D0492721

Techniques of Television Production

McGRAW-HILL TELEVISION SERIES

DONALD G. FINK, Consulting Editor

AGNEW AND O'BRIEN · Television Advertising

BRETZ · Techniques of Television Production

CHINN · Television Broadcasting

DEUTSCH · Theory and Design of Television Receivers

DOME · Television Principles

FINK · Television Engineering

FINK · Television Engineering Handbook

FOWLER AND LIPPERT · Television Fundamentals —Theory, Circuits, and Servicing

GROB · Basic Television: Principles and Servicing

N.T.S.C. · Color Television Standards

WENTWORTH · Color Television Engineering

Techniques of Television Production

Rudy Bretz

Head, Educational Television
University of California at Los Angeles

SECOND EDITION

McGRAW-HILL BOOK COMPANY 1962

New York San Francisco Toronto London

TECHNIQUES OF TELEVISION PRODUCTION

 Library of Congress Catalog Card Number 61-15907

9 10 11 12 – MAMM – 7 5

ISBN 07-007665-2

Preface

One of the problems of television program production is the division at many stations between "technical" and "production" personnel. The distinction is largely arbitrary because the areas overlap widely. One can define the job that a technical man is doing at one station and somewhere else find a production man doing the same thing. The reverse, of course, is also true. At small stations where the staff is limited, each employee will have a wide range of duties. "Technical" people must often perform many production functions, such as operation of cameras and other equipment. "Production" people are frequently required to adjust the video controls, handle the audio console, and do other jobs which are usually considered to be purely engineering.

Television, more than any other field, requires the maximum possible cooperation from all involved. Where engineers have taken no interest in production problems and production people have left "technical things" up to the engineers, this vital cooperation has failed. The production man is generally baffled by the complexity of electronic engineering and gives up trying to learn anything about the equipment, while the engineer hesitates to teach him anything on the grounds that he couldn't teach it thoroughly and "a little knowledge is a dangerous thing." A little knowledge, however, is dangerous only if it is mistaken for a lot of knowledge, and certainly a little is better than none if this mistake is avoided.

The aim of this book is to bridge the gap between the creative production man and the technically minded engineer. The book is directed toward the production man, the director, producer, or worker in any of the dozens of service departments, such as graphic arts, costume, make-up, special effects, or lighting. It is written from their point of view and in answer to their problems. It should be entirely understandable to any production man, and yet it goes quite far into the area he has generally considered "technical" and beyond his powers of comprehension.

The specialist in any branch of production may be familiar with most of the information in the chapter covering his particular field; the other chapters, however, will teach him much about the other fellow's job. This kind of understanding, vital to the close cooperation required in television production, is too often lacking. And certainly the advanced student of television techniques will find much in every chapter that he could discover otherwise only by working in many capacities and at many stations on many different kinds of production.

Since the last edition of this book was prepared, during the early 1950s, many small changes and a few very large ones have occurred in television techniques. Some techniques have changed slowly, by evolution, as new technology became available and improved human engineering resulted in operating equipment better adjusted to the human hand, mind, and eye. Other changes were more sweeping in their various areas. Video tape recording caused a major revolution in the broadcasting industry. New production techniques have developed which are specific to video tape, and accordingly a chapter on television recording has been added to the new edition. During the same period color television reached further development. Although technically it still leaves much to be desired, it is now a common broadcasting medium in America and deserves special coverage in another new chapter. The third added chapter is one that could have been included in the original edition but had to be dropped because of space limitations. This is the new chapter on intercommunication and cuing.

Current trends at the date of publication of the new edition should at least be summarized, since it might be expected that the present book would be subject to obsolescence. First of all, the television production medium is constantly expanding, at least in America, through a broad spectrum of closed-circuit applications in industry and education. Already broadcasting is but a small part of the market for any manufacturer of television equipment. The vidicon camera with its much lower original and operating costs has proved the most practical equipment in this field.

We can expect marked improvements in the field of kinescope recording, which in industry and education has the potential of being a more practical recording method than video tape owing to the simplicity and flexibility of playback. Thermoplastic film holds the promise of combining this flexibility of projection with the erase and reuse feature of video tape.

Technical improvements in color television, particularly in reception equipment, will open the way for future growth of this medium. All electronic equipment will become smaller, cheaper, and more stable in operation as the transistor, the tunnel diode, and molecular construction take over the field. Probably most electronic equipment will soon be based on modular units quickly replaceable and interchangeable between different kinds of electronic equipment. Finally the growth of automated systems, particularly those which are computer-based, will make big changes in TV station operation, as automation has already done in the field of radio. But just as audio automation has not found application in the recording medium, where creative flexibility is required, the techniques of the creation of illusion and other presentation through the television medium will remain much the same as they are today.

Most of this book has been revised away from specific discussion about particular equipment and toward generalizations about basic types of equipment and their operation. It is expected that the techniques described as well as the production materials and equipment involved will remain basically unchanged. Thus the present volume should remain a practical guide and reference book for the production of television, live and recorded, broadcast and closed-circuit, color and black and white, for many years to come.

Rudy Bretz

Acknowledgments

The first edition of this book carried an exhaustive list of the people and organizations that had given the author assistance in the original preparation of the manuscript. While many changes have taken place in each area of TV production since that time, most of the basic information contained in the first edition has been retained. I must then again acknowledge the debt I still owe to those individuals, acting in most cases beyond the line of duty, who gladly took their time to supply information or review the manuscript as it took form. Those people are as follows: Victor Allen, Les Arries, Frank Back, Bob Banner, Ray Barrett, Joe Behar, Gloria Brennan, Bob Bright, John Casagrande, John DeMott, Gil DeStefano, Peter Dimmock, Marshall Diskin, Rolf Drucker, Roy Fee, Don Figlozzi, Shirley Fisher, Joe Fox, Mike Freedman, Otis Freeman, Oliver Fulton, Jim Furness, George Gill, Bert Gold, George Gould, Stuart Griffiths, Bill Guyon, Paul Hale, Don Hallman, Bob Hannum, Howard Hayes, Bill Helion, J. Holubek, Reginald Horton, Austin Huhn, Paul Levitan, Colby Lewis, Warren Jacober, Al Jenkins, Bob Jiras, Irene Kent, Jim MacNaughton, Bill McCarthy, Harry Milholland, Rod Mitchell, Mavor Moore, Jack Murphy, Tom Nagaele, Boyce Nemic, Richard O'Brien, Georg Olden, Byron Paul, Jack Pegler, Louis Pourciau, Al Protzman, Arthur Rankin, Otis Riggs, Dick Robbins, Jack Rose, Ad Schneider, Bill Schwartz, Ernest Sindelar, Irwin Shane, Ray Sherwin, Dick Smith, Neal Smith, Ed Stasheff, Bill Thompson, Dean Wagner, Karl Weger, Don Whitman, S. Young White, Harold Wright, Carol Van Sickle.

In preparing the revision I asked the help of Dick Smith, Larchmont, New York, who is one of the top make-up experts in the television field.

He was good enough to check the make-up chapter and to bring it up to date. Howard Meighan, consultant for the Ampex Company, reviewed and made comments on the chapter on television recording. Peter Dimmock, head of outside broadcasts for the BBC in London, supplied photos of some of the new BBC mobile units, and supplied detailed information on the coverage of the Royal Wedding. Mort Miller, UCLA colleague, helped by reading and commenting on some of the new chapters. Frank Gaskins at NBC supplied information on the NBC switching system and Chroma-Key, and checked these portions of the manuscript.

The author is indebted to the University of California Press for permission to use portions of an article on video tape originally published in the *Quarterly of Film, Radio and Television.*

Rudy Bretz

Contents

1

Introduction

Television programming can be divided into several parts. First there are the live programs which originate in the television studio; second, the live programs which originate at remote locations outside the studio; and third, the programs which are projected onto the television system from motion-picture film. A possible fourth category is recorded live television, either studio or remote, on motion-picture film or video tape. For the average viewer the boundaries between these areas are vague. Much live programming has been looked at under the impression it was film, film has been taken for live, and video tape invariably looks like a live program. In the case of drama, it probably makes little difference to the audience whether the program is live, taped, or on film. The actuality of the moment, which only the viewer of live TV can feel, has little importance beside the effectiveness of the illusion being created.

The final product of television drama is very close to that of motion-picture drama—a story about people involved in situations, presented by actors and translated to a screen in terms of long shots, medium shots, close-ups, and reverse angles. Sets, props, costumes, and acting all contribute to create an illusion that the action is taking place anywhere but in the studio itself. It is inevitable that the techniques of the motion picture should be adopted in large measure. With almost any other type of programming than the dramatic show, however, it is a different story. In the comedy show, the revue, the dance, the panel format, the interview show, and many others, no illusion is attempted. Such programs are better television when their directors make the most of the effect of immediacy—the feeling on the part of the audience that the action on the screen is at that very moment taking place. Some programs, like the classic "Garroway at Large," create illusions but are happy to destroy them as soon as they have served their purpose, knowing that this very act of destruction is often more entertaining and better television than the illusion itself.

Remote pickups usually make interesting television entertainment because of the actuality of the real backgrounds and the immediacy of the real action which is being transmitted. The television cameras at the remote location may simply report on an event and transmit it directly, as in the case of spot news such as fires, and other disasters; they may pick up a show which has been prepared for a regular audience present at the event, as in the case of sports and parades; or they may pick up a special program which has been created expressly for the television show.

Recordings of live television, called "kinescope recordings" because they were motion pictures taken of the face of the kinescope (receiver) screen, provided greater scope for network operation. Stations unconnected to a live network could still carry network programs by film, and stations in the Western part of the United States, two, three, and sometimes four hours earlier in time than New York, could record programs and play them back later at the same clock times for which they were designed. Video tape, when it arrived, immediately replaced film for the latter purpose, and soon, in the case of networks and major stations, took over many of its other functions as well.

PRODUCTION IN LARGE AND SMALL STATIONS

It is very difficult to generalize about television production methods. Techniques differ widely between the small station in a community of limited size and the large network origination station in New York or Hollywood. The small-station producer may have to do a local variety show, for example, for $200, while his colleague on the network may have a budget of $10,000 with which to produce the same type of show. In addition to this, the network director will have a week or more to prepare his show without other responsibilities, and a day for camera rehearsal, whereas the local producer, responsible for several hours of programming per week, must throw the production together and considers himself very lucky if he is allowed any camera rehearsal time at all.

Studio facilities also vary greatly. A network station in New York will have more than a dozen studios, several converted theaters, and two or three mobile units. The total number of cameras owned by a network station may be over a hundred. Each studio will have three cameras, and some may use four or five. On the other end of the scale, there are several stations which have been operated successfully with no more than one studio camera or none at all, programming entirely through network feed and film.

THE TELEVISION STUDIO

At first glance, a visitor to a television studio is apt to remark that it looks very much like a movie set. Then he will note things which remind him of a stage in a theater, and if he has the opportunity to enter the control room, he will feel that the whole thing is, after all, an overgrown radio studio. He will be right in each case. Television has borrowed much from all three of these fields.

Like stage shows, television productions must run continuously through many scenes with a minimum of time allowed for changes of sets and lighting. All the lights must be properly placed at the beginning of the show, and although they may be dimmed or switched on and off during the production, they cannot be repositioned. The lighting, the set, and the action must be planned so that the show can be seen properly from a great many angles of view. In the theater the audience sits in all portions of the house, and in the television studio the cameras shoot from many angles. Most television studios use a type of scenery which is standard in the theater, flats made of muslin stretched on light wooden frames, plus roll drops, cycloramas, traveler curtains, and the like.

Theater-trained people working in television production say that this new medium is like nothing quite so much as summer stock. Everyone is working against time, nothing can be perfect, and the short cut is usually better than the "right way" to do a thing, the main difference being that there is a new show every night instead of every week.

The great French architect LeCorbusier once described the house as "a machine for living in." In the same sense the theater is "a machine for doing plays in." The TV studio, like the theatrical stage, has much of its lighting, sound equipment, scenery apparatus, etc., built in and can also be considered a machine. Television is unlike the stage, however, in one very important way. Television is a photographic medium. Nothing reaches the television audience which has not entered the eye of a camera. The question has been commonly raised: Why cannot the television medium transmit a stage play to the home audience, capturing the immediacy of the performance instead of attempting to simulate the motion picture? Perhaps if a play were televised in one continuous long shot with the proscenium arch of the stage constantly visible, the effect of a stage play would be retained. As soon as the cameras are brought onto the stage, however, and proceed to break the action down into close-ups, two-shots, reverse angles, and so forth, the show no longer resembles a play but has become like a motion picture. The television medium is a medium of the camera and as such has departed almost as far from the live theater as has the medium of film.

The main difference between television and motion-picture studios is that the film studio is not a machine. It is only a space like the photographic studio, within which lights, sets, and cameras may be placed and pictures made. Very little is built in; practically everything rests on the floor. Lights, when they are not mounted on floor stands, are fixed to the top of the sets or to scaffold towers or bridges, which in turn rest on the floor. This is possible in film production because everything may be rearranged between each shot. In television, on the other hand, the production cannot stop after each shot, and the entire floor must be free for the unrestricted movement of cameras.

The salient feature of the television studio which is taken directly from radio is the control room. Sound-isolated from the rest of the studio, the control room is always provided with a large plate-glass window. In radio this window allows the actors to see the director and take visual cues from him. In television, cues are never given through this window to anyone; it is usually impossible to see through it from the studio side because of the reflection of the studio lights. Most stations have installed large sheets of plastic filter material across the glass to cut down the glare from the studio so that the personnel in the control room can see the camera monitors more easily. Very often the studio is so crowded with sets that scenery must be placed against the control-room window, and it becomes more of a wall instead.

The director of a rehearsed show has little need for the control-room window; it is seldom if ever used in dramatic production. Control-room personnel working ad-lib programs, however, are thankful to be able to see more than the cameras alone can show them.

THE ANATOMY OF THE TELEVISION STUDIO

Turning now to the elements which make up a typical television studio, we note first of all that the studio must provide a space or a stage for action. In small studios where there is not enough time to rearrange lights and other equipment between shows, these staging areas will remain quite well set from one show to the next. In a large network studio, however, the designer of a set should be able to use any portion of the studio he wishes, provided, of course, it is possible for the director to get his cameras into place to shoot it. The typical dramatic production will be laid out in a series of small two- or three-sided sets placed around the sides of the studio with an area for camera movement left free in the center. Some of the more complicated productions have reversed this procedure and placed their sets in the center of the studio with camera access provided on all sides. In using this method, however, the director must be careful to plan things so that minor errors do not result in the cameras showing each other in the background of their shots.

Some television sets have been two stories high, and indeed in some of the larger studios the ceiling of lights can be raised, permitting background drops as much as 40 feet high to be used. At the other end of the scale, some very successful productions have been staged without scenery at all, the entire show being done in close-ups of the actors against a background of "limbo" (dark curtains or cyclorama backing which comes out black on the television screen).

The television camera is at once more complicated in operation and more flexible than motion-picture cameras. It is rather unwieldy, but no more so than a large sound camera of Hollywood when enclosed in a soundproof blimp, and it is certainly less cumbersome than the huge technicolor camera.

The cameraman controls the composition of the picture and the focus of the lens when action is approaching or receding from the camera, and he often rolls the camera across the floor ("dollies it") at the same time. The camera is provided with a small monitor, actually a little receiving set, which constantly shows the cameraman the picture that his camera is putting out. This is called an "electronic view finder."

The cameras are connected by special cable (containing 24 different conductors) to the camera-control units in the control room. The camera, its camera-control unit, and the power supply which feeds it the necessary voltages are known collectively as a "camera chain." A camera cannot operate without its entire chain. A video engineer is necessary to operate the camera controls in the control room, and he might very well be classified along with the rest of the camera crew since the camera will not function properly if he is not on the job. Each camera-control unit includes a monitor on which the picture taken by its particular camera is visible as long as the camera is operating.

The studio audio equipment parallels that of a radio studio very closely. A similar audio console is used in the control room, although extensible boom microphones of the motion-picture type are necessary to follow the sound which must necessarily come from actors in movement. Two turntables are usually provided so that recorded music can be used freely as part of the studio show. Sound effects are usually provided by a sound-effects man who handles records and live effects in the studio just as in the manner of radio broadcasting.

THE STUDIO CONTROL ROOM

The camera monitors already described (part of the camera-control units) are usually lined up in a row in front of the control-room window, permitting the director to preview the picture from each camera at all times.

In addition to the camera monitors there is always a master monitor, or on-the-air monitor, which carries the picture that is leaving the control room. Thus when a switch (or "cut") is effected between two cameras, no change is noted on the respective camera monitors, except for small tally lights which indicate which camera chain is on. The master monitor always shows the effect of the cut, however, since it carries the program which the director is creating.

An additional monitor is always present for the purpose of previewing pictures which do not come from studio cameras and do not have their

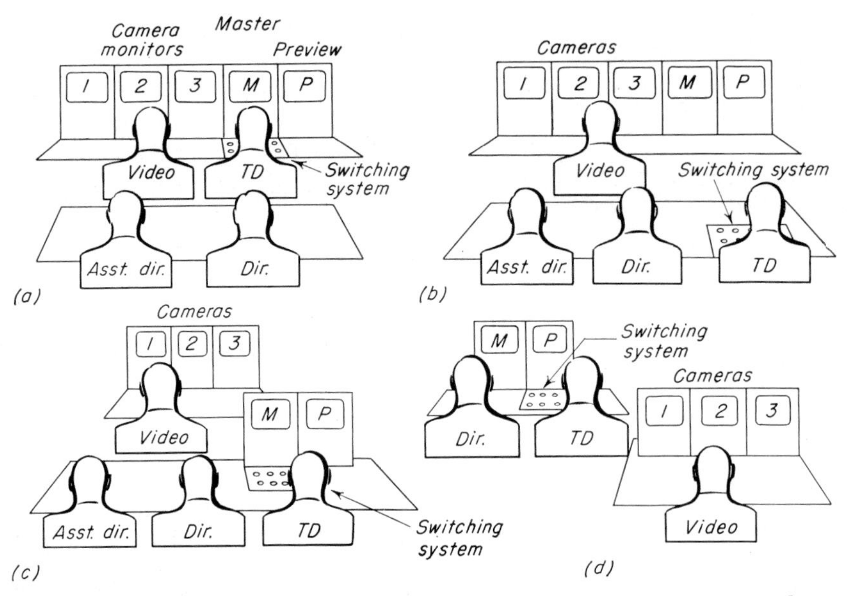

Fig. 1–1. Four typical control-room layouts. (*a*) All controls and monitors on lower tier; (*b*) all monitors below, director and technical director side by side at production desk; (*c*) master monitor and preview monitor mounted on production console; (*d*) camera monitors removed from director's vision—preview monitor used instead. This is the basic NBC system.

own camera monitors in the control room. This is called a "preview monitor." Film and slides from the projection room, pictures from remote locations which are to be integrated with the studio programs, and sometimes pictures from other studios are previewed on this monitor.

Switching from camera to camera is done with a control panel of switches and levers or dials, called the "switching system." Not only straight switching (instantaneous change of scene) but dissolves, fades, superimposures, and sometimes wipes can be done as well. Figure 1-1 shows four different methods of control-room layout. The technical director, who operates the switching system, may sit at the same console with the video engineers (*a*) or he may sit side by side with the director (*b*, *c*, and *d*). This is the preferred method. Some studios place the video men and camera monitors off to the side of the control room and leave the director and the TD alone in front of the control room window. Only a master monitor and one preview monitor are used in directing a show with this control-room layout, each camera having to be specially previewed just before it is used.

Some stations have experimented with using two control rooms instead of one. The engineering and the production functions are thus separated, with, of course, constant intercommunication between them.

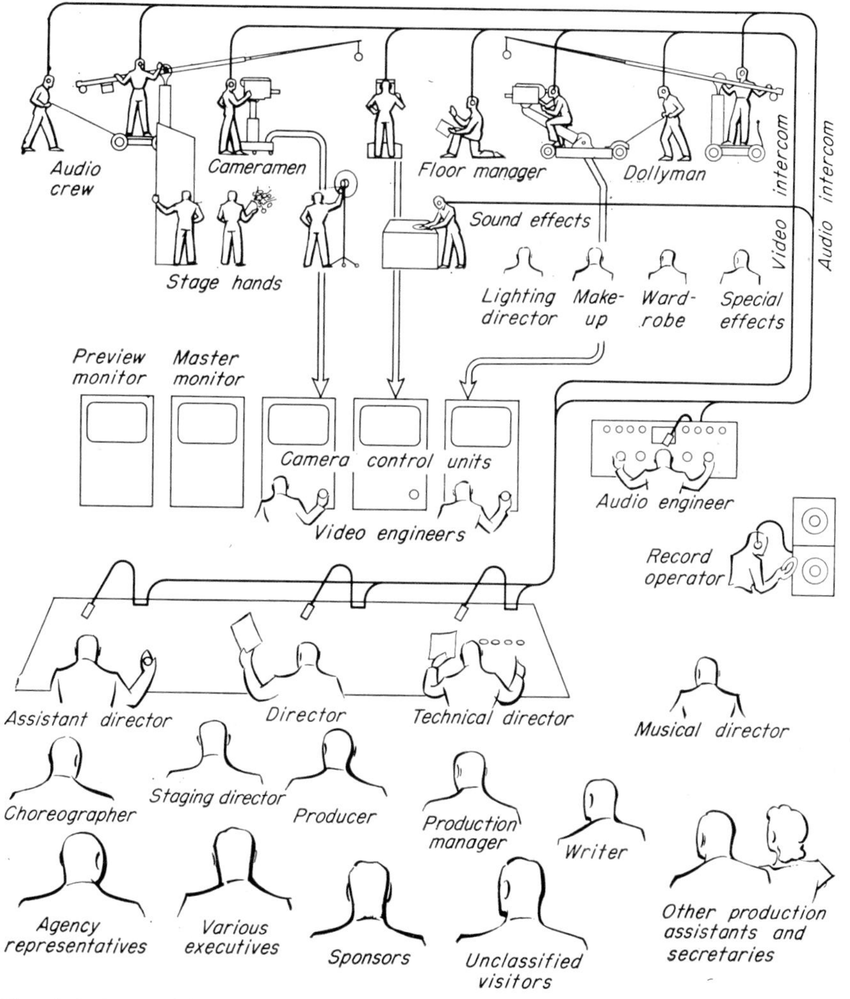

Fig. 1–2. Personnel present during rehearsal of a typical television-network show.

The triple control room is also common in the larger network studios, sliding glass panels separating the production control room in the center from the smaller audio control room to one side and the video control room on the other. Many stations have combined the video control rooms of their several studios, placing this center in the master control area, thus consolidating engineering personnel. Special production monitors displaying each camera are provided in the production control room when the video-control units are installed elsewhere.

It should be noted that television directors often do not use the control room in rehearsing a show, preferring to work on the studio floor, watching the picture on the cameramen's view finders or on the floor monitor, and not entering the control room until time for dress rehearsal. It is certainly very rarely that a director can stay long in the control room during rehearsal of a complex show without having to go out onto the floor and untangle some kind of problem.

THE PROJECTION ROOM

Since a large part of the programming of television is motion-picture film, every station must have equipment for the projection and pickup of films. A typical setup is illustrated in Fig. 1-3. Two television film pro-

Fig. 1–3. A typical television film chain. Two 16-mm film projectors, optical system (multiplexer), and vidicon TV camera.

jectors are shown, pointing into an optical system called a "multiplexer." The image from either projector is then transmitted to the small vidicon film pickup camera shown in the center. Slide and opaque projectors can also be fed into the multiplexer and may become an additional part of such a projection complex. The term "film chain" is commonly used for the entire complex, but more properly refers to the film pickup camera plus its control unit and power supply.

Each film pickup camera must have its camera-control unit just as the studio cameras do. In a network station these may be placed in a special film control room, which is generally laid out in very much the same manner as a studio control room, with two levels, a switching system, master monitor, and audio console.

MASTER CONTROL

In a large station or network, studio programs will not go directly to the station transmitter, but to an intermediate switching point which is called the "master control." This also constitutes a central place for the grouping of amplifiers, synchronizing-pulse generators, and the other technical equipment which is necessary to the television system. Several studios may feed into master control; so may one or more film chains; and there may be incoming lines from outside the station, such as feeds from remote pickups and network programs from the telephone company

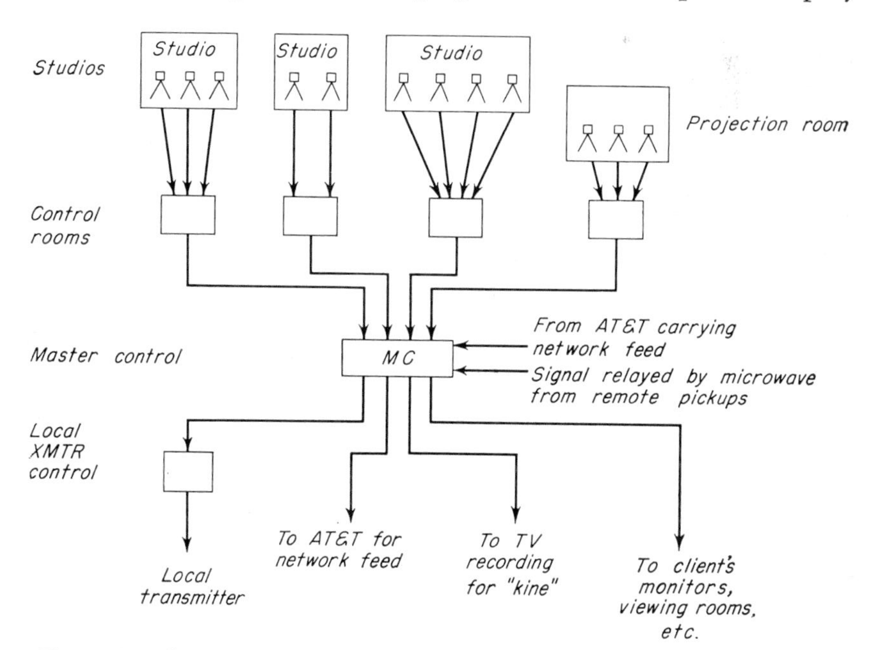

Fig. 1-4. Relationship of studios to master control in typical network plant.

(Fig. 1-4). Master control will in turn feed programs to many different places. Video patchboards, similar in a general way to telephone switchboards, are provided, making a great variety and flexibility of circuits possible. Signals from any of the above incoming lines may be patched down to any studio for preview or for integration into that studio's program. In addition to outgoing lines to each studio, master control may also feed a variety of client and audience monitors about the station, the local station transmitter, and the central offices of the phone company for network feed. Still other outgoing lines will lead to the recording department, where certain programs will be put on film or tape.

SMALL-STATION LAYOUT

Smaller stations will often combine the various control rooms mentioned above in the interest of economical operation. The usual combination is to include the film-control function in the studio control room. This will add more monitors to the control room. Sometimes film control is combined with master control, and occasionally both these functions are incorporated within the single studio control room. A few small operations have combined all this with the transmitter control room so that one control room performs four functions.

Every possible combination of duties has been tried at one station or another in the attempt to reduce operating expense. A typical example is the station where two men operate transmitter, projection, audio, video, switching and directing, and, in the studio, man two cameras. This is achieved by having one man thread the film projectors, operate transmitter and audio controls; the second direct, switch, and control video. In the case of a live show, the first man leaves the transmitter and the audio console after he has opened up the proper microphone, and goes into the studio to man a camera. The second camera is left unattended on a wide shot of the set. Remotely controlled cameras have been used in other stations to make it unnecessary for anyone to leave the control room. Needless to say, these methods of operation necessitate extreme austerity in production technique; it is not expected that personnel at such stations would have an opportunity to put into frequent use the various techniques of production described in this volume.

2

The Television Cameraman

Television is a medium of the camera. All the techniques of television production are related to the functioning of this instrument. Since the camera is basic, any real understanding of the medium must begin with a thorough familiarity with the television camera and its operation.

Before cameras and the techniques directly associated with cameras are discussed, a general picture of the television cameraman will prove valuable. The following chapters will discuss details of equipment and operating techniques—knowledge which a cameraman must have and which a director would do well to acquire.

The requirements of television production and the unique design of television cameras have developed, among better television cameramen, operators of unusual skill. Handling the camera is a highly creative job, and there is a tremendous difference between a good and a mediocre cameraman. The ability of a television cameraman depends on certain basic abilities but is also due in large measure to his attitude toward his job. This in turn seems to hinge primarily on the position of the cameraman within the station organization.

The job of cameraman is only one of a group known as operating jobs. Such duties as dolly pushing, mike-boom operating, audio-console operating, and the jobs of technical director, projectionist, record spinner, etc., are not strictly *technical* jobs. In none of these positions does the operator have to understand more than the mechanics of operation of his equipment. He is not called upon to repair or redesign, but only to operate, and skill of operation rather than engineering understanding is required. A few television stations, as, for example, WHEN and WTVJ, have classified every one of these jobs under the program department. Since in an operating job, an understanding of showmanship is of greater value than a technical background, creative contribution is more likely to result in all these aspects of production. This is not to say, of course, that no engineers have any concept of showmanship. There are many engineers in television who, through particular backgrounds or constant control-room experience in television or radio, have developed an understanding of the elements of showmanship that would qualify them equally well as directors. The best of the technical directors fit this description.

APTITUDES OF THE SUCCESSFUL CAMERAMAN

Whatever the cameraman's classification within the organization, he will become really good only if he has two essential aptitudes. The first is a sense of composition, and the second is a well-developed manual coordination.

The sense of composition comes only from long familiarity with the picture medium. A man who has been a still- or motion-picture photographer, or perhaps has worked on a picture magazine, has been thinking in terms of pictures and developing this sense. Many books are available on composition, but it is not possible for the television cameraman or director to apply rules for composition while he is making pictures. There just is not enough time. The cameraman must have acquired a feeling for a well-composed picture. He must be able to look at a picture, see what is wrong with its composition, and unerringly make a quick adjustment to improve it.

Manual dexterity and coordination come only to those who are endowed with the necessary aptitude. Just as it is impossible to teach some persons to fly an airplane, so it is impossible to teach such persons the smoothness and dexterity necessary to operate the television camera. A man who lacks the feeling for composition but has coordination may learn the former in time; if he lacks the aptitude for physical coordination, he will never be a good television cameraman, no matter how finely developed his pictorial sense.

RELATIONSHIP BETWEEN CAMERAMAN AND DIRECTOR

Most creative decisions about the use of the cameras are made by the television director. He is even sometimes known as the "camera director" to distinguish him from the "staging director," whose concern is with program content.

The usual studio setup puts the director at one end of the studio intercom and the camera crew at the other. He directs the movements of the camera on the air, while at the same time readying his other cameras for the next shots he will use. Then he directs the switching from camera to camera as the show progresses. The director and the cameraman work together as a team. Since the technical director does no more during a show than operate the switching system, this method of operation has been known as the "switcher" system.

In some stations, notably those operated by NBC, the "technical director system" was developed. According to this method of operation the TD not only handled the switching but also acted as a kind of head cameraman, taking charge of the operation and placement of cameras. In theory the technical director (TD) was to be the only person in the control room who gave directions to the cameramen. (The director was given a separate intercom line to the floor manager.) In the case of complex productions, the TD would visit outside rehearsals and have a share in the planning of shots and camera angles.

Proponents of this system saw in it an analogy to the method of Hollywood film production, where each film has essentially two directors, one of whom is the director of photography, in charge of the technical aspects, while the other, nominally *the* director, confines himself to the broader problems of staging and acting.

Where the TD method was used, the TD was of necessity primarily an engineer. The nature of his work, however, required him to learn and to apply all the operational skills of the television director. This is attested to by the fact that some of the best directors in the industry were originally engineers, making the transition through technical directing.

One aspect of the TD system rendered it impractical: the insistence on the TD's being the only one to give directions to the cameramen. During an ad-lib show, camera and switching directions must be coordinated, and they must be issued and acted upon immediately or action will be lost. Sudden instructions to the cameraman cannot be given through the TD, since by the time they are relayed it is generally too late to put them into effect. Stations operating with the TD method found various ways around this restriction; according to one union contract the director was allowed to talk to the cameramen on "unrehearsed" shows. In another studio an open microphone was placed in the control room unofficially, feeding into the cameramen's phones and thus making it possible for the cameramen to hear the director as he gave an original order to the TD and to begin to act upon it before it was officially relayed to them. Since most stations must do the ad-lib type of production primarily, the majority of them have left the director in constant contact with the camera and floor crew.

A good compromise is achieved in some stations where both the director and the technical director may talk to the cameramen at any time. This makes quick decisions possible and at the same time provides a two-director team for the rehearsal and production of the show. After operating under this joint system many people have observed that the usual method, whereby the TD simply operates the switching system under the director's command, wastes the capabilities of this individual, who could be assisting the director at the same time.

THE CAMERAMAN'S RESPONSIBILITY

Opinion is divided as to how much responsibility should be vested in the cameraman for finding the right shot at the proper time. In the case of the unrehearsed show where there is no set sequence of shots, the cameraman is usually relied upon to "hunt for shots" when he is off the air. The director may look at a shot the cameraman has found and say, "No, I don't want to use that," or "That's good; give it to me again when I tell you," or he may switch it immediately into the program.

At the opposite end of the scale is the method of operation where the cameraman makes no move at all, except the very obvious, without instructions from the control room. It is a generally accepted principle that a cameraman should operate like this while his camera is on the air, but most stations give him greater freedom and more responsibility between shots.

In the case of the scripted and rehearsed show, the cameraman will always be supplied with cues from the control room to remind him of his next shot each time he is switched off the program line. In many studios, however, he is expected to take the major responsibility and will keep a cue sheet on the camera, listing each shot as it becomes established in rehearsal. He will often put numbered chalk or paint marks on the studio floor so that he can immediately find the exact camera position that was established in rehearsal for each shot.

Some of the better cameramen are opposed to this method, however. They feel that the important thing is to get the same *shot* they had in rehearsal, not just the same lens and camera position, and since the performer's positions may vary between rehearsal and air, the camera may easily be on the right mark and not have the proper shot at all.

3

Television Cameras

Television cameras are built around several kinds of picture tubes and take their essential size and shape largely from the tube on which they are based. The first electronic cameras in this country utilized the iconoscope tube, which was relatively insensitive to light and large in size, requiring large-diameter long-focal-length lenses for standard studio purposes. Another early tube, the Image Dissector, was too insensitive for studio use, but found broadcast application as a film pickup camera.

The iconoscope went through several improvements in Europe, in its variations being known as the Emitron tube, the Super-iconoscope, and the Image-iconoscope, and finding applications long after cameras employing other tubes had come into simultaneous use.

During the 1940s another large but more sensitive camera, based on the orthicon tube, was in use, primarily for outside telecasts. It was during World War II, however, that military applications hastened the development of the image-orthicon tube, which when it became available in 1947 constituted television's greatest single advance of the decade.

Some French and English cameras were built around the Photicon tube during this period; German technicians developed the Riesel iconoscope, which was in constant use during the early 1950s. Four American manufacturers, three British, and one German were marketing image-orthicon cameras in quantity at this time.

Early in the 1950s also, the vidicon tube was developed. Much smaller and cheaper than the image-orthicon, the vidicon cameras were at first only capable of creating a picture of substandard quality, but because of their low cost they began to open up a wide new field of industrial applications. By 1957 established American manufacturers were doing a greater volume of business supplying the industrial market with vidicon cameras than they were in the broadcast field.

While industrial television with its slightly-lower-than-broadcast standards of quality led to the development of the vidicon camera, the demand for increased quality in broadcast television led to the development of a higher quality image-orthicon tube. Whereas the standard

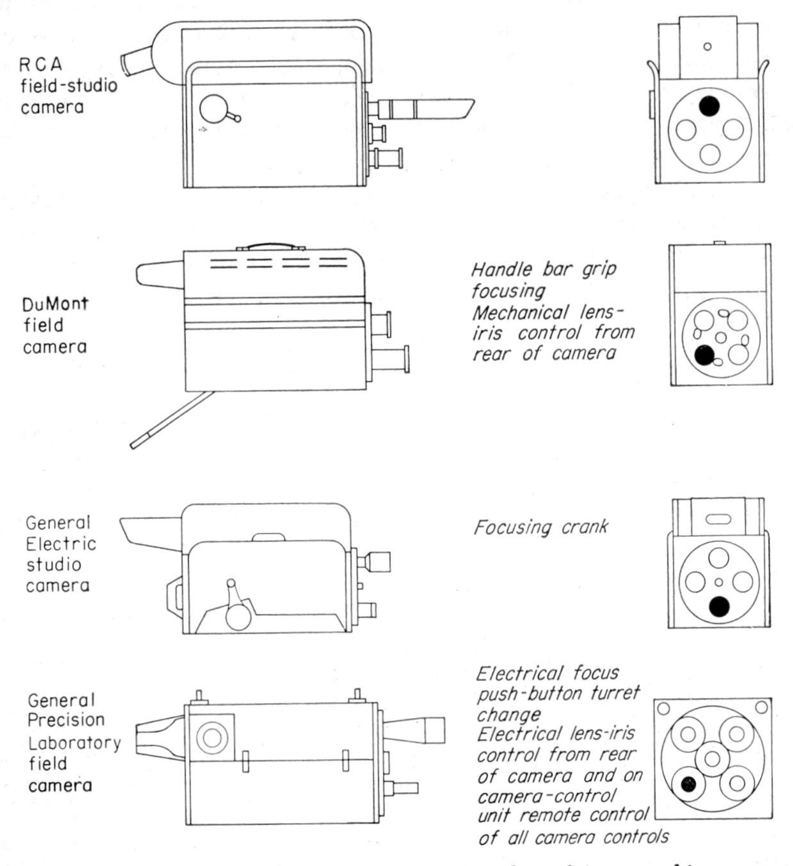

Fig. 3–1. A comparison of the major American makes of image-orthicon cameras. The GPL camera at the bottom is actually manufactured in England by Pye.

image-orthicon tube had been 3 inches in diameter, the new tube was 4½ inches. The pioneering in this field was done by the English manufacturer Marconi, followed by Pye and E.M.I. and joined later by American firms.

The stability of the 4½-inch image-orthicon camera, its improved gray scale and sensitivity, began a new chapter in the history of television cameras. It began to appear in the early '60s that the vidicon camera would supply the mass demand in industry and education, while the 4½-inch image-orthicon would inherit the broadcasting and video-tape field.

VIEW FINDERS

Like motion-picture and still cameras, any really useful television camera must have a view finder to show the cameraman what he is doing. In some kinds of camera work, notably fast sports, it is necessary for the cameraman to have greater freedom and visibility than if his vision were limited to the small area of the scene which the camera is picking up. He then uses an exterior, or *sports,* view finder.

The simplest type of exterior view finder is a frame of wire mounted forward on the camera, with a small ring, or gun sight, near the back of the camera lined up with the center of the frame. If the cameraman puts his eye to this tiny ring, he is sure to see the area of the scene which his camera is seeing.

An inaccuracy is inherent in these view finders since they are mounted on the side or top of the camera. The center of the view finder is thus several inches from the center of the lens, and the view finder is seeing a portion of the scene 8 inches, let us say, *above* what the lens is seeing. This is known as parallax error. In a distant scene, 8 inches doesn't amount to much, but as the subject comes closer, the parallactic error is more serious, until in close-up an error of 8 inches may cause entire loss of the subject.

It is interesting to note here that, even in studio camera work, when the cameraman is provided with an electronic view finder and composition of the shot is his prime consideration, he will frequently prefer to move his head away from the camera and watch the scene directly. To give a simple example, let us say that the cameraman has a close-up of a person seated, showing only head and shoulders, and the subject suddenly rises. If the cameraman's eye is glued to the electronic view finder, the action may occur too suddenly for smooth handling. If, however, his head is away from the camera, he will notice other movements of the subject preparatory to the act of rising—uncrossing the legs, placing hands on the arms of the chair, etc.—which will warn him of what is coming.

View-finder hoods. The view-finder hood, designed primarily to keep stray light from washing out the image on the kinescope tube, is often used as an important element in camera control. Pressure of the forehead on the hood can be used to dolly the camera, to tilt down, or as a steadying force to control other movements of the camera and ensure smoothness.

The importance of an adjustable hood is that the cameraman does not always have to be directly behind the camera in order to see into the view finder. A hood which will pull down to a low angle when the camera is high and pointing down, for example, will allow the cameraman to look directly into the view finder without climbing up on a chair to do so. The RCA studio camera has such a view-finder hood, and the hood on the General Electric studio camera is also adjustable to a certain extent. As the camera tilts, the view finder must be continuously adjusted to the new angle. In the RCA studio camera, tension screws inside the hood can be adjusted so that the change can be made by pressure of the forehead alone without the cameraman touching it with his hand.

Many cameramen prefer to work without a hood at all, using only a cardboard shade above the face of the tube to keep out excess top light. This method increases the cameraman's flexibility since he can see the view finder from any angle and does not have to be directly behind the camera.

FOCUS

If a camera is to be in sharp focus, the photosensitive plate must be placed exactly where the image is formed. However, objects at different distances from the camera are imaged at different distances behind a lens. Rays of light from an object 30 feet from a given lens may be converged into an image 2 inches behind the lens, whereas light from an object 3 feet away will at the same time be brought to a focus, say, 4 inches behind the lens. Since the TV tube cannot be in both places at the same time, one object or the other must be out of focus. Or, to put it another way, as a subject moves closer to the camera, the distance between lens and TV tube must be increased. This is known as focusing the camera. Camera designs solve this problem in one of three ways:

1. Standard photographic lenses are equipped with focusing mounts. By turning a threaded collar on the lens barrel, all or part of the lens is screwed away from or toward the plate. This is accurately calibrated so that the photographer can be sure of his focus even though he may have no ground-glass view finder on which to check it. Image-orthicon lenses, since they are largely standard minicamera photographic lenses, are so equipped. It is difficult, however, to utilize this type of focusing from the cameraman's position at the rear of the camera.

2. The lens can be fastened to a movable mount and racked bodily forward or back by a wheel or handle control, in the manner of a portrait-studio bellows camera. This is the method employed on the three-tube color cameras, where the entire camera turret racks in and out.

3. The tube may be moved back and forth while the lens is stationary. This is the method used on all major image-orthicon and vidicon TV cameras.

Some TV cameras are equipped with a crank handle on the side of the camera which engages a gear train inside. The number of turns for full-focusing range, however, varies considerably from one make and model to another. The GPL (General Precision Laboratory) camera achieves full focus in less than one turn. Other models vary from 4 to 11 turns. The higher the number of turns, the smoother and more delicate the

Fig. 3–2. The General Precision Laboratory, or Pye, camera.

focusing action can be, but the more time it takes for quick changes of focus.

The engineers at KTTV in Los Angeles improved the RCA field cameras by substituting a 6-inch disk for the focusing-crank control. This allows more delicate adjustment, and since the leverage is greater at the outside of the wheel, the wheel can be moved very easily with only the pressure of the finger tips against the side. In following focus as the camera or subject moves, some cameramen have found it helpful to keep shifting focus constantly, very slightly back and forth. This gives them a fluidity which is necessary for the best control.

The Marconi camera (British) attaches a long handle instead of a crank to the focusing shaft, and since the handle moves in an arc with an 8- or 10-inch radius, it achieves rather delicate adjustments of focus within a total focusing range of less than half a turn of the shaft.

A second type of focus control was found on the Du Mont camera. This is the so-called "motorcycle grip" in which the focusing is accomplished by rotating a section of the handle. A smooth continuous focus over a wide range is difficult to achieve with this design, since the wrist can turn only so far before the hand must release and take another grip. One way of getting around this is to put the flat of the hand or the fingers against the rotating grip and roll it down the palm, the wrist, and even the forearm if necessary.

On the GPL camera (Fig. 3-2) focusing can be done with either hand. The focusing knobs are potentiometers (the same as "pots" or fading dials on an audio console), and the actual movement of the tube is achieved by means of an electric motor.

THE LENS TURRET

Standard design in most film and television cameras includes the use of several lenses mounted on a rotating turret. Television cameras have been designed so that the cameraman can change lenses quickly by means of a handle on the back of the camera. It is desirable for the cameraman to mark or memorize this turret control so that he can know which lens is in place and in which direction to turn to reach the next lens he may want.

The reader will note that there is no handle at the back of the GPL camera. The desired lens is selected by the row of four punch buttons at the bottom of the camera back, and the turret is motor-operated. It takes about 1½ seconds for an adjacent lens to come into place and about 3 seconds if the lens is at the far side of the turret. This is slightly longer than a quick manual change. Another saving in time is accomplished, however. Each time a lens is changed, the camera automatically compensates for the change in focal length by racking the tube forward or back so that the new picture quickly comes into focus. With any of the other cameras a moment of manual focusing is necessary whenever a lens change is made.

THE LENS DIAPHRAGM

Under ordinary circumstances control over exposure (the amount of light entering the lens) is not part of the cameraman's responsibility. Exposure is a part of "picture quality," an engineering term referring to such factors as the accuracy of tonal reproduction, freedom from "noise" (rain or snow in the picture), and clarity of the image. When the cameraman adjusts the lens diaphragm to admit more light to the camera tube, he does it at the direction of the video man, who has found he must have more light for a satisfactory picture.

In the first RCA and the GE cameras this is done by reaching around to the front of the camera and adjusting the diaphragm control on the lens. The Du Mont, GPL, and subsequent RCA cameras allow this operation to be done from the back of the camera. In the Du Mont camera this is accomplished by a shaft through the camera and a gear on the lens turret which engages the lens collar controlling the diaphragm. Specially adapted lenses are necessary for this type of operation, and there is some doubt whether it is entirely necessary. There are times when it is undoubtedly helpful—as when the sun goes in and out all afternoon during a ball game, or in the late afternoon as the light is failing—but usually the lenses are all set to a standard opening when the cameras are lined up and are not touched during the program. (Studio lenses may be set anywhere between *f*/5.6 and *f*/11, depending on the age of the camera tubes in use and the studio illumination.) Low-level lighting on remote programs frequently requires the use of the widest *f* stops possible. The GPL camera controls the iris diaphragm electrically. A pair of "open" and "closed" push buttons are provided just above the focusing knob. Far more important, the video engineer also has a similar control on the camera-control unit. A small meter on the back of the camera and another on the camera-control unit indicate the diaphragm opening (*f* stop) at which the lens in the taking position is set.

GPL was the first firm to provide a remote-control unit containing focus knob, turret-change buttons, and controls for an electrical pan and tilt apparatus. Some stations (such as WHUM-TV, Reading) installed GPL remote-control apparatus and eliminated studio cameramen, the director handling the camera controls along with his other duties.* Control was surprisingly delicate, but camera flexibility was limited and the director extremely busy. This equipment appears to be practical only for the simplest type of studio production.

Less delicate remote-control equipment has been provided by several manufacturers for use with vidicon cameras in industrial applications.

LINING UP THE IMAGE-ORTHICON CAMERA

Lining up the camera is strictly a technical operation, and it is performed under the direction of the video engineer. However, it is well for the cameraman to be familiar with the process since his help is usually required. The following discussion is nontechnical and is intended only

* Including, in this case, video control, switching, and remote control of film and slide projectors.

to assist the student cameraman toward a better performance of his part in the operation.

Alignment. The first step in the lining-up process is called alignment. If a camera is improperly aligned, this is because the scanning beam is not moving down the center of the tube. There is considerable disagreement among video engineers as to the best procedure in aligning the camera, and the cameraman may be asked to proceed in different

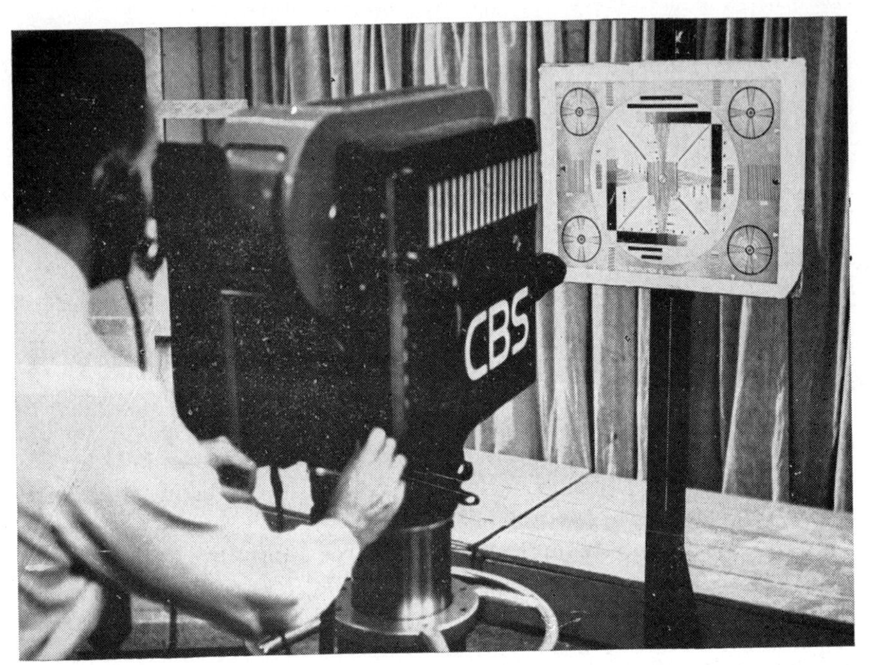

Fig. 3–3. Cameraman lining up on test chart.

ways when working with different engineers. Some will do the entire alignment with the lens capped up. Others will prefer to point the camera at a test chart or a flatly lit dark area. Still others feel that proper alignment cannot be obtained unless the camera is focused on a scene of average brightness and contrast range.

Whichever of these alternatives the engineer will choose, he will proceed to turn up the "orth-focus" control on the camera-control unit so as to bring out one or more tiny white "dynode spots" as close to the center of the picture as possible.

The engineer turns the orth-focus control back and forth to bring the spots in and out of focus. The cameraman, in the studio, listens to the engineer's instructions on the earphones and watches the effect on his camera monitor. If the camera is not properly aligned, a dynode spot will arc back and forth across the screen instead of blinking in and out. It is then the job of the cameraman to rotate his alignment knob in whichever direction is necessary until this arcing is reduced to blinking. The video engineer continues to turn the orth-focus knob back and forth until he is satisfied that the adjustment is correct. If the cameraman cannot stop the spot from arcing by means of the alignment knob, he must open up the side of the camera and make a screw-driver adjustment on the alignment coil inside. He may have to adjust both the knob and the

Fig. 3–4. Vidicon "R-F" or wireless camera which does not require a cable. (R-F: radio frequency.)

screw-driver control at once to find the exact combination which will properly align the camera.

Aspect-ratio adjustment. If he has not done so before, the cameraman now focuses the camera on a test pattern, or resolution chart (Fig. 3-3). He will not adjust his view finder until the video engineer is satisfied that the height and width of the picture are correctly adjusted.

The cameraman is asked to reduce both height and width until the camera is greatly overscanned. Almost the entire end of the circular image-orthicon tube is then visible on the camera monitor. The video engineer will now direct the cameraman to pan and tilt, or dolly in or out, until the image of the test pattern fills the correct scanning area on the end of the tube. This should be as large as possible—most engineers scan very slightly onto the curved edges of the tube, knowing that the resultant corner distortion will be cut off in monitors and receivers.

Now the cameraman is asked to expand picture width and occasionally adjust horizontal centering and linearity, until the video engineer "gets sides." This means that the edge of the test chart just touches the edge of the camera-control monitor screen. The cameraman then adjusts his own view-finder width and centering controls until his sides are also

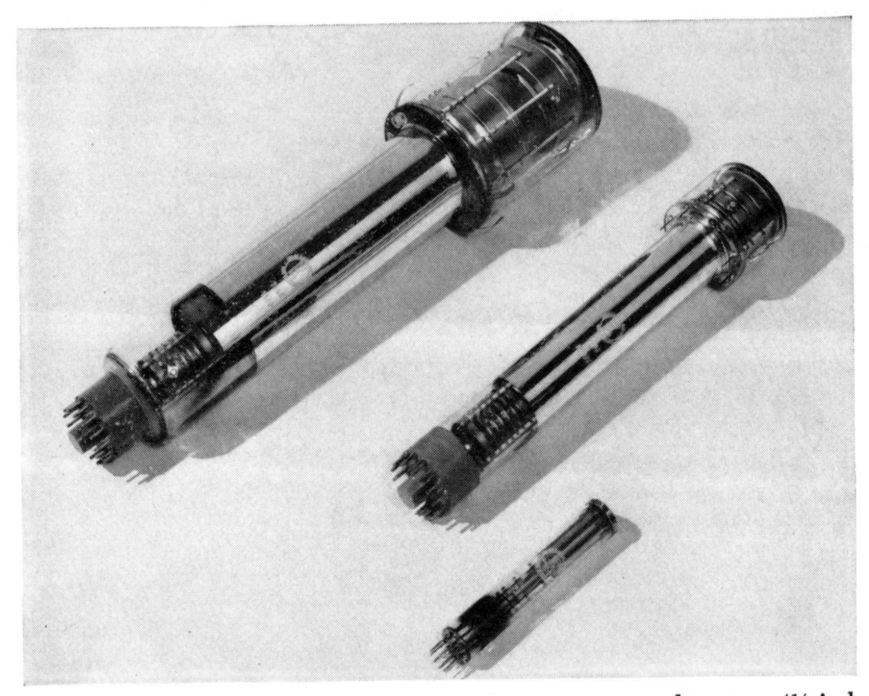

Fig. 3–5. The three most commonly used television camera tubes, top: 4½-inch image-orthicon; middle: 3-inch image-orthicon; bottom: vidicon (1-inch diameter).

correct. Owing to the difference in blanking signal at the camera and at the control unit, the cameraman should be able to see a slightly wider area than will be visible on the control-room monitor. This same procedure is then followed in respect to height until the video engineer is satisfied that he "has top and bottom."

Shading. The video engineer will refer to the oscilloscope trace on the camera-control unit for a check on shading. The "grass" on this waveform monitor must be of a uniform height; the cameraman may be asked to rotate the shading control on the camera until this is achieved. The effect on the picture is to lighten or darken one side against the other but is too subtle for the cameraman to make the best adjustment by eye alone.

S distortion. The engineer will ask the cameraman to pan back and forth across the test pattern to see whether horizontal lines stay horizontal or whether they tend to twist up or down as the camera moves across. If this effect is seen, the image-accelerator knob must be adjusted until S distortion disappears.

High-peaker. For this test the cameraman will be asked to dolly in for a close-up of the two heavy dark bars located below the circle on the test chart. As the high-peaker control is turned back and forth, the bars will be found to streak white when it is too far in one direction and to streak black when it is too far in the other. The control must be adjusted so that neither of these effects is visible.

There are other adjustments, such as the G-5 control, which will change the sharpness in the corners of the picture. Most of the lining-up process, however, is contained in the directions given above. The cameraman will make whatever contrast and brightness adjustment on his view finder he may wish, but he should not change the height, width, centering, or linearity once the lining up has been done.

VIDICON CAMERAS

Intended originally for the industrial market, the first vidicon cameras were built without view finders and designed generally for unattended operation. Remotely controlled pan, tilt, lens change, and lens adjustments were standard items. Underwater housings were provided by several manufacturers, as well as explosion-proof housings. Small cameras were ruggedized so they could be shot off in missiles and remain operative. It is not within the scope of this book to discuss industrial applications of TV equipment. However, vidicon cameras constantly improved and soon began to interest schools as a visual aid in the improvement and extension of teaching and as equipment for school studios where television techniques were taught. Small broadcasting stations began to use vidicons and the Armed Forces Radio and Television Service equipped twenty-four low-power stations at far-flung United States bases with vidicon gear.

In Fig. 3-6 a representative group of industrial vidicon cameras is pictured. Figure 3-7 shows several makes of vidicon cameras equipped with view finders, manual-focus controls, and lens-turret handles so they can be operated by cameramen. Industrial cameras without view finders have been used for studio production, the cameramen relying on a studio floor monitor which, of course, could only show the camera actually on the line. Lining up on a new subject while off the line had to be done through directions from the control room, an unsatisfactory procedure attempted only where nothing better was economically feasible.

The simpler external circuitry of the vidicon camera, as compared with the image-orthicon camera, made possible smaller and less expensive cameras. Another advantage of the vidicon for educational and industrial applications was the lower operating cost. Whereas the image-orthicon

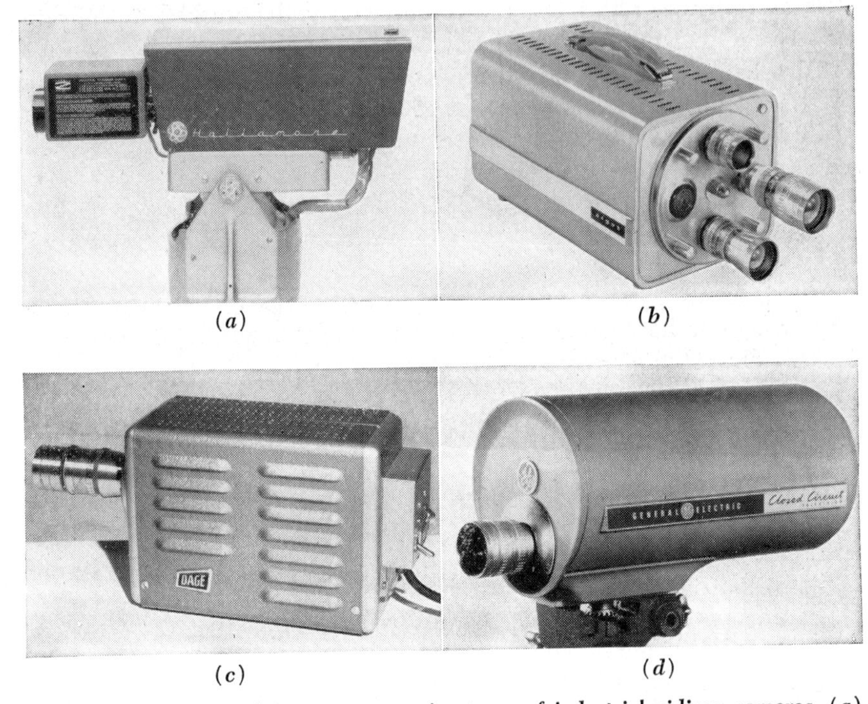

Fig. 3–6. A selection of four representative types of industrial vidicon cameras. (*a*) Hallamore, (*b*) Argus, (*c*) Dage 63A, (*d*) General Electric TE9A. Cameras *b*, *c*, and *d* are entirely self-contained, requiring no further equipment for operation. Camera in (*a*) is shown with remote-control pan and tilt apparatus and remote-control Zoomar lens.

depreciates over a 500-hour guaranteed life, the vidicon can be used up to ten or fifteen times as long. Since its initial cost is about a quarter that of the image-orthicon, the advantage can be very great.

The vidicon tube was built into film pickup cameras, which gave such fine results in broadcasting that the iconoscope film pickup camera was soon rendered obsolete. Lower light sensitivity, general instability, and a tendency to smear on movement kept the tube from producing first-rate pictures in the studio. However, more recent improvements in sensitivity, plus the fine gray-scale rendition which has always characterized the vidicon, have led some persons to the conviction that the vidicon would soon challenge the pre-eminence of the image-orthicon as well.

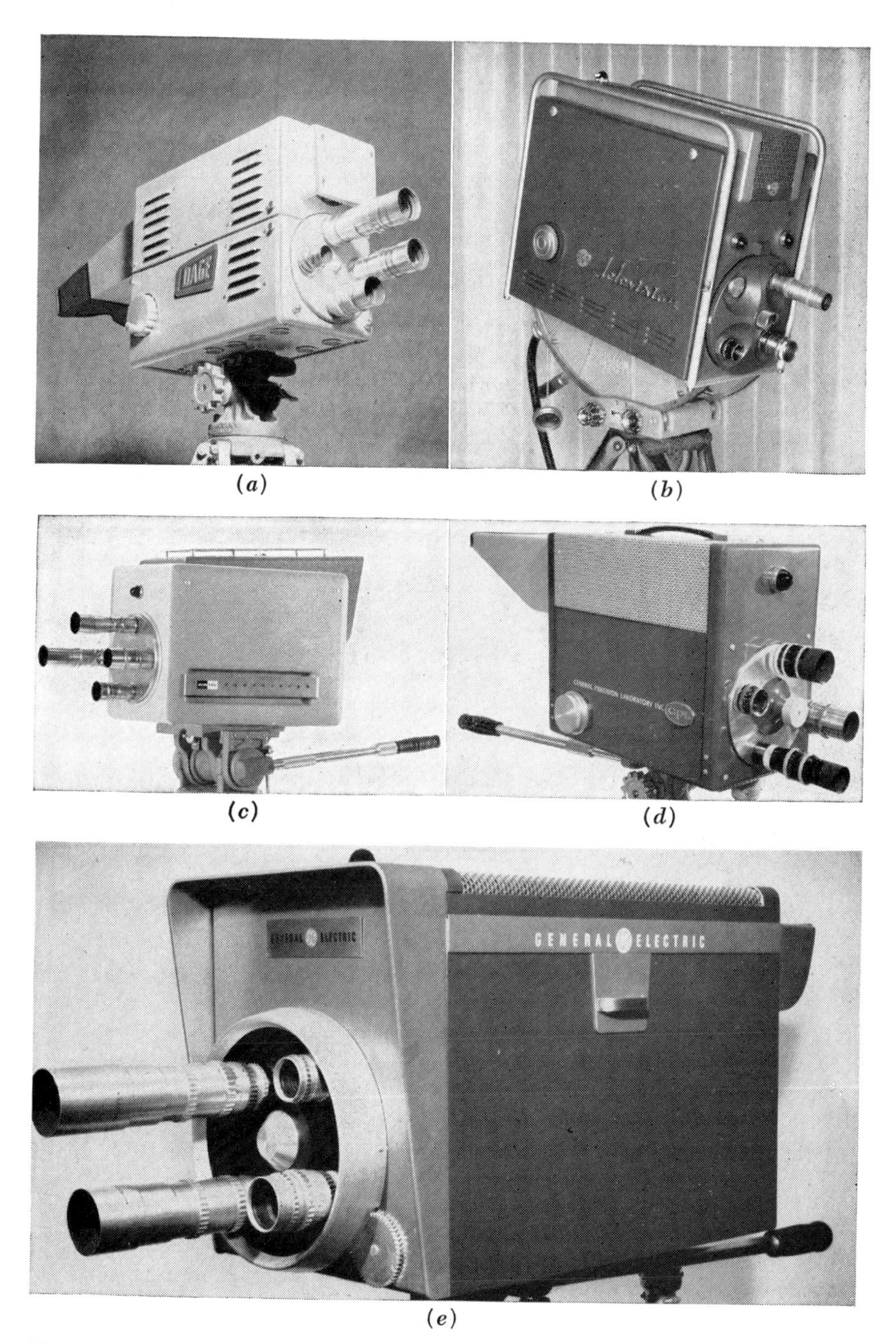

(a) (b) (c) (d) (e)

Fig. 3–7. Several representative examples of studio vidicon cameras intended for broadcast purposes. (*a*) Dage 320A, (*b*) RCA TK15, (*c*) Kintel, (*d*) GPL PD250, (*e*) General Electric TG2.

THE 4½-INCH IMAGE-ORTHICON CAMERA

The development of a superior image-orthicon camera tube changed the picture considerably. Although 4½ inches in diameter instead of 3 inches, the new tube used the same lenses as the standard image-orthicon. The increase in size was effected in the image section of the tube; the photocathode on which the image is focused is standard size. The electron

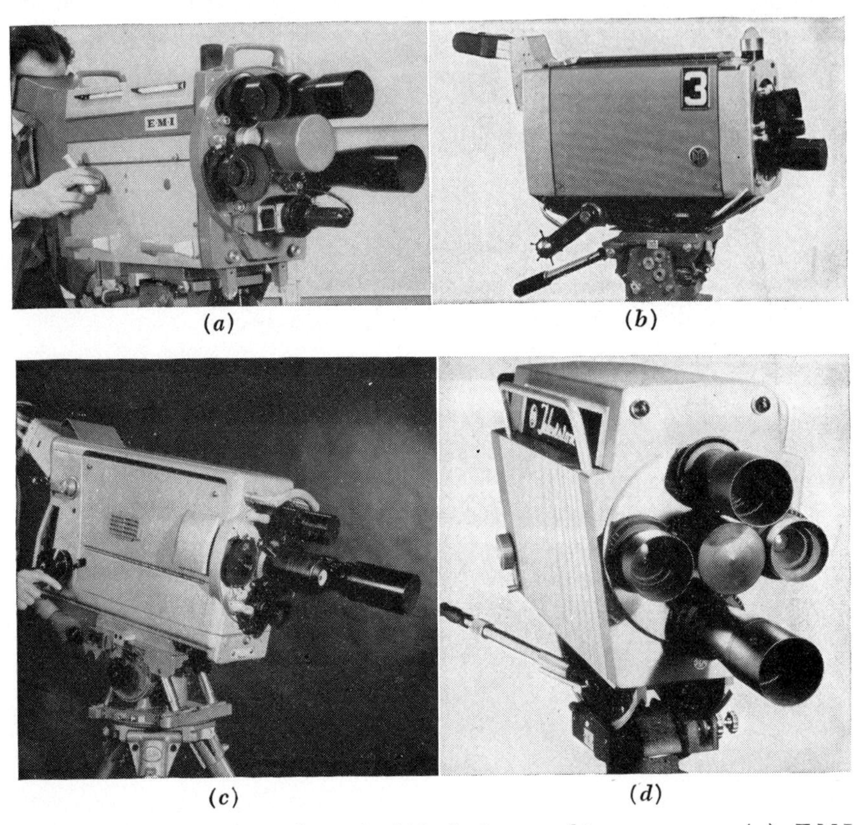

Fig. 3–8. Four major makes of 4½-inch image-orthicon cameras. (*a*) E.M.I. (Electro-motive Industries, British), (*b*) Pye (British), (*c*) Marconi (British), (*d*) RCA.

image is expanded as it is moved back to the target at the back of the image section. The larger target area makes possible better resolution as well as virtual elimination of the "halo" effect. A further discussion of the characteristics of the 4½-inch image-orthicon tube will be found in Chap. 8. Figure 3-8 illustrates several cameras built around the 4½-inch tube. Note that the E.M.I. camera provides a fifth turret position to accommodate a small 2-by-2 slide projector for test-chart or title-slide purposes.

4

Camera Handling

There are four different ways of using the camera in television. The first of these is exemplified by the standard *objective* camera of dramatic films, the presence of which is completely unnoticed by everyone in the scene with it. Camera consciousness in the viewer is to be avoided. Rough camera handling can have the result of calling attention to the camera and destroying the story illusion.

A second way of using the camera is the *subjective* technique. Here the camera takes part in the drama, becoming one of the actors. The audience at home, the camera, and the character in the drama are all one. Actors address this character by speaking directly into the camera lens. Rough camerawork may not result in camera consciousness since movements of the camera are interpreted as movements of the identified character.

A third way to use the TV camera is simply as a receiving instrument, like the radio microphone, into which people can talk and look in order to reach the viewing audience. The camera is used in this manner on most nondramatic programs where no illusion is attempted. The camera is like a window, having no importance in itself except that it allows the people on one side of a wall to see through to the other. There is still an element of the formal presentation across the footlights in most shows produced by this technique. Camera consciousness is not fatal but is definitely to be avoided, and so smooth handling is essential.

The fourth camera technique is similar to the third, except that the camera is very much a part of the scene. No attempt is made to hide one camera from the view of another or to preserve the anonymity of the television crew. The performer, the cameraman, the camera, and the audience are more nearly one. This represents the complete loss of theatrical illusion, of aesthetic distance, of the footlights separating audience from stage. Front stage and back stage are the same. In this technique, camera consciousness need not be avoided. Rough camera handling—changing lenses on the air, abrupt panning, or bumpy dollying—is not at all the crime it is otherwise held to be. Small hand-held television cameras extend the possibilities of this technique.

Creative camera work must be originally conceived and planned by the director. On a dramatic show this is usually done while the production is still in the paper stage. The director weighs the various possibilities in each case, visualizes the final shot on a receiver screen, and makes his selection. The choices that he must make fall within several categories and can be listed as follows:

1. Choice of field of view. The director must decide how much of the subject should be included in the frame.
2. Choice of camera angle. The director must decide from what direction the camera will view the subject.
3. Choice of camera movement. This will include rotation of the camera on a vertical or horizontal axis, bodily movement of the camera as in dollying and trucking, and vertical movement (i.e., raising or lowering the camera).

STAGING FOR THE TELEVISION CAMERA

A great deal of what the camera is able to do depends on the staging of the action before it. People with stage experience, for example, have had to learn that in a television studio the stage for action is altogether different from what it is in a theater. Instead of being crosswise to the audience, the television stage is lengthwise. It is a long, cone-shaped area, wide at the back and tapering to a point at the camera lens. If a director conceives of this area as his stage, he will stage action in depth, making his important entrances and exits either near the camera or at the far back. He will also remember that every time he cuts to another camera he is creating a new stage. This then means that camera shots and action are best constructed together.

Staging of static scenes is also important. As soon as the camera holds a static shot, pictorial composition becomes important. The director will often try to group his people so that they make as simple a form as possible. Three people standing separately are only three people, but the same three standing together or one before the other so that they overlap on the television screen will make a single form. This is usually a simpler and better composition. Of all the many shapes a form may take, perhaps the pyramid is the strongest. The apex of this form is a compelling spot in the composition and lends dominance to whatever may be placed there. Here again, an early decision in regard to the use of the camera will in many cases dictate the grouping and composition of the subject itself.

CHOICE OF FIELD OF VIEW

On the first reading of the dramatic script a director will begin to make his decisions about field of view. He will decide whether he wants a single or a two-shot (one or two people), a full-length shot, or head and shoulders. The terms long shot, medium shot, and close-up, commonly used to designate various fields of view, have no exact meaning. A shot is long, close, or medium only in relation to the other shots that are used with it. Many TV directors identify the type of shot they want by describing in one word where the lower edge of the frame cuts the actor. The use of such specific terms as knee shot, thigh shot, waist shot, shoulder shot, etc., will result in nearly the same kind of framing every time.

The cameraman works for a pleasing composition largely by adjustment of the field of view. This is known as "framing." A better composition is sometimes asked for in the simple command "Frame up." The cameraman pans, tilts, or dollies in or back until the composition is pleasing. The framing is considered tight when the subject is crowding the sides of the frame and loose when there is considerable space around it. A loose composition is always safer since the camera can be ready for broader action, but a tight composition is usually the more pleasing.

The actual physical size of the subject on the television screen is an important dramatic factor. A close-up emphasizes that subject or that part of the subject which is shown. Greater importance is imparted to the larger objects in the scene. A long shot may have dramatic value also, in the opposite way. Sometimes when a character feels lost, rejected, and very small in relation to the world, a long shot which actually shows him small in relation to his surroundings will enhance the dramatic mood.

CHOICE OF CAMERA ANGLE

A good camera angle can often improve composition by introducing variety of size (the principle of subordination). If the camera is placed so that all the people in the picture are the same size, the shot is usually less interesting than when some people are larger on the screen than others. Proper staging in depth can make this possible, or placing the camera to the side of the set instead of shooting everything head on.

Variation in height is another important factor in good composition. From a lower-than-eye-level camera position, near people are high in the picture and far people lower. If the camera is higher than eye level, this relationship is reversed.

As for the dramatic values of camera angles, the proper placement of the camera can often enhance the dramatic relationship of one person to another. This is the principle of dominance. A larger object dominates a smaller one, and a person higher in the picture tends to dominate one who is lower down. Moreover, if one is looking up at an object (such as a statue high on a pedestal), it takes on a greater importance than the viewer. We feel that we are figuratively as well as actually "looking up" to it. Conversely, if the camera shoots down on someone, he is less important than we are.

Most television cameras are equipped with tripods and tripod dollies which will not allow any change in camera height. Only the larger studios have pedestals and boom dollies which can be raised or lowered. Even there, however, cameras are operated most of the time at eye level. This is a matter of necessity, since no cameraman could be asked to operate for several hours at a stretch in anything but the most comfortable position.

High-angle shots are sometimes obtained by mounting a camera on a lighting catwalk or other vantage point in the studio. This entails taking it off its regular mount and devoting it entirely to that one use. Usually it means leaving the camera in its high place during the entire broad-

Fig. 4–1. Camera suspended on batten for top shot above stage (35-mm lens in use).

cast evening. Such cameras have been left unattended, set up for only one shot.

There are several methods of obtaining a high-angle shot through the use of one or two mirrors. These techniques are explained in detail in Chap. 11 in the section on the use of mirrors.

It is interesting to note that the *effect* of a high- or a low-angle shot can sometimes be achieved although the camera is in reality shooting from a normal angle. On the Du Mont program "Hands of Mystery," a top shot of a man in bed was achieved by standing the bed up vertically and pinning the bed sheets up around the actor, who then stood in bed in front of the camera. Again, on this same imaginative program, a low-angle shot was obtained by building a flat to resemble a ceiling with a cheap electric fixture attached to it and holding this at an angle behind the actor. The actor leaned slightly backward, and the resultant shot looked exactly as if it were taken from a low angle shooting up against the ceiling.

In some studios an industrial machine known as a "stacker" has been experimented with. It provides an adjustable platform on which the camera and cameramen can be raised to a high position by manual means. In the case of this particular apparatus the raising or lowering operation is noisy; so it cannot be adjusted during the program, nor can it be moved about while the camera is shooting.

THE CANTED SHOT

When the camera is tilted sideways, vertical lines are no longer vertical and horizontal lines no longer horizontal on the screen (Fig. 4-2). This movement can be called a "roll," since it is analogous to the rolling of a boat. The angle shot which results, however, is called a "canted" shot. The composition of such a shot is often quite dramatic owing to the predominance of strong diagonal lines across the screen. A special camera setup must usually be made, however, and because of the special preparations involved, the canted shot is not often used. None of the regular controls on television cameras will permit this canted effect. Below are listed several ways to achieve the canted shot:

1. A special setup can be made with an unevenly set tripod. This is the method usually employed in films, but it is not practical for television unless the camera is to serve no other purpose in a production.

2. The tripod head may be set at right angles to its regular position, or if standard tilting cannot be sacrificed, two tripod heads may be mounted one on top of the other, at right angles to each other. Special shopwork is required, however, to fit the tripod heads together, and the camera is raised quite high.

3. The image-orthicon tube can be twisted with its yoke inside the camera. This again requires special preparation and eliminates the camera for any other use.

4. The image-accelerator control on the camera will tilt the picture slightly to left or right. This is a quick adjustment that the cameraman can make, but it rarely produces quite the effect desired.

Fig. 4–2. Canted shot obtained with a dove prism.

5. A mirror shot has often been resorted to for this effect. The mirror is placed to the side of the subject and slanted a little out of vertical. This is described in greater detail in the section on mirrors in Chap. 11.

6. When the Fearless Panoram dolly is used, still another possibility is open. Beneath the panhead on this dolly are two small leveling screws, one on each side. If these are taken out and wood blocks substituted, the leveling can be greatly changed very quickly by changing the blocks. A large block on one side of the head, for example, and none on the other will cant the camera a considerable amount, which, if combined with the image-accelerator effect, is said to be quite useful.

7. The simplest and most practical method involves a large dove prism (see Fig. 11-14, page 200). The prism is placed endwise in front of the

lens and is suitably mounted so that it can be rotated. Ninety degrees of rotation will turn the picture upside down. The prism, like the single mirror, will reverse the image from left to right, so scanning reversal is generally employed to correct it.

CAMERA MOVEMENT—PANNING

Movement of the camera on its vertical axis (that is, twisting it from one direction to another) is called "panning" (from panorama). Tilting the camera up and down is often combined with the pan shot and is subject to the same considerations (Fig. 4-3). In fact, the tilt shot is frequently called a pan in television; the director calls for a pan up or pan down, just as he does for a pan left or right. The following discussion of panning should be understood, therefore, to include tilting as well.

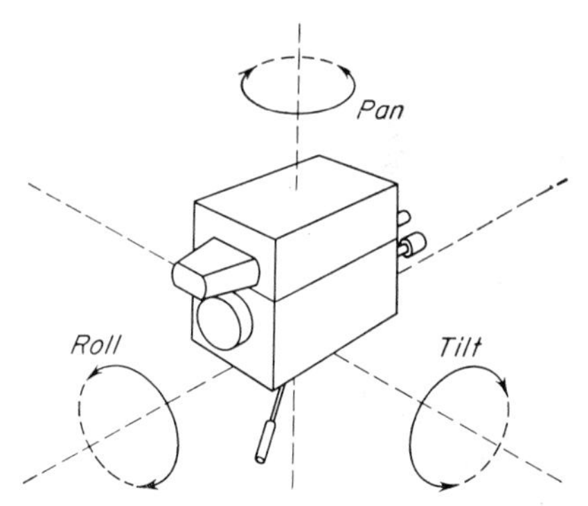

Fig. 4–3. Rotation around three camera axes.

Panning is the most common camera movement or adjustment, and it is one of the first things that the cameraman must learn to do. He must learn smoothness, control, and how to make his movements definite and deliberate. The best-executed pan shot, however, does not always work. One or more static shots are better in many cases. There are certain qualities that camera movement must have; lacking these, it may be more of a detriment than a help.

Every camera movement (as indeed every device of production) must first be motivated. In other words, the audience must *want* the camera to be moved. Second, each camera movement must retain interest and be continuously gratifying throughout its duration. Finally, camera movement must achieve a purpose and have some value to the production as a whole. Let us examine these various requirements in greater detail, though not necessarily in the order in which they have been mentioned.

The pan must be smooth. Smoothness is partly a matter of manual dexterity and partly of quality of equipment. A pan shot should not be jerky; if it is following action, it should not lag behind the motion of the subject; and it should start and stop smoothly. Sometimes it is possible to start a pan slowly, gather speed, and then slow down smoothly at the end. If the pan must follow an irregular action, the cameraman must smooth out the motion of the camera and not attempt to follow every jump and jerk exactly.

A camera is panning too fast when the picture is hard to watch on the screen. Normally a pan which follows the motion of a subject can be made at whatever speed the movement requires, as long as the camera can stay with the subject.

If the pan is not following action, the speed of panning must necessarily be much less, because everything is in motion across the face of the screen. If the scene is relatively a plain and simple one, such as quiet sea and sky, the camera can slide over it much faster than it can over complicated and detailed backgrounds. The more there is for the eye to examine, the slower the pan must be.

If, for some reason, the camera must pan fast across a stationary scene, then it should pan *very* fast, so that the eye is not tempted to identify objects in the blur but just lets the whiz go by. This type of shot is sometimes called a "whiz," or "swish," pan. It has a definite dramatic effect but cannot be used indiscriminately without the danger of calling attention to the camera.

The pan must be continuously interesting. The pan shot, like anything else in showmanship, must be continuously interesting to the audience. It must have a beginning, a middle, and an end. The motivation for the pan gives it a beginning; the ultimate purpose is usually recognizable at its conclusion and gives it an end; but a frequent error in camerawork is to forget about the middle.

It is a mistake, for instance, to pan across large open areas lacking in visual interest. Often the camera must pan between two people, and

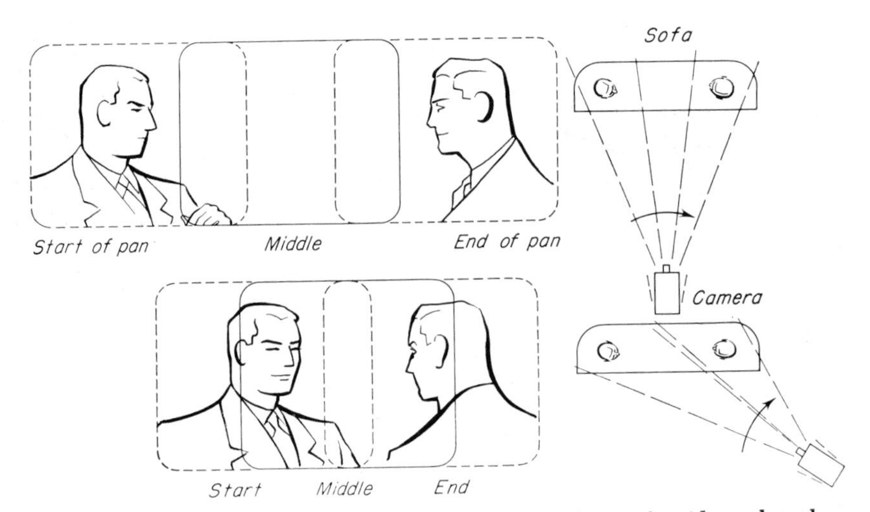

Fig. 4–4. The pan shot with the uninteresting middle. Choice of a side angle reduces the length of the pan. The new subject can start to enter the frame as soon as the camera starts to pan.

there is nothing of importance to show in the process of panning (as in the case of two people conversing on a sofa).

Figure 4-4 shows a common problem in camera coverage. By the first method, with the camera perpendicular to the sofa, a relatively long and uninteresting middle is necessary to link the beginning and end of the pan shot. Unless the two subjects can be moved closer together (and this is sometimes not possible), the camera must find another angle from which a shorter pan can be made. By the second method, the uninteresting middle is eliminated from the pan entirely. The second person enters the frame of the picture before the first has disappeared from sight. Standard practice is to seat people closer together than they would normally seat themselves.

The pan must be motivated. The audience must *want* the camera to pan. If the camera pans without motivation, the viewer will be, so to speak, dragged away from something he is looking at. He will resent this, if only subconsciously; and his conscious mind may even be called to the camera and away from the subject of the shot. Camera consciousness is always to be avoided when a story illusion is being conveyed, since the illusion is broken when attention is called to the mechanics of production.

Equipment and techniques for panning. The action of panning is not performed by the camera, of course, but by the tripod head on which the

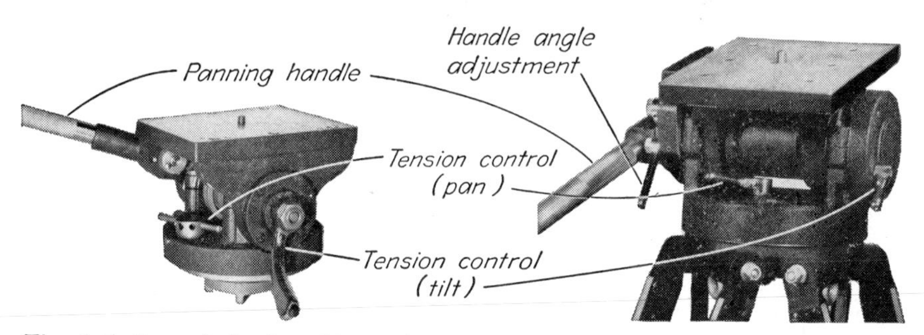

Fig. 4–5. Two of the best friction heads: Fearless (left) and Camera Equipment Co. (right).

camera rests. Standard motion-picture equipment is used for this purpose, since the demands of television panning are not very different from those of film.

The standard type of tripod head is the "friction head" (Fig. 4-5). As the name implies, the friction head provides friction surfaces which slide across each other as the camera pans. Controls on the tripod head regulate the pressure with which these surfaces press against each other and thus provide varying resistance to movement.

Since television cameras are considerably heavier and bulkier than all but the largest studio film equipment, they have a higher center of gravity. As long as this center of gravity is over the base of support, the camera will not be out of balance; but as soon as it is tilted forward so that the center of gravity is beyond the base, the camera acts like a lever, with its weight pushing the head into a steeper and steeper tilt. To counteract the overbalancing effect, friction heads are designed with heavy steel springs coiled around the tilting axis so that the farther forward the camera tilts, the stronger is the spring tension opposing that movement.

A tripod head known as the "cradle" type (Fig. 4-6) completely eliminates the overbalancing effect by removing its cause. Since the

Fig. 4–6. Houston-Fearless cradle head.

cradle tilts by rolling forward and back, its center of rotation is well above it, at the center of curvature of the cradle. This is so designed, in the case of the TV cradle head, as to be at the center of gravity of the average image-orthicon camera. Thus the camera's center of gravity never moves as the camera tilts, and the same balance is maintained at every position of tilt.

The cradle-head design was developed originally for heavy motion-picture cameras but was built for gear operation, requiring the camera operator to use one hand on the panning and the other on the tilting crank. Since the TV cameraman must have a hand free with which to follow focus, a free-moving type of cradle head was designed, controlled by a single pan and tilt handle. The three-tube RCA color cameras (see

Fig. 21-1) are, because of their great bulk, necessarily mounted on cradle heads of this same type, but of a heavier design.

CAMERA MOVEMENT—DOLLYING

Bodily movement of the camera is similar to panning in its basic requirements. Here again we may say that camera movement must be smooth, continuously interesting, motivated (in the beginning), and purposeful (in the end).

Smoothness is a result of the skill of cameraman and dollyman but is also dependent on the equipment the cameraman is given, the size of the dolly wheels, and the smoothness of the floor. In motion-picture work, absolute smoothness has usually been achieved by laying metal tracks ahead of the dolly. Where this has been attempted in television, more has been lost than gained, because of the resultant inflexibility of camera movement and positioning.

Smoothness of dollying is also dependent on the focal length of the lens in the camera. A long lens magnifies the scene and also the irregularities of camera movement. The shorter the lens (the wider the lens angle), the smoother the dolly movement appears to be. The 50-mm (wide-angle lens) provides the smoothest dolly, but the 90-mm (normal lens) is more commonly used for all purposes and hence for dolly shots as well. The extremely wide-angle 35-mm lens exaggerates the speed of forward or backward motion of the camera and must be used with caution except for special effects. The 135-mm lens is too long for smooth dollying on anything but the smoothest equipment and studio floor. Anything over this length is impossible to handle smoothly on a moving camera.

The zoom lens has been used in some studios to replace dollying (see pages 69 to 75 for an explanation of the variable-focal-length lens). Perfect smoothness is obtained with a zoom lens since the camera does not actually have to move at all.

Motivations of dollying. Only fast dolly movement has to be motivated. A slow dolly, if smoothly executed, often goes unnoticed, even without special motivation. Thus the slow dolly can be arbitrarily used for a variety of purposes. Some of the best television cameramen keep their studio pedestals almost constantly in motion, achieving a great fluidity and flexibility by this means. Fast dolly movement can be motivated by intense dramatic action or by motion of the subject which the camera is following. Unmotivated fast dollying causes camera consciousness.

A dolly movement which follows action is usually well motivated. A person moves from the back of the set up to a position at the front, and the camera dollies back in front of him, keeping him always the same size in the frame. This kind of camera work is sometimes called a "follow shot" or a "travel shot." In motion pictures it is usually termed a "trucking shot" because of the method of putting a camera in a truck and trucking up the road in front of the galloping cowboy, keeping always the same distance from the action. The term trucking shot is used in television more often to mean any kind of camera movement which is not toward or away from the action. Thus the television cameraman is asked to dolly in or pull back but to truck left or truck diagonally in to the right.

The dramatic effect of fast movement. Man's sixth sense is the kinesthetic, the sensation of bodily movement perceived through all the nerves of the body and of course accompanied by a strong visual sensation of movement.

Whereas we cannot transport the viewer through space, we can give him the visual sensations of movement by moving the camera, and the faster this movement, the stronger the kinesthetic effect. A fast dolly or a fast zoom with the zoom lens will carry the spectator in breathless flight through space and add a strong dramatic emphasis to the action. This has frequently been used in dramatic shows at moments such as a dramatic entrance, a sudden accusation of murder, or a sudden realization of the "awful truth." At all these moments a big close-up of the actor is called for, and a sudden dramatic swoop of the camera can intensify the dramatic effect.

VERTICAL CAMERA MOVEMENT

The ability of the cameraman to move his camera vertically depends on the equipment he is given. Some camera mounts (the counterweighted crane dollies) can raise and lower the camera so easily that there is a tendency to overdo the effect and raise or lower the camera without sufficient motivation. Many television studios, on the other hand, are provided with no equipment whatever for vertical camera movement.

Dramatic purpose can sometimes be served by a camera which is in slow vertical movement, changing its camera angle during a scene. For example, imagine a scene in which two people carry on a conversation during which the relation of one to the other is slowly reversed. One person dominates the scene at the beginning, let us say, while at the conclusion the other person is in control. If the dominant person is placed in the background of the shot and the camera is placed somewhat above eye level, he will be higher in the picture than the one in the foreground. This will give him a dominant position in the composition. When, during the conversation, the foreground person comes to dominate the

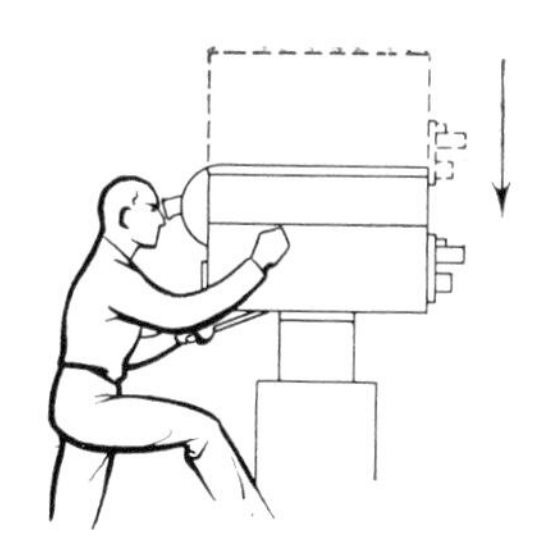

Fig. 4–7. At beginning of scene, *A* is dominant; at end *B* has become the stronger. Camera contributes to this dramatic change by a slow, vertical movement to a lower camera angle.

scene, the camera slowly lowers its height until it is lower than eye level and the foreground figure becomes the higher of the two and the dominant element in the composition (Fig. 4-7).

CAMERA MOUNTS AND EQUIPMENT FOR MOVEMENT

Camera mounts are of several types. The simplest is the tripod on a three-castered base and the most complex is the counterweighted crane. Flexibility and quality of camera movement, as well as freedom in repositioning the cameras between shots, are dependent in large measure on the equipment on which the camera is mounted.

Camera movement and camera repositioning are two different things and must not be confused. Camera movement refers to the movement of the camera while it is on the air. Repositioning, however, is done while the camera is off the air, in setting up for its next shot. Some of the dolly equipment mentioned in the next section is well adapted to one of these functions and not the other.

Examples of the principal types of camera mounts are described in detail in the following sections. From this discussion the reader should be able to evaluate the equipment available to him and determine the best methods of operating it.

The requirements of good dolly design for repositioning between shots are as follows: (1) Maneuverability. The dolly should be able to move in any desired direction without much backing and steering. (2) Speed. The dolly should be able to reach the next camera position in the shortest possible time. Of course noiseless operation is required, but smoothness is not a consideration. Thus wheels of the castered type are well suited for repositioning.

On-the-air dollying must be smooth, and it must be controlled. Caster wheels have a habit of going in the direction offering the least resistance and will often make the direction of movement hard to control. Locked wheels, on the other hand, are certain to go in a straight line. The larger the wheel, the smoother it will roll in most cases.

TRIPOD DOLLIES

Turning now to camera mounts which will permit both quick repositioning of the camera between shots and camera movement on the air, the first to be considered is the tripod dolly. This is simply a three-wheeled base on which a tripod can be mounted. Many stations have built these themselves at little cost out of a triangular piece of plywood and three large casters (Fig. 4-8). If the casters swivel easily and roll

Fig. 4–8. Station-built tripod dolly with caster wheels. Lack of cable guards is serious disadvantage.

smoothly, this dolly can be used for simple on-the-air moves, at least in straight-line movement, although before a shot a little advance preparation is needed to get the wheels lined up in the right direction. A particularly skillful cameraman can control direction to some extent during a movement on one of the better tripod dollies and simulate what can usually be done only with a two-man-operated boom dolly. This is definitely the exception, however, the tripod dolly being primarily a device to provide mobility for the camera between shots while it is off the air.

The RCA tripod dolly (Fig. 4-9) is highly flexible and will permit movement in almost any direction at any time. It is collapsible and

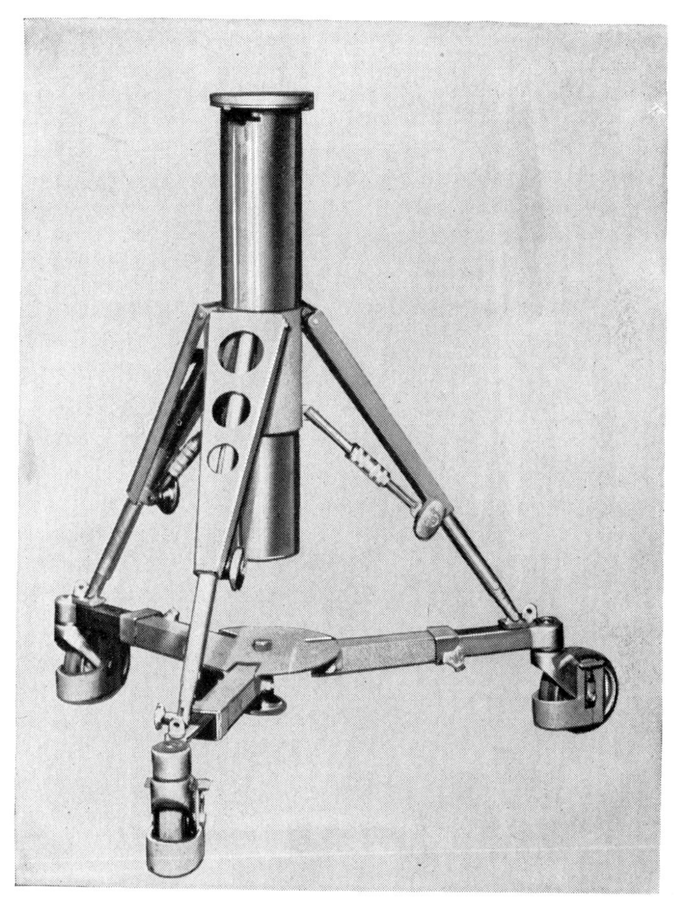

Fig. 4–9. RCA tripod dolly with caster wheels.

may be used on "remote" work if desired. Large caster wheels ensure smooth movement.

Some television stations have acquired tripod dollies which have only one steerable wheel. This is a very great disadvantage in television studios. No matter what kind of wheeled camera mounts are used, all wheels should be steerable so that backing and turning will not be necessary.

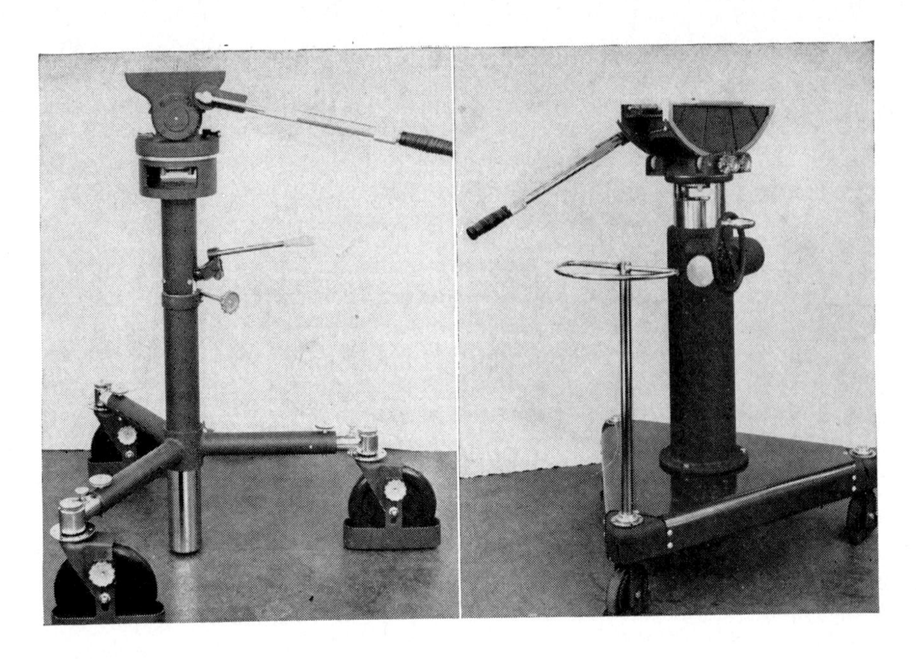

Fig. 4–10. Three models of Houston-Fearless pedestals. Top left: PD 10; top right: PD 7, which has synchronous steering, but steering post is difficult to reach from opposite side of dolly. Bottom left: Counterweighted pedestal at lowest height. Note that steering ring is equally handy from all sides of dolly. Smaller ring is lock for lowering and raising action. Bottom right: Counterweighted pedestal at highest extension.

STUDIO PEDESTALS

Many people consider that the nearest thing to a final answer to the maneuverability problems in the television studio is to be found in the studio pedestal type of camera dolly (Fig. 4-10). With this equipment one man can often achieve the same quality of camera movement that two men usually produce with more complicated dollies.

The three wheels on the pedestal are joined with a counterweighted chain so that they are locked together and must all point the same way. Steering is controlled by a handle which circles the pedestal at about waist height. Motion in any direction is possible as soon as the wheels are correctly aligned. On-the-air movement was not intended by the manufacturers, yet cameramen constantly achieve excellent dolly shots with studio pedestals.

Steering during on-the-air movements is possible only if the cameraman can release his hold on the focus control to steer the pedestal. Sometimes an assistant can help the cameraman by steering the pedestal for him. However, two-man operation of the pedestal usually is considered only an emergency measure in the event that another camera has failed.

Many cameramen prefer the studio pedestal to one of the larger boom dollies. For one thing it can be started into motion faster. The weight of the larger dollies prevents quick reactions of this sort. Another advantage is the small size of this unit, making it possible to move the camera through tight places, get it behind sets to shoot through doors or windows, and squeeze it between mike boom and other studio equipment for greater maneuverability and choice of camera position. A third factor, which has led some cameramen to request this unit when they could have had a Fearless Panoram dolly and dolly pusher for a dramatic show, is that all motions of the camera are under the cameraman's complete control.

When the camera is at minimum pedestal height (lens height 3 feet 10 inches), the handle for steering and movement control is too low to reach properly and moving the pedestal is very difficult. On-the-air moves are much easier at standard height (which is, of course, the height at which the view finder is just at the cameraman's eye level). The pedestal will raise the camera until the lens is at a height of 6 feet from the floor.

The control of height in some studio pedestals is manual; a hand crank projects up from the base of the pedestal for the purpose. This adjustment can be made while the camera is on the air if an assistant can handle the crank. Some cameramen who have had considerable experi-

Fig. 4–11. Pat McBride adjusts pedestal height while his camera is on the air. (Courtesy of Popular Science.)

ence with this equipment have found that they can operate the hand crank with the foot (Fig. 4-11).

BOOM DOLLIES

A boom dolly requires two- and sometimes three-man operation and is thus for the great majority of small stations too expensive to operate. Most models are almost a direct transplantation of motion-picture equipment, to which have been added a few new wrinkles to adapt them to the different requirements of television use.

The Fearless Panoram dolly. Nearly every station which attempts dramatic shows is equipped with a Panoram dolly (Fig. 4-12). This boom dolly permits many kinds of camera movement and a large choice of camera angles, both of which are of great importance in creative camera work. The cameraman may ride the boom on the dolly, he may stand on the platform below, or he may pull the boom over to the side and stand on the studio floor. A good cameraman or cameraman-dollyman team, working with this equipment for a year or so, will develop such skill and precision that they may be operating far beyond the methods for which the instrument was designed or the ways in which it was ever used in the motion-picture field.

Fig. 4–12. Fearless Panoram dolly.

Since the dolly pusher on this team has no view finder, he is in a sense working blind, largely on orders from others, either the director or the cameraman himself. The cameraman at WPIX rigged up a small push-button and light system, so that red and green lights controlled by the cameraman on his pan handle would cue the dollyman for forward and backward movements. Thus the cameraman was able to signal without taking his hands off the camera controls. As he becomes more experienced, the dollyman will develop the ability to keep a constant visualization of the shot the camera is taking, assisted by an occasional glance at the floor monitor or into the camera view finder over the cameraman's shoulder.

This dolly comes equipped with two seats. One of these is on an extended arm and is intended for the assistant camera operator during motion-picture shooting. This is immediately discarded by every television studio. The other, attached to a small arm part way up the boom, is usually retained. Howard Hayes, a top cameraman, used the seat for two years and subsequently abandoned it entirely. He felt he had doubled the flexibility of the instrument by removing this limitation.

It is undoubtedly true that a cameraman who is fastened to a seat is limited to the angles he can shoot from that single position. He is limited in how far to the side he can pan without losing good control or a good view into the view finder. He is limited to one height and to only a narrow lateral range of camera angles. One Western station went so far as to put stirrups on the boom to increase the comfort of the cameraman but admitted they were rather useless when it came to real operation.

The boom, or "tongue," of this dolly is mounted on a turntable in its base. When the seat is used as an operating position, rotation of the turntable is sometimes used as a means of panning. The cameraman holds his camera more or less stationary and swings the boom across the set by cranking the small turntable control wheel. This is often called "tonguing" left or right. It is useful in following action, since it provides at once a panning shot, which keeps the actors in frame, and a transverse camera move, which keeps the relation of camera and actor more nearly the same (Fig. 4-13).

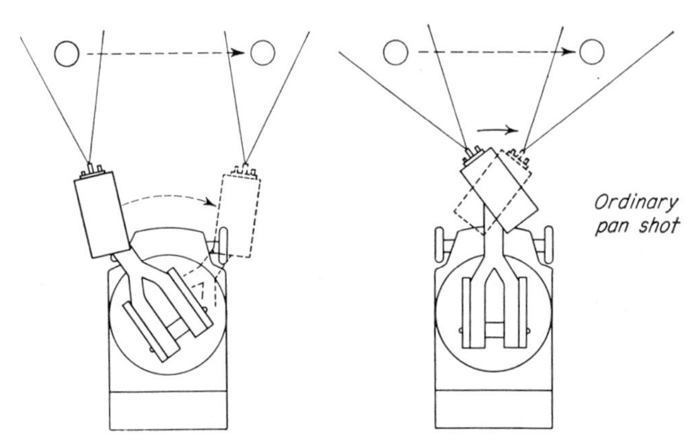

Fig. 4–13. Tonguing to follow action versus panning the camera.

A cameraman will often prefer to achieve a dolly-in effect by moving the boom rather than by rolling the wheels of the dolly. Many cameramen prefer to work with the boom out crosswise from the dolly, their feet on the floor, dollying by walking forward or backward with the camera. The movement is in an arc rather than a straight line, but this makes very little difference. The important thing is that all movements of the camera are under one man's control. If he pushes forward, he can correct focus at the same time; his hands need not leave the controls even for brief signals to the dollyman. A completely coordinated move is the result.

If the dolly is placed almost crosswise to the set (at a slight angle as indicated in Fig. 4-14), the camera can be quickly placed at any point

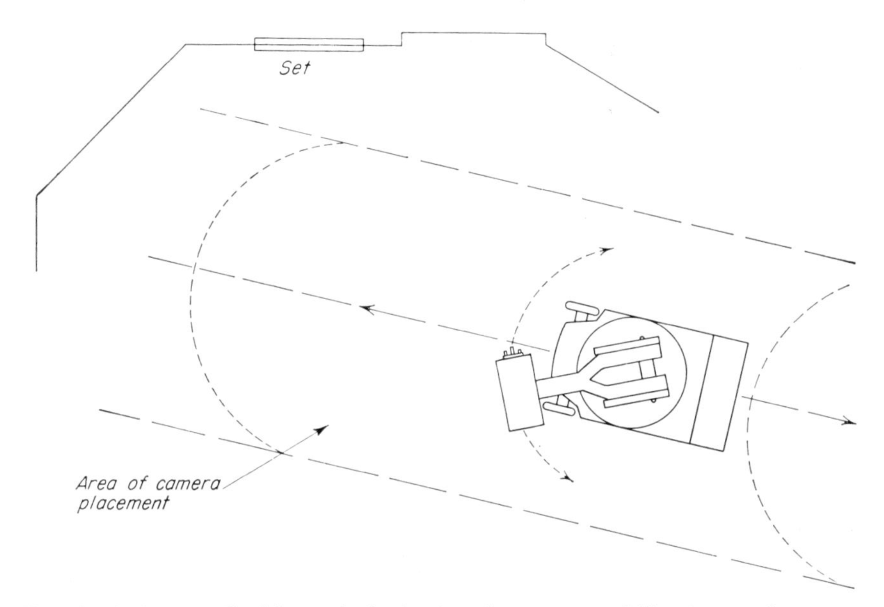

Fig. 4–14. A more flexible method of using the Panoram dolly. Camera has great freedom of positioning, and cameraman has freedom of forward and backward movement.

within the working space indicated. Only two moves are necessary, one by the cameraman (pushing the camera in or out) and one by the dollyman (pushing the dolly forward or backward along the set).

Even without movement of the dolly the cameraman can place his camera in a great variety of positions by utilizing the full possibilities of the camera boom. Speaking three-dimensionally, he can put the camera anywhere on the periphery of a hemisphere which is about 6 feet across and rises to maximum boom height, about 7 feet, in the center (Fig. 4-15). In combination with the choice of lenses instantly available, this provides a great variety of shots without moving the wheels of the dolly at all. Several Panoram dollies at CBS-TV were made more flexible for this kind of use by the addition of a 3-foot extension to the boom. The

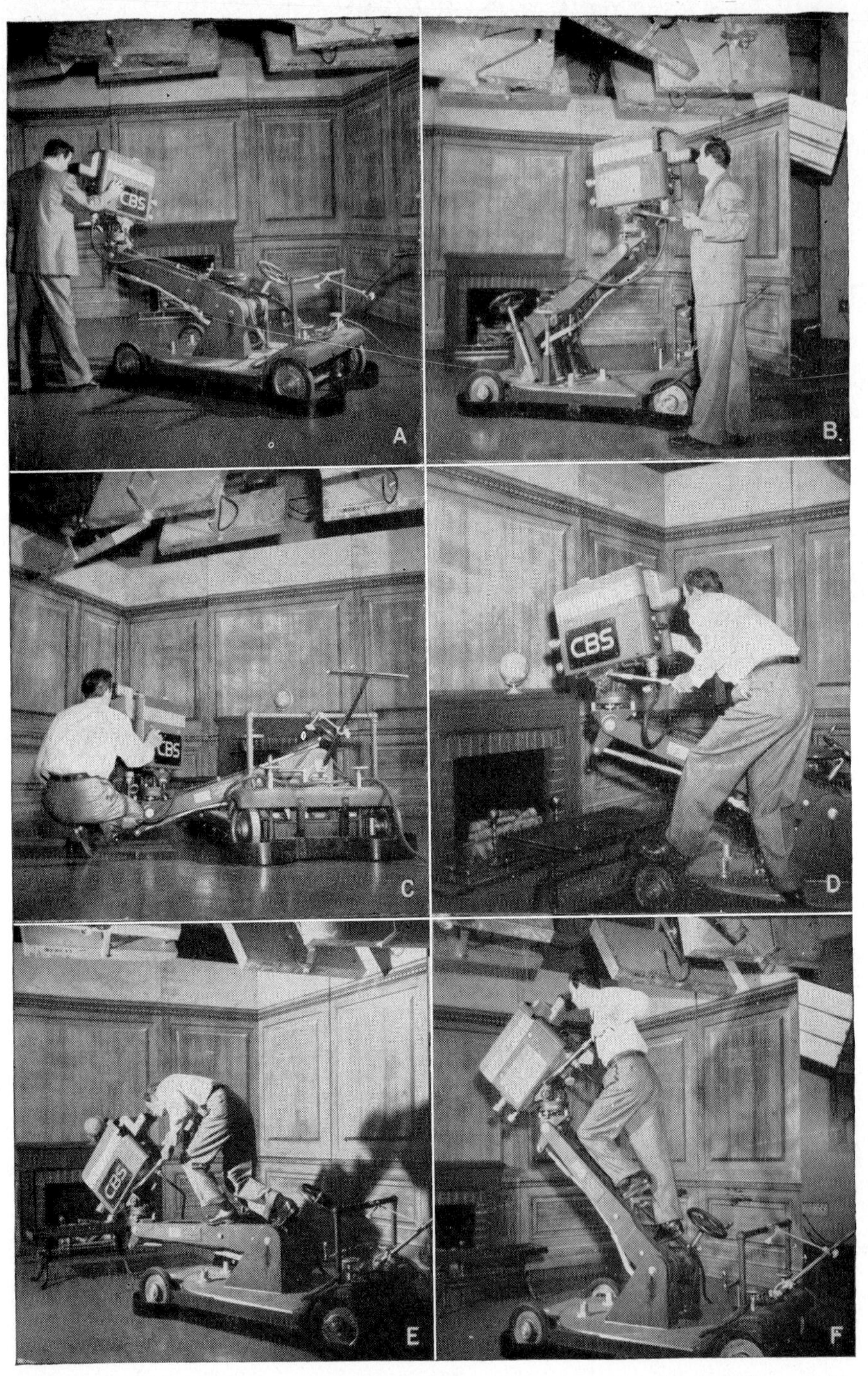

Fig. 4–15. Howard Hayes, top CBS cameraman, demonstrates the flexibility of the camera when mounted on the Panoram dolly.

additional weight was counterbalanced by a concrete weight just on the opposite side of the point of support (Fig. 4-16).

Adjustments in camera height are almost always off-the-air moves, although for special reasons it is sometimes desirable to make a vertical

Fig. 4–16. Fearless dolly adapted by CBS with 3-foot extension on boom counter-balanced by large weight (foreground). Note that auto steering wheel replaces standard handle.

move during a shot. This can be done very easily going down; the cameraman can often control the move himself by reaching back with his foot and spinning the vertical control wheel. Under the weight of the camera—and cameraman—the wheel will spin freely until he again brakes it with his foot, giving him accurate control over the speed and length of the vertical move.

An on-the-air vertical move from low to high must be done by the dollyman since the wheel must be cranked continuously to make the boom rise. If the cameraman is riding the boom, the cranking becomes very difficult; so these moves are usually made with the cameraman standing beside the boom. After the camera is up to the highest point at which he can still control it, he will carefully climb onto the boom. His weight is now less of a factor because the boom is more nearly vertical, and he can easily be cranked up to full height if necessary. Minimum lens height is 28 inches from the floor, obtained when the boom projects from the side of the dolly. Maximum lens height is 7 feet.

The standard Panoram dolly provides for back-wheel steering only, controllable by a handle bar which is lowered to a height most convenient for the dollyman. Pulling the handle to the side will turn the rear wheels. CBS installed an automobile steering wheel on one of its dollies in place of the handle and found it very useful (Fig. 4-16). The dolly could be steered from the side, as well as from behind, and could back up close against sets or the studio wall. Side operation is very important, since from that position the dollyman is able to reach all the boom controls. Very delicate camera movements or adjustments are best made by handling one of the front wheels. Marshall Diskin, who, before he became a director, was one of the best dollymen in the industry, always wore gloves so that he could roll the dolly or at least start it into motion with the wheel.

Formerly the front wheels on the Panoram dolly were individually mounted on swivels so that they could be unlocked from the forward direction and one by one locked into a transverse position. The move took too long for television, however, and so was never used, the cameramen preferring to pull the dolly back and go in again on a different line to find a new position. The later models of this dolly have an additional control to turn both front wheels at once, located toward the back of the machine, where the dolly pusher can reach it easily. At the same time that the front wheels turn, a caster is lowered at the rear of the dolly, lifting the back wheels. The dolly can then be immediately pushed sideways without further steering. Men at some stations use this model freely and find it a valuable addition, since it makes sideways movement a practical thing; other cameramen use it very rarely. It is far from noiseless in operation and must be very carefully handled.

COUNTERWEIGHTED CRANE DOLLIES

Recently several studios have invested in a larger and more elaborate type of dolly with a counterweighted crane. In the Fearless Panoram dolly just described, the weight of cameraman and camera at the end of the boom is balanced by strong coil springs underneath the boom (Fig. 4-17). In the dolly with the counterweighted crane, this weight is balanced by another weight at the other side of the point of suspension of the boom. This weight is adjustable and can be increased or decreased to balance exactly the weight of any cameraman. Raising or lowering

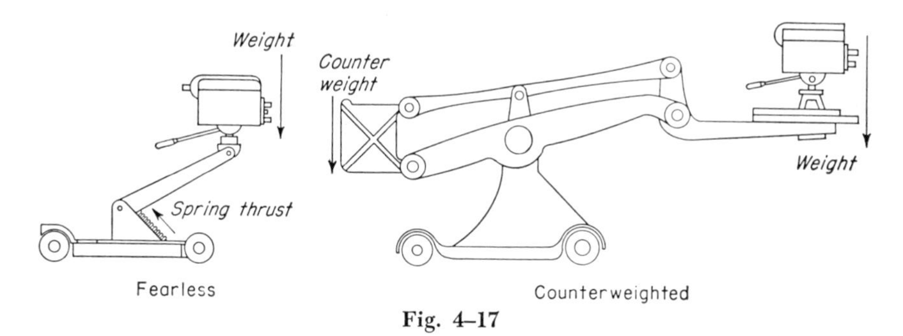

Fig. 4–17

the boom can be accomplished with very little effort, and no cranking is necessary. The camera platform, the boom, and the counterweight are all provided with handles so that the boom man can operate from almost any position.

The Houston-Fearless counterweighted crane. The Houston crane (Fig. 4-18) is standard motion-picture equipment which has been

Fig. 4–18. Houston crane in use at ABC-TV, New York.

adapted for television by the addition of cable guards around the dolly base. It is a three-man operation since the dollyman operates from so far behind the machine that he cannot reach the boom. Steering is controlled by a handle similar to that of the Panoram dolly, and the dolly is motor-driven, under the dollyman's control. The central pedestal of the dolly can be hydraulically raised or lowered 15 inches by a handle at the side of the base. Sometimes it has been found necessary to make more delicate dolly movements than the motor can handle (as when the camera is on a close-up and a slight movement makes a big difference in the picture). It has been found that it is possible to push the machine manually if it is put in gear but power is not applied. This gives a slow and regulated movement not possible with the use of the motor.

In recognition of the very real need of the dollyman for a view finder, both CBS and ABC have installed monitors on the back of the counterweight boom. (The monitor is fed from the camera view finder through a stabilizing amplifier.) With a view finder for the dollyman, and the boom man too, if he works from behind the dolly, it has been found possible on complicated shows to achieve a smooth flow of movement, in time with the music, and coordinated with the actors or dancers in a way which would never be possible if the dollyman had to wait for directions from the cameraman or the control room. On the Paul Whiteman revue, a particularly intricate dance and musical production, the camera on the Houston crane sometimes carried the entire show alone for as long as four minutes at a time, moving in and out, up and down.

The camera platform (turret head) on the Houston crane rotates around a point of support directly under the camera and carries the cameraman's seat around with it so that he is always directly behind the camera. Foot-pedal control operates this, pressure on the right pedal panning the camera left, and pressure on the left panning it to the right (Fig. 4-19). The panning head on the camera is usually left free also, for smaller adjustments, while the cameraman executes the larger movements of panning with his feet. The turret table can be rotated through 180 degrees, and it can be set for any degree of friction by a control within the cameraman's reach.

The boom is capable of carrying the camera lens to a height of 10 feet from the floor and lowering it (when the central pedestal is down) to a height of only 2 feet above the floor. It will rotate around a 360-degree arc, and both panning and tilting of the boom can be set for any desired amount of friction. The entire crane weighs about 1,200 pounds and will pass through a doorway 3 feet wide and 6 feet high.

The Sanner dolly. Another type of counterweighted crane dolly was designed and built by Sid Sanner, a cameraman at KTTV in Hollywood and a design engineer with considerable motion-picture background.

The most important aspect of the Sanner dolly is the method of steering. Whereas all other two-man dollies are steered only by the back wheels, the Sanner dolly steers with all four. A steering wheel is used instead of a handle, and next to the wheel is a lever which will shift between two types of steering.

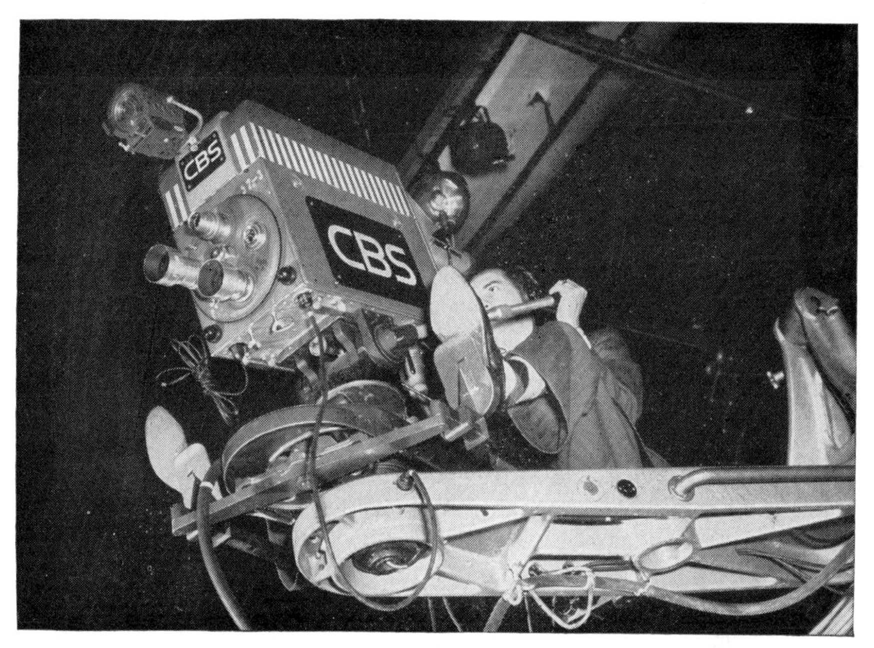

Fig. 4–19. Cameraman on turret table of Houston crane.

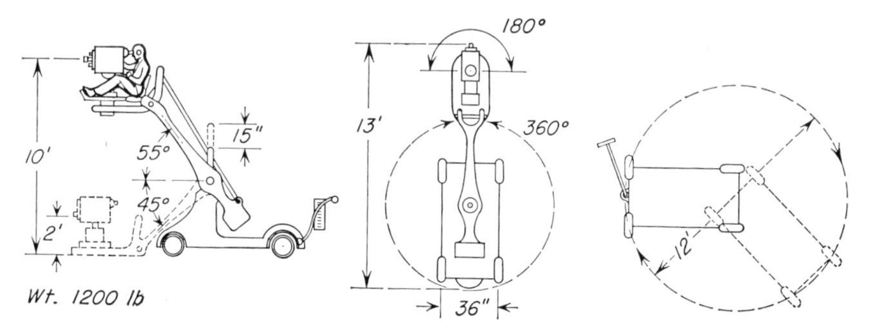

Fig. 4–20. Dimensions and range of movement of Houston crane.

The first type of steering is *synchronous,* i.e., all four wheels change direction at once. This makes it possible to move the dolly in any direction without changing its orientation. The same flexibility of movement which characterizes the studio pedestal is here incorporated into a crane dolly.

Fig. 4–21. Sanner dolly (Sid Sanner behind camera).

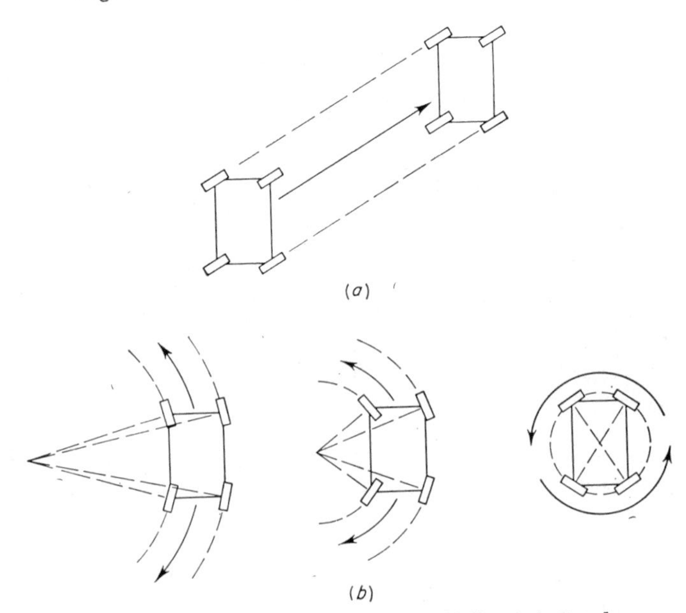

Fig. 4–22. The two steering modes of the Sanner dolly. (*a*) Synchronous steering. (*b*) Differential steering.

The second type is *differential* steering. The back wheels turn in a direction opposite to the front wheels and follow exactly in their tracks. Thus the dolly is able to rotate in a wide or narrow circle or even to rotate on its own length, turning completely around in a circle with a 9-foot diameter. These two methods of steering are a great advantage in the usual television studio, where maneuverability is so highly important.

In a small studio, where a great amount of dolly movement is not necessary, the original Sanner dolly was operated by only two men. Since the steering controls can be reached from the side of the dolly, the dollyman could easily take his position where he could handle the boom. Two men who have worked together for a month or two could operate this dolly all day without rehearsal. The usual practice at a small station which does not allow rehearsal time is for the director to turn over the show for certain periods to the cameraman-dollyman team. On a piano number, for instance, the director may say to the crew, "Take over; the next three minutes are yours" (Fig. 4-23).

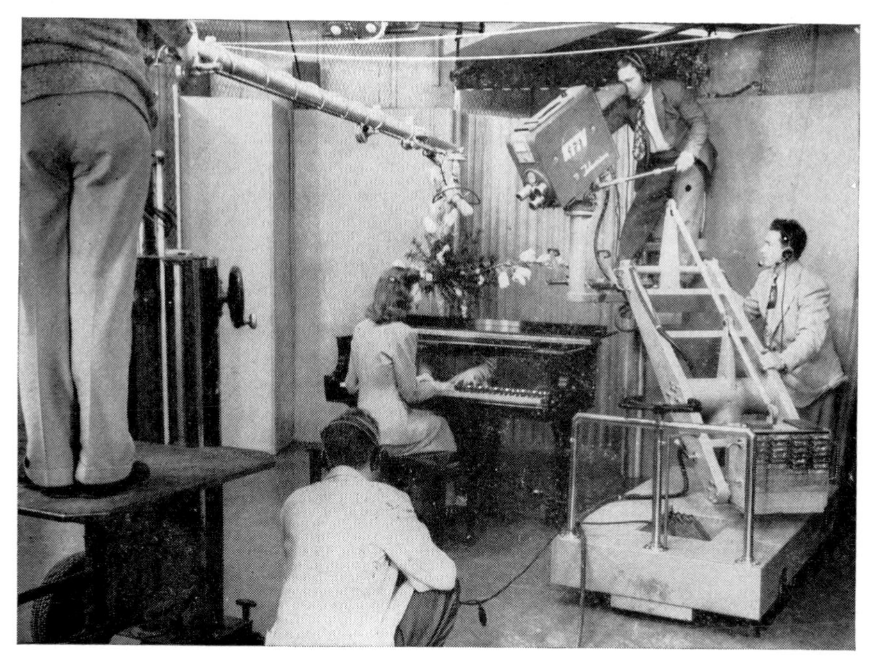

Fig. 4–23. Dollyman-cameraman team working the original Sanner dolly at KTTV, Los Angeles.

One serious drawback to the Sanner dolly, however, is its lack of a motor. Its heavy weight makes it very difficult to start into motion rapidly, and fast moves, either for repositioning between shots or on the air, are a constant requirement in every complex show. Several studios have found it best to assign four men to this dolly: cameraman, boom operator, and two dolly pushers—the strongest and heaviest boys on staff. The excess weight is caused by the fact that the dolly base and other large parts are made of heavy castings. In the original Sanner prototype models all parts were made from plate metal. The change to castings for economy in manufacture added 1,000 pounds to the weight.

The camera platform rotates 180 degrees under control of the cameraman's feet just as in the Houston crane, except that the cameraman may, after reaching the limit of rotation, reach down, release the pedals and reverse them, and then engage them again for another 180 degrees of rotation. If the cameraman should want to stand on his feet, as he often has to for high-angle shots, he can stand on running boards fastened to the same shafts as the foot pedals and continue to control the camera in the same fashion.

McAlister Crab dolly. Probably the most admired dolly is the McAlister Crab dolly (Fig. 4-24). This ingeniously designed dolly has been found very useful in both motion-picture and television work. It lacks a rotating boom, but sidewise motion in any direction is readily pro-

Fig. 4–24. McAlister Crab dolly.

vided by movement of the small and extremely maneuverable dolly base. Smooth vertical movement, within limits similar to those of the camera pedestals, is hydraulically controlled. The dolly base is 5 feet long and 32½ inches wide and weighs only 525 pounds. Since eight wheels are used, the weight of camera and cameraman on each wheel is very little, making the dolly easy to move. Large (12-inch) wheels are used at 70 pounds pressure. All tread is removed from the tires to pre-

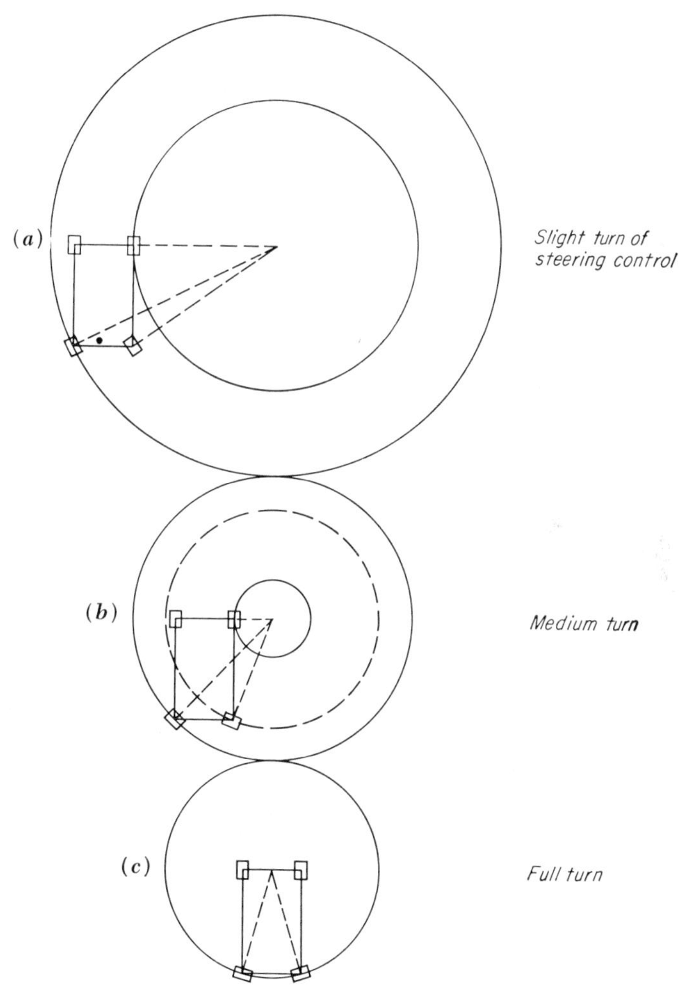

Fig. 4–25. Circular steering with the crab dolly. (*a*) With a slight turn of the steering control the dolly turns on a wide circle. (*b*) With a medium turn of the handle the circle is smaller. The center of rotation is still in line with the front axle. Note how the two steering wheels must turn different amounts. (*c*) With a full turn of the handle the dolly rotates around a point between the two front wheels.

vent squeaking. An important feature, especially in motion-picture work, is that the camera moves exactly vertically when elevating, instead of in a vertical arc like most torque or boom dollies, moving farther from the subject the higher it goes. Steering is controlled by a vertical shaft which

Fig. 4–26. Special remotely controlled pan, tilt, and crane apparatus used by NBC on the daily "Home" program. Camera operators watch view finder in control point overlooking the studio.

allows the dolly to back up against a wall and still be controlled from the side.

Two types of steering are provided, square and circular. Square steering is synchronous, like that of the studio pedestals, all wheels pointing the same direction. Circular steering involves only the back pair of wheels, but because of the short wheelbase of the dolly, this is not a limitation. A special cam arrangement turns each of these back wheels at different rates and angles so each wheel will be always perfectly lined up with the direction in which it is moving. This point can be understood with reference to Fig. 4-25, where the dolly is shown turning in a series of arcs about several centers of rotation. Since each of the rear wheels is a different distance and direction from the center of rotation, each rear wheel must have a different direction of motion. In dollies where this differential relationship is not worked out, one or both of the steering wheels will have to skid or twist a little as it rolls, increasing the drag and the danger of squeaking.

When the dolly operator sets the control for circular steering, only the back wheels respond to his turn of the steering handle. Pushing the dolly then rotates it around a point somewhere on the axis running through the two front wheels. With a minimum turn of the steering handle, this point is far outside the dolly; as the handle is turned farther, the point of rotation approaches the center of the dolly, until at the farthest turn the dolly rotates about a point directly under the camera lens.

5

Television Lenses

Complete familiarity with television lenses is essential to both the director and the cameraman; yet among directors there is a wide variation in methods of working with lenses. Some directors don't try to keep track of each lens during rehearsal, simply asking the cameraman for a wider or a tighter shot and leaving the choice of lens and the responsibility for getting the same lens again on the air show entirely up to him. Others, and these are usually the better directors, come to rehearsal with a very exact idea of which lens will be used on each shot, ask the cameraman to "change to the 135" or "try the 50," and can often tell by looking at the picture which lens is on the camera.

Almost anyone who has worked at all in television production becomes familiar with the fact that a change of lens means a change in angle of view. A wide-angle lens takes in more of the scene than a long lens. Of course, when a larger area of the studio is included, everything becomes smaller in size. Conversely, since the narrow-angle lens takes in less of the studio, objects appear relatively larger. Narrow-angle lenses are ordinarily used for close-ups, wide-angle lenses for long shots.

It should be noted here that a shot made with a narrow-angle lens far from the subject and a shot made with a wide-angle lens close to the subject will not be identical. They will be similar only in field of view. There are other differences in the picture, described later.

THE PARTS OF A LENS

Let us look more closely at a lens now and see what we can discover about it. We notice:

1. The lens is built inside a metal cylinder (called the lens barrel).
2. The lens itself is made of several pieces of glass, and the surfaces of the glass are curved.

3. There are two sets of calibrations marked around the barrel or rim on the front of the lens, and the lens can be adjusted to these calibrations by turning portions of the lens barrel. These are:
   a. The focusing scale. Settings for distance to subject marked off in feet (or meters in the case of European lenses).
   b. The diaphragm scale. An iris diaphragm is included in standard lenses, which can be closed down to a tiny pinpoint under brilliant lighting conditions or, when the light level is low, opened up to a circle as wide in diameter as the lens itself. The diaphragm scale is marked in *f* stops (described later). The larger the *f*-stop number, the smaller the diameter of the diaphragm opening. Lenses are often described in terms of their largest *f* stop. A lens capable of opening up to *f*/1.9, for instance, lets in a great deal of light and can take pictures under low-light conditions. It is known as a fast lens. A lens which cannot be opened wider than *f*/8, for example, is known as a relatively slow lens.

4. The lens is fastened to the lens turret by means of a screw base. Some of the longer lenses are fixed with a "bayonet" mount, which makes it possible to change lenses quickly and without the danger of damaging threads. The bayonet mount requires only one twist to secure it. The lens turret on television cameras is made to take threaded lenses; so an adapter for the bayonet-mount lenses is first screwed into the regular lens position.

STANDARD TELEVISION LENSES

To give a broad picture of the variety of lenses available for television, the most common lenses found on television cameras are listed below. Lenses are usually known by their focal length (a term which will be explained later in this section). Focal length bears a close relation to angle of view: long-focal-length lenses take in a narrow angle; short-focal-length lenses, a wide angle. The most common lenses are the 50-mm, 90-mm, and 135-mm, sometimes referred to as the 2-inch, 4-inch, and 6-inch (Fig. 5-24).

These three lenses are used on almost every studio camera. An extremely wide-angle lens, the 35-mm, is used in studios which are very small and on programs which take advantage of the exaggerated effects which this lens is able to achieve. The 8- or 8½-inch lens is also commonly seen in studios. The use of this long a lens enables the cameraman to get extreme close-ups without having to move his camera in so close that he might enter the field of the other camera. There is a wide gap between the field of the 50-mm lens and that of the next longest lens, the 90-mm. Some studios have added an intermediate lens, the

75-mm, or 3-inch, to bridge this gap. Unless the producer specifically requests these additional lenses for his show, however, the assignment of studio facilities generally includes the use of only the 50-, 90-, and 135-mm.

Lenses of 13-inch to 25-inch focal length are supplied by a number of manufacturers. These lenses are too long to be of frequent use in the studio; their greatest application is in field work where the cameras must be placed at a much greater distance from the action.

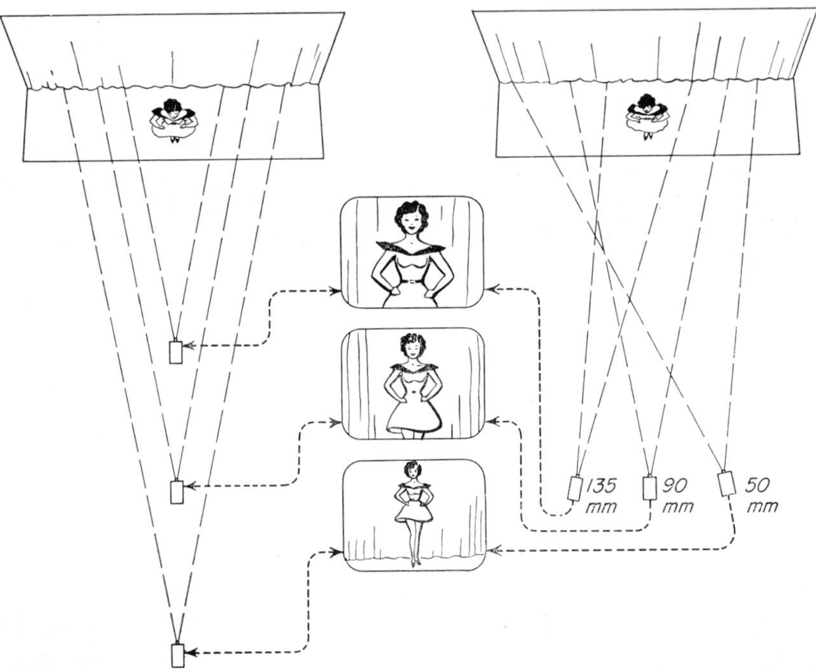

Fig. 5–1. Three standard shots—long shot, medium shot, and close-up—taken by (left) a 90-mm lens from three different distances and (right) three different lenses from the same distance.

The 50-, 90-, and 135-mm lenses in the Ektar series are modifications of standard photographic lenses, originally designed for the Eastman Ektar and other 35-mm minicameras. This use is possible because the size of the photocathode in the image-orthicon tube is very close to the size of the 35-mm double frame (the film used in minicameras).

There is a simple formula for arriving at the lens angle of any given focal length which, although not mathematically accurate, is close enough for any production purposes.

$$\text{Horizontal angle of view} = \frac{1{,}700}{\text{focal length in millimeters}}$$

or

$$\text{Horizontal angle of view} = \frac{68}{\text{focal length in inches}}$$

With the application of this simple formula it is possible to find the horizontal lens angle of any lens of known focal length. The vertical angle of view is always three-quarters of the horizontal angle, since the height of the picture is three-quarters the width.

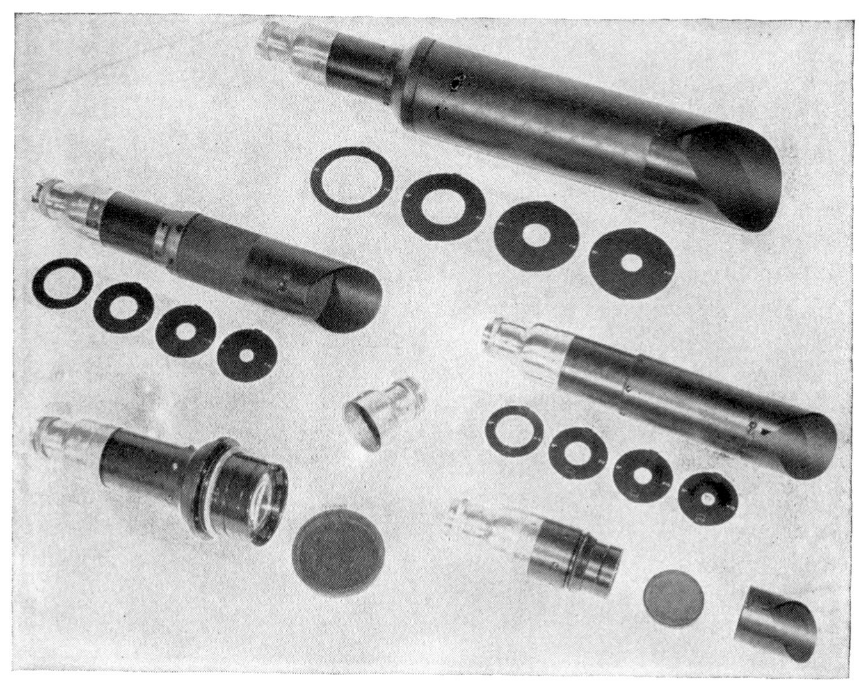

Fig. 5–2. A selection of field-camera lenses supplied by RCA. Lower right: 8½-inch lens with lens cap and sunshade; lower left: 13-inch *f*/3.5; center right: 15-inch; center left, 17-inch; top, 25-inch. Waterhouse stops (described on page 86) accompany the three largest lenses in stops of *f*/8, *f*/11, *f*/16, and *f*/22.

The actual angle of view that the camera is transmitting is not, however, always exactly that listed above. Electronic adjustments within the camera can alter it somewhat. If the video operator happens to adjust his horizontal width to scan a picture slightly under the full photocathode size, then the picture which appears full-screen on the monitor will be less than the entire picture that the lens has produced. The effective angle of view of the lens is thus reduced.

LENSES FOR VIDICON CAMERAS

The photosensitive plate on the vidicon tube is one-half inch in width, which is slightly wider than the picture gate on a 16-mm motion-picture camera (16-mm frame: 0.41 inch wide). For most purposes lenses intended for use on 16-mm cameras perform adequately on vidicon cameras; occasionally distortion or aberration will be noticed around the border areas. This can be because an extended area of the image is being used which in a 16-mm camera falls beyond the area of the picture gate and thus need not be designed to give a good quality picture. In the case of focal-length lenses shorter than 20 mm, the standard 16-mm-camera lens is likely to cause a vignetting effect (circular picture surrounded by dark area) and lenses of such short focal lengths must be specially designed for the vidicon camera. This effect is also seen when some of the shorter 16-mm-camera zoom lenses are used on the vidicon.

The "normal" lens for the vidicon is the 1-inch (25-mm). The 2-inch (50-mm) is the next most frequently used in studio work. Three-inch or four-inch lenses are sometimes used, and a shorter lens than the 1-inch can prove useful if one can be found which does not cause the vignette effect.

The horizontal angle of view of the standard vidicon lenses is easy to learn; one need only remember that the 1-inch lens gives a width of scene just half as wide as the distance of that scene from the camera. A glance at Fig. 5-3 will explain why this is so. A lens 1 inch distant from a ½-inch plate is represented graphically by a triangle with a height twice the base and an angle at the apex of 30 degrees. This is naturally the same as the horizontal angle of view, which is represented by a projection of these same lines forward of the lens into the scene. Thus the horizontal angle of view of the 1-inch lens is 30 degrees, the 2-inch lens just half of that, and so on. Simply divide the focal length of the lens into 30, if it is given in inches; into 750 if it is given in millimeters. Thus a 6-inch lens would have a viewing angle of 5 degrees, a 100-mm lens 7½ degrees, and so on.

$$\text{Horizontal angle of view of vidicon lens} = \frac{30}{\text{focal length of lens in inches}} = \frac{750}{\text{focal length in mm}}$$

Note that a lens of 50-mm focal length, when used on an image-orthicon camera, gives an angle of 34 degrees, and is known as a "wide-angle" lens. On a vidicon camera, however, a 50-mm lens gives a 15-degree angle of view and is known as a "long" lens. To put it another way: a 50-mm lens on a vidicon gives about the same angle of view as a 135-mm lens on an image-orthicon. It will be seen later in the discussion of depth of focus how the vidicon has an advantage in this respect, since shorter-focal-length lenses have greater depth of focus.

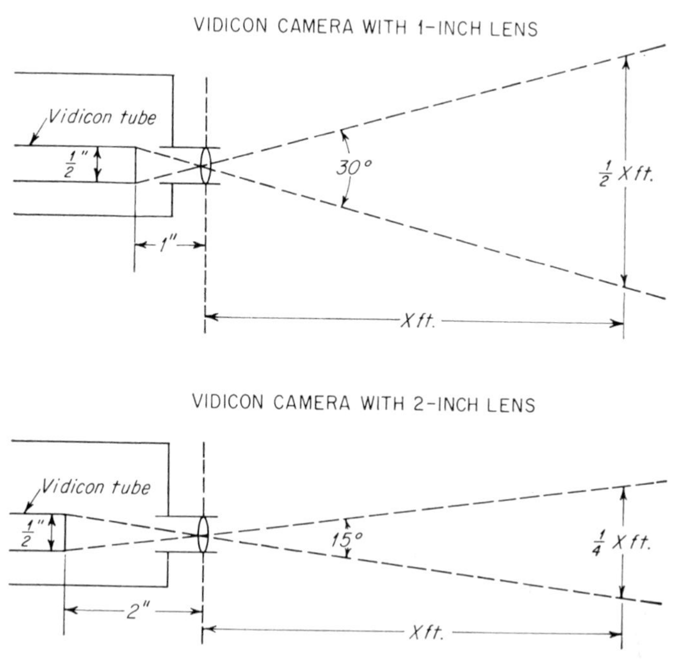

Fig. 5–3. Field of view of vidicon camera with two standard lenses. Above, with the 1-inch lens. Simple geometry of diagram shows similar triangles behind and in front of lens. Since vidicon tube is ½ inch across and focal length of lens is 1 inch, both triangles are thus half as wide as they are high. Below, same camera with a 2-inch lens. Ratio is now 2 inches to ½ inch; each triangle is one quarter as wide as it is high. Conclusion: Field of view of vidicon camera with 1-inch lens is half as wide as its distance from the camera. Field of view with the 2-inch lens is one-quarter as wide as its distance from the camera.

In addition to the standard lenses for image-orthicon and vidicon cameras, there are several special types of lenses which deserve individual discussion.

THE REFLECTAR LENS

The Reflectar is a lens of radically different design. Instead of using lens elements to form the image, the Reflectar uses a concave (focusing)

Fig. 5–4. Video Reflectar lens in use.

Fig. 5–5. Video Reflectar lens (early model) focused on people in the stands across a football field. The camera's picture is visible on the monitor in the foreground.

mirror. Although only 16 inches in over-all length, the Reflectar produces a picture equivalent to that produced by a 40-inch lens; thus its focal length is almost twice that of the next longest television lens. Figure 5-4 shows the Reflectar mounted on the lens turret of a WFBM-TV camera. It will be noted that the shortest-focal-length lenses can be used on the same turret without danger of the Reflectar showing in their pictures.

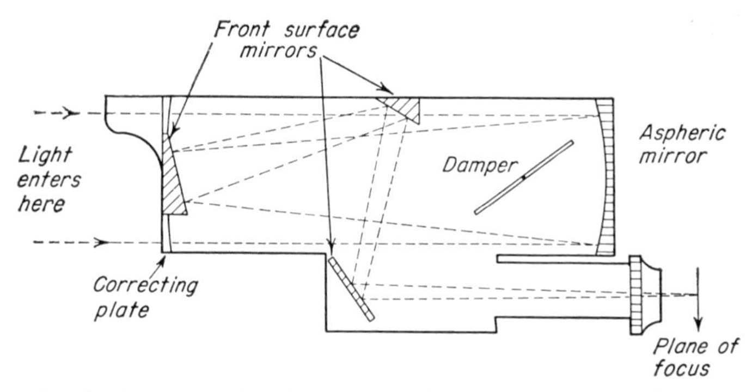

Fig. 5–6. Sketch of interior of Video Reflectar lens. Exposure control is accomplished by means of a simple damper. When this is horizontal, the lens is rated at *f*/8.

Fig. 5–7. A 110-inch lens at KOMO–TV, Seattle. Horizontal angle of view: 0.6 degrees. This is sufficient to fill the entire camera field with a close-up of the sun or moon. Here the lens is shown following hydroplane races on Lake Chelan.

ZOOM LENSES

A good zoom lens is probably the most important single accessory that can be added to a TV camera. A zoom lens is technically referred to as a varifocal lens, since its focal length can be changed within certain limits while the camera is in operation. As the focal length changes, so does the angle of view, and the picture may be smoothly changed from a long shot to a close-up and back again. The effect is very much like that of moving the camera toward or away from the subject, and makes these effects possible in places where (1) the camera cannot be mounted on a dolly, (2) there is no suitable surface for dollying, or (3) the required movements would have to be too rapid for smooth dollying and focusing. An example of this third situation can be cited from the ABC production "Stop the Music," where it was desired to have a very fast zoom shot into a telephone at the moments when the telephone ring interrupted the program. A cameraman could not have done this by dollying and still have held focus. The phone had to be too close to the camera, and the speed was too great. Moving the telephone on a track toward a stationary camera would still have required a very fast follow-focus. The solution was found in the use of a zoom lens. No focusing was necessary since the telephone remained the same distance from the camera during the zoom.

Zoom lenses are designed to hold focus on a given distance during the act of zooming, so the image after the zoom is completed is as sharp as it was at the start. In order to do this, the lens itself must be focused on the proper distance, according to the focusing scale on the lens barrel. The usual method of focusing the TV camera, racking the tube forward and back, can no longer be used. If, for instance, the lens is focused on a player 30 feet away, the lens may be zoomed from one end of its range to the other and the subject will remain in focus. If the player moves toward the camera, say, up to as close as 10 feet, the lens will need to be refocused, just as any lens, or the player will become progressively more and more out of focus. If this refocusing is done with the camera tube, the lens itself will remain focused on 30 feet, and attempting to zoom on an object 10 feet away will result in the lens not holding focus throughout the zoom. Follow-focus, then, must of necessity be done with the lens itself.

Lining up a zoom lens. The best way to line up a zoom lens so it will hold focus whether zoomed on near subjects or on distant subjects, is to follow the steps outlined below:

1. Point the camera at a stationary object.
2. Zoom the lens in to the long-focal-length position. It is now operating as a long lens and as such has a relatively short depth of *field,* but relatively long depth of *focus* (Fig. 5-8). (See page 90 for definition of these terms.) Taking advantage of this fact:
3. Focus the distance scale on the lens until the picture becomes sharp. The lens is now focused within this short depth of field.
4. Zoom the lens back to short-focal-length position. It is now a short-focal-length lens, having a long depth of *field* and a short depth of *focus* (Fig. 5-8). Working now within this short depth of focus—

5. Focus with the camera focus control until the picture is again sharp. If the camera has no focus handle, the vidicon tube must be slid forward or back by other means.

If the subject on which the camera has been focused was at infinity, the lens will now hold focus during the zooming action. If the subject was closer to the camera than 300 feet or so, it may be necessary to refine the adjustment by going through the above process a second or a third time before the lens will hold its focus during the zooming action.

After the lens has been thus lined up, the camera-focus control (which slides the tube back and forth in the camera) must be taped down or

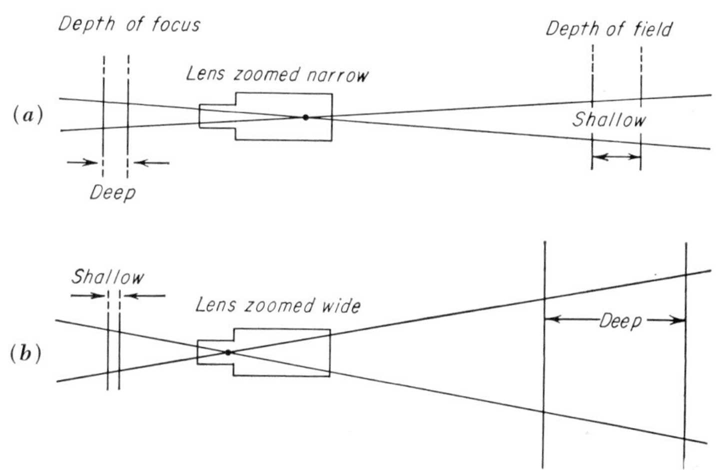

Fig. 5–8. A zoom lens, its depth of focus and its depth of field. (*a*) Zoomed in (narrow angle, close-up shot), it is a long focal-length lens; thus it has a large depth of focus and shallow depth of field. (*b*) Zoomed out (wide angle, long shot), it is a short lens, having a shallow depth of focus and a large depth of field. (Diagram not to scale.)

locked. All adjustment for distance must be done by the optical focusing means provided on the lens itself. If this rule is followed, it should be possible to alternatively or simultaneously dolly the camera and/or zoom the lens, focusing on subjects both near and far, with certainty that every time the lens is zoomed on a stationary subject (and the camera is also stationary) the picture will remain sharp. Naturally, if the distance between camera and subject changes, the cameraman will have to follow-focus, just as with any other lens. The only difference is that this must be done with the distance scale on the lens itself, not with the focus handle on the camera. Only then will the zoom lens continue to hold focus during every zooming action.

A zoom lens is valuable, even without utilizing the zoom effect. It provides an infinite number of focal lengths within the limits of its range, and can replace an entire complement of lenses of different focal lengths. When it is not being used for on-the-air zooming, but simply to provide a multi-purpose lens of many focal lengths, changes of focal length can be made between shots while another camera is on the air. In such a case the *camera* can be refocused for each new setting of focal length, as indeed must always be done when changing from one focal-length lens to another.

An early model of the Zoomar lens (Fig. 5-9), although it has been superseded by improved models, will serve best as an example of the operation of these lenses since more of its parts are revealed.

Fig. 5–9. The first model television Zoomar. Control handle is visible at rear of camera.

Control over the zooming section is exercised by means of a long plunger which is extended through the camera to the back, where it emerges in the center of the turret-control handle. A simple pulling or pushing motion is sufficient to achieve the zooming effect. The plunger can be rotated to change focus. This is achieved by fitting the forward end of the plunger with a long spline, which engages a collar gear at the front of the lens. Rotating the plunger will turn the collar; focus is maintained by controlling the lens, not by the usual method of racking the tube toward or away from the lens.

Many stations utilize zoom lenses in the studio. Used in the studio, the zoom lens constitutes an alternative to dollying the camera, although a totally different effect is achieved. When the camera is *dollied* forward, not only does the subject get larger in the frame but the perspective also is changed. Near objects move in relation to farther objects, the view through a doorway, for example, will widen out and more of the room behind can be seen.

The only similarity between the dolly and the zoom effect, however, is that the subject grows larger in the frame. Since the camera equipped with the zoom lens stays the same distance away, the *perspective* remains the same. An object in the background which is obscured by a foreground object will remain obscured even in the close-up view. It is usually possible to distinguish very quickly between the zoom and the dolly effect (Fig. 5-10).

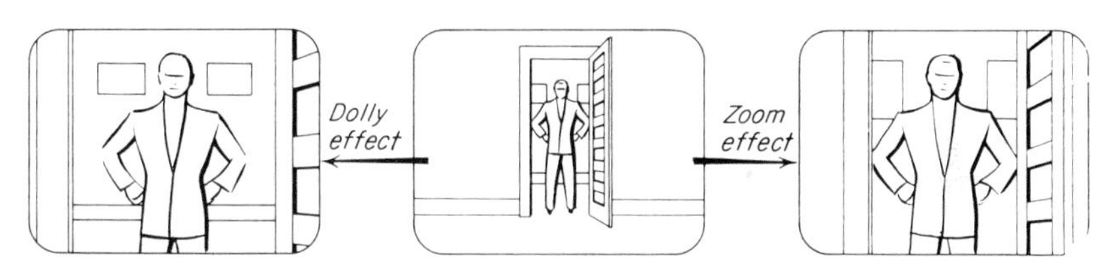

Fig. 5–10. Comparison of dolly and zoom. Starting with the center picture, the dolly effect (left) alters the perspective in the shot. As the camera approaches the door, it can see around the sides of the man, and he becomes smaller in relation to the door frame. During the movement the sides of the door frame move outward against the background. In the zoom effect (right) the same perspective is maintained throughout the shot, and the man still fills the doorway. There is no movement of the door frame against the background.

Zoom lenses of shorter focal length and a more limited range have found considerable use in television stations. One of these was called the Electra-Zoom lens because the zooming action was electrically controlled by a toggle switch mounted on the camera-panning handle. With its range of 2⅝ to 7 inches it could almost replace an entire normal complement of studio lenses on the camera turret. The horizontal angle of view varied from 27 degrees, not quite as wide as the 50-mm lens, to about 10 degrees, nearly the same as the 8-inch lens. Wide open it was rated at $f/2.8$. A drawback, however, was that the zoom action proceeded at a slow fixed rate and could not be controlled according to the needs of the action or the dramatic effect desired. For this reason some of these lenses were adapted by their users to operate manually.

Another lens, the New Studio Zoomar, had the advantages of fitting onto a turret with other lenses, and manual operation as well. A plunger through the camera controls this lens in the same manner as the original Zoomar described above. The range of focal lengths is from 2¼ to 7 inches (a 3-to-1 ratio) and the maximum speed, $f/2.8$. A more recent lens, the Super Studio Zoomar (Fig. 5-11) is similar in operation and has a range of focal lengths from 55 mm to 180 mm, or a ratio of 3½ to 1; the speed is $f/2.7$.

Fig. 5–11. Super Studio Zoomar lens on RCA color camera. Turret may be rotated for other lenses.

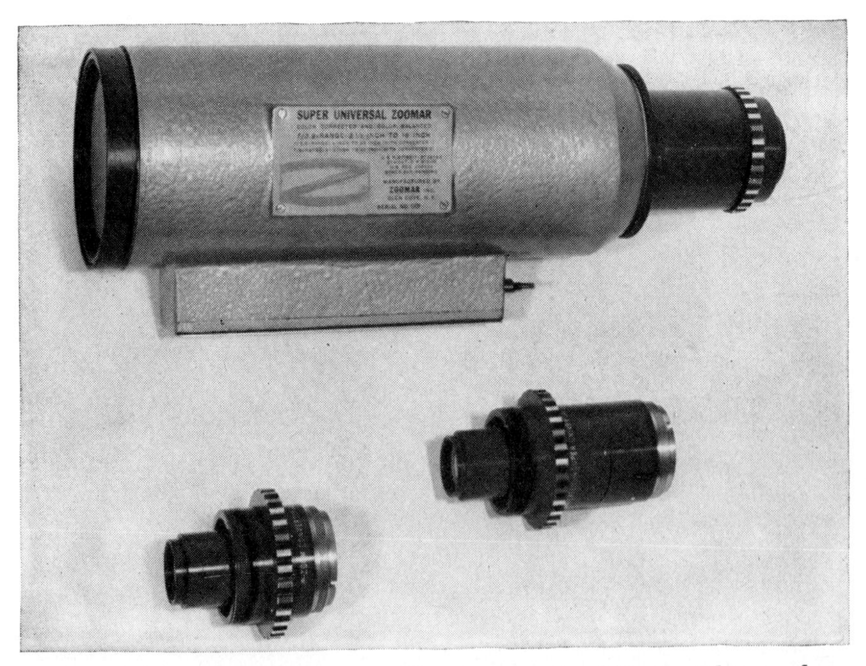

Fig. 5–12. Super Universal Zoomar with converters. Focal length of lens as shown above: 2½ to 16 inches (*f*/3.9). With converter at lower left: 4 to 25 inches (*f*/5.6). With converter at lower right: 6½ to 40 inches (*f*/8).

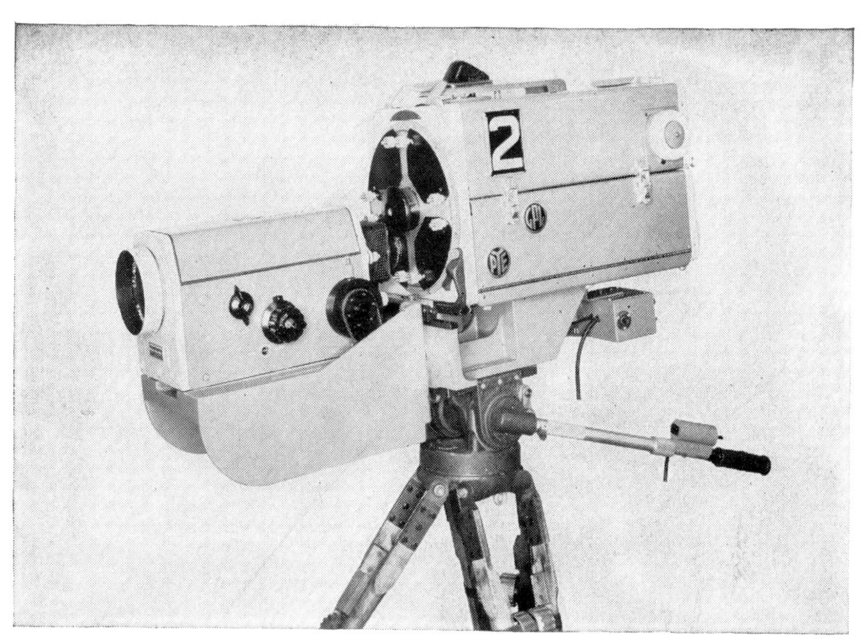

Fig. 5–13. Watson zoom lens (British make). Zoom ratio: 5 to 1, electrically controlled. Lens is first attached to tripod, then camera is placed on lens.

Lens	Range of focal lengths		Zoom ratio	Speed
Field Lenses				
Field Zoomar		5″–22″	4.4–1	*f*/8
Universal Zoomar and Super Universal Zoomar	62 mm–400 mm	2.5″–16″	6.4–1	*f*/3.9
Watson		3″–15″	5–1	*f*/6.3
		6″–30″	5–1	*f*/6.3
Studio Lenses				
Field Zoomar with wide-angle front lens	75 mm–325 mm	3″–13″	4.3–1	*f*/8
New Studio Zoomar	56 mm–175 mm	2¼″–7″	3.1–1	*f*/2.8
Super Studio Zoomar	55 mm–180 mm	2⅕″–7⅕″	3.5–1	*f*/2.7
Electra-Zoom	65 mm–175 mm	2⅝″–7″	2.7–1	*f*/2.8
Zoom Lenses for Vidicon Cameras				
Pan Cinor	20 mm–60 mm	⅞″–2½″	3–1	*f*/2.8
Pan Cinor	25 mm–100 mm	1″–4″	4–1	*f*/2.4 and *f*/3.4
Perkin Elmer	30 mm–150 mm	1¼″–6″	5–1	*f*/2.8
Zoomar	20 mm–120 mm	⅞″–5″	6–1	*f*/3.9
Zoomar Mark IV	17 mm–70 mm	.68″–2.8″	4.1–1	*f*/2
Zoomar Mark VI	25 mm–150 mm	1″–6″	6–1	*f*/3.5
	40 mm–240 mm	1.6″–9.6″	6–1	*f*/5.6

NOTE: Som Berthiot also makes a Pan Cinor lens which has a 17- to 70-mm range. However, this is entirely suitable only for 16-mm cameras since a vignetting appears on the vidicon picture when the lens is zoomed wider than 20-mm focal length.

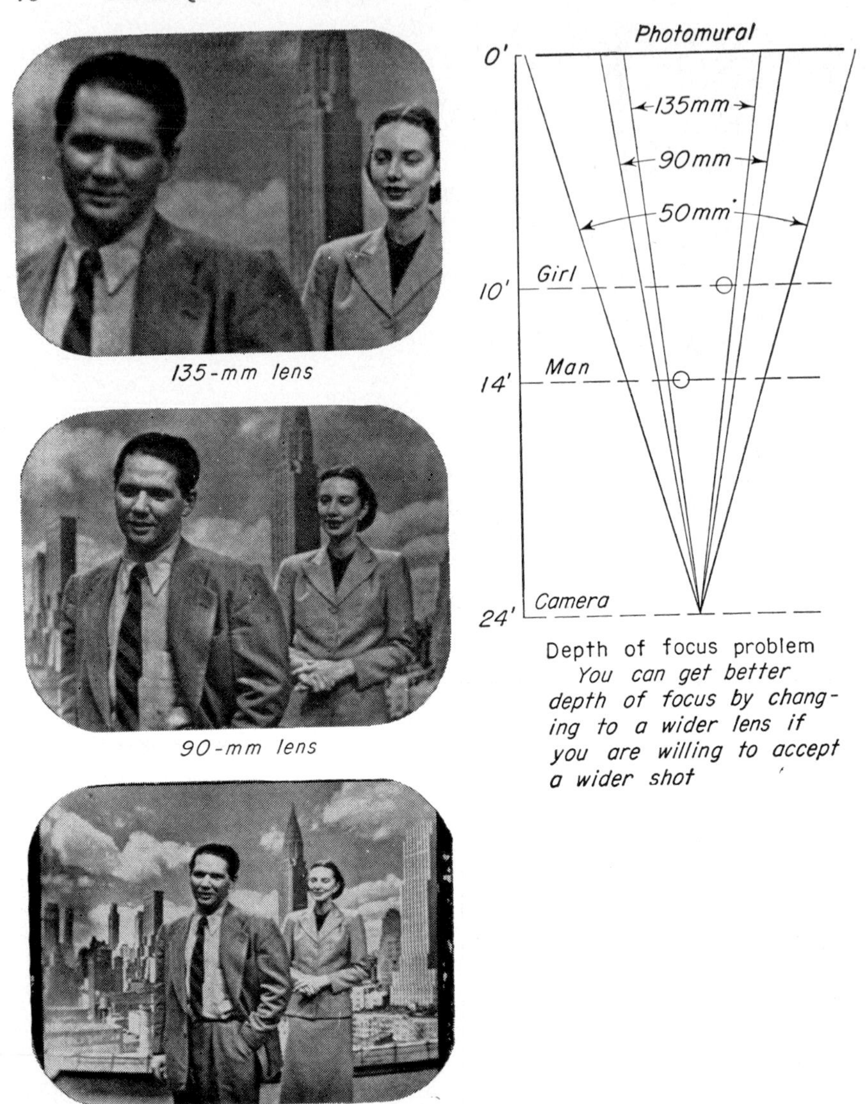

Fig. 5–14. Three shots taken from one camera position with three different lenses. Note that relative size of man, girl, and building remains the same. Only the field of view changes. Note also the improved depth of field in the wide-angle shot. (All lenses were opened to $f/3.8$ to exaggerate this difference in depth of field.)

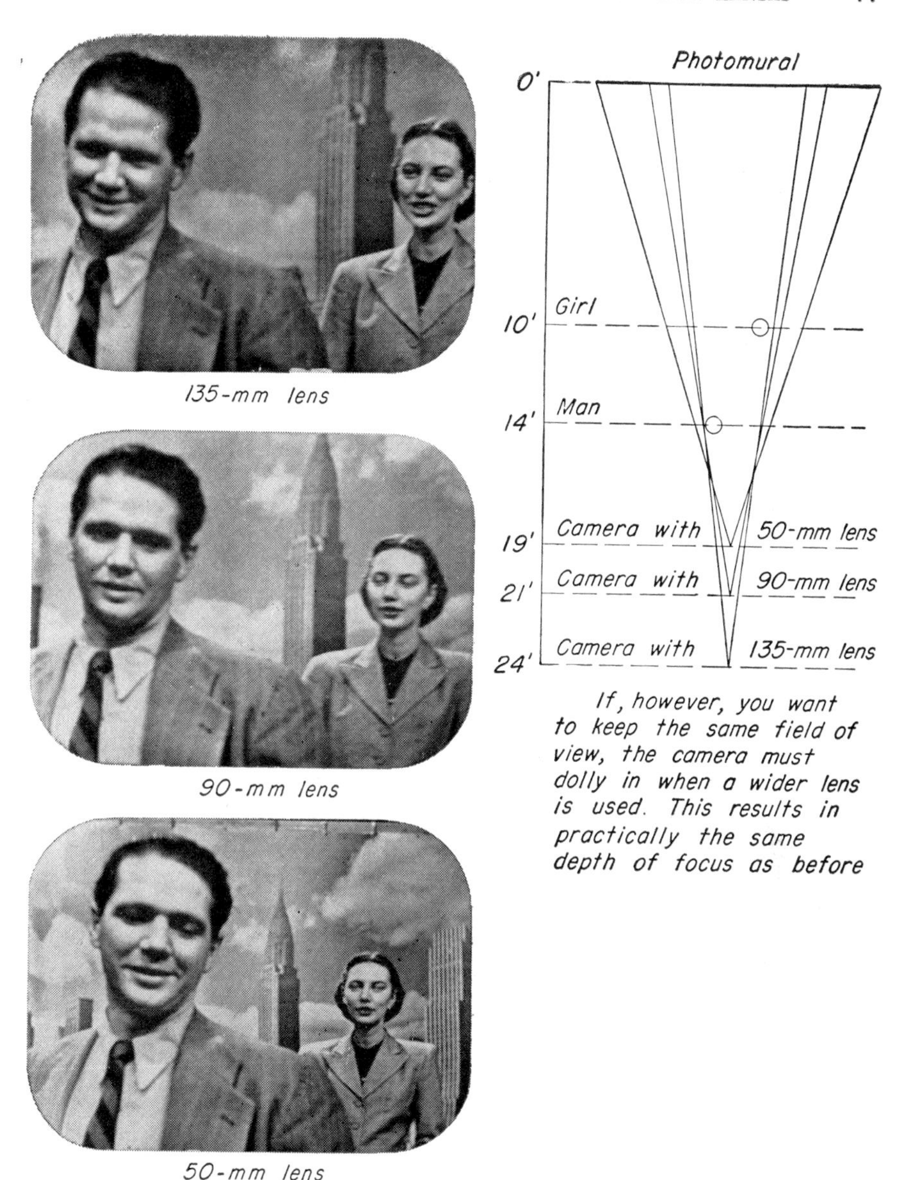

Fig. 5–15. Three shots with three lenses from three different camera positions maintaining the same approximate field of view. Man in foreground has been kept the same size. Note difference in relative size of girl and building in the three shots. Note also that there is very little difference in depth of field.

In an attempt to fill the needs for both studio and field purposes with one lens, the Zoomar corporation developed yet another lens, the Universal Zoomar, which soon became the Super Universal Zoomar (Fig. 5-12). These lenses had a more than 6-to-1 ratio, the greatest range of focal lengths yet produced in a lens for image-orthicon cameras. With a reasonably fast speed of *f*/3.9, considering the focal length (2½ to 16 inches), this lens quickly became widely accepted. The chart shown on page 75 lists the better-known makes and models of zoom lenses, together with their speeds and ranges of focal lengths.

PERSPECTIVE IN LONG AND SHORT LENSES

It has been said that the shot taken by a camera with a long lens far from the subject is a different picture from that taken by a wide-angle lens closer to the subject. This is true, in spite of the fact that each may take in the same actual area of the scene. The difference is in the perspective in the picture—the way in which the camera registers the dimension of depth. If the scene had no depth, there would be no difference between the two shots. The image of a title card, for instance, if it fills the screen in each case, will look the same no matter what length of lens is used. But a scene in which some objects are close and others far away will look quite different. A wide-angle lens exaggerates the depth dimension. A long lens, on the other hand, squeezes the near objects up against the farther ones, so that they are all about the same size, and decreases the dimension of depth.

To understand this more clearly, consider a very simple illustration. Two actors are in a studio set, one about 4 feet in front of the other. A set of off-the-tube pictures is shown in Fig. 5-14 illustrating the shots obtainable with the three standard lenses from the same camera position. There is no difference in perspective; the relative size of man and girl is the same in each shot. In the second series of shots (Fig. 5-15) the same field of view has been maintained. This of course required repositioning the camera each time the lens was changed.

By changing the position of the camera we have changed the *relative* distance from the camera to the two subjects. In the bottom picture, taken with a 50-mm lens, the camera is 5 feet from the man and 9 feet from the girl. She is almost twice as far away, hence half the size. In the top picture, taken with the 135-mm lens, the camera is 10 feet from the man and 14 feet from the girl. This is a ratio of 2 to 3 rather than 1 to 2: Less relative difference in distance from the camera, hence less difference in size. If the camera had gone even farther back, using longer and longer lenses to keep the field of view the same, the 4-foot difference between the two people would count for less and less in relation to the camera distance and they would even more closely approach the same size.

Another series of pictures (Fig. 5-16) serves to illustrate how this same thing affects the shots we take in remote pickups outside the studio. The camera is set up to shoot through an archway at a fountain beyond.

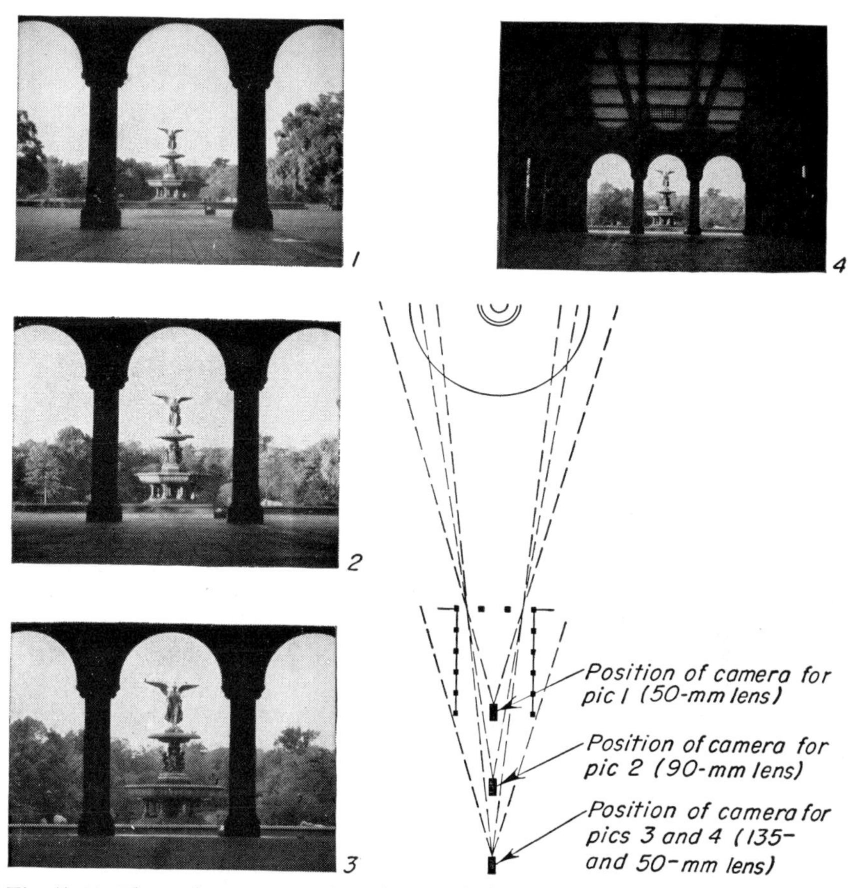

Fig. 5-16. Three shots, Nos. 1, 2, and 3, made from different camera positions with different lenses, keeping the arches the same size. Note that wide-angle shot 4 from same camera position as 3 shows the same relative size of fountain and arch.

Three shots are included, taken by the three standard lenses, and since the arches are the same size, it is obvious that the camera has repositioned each time a new lens was used. It will be noted that the relative size of the fountain has changed considerably.*

* The author used an Exacta 35-mm camera in taking these pictures. Since the area of the 35-mm double frame used in minicameras of this design is practically the same as the area of the image-orthicon photocathode, the results of the three lenses used above are substantially the same as though they were used on television cameras.

It is not the choice of lens which has made the difference in perspective between these shots, but the repositioning of the camera which had to be done to keep the arches the same size in the frame. The size relationship between arch and fountain shown in the 135-mm shot (No. 3), for example, is due not to the fact that a long lens was used but to the fact that the camera was placed farther back from the subject. This same size relationship would exist in the shot taken by any lens, even the 50-mm (No. 4), as long as it were from this same camera position. This is the perspective which exists; it is not something created by the long lens; it is the same relationship which an observer would see if he were standing next to the camera. A long lens simply takes a small portion of the distant scene (with its distant perspective) and enlarges it to full-screen size, giving the viewer the illusion of a closer camera position. If perspective then looks distorted, it is because the viewer assumes from the size of the objects that the viewpoint is closer and cannot reconcile a close viewpoint with a distant perspective.

A common shot in television is the piano keyboard, from the side looking down the keys. If this shot is taken with the 135-mm lens, the perspective looks very strange. The keyboard looks abnormally short, simply because the camera is far away (Fig. 5-17A). *B* illustrates the same piano

Fig. 5–17. Piano keyboard taken with (*A*) 135-mm lens from a distance, (*B*) 50-mm lens up close, and (*C*) 90-mm lens from intermediate position.

keyboard taken from a closer camera position with a wide-angle (50-mm) lens. Here it has the perspective of a near object, and the keyboard looks abnormally long. *C* was taken with a normal lens (90 mm).

THE NORMAL LENS

The term "normal" (normal-length) lens has been used earlier without any exact definition. If we understand now what is meant by a normal lens, we can better understand why long or wide-angle lenses give their unusual effects. When we stand in front of a scene and draw, paint, or photograph an area of it into a two-dimensional picture, we intend that picture to be viewed from a certain distance. The area of the scene itself is seen within a certain angle of view from the eye. If we draw or photograph that scene so that the final picture is looked at with this same angle of view, as far as perspective is concerned we have come as close as we can to creating in two dimensions the effect of reality.

The angle of view with which a picture will be seen determines the angle of view with which it should be taken, if it is to have correct perspective. In motion pictures, an angle considerably narrower than 50 degrees is considered a normal angle of view, since the viewer usually watches the movie screen from a relatively greater distance than that from which he looks at a photograph or a painting. Between 20 and 25 degrees is used as a normal angle of view in 16-mm and 35-mm motion pictures. The 1-inch lens is considered normal for the 16-mm camera, and the 2-inch lens is normal for the 35-mm.

Generally speaking, the televiewer sitting in front of his set is 4 to 8 feet from the screen. If the screen is 20 inches wide and the viewing distance 6¾ feet away, then the angle of view is some 14 degrees. The

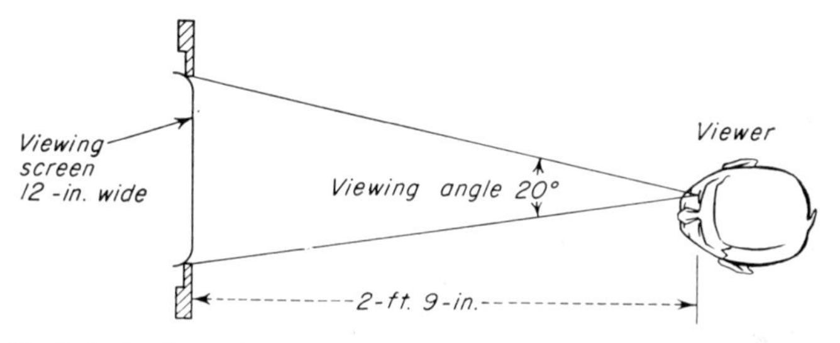

Fig. 5–18. Relationship of screen width and viewing distance to viewing angle.

normal lens for this viewer is 135 mm. When fewer people are around a set, they generally prefer to sit somewhat closer, say about 5 feet away. The angle of view is about 19 degrees from such a position for a 20-inch screen.

If the normal angle of view for television viewing is 19 degrees, then the normal-length lens should have an angle of view of 19 degrees also. The 90-mm lens fits this description. As long as television viewing screens were, on the average, rather small and the distance between viewer and screen proportionately large, the lenses longer than 90 mm could be used without seeming to distort perspective too much. However, with the larger screens becoming more popular, unless people sit farther back, the screen will subtend a greater angle at the eye and the long-lens effects will, of course, be more noticeable.

WIDE-ANGLE LENSES

The exaggeration of depth in a wide-angle shot makes the studio look much larger than it really is and exaggerates the speed of movement toward or away from the camera. Dancers loom up very rapidly or dwindle quickly as they go away.

Caution must be exercised, however, in using wide-angle lenses. If the cameras get too close to a person's face, a very undesirable type of distortion will result. This is noticeable in the 50-mm lens when the camera is so close that the person's head is half the height of the screen. With the 35-mm lens the effect is perceived even sooner, when the head is one-third of screen height.* Since the nose is the closest thing to the camera, and considerably closer than the ears, it takes on an exaggerated

Fig. 5–19. Distortion of close-up taken with wide-angle lens.

size. The rest of the face then curves away from the nose like the sides of a ball (Fig. 5-19).

Barrel distortion is another difficulty encountered with the wide-angle lenses, especially the 35-mm. Vertical or horizontal lines near the edges of the screen seem to curve outward. This may not be noticeable in a static shot, especially if there are no definite lines to appear distorted. When the camera moves, however, and particularly when it pans, objects move from distorted to nondistorted portions of the screen and can be seen to change their shape and bend around.

HOW TO CHOOSE LENSES

When a remote pickup is to be made from a new location, a preliminary survey is always made, and usually a member of the program department

* This is between 3½ and 4 feet from the camera in both cases.

accompanies the engineer who makes it. He is primarily concerned with camera positions and the kind of shot he can get. Standing where the cameras are to be, he must be able to visualize exactly what each of his lenses will cover.

There are portable view finders on the market which can serve this end. The adjustable finder for the Leica camera, for example, carries view finders for at least the three standard lenses. It is not necessary to go to that expense, however, for a simple shoe box can be adapted very easily to serve the purpose.

Cut a peephole in one end of the box; in the other, a window just wide enough to show you the angle of view of, say, the 135-mm lens. To determine the size of this window, lay out the lens angle (13 degrees)

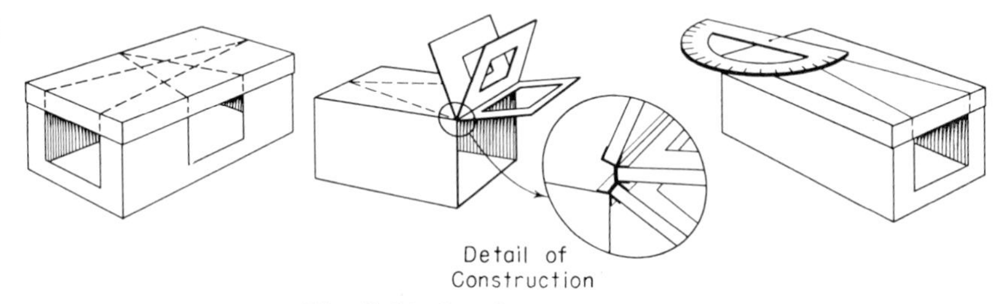

Fig. 5–20. Simple viewing boxes.

with a protractor on the top of the box. If the box is too long for this, turn it sideways. Just be sure you can get your eye right up against the peephole; otherwise the angle of view that you see will be too narrow. Directors have at times made these viewing boxes with only one peephole and a number of flaps that hinge down in front of one window.

An even more practical type is a simple cube box, conceived by the author and known as the "Bretz box," which has windows on all sides. The window for one lens serves as the peephole for another, when you turn the box around.

This box is very easy to make. Simply cut six pieces of cardboard, each about 6 inches square. Lay out all the lens angles on one of them, as if it were the top of the box. Using this for a gauge, mark out a different window in each of the other pieces. The lens angles given are horizontal angles. To find the height of each window, figure three-quarters of the width, since the screen-aspect ratio in television is 3 to 4 (three units high, four wide). After the holes are cut with a razor blade, fasten the sides together with scotch tape. Mark the lens numbers on the windows, so there can be no confusion. A good place is on the inside of the box before you put the pieces together. If the interior of the box is black, it is easier to visualize the window as a television screen.

This box will show you everything that the camera and lens itself will show you. In it you can see the effect of distortion of depth with wide-angle lenses and long lenses. You can take it in your hand and walk up to or away from the arch, in our recent example, and determine ahead of time just what camera position is necessary for the desired size relation between arch and distant fountain. The only thing the box will *not* do is

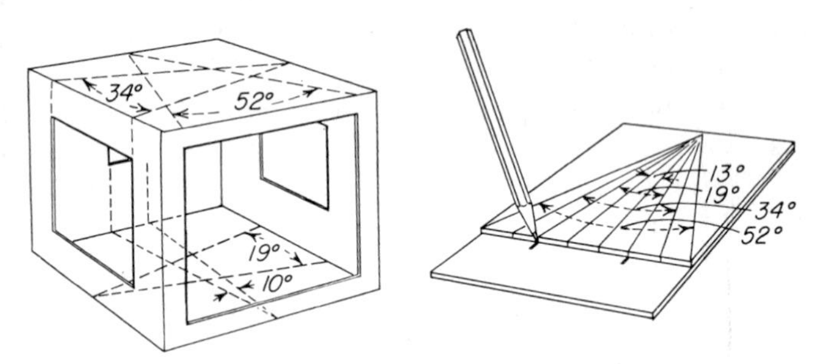

Fig. 5–21. Bretz box, with method of laying out windows.

to show you these pictures full-screen. You have to look through a large window for a wide-angle shot and through a small window for a long-lens picture. This is where your imagination must help. You must visualize each of these various-sized windows as a full-screen picture on the television monitor, and if you can't do that, the box will help you learn.

FOCAL LENGTH

When the lens is focused at infinity and the image-orthicon tube is as close as it will ever be, the distance between what is known as the optical center of the lens and the photosensitive plate is measured; this is known

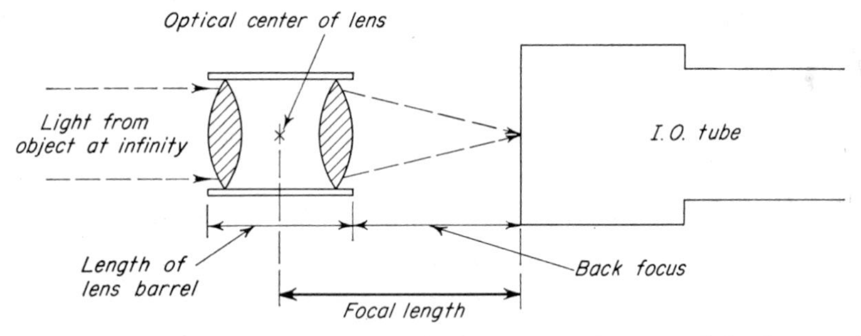

Fig. 5–22. Focal length is the distance from the optical center of the lens to the focal plane when the lens is focused on infinity. It is not to be confused with back focus or the length of the lens barrel.

as the "focal length." Focal length is not the same as the distance between the back of the lens and the tube; that is known as "back focus." Nor is the focal length the same as the length of the lens barrel itself.

TELEPHOTO LENSES

The telephoto is a lens which is actually much shorter than its focal length. It is not correct to call any long lens a telephoto. To be sure, they all produce the effect of a telescope—a great enlargement of a small area of the scene. But that is not the full meaning of the term. A 20-inch regular lens would have to be somewhat over 20 inches in actual length; whereas a 20-inch telephoto lens, owing to its different design, could be less than 15 inches in length. Both 20-inch lenses would have the same focal length, angle of view, etc., and would function, to all intents and purposes, identically. This is such a great advantage in photography that most long lenses today are made in the telephoto design. This has given rise, of course, to the confusion in terms.

The telephoto principle, very simply, is this: an additional *negative* lens element is added behind a regular short-focal-length lens. The effect of a negative lens is to diverge the rays of light. This causes them to converge to a focus farther back than they otherwise would. They converge, however, at such an angle that were they coming from a regular lens, that lens would have to be much farther away. The optical center of the lens,

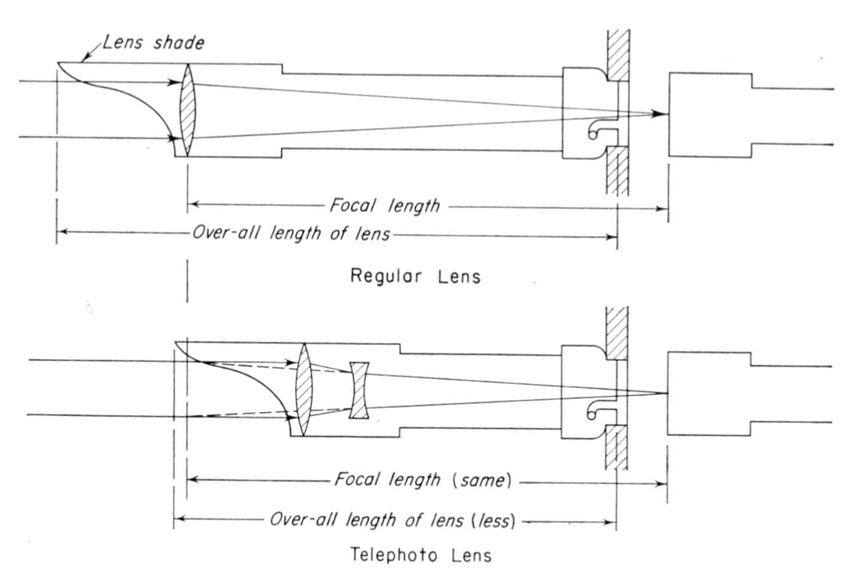

Fig. 5–23. Comparison of regular lens with telephoto lens of the same focal length. Both produce the same picture.

the point at which the rays are bent to converge into an image, is, in the case of the telephoto, actually outside and ahead of the lens. Of course, the rays are not *actually* bent there; they are *effectively* bent there. As far as the television tube is concerned, the rays of light that fall upon it through a 20-inch telephoto lens are converging at the same angle as they would from a 20-inch regular lens. Figure 5-23 explains this.

DIAPHRAGM OPENINGS

The iris diaphragm in most lenses is adjustable. It is made of a great many small leaves which overlap each other in a circular fashion and which can be made to open up to allow a large amount of light into the lens or to close down to a small opening so that only a minimum of light can enter (Fig. 5-24).

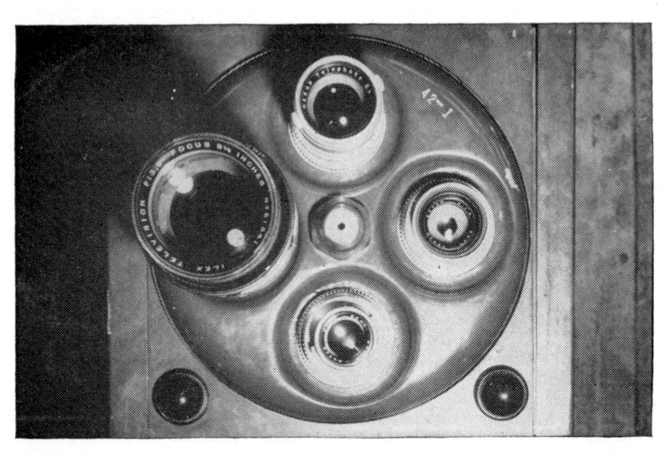

Fig. 5–24. Four standard studio lenses. The iris diaphragm can be seen within each lens, partially stopping it down. Top, 135-mm; left, 8½-inch; right, 50-mm; bottom, 90-mm. All these lenses are set at the same *f* stop. Notice that the longer the lens, the larger the diameter of the opening which is necessary to produce the same image brightness on the face of the tube. Note that the 50-mm (right), being a faster lens than the others, is far from wide open.

Some lenses are not so equipped. To cut down the amount of light which can enter such lenses, pieces of cardboard or metal, with holes of different sizes, are inserted in the lens barrel. These are known as "water-house stops." Some of the long lenses used in the field make use of this simple method of controlling the lens opening (Fig. 5-2).

The size of the lens opening is calibrated in stops. To open the lens one stop means to allow twice as much light to enter. Two stops will quadruple the light; three stops will multiply it by eight. Conversely, closing the lens one stop will cut the light down by one-half; two stops, by one-fourth; three, by one-eighth.

Stops have, until recently, been designated almost exclusively by *f* numbers. The *f*-number calibration for a lens is calculated by dividing the focal length by the diameter of the lens opening.

$$f = \frac{\text{focal length}}{\text{diameter}}$$

Thus, if a lens has a 2-inch focal length and can be opened to a diameter of 1 inch, we call it an $f/2$ lens. Such a lens can take pictures under very low light conditions. Closed, or "stopped," down one stop, to $f/2.8$, it admits half the light. The lens diameter is then about ¾ inch. Stopped down two stops, to $f/4$, one-quarter of the light now passes the lens, and the diameter is ½ inch.

All lenses, when set to the same *f* stop, produce about the same illumination on the plate of the tube. This is the reason the *f*-stop method of calibration was devised, so that a photographer might use several lenses on the same scene and put them all on the same setting. The reader may have noticed from the chart of lenses, however, that only the shortest lenses open up to large stops, the longest ones being relatively slow. We have said that

$$f = \frac{\text{focal length}}{\text{diameter}}$$

and that

$$f/2 = \frac{\text{2-in. lens}}{\text{1-in. diameter}}$$

What diameter would a 20-inch lens need in order to achieve an $f/2$ rating? It is easy to see that a lens of that bulk would be impractical. The 20-inch lens for the television camera opens up only to $f/5.6$, which means its diameter need be only about 3½ inches.

The usual range of stops marked on television lenses is as follows: $f/2.8$, $f/4$, $f/5.6$, $f/8$, $f/11$, $f/16$, and $f/22$. Each of these is a full stop different from the next.

The particular diaphragm opening which will produce the best picture will vary according to the sensitivity of the camera tube, the amount of light incident on the scene, and also the reflectance of the scene (dark objects need more exposure). The best practice in determining the correct lens setting is to open the lens one stop beyond the point at which the highlights begin to compress. The engineer will determine this point by watching his waveform monitor as the lens is opened.

When the 5820 image-orthicon is used outdoors, very brilliant illumination is frequently encountered. Bright sunlight may register as high as 10,000 foot-candles—100 times as bright as the usual studio illumination. This would require stopping the lenses down as much as six or seven stops from their studio openings. Since the smallest stop on most lenses is *f*/22 (only three or four stops smaller), neutral-density filters which cut out at least nine-tenths of the light must be used. The use of a 10 per cent transmission is equivalent to stopping down the lens three stops. *f*/16 can be effectively changed to *f*/45. When more stopping down than this is necessary, filters of only 1 per cent transmission have been used.

Occasionally it is possible in some stations for program people to have a word in a few of these technical matters. Some directors, for instance, like to see larger lens openings used. Less light is necessary, for one thing, and subtler nuances of light can be achieved at lower levels. Another reason is that the depth of focus is reduced at larger lens openings. It is not always desirable to have everything in the picture in sharp focus. A great depth of focus is particularly unwelcome to set designers, who notice all the wrinkles, cracks, and blemishes showing up clearly on their scenery in the background.

T stops. The system of rating the light transmission of lenses in terms of their focal length and diameter was never too accurate. There were many factors which this formula did not take into account. Most lenses today are antireflection-coated and transmit more light as a result. But their *f*-number calibrations remain the same. To improve this condition, a new method of rating lenses, which calibrates them according to their actual transmission of light, has come into use. The emergence of this "*t*-stop" method of calibration is of greater importance to photography than to television. The photographer cannot see the result of his work until after he has developed his films, and accurate exposure is his main control over picture quality. In television, it would be possible to do without any lens calibrations at all, since you can see the picture as you are taking it, and making the proper lens setting is only a matter of adjusting the lens until the picture is the way you want it. The value of lens calibrations, however, is not to be forgotten. Standardized diaphragm stops make it possible to set all lenses quickly to transmit the same amount of light and to reproduce accurately the conditions of a previous pickup.

FOCUS

Anyone who has operated a camera of any kind understands the problem of focus. The lens must be set for the right distance, or the image will be soft and fuzzy. If the subject moves toward or away from the camera, it will go out of focus unless the lens is readjusted. The larger the size of film or photosensitive plate in the camera, the greater the number of focusing adjustments that must be made. A camera with a small-size film, say 16 mm, can hold focus through a much greater depth without adjustment than can a 35-mm camera or a television camera. The smallest movie camera, the 8-mm, needs no focusing adjustments at all under ordinary conditions. The lens for this camera is made "fixed-focus" without a focus scale. Everything from 2 or 3 feet to infinity is in focus at once, since the lens is set at the proper intermediate point (called the hyperfocal distance).*

TV-studio lenses are usually set at infinity, but there is a difference in practice here between one studio and the next. Some studios set all lenses at 15 feet. This is done in an attempt to reduce the amount of refocusing which is necessary, especially at close distances, after switching from one lens to another. If all four of a camera's lenses are set on infinity and the camera is focused on this distance, lenses can be changed without readjusting focus. However, when the camera focuses on a closer subject, each lens requires a different amount of tube travel. With the RCA camera, for instance, to focus down from infinity to, say, 2 feet, with the 50-mm lens requires less than two counterclockwise turns of the crank. With the 135-mm, on the other hand, six turns are necessary to focus on the same subject. In other words, in changing from the 50 to the 135 while focused on 2 feet, the crank handle must be turned counterclockwise about four turns to readjust focus.

The GPL camera, as described before, has solved this problem in a unique way. As the turret is changed in this camera and a new lens comes into position, the tube automatically slides forward or backward the necessary amount so that the new lens is immediately in focus.

DEPTH OF FOCUS

When the rays of light emitted by a single point, such as we have been discussing, are brought to a focus, they form a cone of light behind the lens. After they have come together, they cross and proceed to diverge again in another cone. It is only when the photocathode is placed exactly in the focal plane that the image of the point is actually a small point itself. As the tube is moved away from this plane, the point becomes a small circle which gradually increases in size, the farther the tube is

* The hyperfocal distance is the nearest point at which objects are in approximately sharp focus, when the lens is focused on infinity. When the focus is fixed on the hyperfocal distance, everything from half that distance to infinity will be sharp. The hyperfocal distance depends on diaphragm opening and focal length of the lens: the longer the lens and the wider the opening, the greater the hyperfocal distance.

moved. When all the points which go to make up an image register as circles, the image becomes soft and indistinguishable. There is a short distance within which the tube can be moved, however, without making any noticeable difference in the sharpness of the picture. This is because there is a certain maximum size of circle below which it is, to all appear-

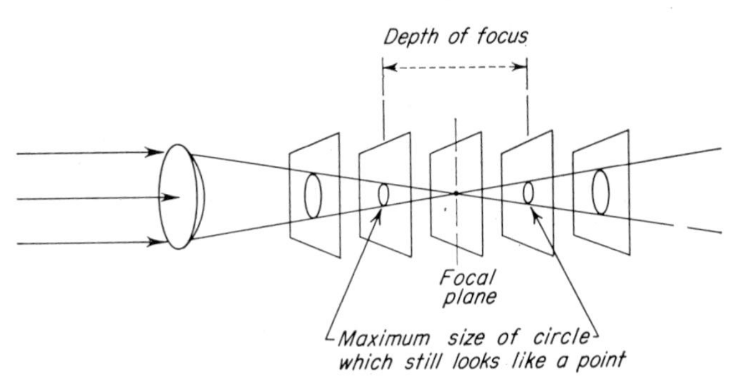

Fig. 5–25. Depth of focus.

ances, still a point. This maximum size will, of course, vary according to the final size in which the picture will be seen. For television it is of the order of 1/200 inch (0.005 inch).* For those who want a clearer definition, it might be added that this is called the "circle of confusion."

Inside the camera, then, the distance within which the plate can move toward and away from the lens without throwing the image out of focus is called the depth of *focus*.

DEPTH OF FIELD

Assuming no camera adjustment, the depth within which a *subject* can move toward or away from the camera without going out of focus is called the depth of *field*. To put it another way, depth of field is the distance between the nearest sharp object and the farthest sharp object. Depth of field is often erroneously called depth of focus. This misnomer has become so widespread that it has almost become general usage.

Depth of field depends on three factors: (1) the distance from the camera, (2) the diaphragm opening used, and (3) the focal length of the lens.

The first factor seems self-evident. Any cameraman can tell you how hard it is to keep in focus when he is holding a large close-up. He has

* Box cameras, 1/60; folding Kodaks in low-price range, 1/200; 35-mm cameras, 1/500; 16-mm, 1/1,000; Leica Summar lens, 1/1,500.

a much shallower depth of field when focused close, and even a slight movement may exceed it.

Figure 5-26 is a diagram of the depth of field which a 90-mm lens can hold when focused at different distances.

Diaphragm opening and depth of field. The diagram in Fig. 5-27 also indicates the difference that diaphragm opening makes in the depth of focus. When this particular lens is used wide open ($f/3.5$), the depth is

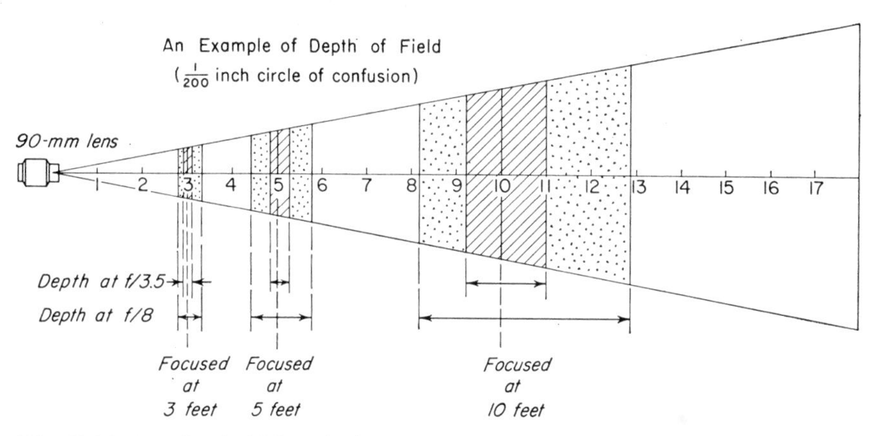

Fig. 5–26. Depth of field with the 90-mm lens. The farther the point of focus is from the camera, the greater the depth of field. Depth of field is increased by stopping down the lens.

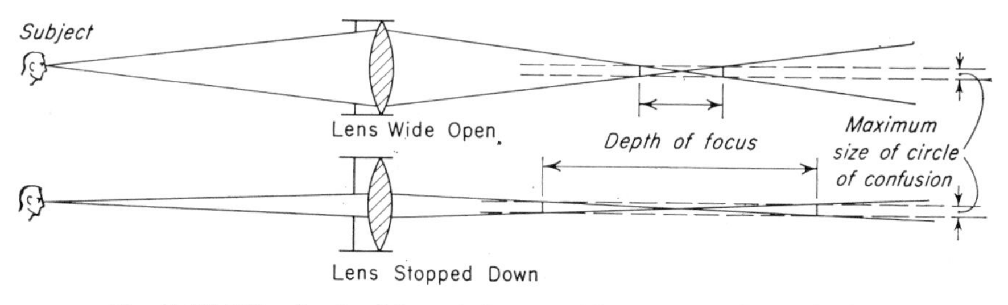

Fig. 5–27. Why depth of focus is improved by stopping down the lens.

very shallow. As it is stopped down to a smaller and smaller opening, the depth of focus constantly increases.

Consider again the light from a single point, gathered together by a lens and concentrated into one spot to form an image. It is clear from the diagram that a smaller lens opening, producing a narrower cone of rays, will cause the maximum tolerable circle of confusion to fall farther from the plane of exact focus, both ahead and behind. Thus the depth of focus is increased by stopping down the lens.

It should be pointed out that when the lens is stopped down, fewer rays of light enter it and the image loses brilliance. More light is necessary on the subject to give the same illumination on the photosensitive plate.

Figure 5-28 explains what stopping down the lens means in terms of depth of *field*. In drawing (*a*) the depth of focus is not sufficiently great to hold two objects, *A* and *B*, sharp at the same time.

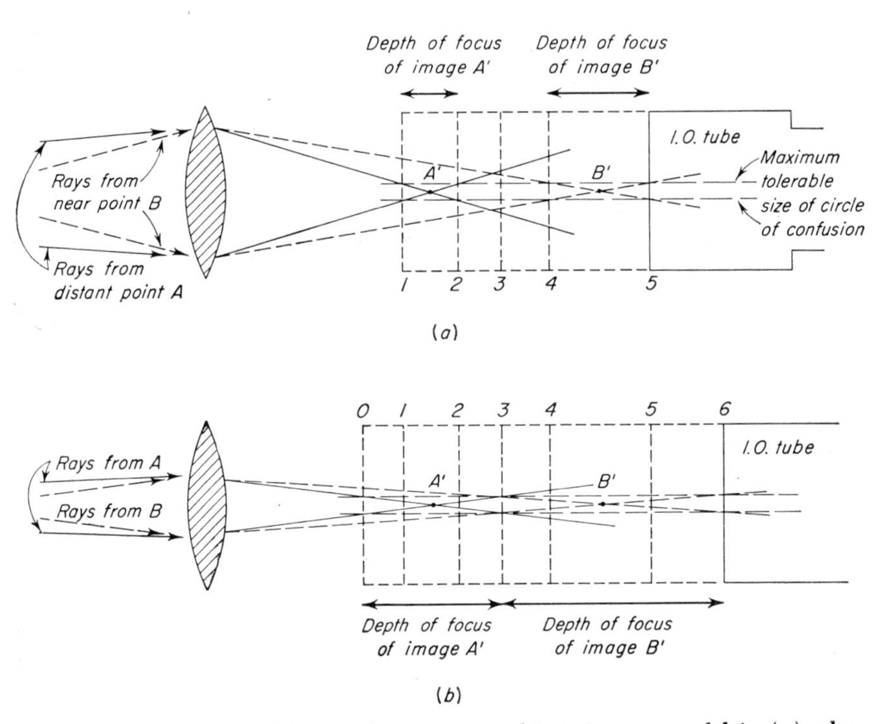

Fig. 5–28. Attempt to split focus between two objects is unsuccessful in (*a*) when lens is wide open, but succeeds in (*b*) when lens is stopped down. *Note:* Amount of movement of the tube is exaggerated for purposes of illustration. The possible length of travel is only a little over 2 inches.

The end of the tube could be placed anywhere between positions 1 and 2, and the image of the distant point, *A*, would be in focus. Critical focus would exist only at *A′*, where all the rays from *A* join to form a point of light. Between positions 1 and 2, however, the circle which these out-of-focus rays cast is within the tolerable limits and still looks like a point. The rays from point *B*, however, are forming too large a circle in this region, and *B* is definitely out of focus. *B* will be in focus only if the end of the tube is placed between position 4 and position 5. But these two regions where *A* and *B* are in focus do not overlap, and any attempt to "split focus" by focusing on a point midway between A and B (position 3 with the tube) results only in both points being out of focus.

Figure 5-28*b* illustrates the effect of stopping down the lens in solving this problem. Point A is now in focus from tube position 0 to position 3; point B is sharp from position 3 back to position 6. By splitting focus and placing the tube at 3 we can now get both A and B sharply defined at the same time. In front of the camera the depth of field has been increased until it is now as great as the distance from point A to point B.

Focal length of lens and depth of field. The third factor which determines depth of field (and depth of focus) is the focal length of the lens. A short lens has a greater depth of field than a long lens, when both are set at the same diaphragm stop and *focused for the same distance*. Figure 5-29 shows the differences in the depth of field of three standard lenses.

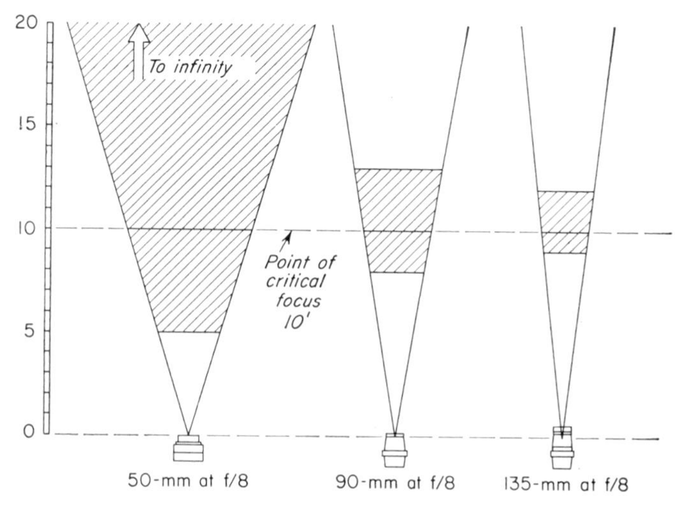

Fig. 5–29. Comparison between depth of field in three standard lenses focused on a point 10 feet distant.

All three are open to the same *f* stop and are focused on a subject 10 feet away. The shorter the focal length, the greater the depth of field. Cameras which use smaller sizes of film need relatively shorter-focal-length lenses to cover the same angles of view. This is why these small cameras have a greater depth of field, why the 8-mm movie camera never needs to be focused at all. The standard lens on these cameras is only ½-inch focal length. The three photographs in Fig. 5-14 demonstrate the improvement in depth of field with the use of a wider lens.

It should be noted, however, that you cannot get something for nothing. In changing to a shorter-focal-length lens to increase the depth of focus, you also greatly increase your angle of view. If this is undesirable, the next move will be to dolly the camera in closer to the subject. But as the distance to the subject decreases, so does the depth of focus. When the camera is in close enough to cover the same width of stage as it did before with a long-focal-length lens, the depth of field achieved with the wide-angle lens is not very different (Fig. 5-30).

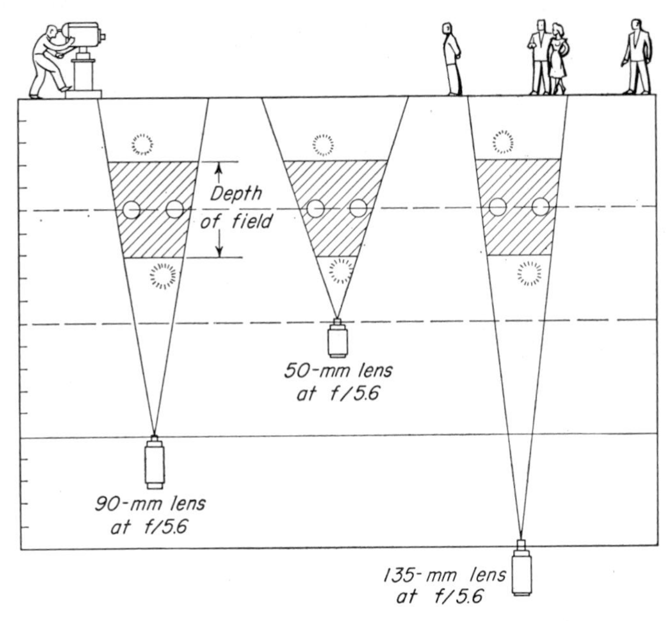

Fig. 5–30. Comparison between depth of field when same width of scene is maintained in shots taken by three standard lenses. You cannot improve depth of field by changing lenses unless you accept a wider angle of view.

Depth of field of a given distance depends on the diaphragm opening and the focal length of the lens. All lenses of the same focal length have the same depth of focus, no matter what cameras they are used on. If you want to look up the depth of focus of a particular lens you plan to use, you can consult photographic tables concerning lenses used on any size camera. A 2-inch lens, for example, will have the same depth of field no matter what camera it is designed for. Caution: Different depth-of-field tables are calculated around different maximum circles of confusion. If the maximum tolerable circle size is only 1/1,000 inch, for example, the depth of field of a lens at any particular lens opening will be a lot less than it would be for a television camera, where the circle size can be $\frac{1}{500}$ inch or less. Look then for tables calculated at this size circle, such as the table for 35-mm-film camera lenses in the handbook mentioned.

6

Television Cutting

In motion pictures a change from one scene to another is accomplished by cutting the unwanted portions off the end of one scene and the beginning of the next and then joining the two together with a splice. This process is called "cutting." To cut a film does not mean simply to reduce it in length by taking out unwanted portions. It is the whole process of putting a film together: choosing which shot shall follow which, and determining the precise length of each and the exact frame on which each cut shall be made.

The cutter is the one who does the physical work of handling the film. The creative decisions are usually made by a film editor, who may sometimes do his own cutting. Motion-picture cutting is recognized as a vitally important aspect of the film art. It is a profession in itself. Some film makers have gone so far as to say that in the technique of cutting lies the entire process of creative film art.

In television a change in the scene is made with a switch, not with the scissors and splicer. Strictly speaking, we should call it "switching" instead of cutting. But the word "cut" has come to mean an instantaneous change of scene; and since that is what we produce by pushing buttons, it is still correct to call the process cutting. The two terms will be used interchangeably here: "cutting" when the creative aspects of the process are being considered; "switching" when the discussion is on the technical side.

The process of cutting television is very similar to that of cutting motion pictures in end result, but the method is entirely different. A film editor may take weeks to cut a show, deliberating over each decision. A television director has to do his job during the show itself. He must rely on fast thinking, quick reaction time, and thorough preparation. In some cases he relies on his script or on his assistant, who follows the script. The sight of the television director excitedly calling shots ("Take Two!" "Take One!") has led some to think that shot calling is all there is to television directing. Some directors actually do forget to make full use of their cameras because they are so occupied with just the problem of cutting.

In creative production a good director plans his cuts, just as he plans his camera shots—on paper. If he has had enough experience, he can visualize the effect of a cut, even between two shots which also exist only in his mind or as thumbnail sketches on the margin of the script. He will not limit himself to what he has planned, however, once he has produced the shots with cameras and watched the effect of the cut on the master monitor. He may change the camera shots to improve the cut, or he may change the timing of the cut itself.

By far the greatest number of television shows, however, are produced with little or no rehearsal; and the cutting cannot be planned in advance. Even if camera shots are set in rehearsal, the cutting is often not the same on the final air show. This is because the timing of the cut or the choice of camera depends mainly on the performers. If they deviate from the rehearsed routine or go through actions which have not been rehearsed at all, the director must be on his toes to adapt his cutting to their performance. This is called "off-the-cuff" shooting, "ad-lib" cutting, or "winging" the show.

METHODS OF CONTROL-ROOM OPERATION

Under both the technical-director and the switcher systems of control-room operation (described in Chap. 2) an engineer known as the TD (technical director) operates the switching system and actually punches the buttons. He may take the cues directly from his own script or the action on the screen, or he may, as in most cases, wait for the director to call the shot before he punches the button.

Another method of control-room operating which is used in many of the small stations could be called the "director-switching" system. Under this method the director has the switching system before him and operates the buttons and faders himself. Some stations have adopted this method for reasons of economy and because there was no union jurisdiction over the job. Others have chosen it because they believe it to be the best method of operation. The exact moment when a switch is made is very important, and a split second's delay can often mean the difference between a good and a bad cut. In baseball pickups a bad cut is much worse than that—it is a lost play. A majority of the stations have adopted the director-switching system at least for baseball and other sports remotes.

This method of operation works out fairly well in small stations and on programs which are not too complicated. However, in the production of dramatic shows, it is well that the director can dispose of the burden of handling several rows of push buttons and fader controls.

It is very important for the switcher or TD who punches buttons to know ahead of time which camera is to be taken next. His reaction time is faster then. He has only to punch the button. He doesn't have to decide first which button to punch.

The director's best method is to give a "ready" cue whenever possible. This is appreciated also by the cameraman, who is not so likely to be caught changing lenses or adjusting focus at the moment of the cut. "Ready Two" can be said almost automatically while you are watching the action on camera 2. Where the cut must be precise, a further "Take—" will keep the TD poised. Then the number can be thrown very quickly, accompanied if desired by a hand signal, and the reaction is almost as fast as though the director himself pushed the button.

The most logical method the author has encountered was in Finland. There the director says essentially "First one—now. Second one—now." The sharp final command ensures accurate timing, while the number is given just a little earlier as a safeguard against error.

PRINCIPLES OF CUTTING

The principles of cutting outlined here are the same that have governed film editing in all but the most esoteric types of film or film sequences. These are the techniques which achieve a "smooth cut" and assure a visual continuity. Good cutting, by this criterion, is unnoticeable. Two shots are joined in such a way that the audience is completely satisfied by the result; and attention can properly remain with the action, rather than the method of production. Subject is more important than form in this type of production.

Basically, the responsibility of the television director is to satisfy the viewer. When something is going on and the director is making pictures of it, he must show it properly or the viewer will be dissatisfied. He must show the viewer what he wants to see. Almost fifty years of an ever-improving motion-picture art have educated the viewer to expect a lot. He wants close-ups on essential action; and he wants them quickly, just as he is used to getting them in the films. He wants to look around and know where he is, and he expects good orientation. Above all, he doesn't want to miss anything that happens, and he doesn't want to be confused.

The director must show the viewer what he wants to see when he wants to see it, and cause him no confusion in the process. If the television director can achieve even so much as this, he will be a good director. Fancy angles, subjective camera, montage cutting—these have their place too, but they can never substitute for these basic requirements.

Showing the viewer what he wants to see might better be classified under camera handling than under cutting. But showing it to him when he wants to see it is definitely a principle of cutting. The timing of the cut is perhaps the most important single thing about it, and the one thing which is most likely to be a little off in television. Film-editing procedures take account of this and usually include a "rough-cut" stage where all the scenes are overlong. When the film is projected and studied in this condition, better decisions can be made as to the exact timing of the cuts. In television such a thing is impossible. A long shot and a medium shot which are to be cut together exist side by side on two monitors. A switch between them is instantaneous and irrevocable.

Within a sequence of shots taking place in one scene, the actual length of an action cannot be changed. An actor crosses the room, and we cut to a close-up when he reaches the other side. In film editing there is a possibility of shortening the actual time of the cross. If the actor walks out of frame on the first shot and into frame on the second, the entire intervening time can be eliminated. This is known as creating "filmic time." In television we can condense time in this way only between sequences or by special devices, but not in the regular run of cutting. We are limited to actual time, since television is basically an art of actuality. The choice, by the director, of the best segment of this actuality, at the best time, is the process of artistic selection, which is a good part of what might be called the creative art of television.

Dependence on actual time, however, simplifies television cutting as compared with cutting film; there is no need to worry about matching of action. In film shooting it is always a constant worry to be sure the action is the same when you shoot a close-up as it was when you shot the medium shot just before. If an actor sits down, he must do it at the same speed each time, hold the chair with the same hand, cross his legs in the same direction, etc., or joining the two pieces of film will be a great problem. Then (in film cutting), even when you have two shots with identical action in them, there is the problem of cutting between them, so that the action, which begins in one shot and ends in the other, will be smooth and continuous. There must be no overlapping, nothing missing. This also we are spared in television.

CUTTING ON ACTION

The principle of cutting on action is just as important in television as it is in films. There is nothing that will so disguise the fact that a cut has been made as a strong and positive action to carry across from one shot to the next. The cut should be made during the action itself, not just before it, and not after it. As a director you must watch your monitors very closely, have the second camera ready, call the first half of your order, "Take—," and, just at the moment of the move, call the camera number. If it is a short movement, like a dancer's leap, for instance, and there is any delay at all, the cut will come after the leap is over.

Cutting on action is possible, however, only if the attention of the audience is definitely centered on the action through which you intend to bridge the two shots. If you start with a long shot which includes several actions, the audience is as likely to be watching one as another. If the shot, let us say, shows four football players warming up before a

Fig. 6–1. Cutting on action is an unsure method in this case because there is no way of knowing which action the audience may be watching.

game by kicking punts and the director should wish to cut to a close-up of one of them, he cannot do this on the action of the kick. There is a 3-to-1 chance that the viewer may not be watching the same player that the director is looking at. If the viewer's attention happens to be on the wrong player, the new shot will suddenly be upon him in the midst of an action. It would be best in this case to cut before the kick, so that the complete action would be included in the close-up shot, just as one would do in cutting to another scene, when matching of action is unnecessary.

CUTTING ON REACTION

One of the most powerful motivations for a cut is to have someone in the picture look outside the frame. Immediately the audience wants to see what he is looking at. A shot of another subject—anything under the sun—is accepted, at least momentarily, by the eager viewer. The viewer has been given what he wanted to see. More than that, the director has contrived, by the device of having someone look, to make the viewer *want* to see the thing he is going to show him next. He can cut to almost anything at all and make a good cut. For a joke, he can even put in something ridiculous. If the shot is entirely impossible and incongruous, the viewer will laugh at himself for having accepted it, but only after a smooth and natural cut has been foisted upon him. The same general principle applies in the case of an actor pointing a camera or a gun. The audience wants to see what the actor is pointing at.

Such a device can be used to motivate a cut to a very big close-up from a medium or long shot. Usually it is best not to make the change of shot too extreme. Long shot to medium shot, medium to close-up, close-up to big close-up is the normal progression. But if a person picks up a picture or a letter or obviously concentrates his attention on a very small portion of the scene in front of him, a cut to that small area is perfectly motivated.

Cutting is often motivated when the audience wants to see someone's reaction to what has just been said or done. In the audience-participation show, a contestant may be blindfolded and put through some silly stunt. A shot of his wife's reaction to his asininity is completely motivated (provided she is reacting at all). In the dramatic show, when two people are in conversation, it is often desirable to cut to a close-up of the person who is not talking, in order to watch his reaction to what is being said. Standard procedure under other circumstances, in covering a conversation, is to show at all times the person who is talking and to cut back and forth on every speech. You have to show the viewer what he wants to see, and he is interested primarily in the source of sound. Noises off screen, the opening of a door, or a voice will make the viewer want to see where the sound is coming from.

THE CUT-IN, OR INTERCUT, SHOT

Sometimes during an event or a performance it may enrich the show to cut away from the event and interpose a shot of something else. A spectator reacting to a sports event or not reacting, as the case may be, is a good example. The newsreels frequently intercut a close-up of screaming fans just after a good play, or show a long shot of the stands if the preceding action has not been too exciting. But in films this serves a practical purpose, which does not hold true in television.

An intercut shot in a film can be used to separate two shots that do not match and cannot be cut together. A smooth continuity results. Moreover, the film audience does not mind being taken away momentarily from the primary action because it knows the film editor has included the rest of the scene in the reel and that it is not going to miss anything. The television viewer, on the other hand, feels no such certainty. He is afraid, while he is watching the frenzied fans jumping in the stands, that he is missing something going on down on the field. The same is true of audience-participation shows, comedy shows, variety shows, and many other kinds of spontaneous programs. If intercut shots are to be used at all, they must be used at a time when nothing of importance is likely to happen elsewhere or they will not be what the viewer wants to see.

The television dramatic show, on the other hand, is closely akin to the dramatic motion picture in this as well as most of its other aspects. All the cinematic techniques are applicable to television dramatic shows if they can be physically accomplished at all. Intercutting of extraneous shots for purposes of contrast, irony, flash back, etc., can be accomplished as well in television as in film medium. The reader is referred to such books as Rudolf Arnheim's "Film," Raymond Spottiswood's "A Grammar of the Film," and Ernest Lindgren's "The Art of the Film" for full analysis of these techniques.

LENGTH OF SHOT

Some people hold the theory that a lot of cutting increases the tempo of a production. This is carried so far that statements like this have been heard: "There should be a cut at least every 20 seconds in order to keep audience interest." This is by no means always true. A shot should be as long as the proverbial piece of string. Tempo is not controlled only by the rate of cutting, except perhaps in newsreels or documentary films. In the newsreels or in the documentary films which are built from a series of more or less disconnected shots, scenes of three or four seconds in length are standard. A shot containing action should be continued as long as necessary to complete the action, or cut as short as possible, one might rather say, without *losing* any of the action. "The True Glory," a war film made from thousands of stock shots taken by a great number of Signal Corps cameramen, was cut to a very rapid place. The shots were, straight through the film, less than two seconds in length. This resulted in a picture which was very hard to watch.

Cutting, in this type of film, does control tempo because it controls the speed at which the film progresses from subject to subject. Television production, however, is not like this at all. Cutting, in television, is generally not from one subject to another, but from long shot to medium shot to close-up, etc., all parts of the same scene or subject. The speed at which the performers progress from action to action is what determines tempo. All the frantic cutting in the world can't speed up the show.

I remember once, as a young director, being given a sports interview show to direct. The MC and the interviewee sat together on a sofa and talked. Here was my great opportunity to do a real production. I dollied the cameras in and out. I cut from one angle to another—big close-ups, high two-shots, timing each cut accurately with the phrasing of the conversation, building up what I thought must be a terrific pace. But I succeeded only in sweating up the camera crew and making it hard for the audience to relax and pay attention to the interview. The show remained nothing more than two people sitting on a sofa and talking.

"What is the absolute minimum length of shot?" is a question that is sometimes asked. Four frames of film are enough to give the audience a glimpse of a subject; there are shots of this length in some of the montage sequences in Hollywood films. It is amazing how quickly the eye can take in a picture. Back in the Keystone Comedy days they found they could get a better laugh if they cut in close-ups of action. If the action was only a pie hitting face or a quick change of expression on a comedian's countenance, it was included in a few frames of film and there was no need to run the shot even as long as one second to show what had happened.

Fast cutting is very rarely desirable in television, and hardly ever possible. For one thing, you run out of shots too quickly. You only have two or three cameras, and you have to allow time between takes for the cameramen to line up new shots or you will be repeating yourself.

Furthermore, television doesn't call for the pace of the motion picture. The two media are different in this respect. Since the viewers are watching reality in the case of television, they are content to let events take their own natural time. It is hard to imagine a group of people sitting through a 2½-hour film of a football game in the way that they will watch a full-game telecast. In a motion picture they are used to a condensation of time and a tempo of production which is purely filmic.

CUTTING VS. CAMERA MOVEMENT

Since the film is a construction made out of shots spliced together, it is natural that the cut would be accepted as the normal thing. Television, on the other hand, is an electrical pickup of reality. The television camera makes pictures continuously, as long as it is turned on and the beam control is up. Theoretically, the long continuous shot is more natural to the television medium. Furthermore, a television pickup is usually less of a construction than it is reality itself. The television viewer feels toward the receiver as though it were a kind of window through which he can see distant events. The more real this view, the stronger his feeling. These theoretical considerations seem to indicate that cutting is something to be avoided in television.

Camera movement is, of course, the alternative. Instead of cutting to a closer shot, why not dolly in? Is it not better to use a Zoomar lens on a baseball game than to cut from camera to camera? By and large, this is true. Willys Cooper in his "Volume I," "Escape," and "Stage 13" series did some very fine dramatic shows with only one camera. There are times, however, when the advantage of a cut over camera movement is very great. Several such advantages can be listed:

1. One practical consideration is time. It takes time to dolly in to a close-up and back again. The action must be slowed down for the camera. It is much better to cut to a close-up and cut away from it again in a matter of seconds and get along with the show.

2. Rehearsal time is also involved. A dramatic show can be planned with a great deal of actor and camera movement, or it can be done by cutting between a series of static shots. A lot more rehearsal time is needed to produce a show with camera movement. The movement, the positions of the actors, and the coordination of the camera—all have to be carefully worked out and well rehearsed if they are to work at all. Simple cutting from one shot to another can be worked out in much less time.

3. Reaction shots, also, cannot often be done by panning or dollying the camera. When the viewer sees someone look at something, he wants to see immediately what the actor is looking at. The viewer is seldom content to wait through a long pan shot across unimportant background to see it.

4. Another consideration is the dramatic value of the cut itself. The sudden appearance of a new picture on the screen can be put to good use sometimes, entirely for its shock value. This is particularly the case if cuts have been used sparingly in the sequence just before. A sudden dramatic moment can be enhanced by sharp cuts. A cut is useful for punctuation, something that is more difficult to accomplish with camera movement.

MATCHING CENTER OF INTEREST

The composition of the two shots involved has a definite effect on the smoothness of cutting between them.

When a cut is made, the eye must quickly adjust itself to a new composition. The easier the readjustment, the less noticeable and smoother the cut. One factor which determines this smoothness is the composition of the two shots and the relative position in the frame of the center of interest in each case. In the first shot in Fig. 6-2 the center of interest

Fig. 6–2. The importance of matching center of interest.

is the woman talking, in the lower right-hand corner of the screen. If a cut is made to a close-up of the same subject, but composed so that the woman is then to the left of the screen, a readjustment of the eye is necessary. The eye remains focused on the lower right-hand corner after the cut, with nothing particular to look at. It must travel across the picture to find the center of interest again in its new position on the screen.

This is really a minor point in television, since there are usually so many other more important things to be desired. Where greater perfection is necessary, however, it is something to consider. An example is in the pickup of sports. The smoothest possible cutting is necessary in covering sports because even momentary confusion is enough to cause the viewer to lose track of a play, particularly in a fast game. Naturally it is not possible to order the cameramen to place the ball in any particular corner of the screen (although methods for doing this very rapidly

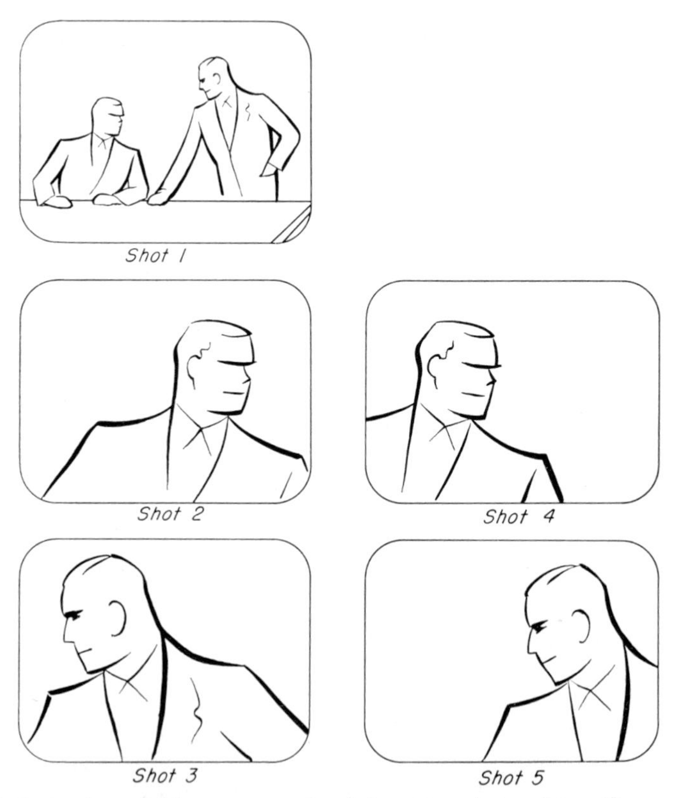

Fig. 6–3. A simple switching sequence involving a two-shot and two close-ups. If the close-ups are composed as in shots 2 and 3, a smooth cut between them is impossible. Shots 4 and 5 cut together well. Note that shot 4 cuts after shot 1 better than shot 2 does because there is less change in the center of interest.

have been suggested). It is about all you can hope for if each camera merely centers on the action. If each camera centers the ball, at the moment of the cut the ball will remain in the same place on the screen.

The series of pictures in Fig. 6-3 illustrate a common error in composition made by television students. Sometimes a framing may be very good in and of itself but may lead to confusion when cut into a sequence of other shots. A sequence of three shots is shown, a covering two-shot and two waist shots of individuals. When these two single shots (shot 2 and shot 3) are cut together, the two people do not seem to be looking at each other but, instead, seem to be back to back looking in opposite directions. Each one is looking out of the frame, away from the place where the other man's head will be after the cut is made. In order to make these shots usable in this succession, good balance must be sacrificed and both shots framed up so the people are looking into the frame and at each other (shots 4 and 5).

Another common fault is the sequence of shots which are composed in such a way that the subject appears first in one part of the frame and then in another. The sequence of shots in Fig. 6-4 illustrates this.

Fig. 6–4. Two-shots that cut together very badly. Character *A* appears to jump from one place to another on the screen.

Whereas the composition of the individual shots may be entirely adequate, when they are used in succession the character *A* seems to jump from one part of the picture to another. This is made particularly noticeable by the fact that he is the same size in both pictures.

CUTTING TO THE AUDIO

Sometimes, the phrasing of sounds will provide a natural place to cut. For instance, all else being equal, it is smoother to cut at the end of a sentence rather than in the middle of one. The phrasing of music forms a very compelling pattern for cutting, especially when the music plays an important role. The music is reinforced if the visual change follows the changes of tone color, chorus, and verse. Clark Jones, one of the best directors in this field, is known for his accurate cutting in musical shows.

His shots will be 8 bars, 4 bars, sometimes only 2 bars in length depending on the change in tone color of the music, and the cut is always made precisely on the beat, showing the new musician just as he begins to play. When tone color changes every 2 bars, so do the cameras; when a vocalist sings 32 bars without a break, the camera rests quietly with the subject.

WHAT NOT TO DO IN CUTTING

To the tyro director who has had little experience in the film or television medium the author would direct the following words of caution:

1. *Don't cut too much.* You are likely to make the show harder to watch or to irritate your audience. If you have time to work it out, camera movement or actor movement is smoother. Use the cut for dramatic punctuation or to get a shot on the air quickly. Don't go crazy with "brilliant" cutting unless you know what you are doing.

2. *Don't cut blindly.* Some directors seem to close their eyes and say "Take Two." They are afraid to take their eyes off the master monitor. Keep looking back and forth; try to watch all the monitors at once. And look at the camera monitor just before you call the take. You'll get fewer lens changes and out-of-focus shots on the air if you do.

3. *Don't cut between similar shots of the same subject.* Don't cut from one two-shot to another two-shot. Of course, the second one may be from a different angle, but does it show the audience anything more? The only exception to this is in the case of "reverse-angle" shots, where the first camera looks over one man's shoulder to see the other full face and the second camera does the opposite from the other side (Fig. 6-5).

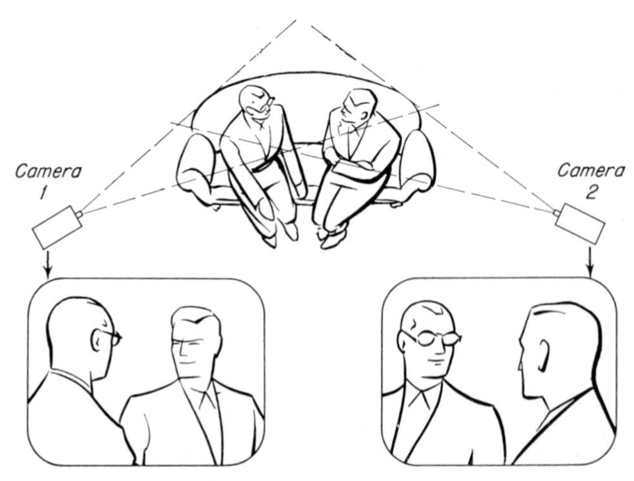

Fig. 6–5. Reverse-angle two-shots. This is an exception to the general rule against cutting between similar shots.

Never let two cameras give you the same shot. See that one of them changes lenses or repositions. Otherwise you might as well not have it out there. Sometimes a director may get stuck and have to cut between two identical shots, bad as such a cut may be. He may find, for example, that he has to release the camera which is on the air for some sudden need. He must cut to another camera. His only possibility is an identical shot, and he hasn't time to change it to something else. The viewer doesn't know these problems, however, or hear the director's excuses.

A cut between two similar shots will often give the effect of a sudden jump in action. There is a certain shift of position on the screen which blends in the eye like stages of an animation to give the effect of motion. This is similar to the familiar jump cut, in unedited films, caused by the camera being turned off and then on again.

The worst example the author can recall of cutting between similar shots occurred on a variety show. There were three cameras; one presenting a full face of the girl singer, one a three-quarters left profile the same size, and the third a right profile, also the same size. During the song the director changed shots often. There might have been some reason for this because of the variety obtained by the change of angle, except that the performer was too smart for them. She was on to television. As soon as the camera changed, she spotted the red lights out of the corner of her eye and turned to face the new camera. Thus wherever the director shot from, he always got a full-face close-up. The singer continued to chase the cameras around for the rest of the number.

4. *Don't cut to an extremely different angle.* What constitutes too great a change in angle is hard to define. The main thing is to be sure the subject is immediately recognizable and doesn't look like something else in the new shot. A shot from an angle that is so far different that an altogether different background is seen behind the subject will cause confusion. Sometimes a change of angle will make a great difference in the lighting. What is contrasty side light from one angle may be flat front light from another. The difference may be so great that the subject is unrecognizable, at least for a moment. The author has seen a profile shot of a news commentator cut in suddenly after a full-face shot, with the result that the profile shot looked momentarily like someone else sitting across the room watching. The viewers have no way of knowing that the new shot is taken from a different camera angle until they have seen the shot and comprehended it. The natural assumption is that it is taken from the same place, but looking in a different direction, just as an observer on the scene would turn and take in another view. The problem of camera placement in the pickup of baseball and other sporting events is directly tied in with this. A further discussion of the relation between cutting and camera angle is to be found in Chap. 20 in the section on

baseball. One point should be made here, however. When an action takes place *between* two cameras, so that they see the subject from opposite sides, the direction of the action will be completely reversed when a cut is made. Nothing can be so utterly confusing (Fig. 6-6). It is usually

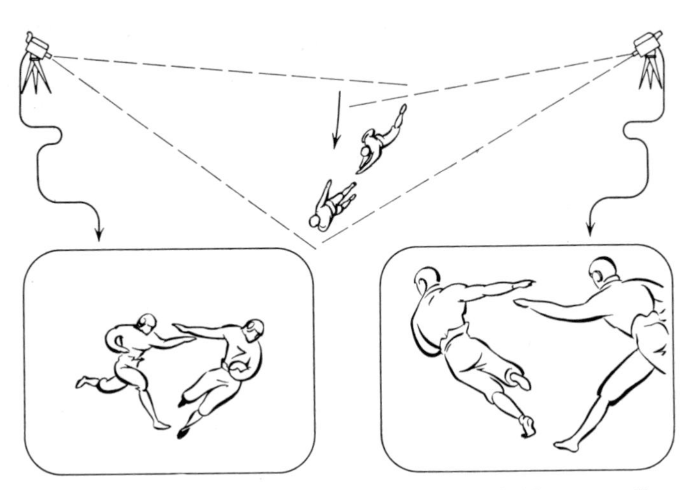

Fig. 6–6. If cameras are placed on opposite sides of the field, a cut will reverse the direction of action taking place between them.

best to keep at least the main two or three cameras as close together as possible on most sports pickups.

5. *Don't cut on a pan.* Don't cut from a camera that is panning to one that is static or from a static camera to one that is panning. Try it once, and you will see that it just can't be done. You *can* cut from pan to pan very nicely, provided they are both going in the same direction and at the same speed. When two cameras are following the same action, for example, the cut is usually quite smooth. At a football game, if both cameras center the ball as they follow a runner, it is perfectly possible to cut from medium shot to close-up without the slightest confusion, since both cameras will be panning, and in the same direction.

6. *Don't spoil exits.* As far as the audience is concerned, once an actor has left the frame of the picture, he has made his exit. Don't rediscover him and exit him again in the background of the next shot. The same thing goes also for entrances. Don't make an actor enter twice.

THE DISSOLVE

The dissolve, lap dissolve, or cross fade is the method of transition in which the first picture becomes steadily weaker while the second becomes stronger on the screen. It is really a fade-out simultaneous with a fade-in. If the dissolving process is stopped at the mid-point, a superimposure is the result—each picture at half strength.

In films, the dissolve has been used with a certain connotation. By unwritten agreement, all film makers found it best to reserve the dissolve for a particular purpose. (The expense of having dissolves made assisted toward this end.) The meaning of a dissolve in dramatic films is transition in time or, occasionally, transition to another place at the *same* time. You dissolve between sequences—to a later time or to another place, or both. Dissolves within a sequence where no change of time or place is intended are rarely done in films, unless by an amateur fascinated with the dissolve mechanism on his camera, who dissolves between the long shot of a garden and the close-up of a flower.

In television, unfortunately, a dissolve is no harder to do than a cut and costs no more. Instead of going to another day's work, as you do in films (taking out the proper negatives, sending them out for opticals, splicing back the dupe negatives into the reel), in television you simply turn a dial or move a handle, as the case may be. With the Du Mont equipment (described in Chap. 7) you punch the same button you ordinarily punch for a cut, and a dissolve is automatically effected.

The result is a very free use of dissolves, often in places where a cut is really preferable. Dissolving within a sequence is often done on television. This is not generally true of dramatic shows, because this type of production follows the motion-picture technique rather closely. In musical productions, variety shows, and the like, however, a director feels less confined to the motion-picture tradition. The result is that in television there is a new connotation (or a loss of any connotation at all) for the dissolve.

Dissolves are commonly used in nondramatic television shows for their own sake, or their decorative value, not for any meaning they may carry. In a fashion show, for instance, with lovely models, smooth music, slow movement, a dissolve from long shot to close-up, as the model turns, is more in keeping with the mood than a sharp cut. Similarly, in shooting a smooth dance number, dissolves may help retain the continuity of movement. In dissolving, as in cutting, the midst of an action is the best time to make this transition, except that, in the case of the dissolve, a longer action is needed. The dissolve on a twirl or turn is particularly smooth. The length of the dissolve depends on the mood at the time, the length of the action behind it, and the pace of the show. Very fast dissolves which are almost like a cut are sometimes seen. Don't forget that the audience is temporarily confused during a dissolve. Whether that is to be a pleasant lingering confusion or as short as possible so you can get on with the story is up to your creative judgment.

Don't go dissolve-happy. Don't use a dissolve where a cut would be better. Don't use a dissolve or a cut when camera movement would be better.

THE FADE-OUT AND FADE-IN

The motion-picture connotation of the fade-out has been retained in television. The fade-out is sometimes called the "dissolve to black" in television because of the way it is done with the dissolve control. It has a connotation of finality; it indicates an end to something. It may be used in place of a dissolve to link sequences together where there is a greater change in time or place than is usually indicated by a dissolve. A dissolve retains continuity; a fade-out–fade-in breaks the sequence. It is not good, for instance, to fade in and fade out a series of titles, since the audience will think with each fade-out that they have seen the last of the series. Similarly, a play divided into a number of short scenes with fades between will lack the unity it might have had if other devices had been used. If the fade-out–fade-in is done rapidly (in less than two seconds all told), it does not end continuity so completely and can be used for many of the same purposes as the dissolve.

The most dangerous aspect of using fade-outs in television is that the length of blank screen between fade-out and fade-in may be too long. Audience interest drops very rapidly when there is nothing on the screen. There may be exceptions to this rule: certainly when sound or music carries through, the wait is not so bad. However, the timing of the fade-out, the blank screen, and the fade-in should always be carefully planned and rehearsed. The shortest possible blank screen is particularly important when the fade-out comes at the end of a program or spot announcement. Every second's delay in bringing up the next picture means an increasing loss of audience. Dial turning on television is a much greater problem than radio ever had to contend with. In stations where the same control-room crew must do one show right after another there is a great tendency on the part of directors and technical directors to fail to look ahead past the conclusion of one program and plan the moves that must be made to begin the next. They wait until the final fade-out, heave a big sigh, and then start hunting frantically through their schedules and routine sheets for the next move while the screen remains patiently blank.

There are other ways of doing fade-outs in a program than by simply turning down the gain, or dissolving to black. Fade-outs can be done with the lights on stage: the old familiar blackout. This is easier if the number happens to be lighted by one spotlight, which is all that needs to be cut. The light can be moved off the subject, or the subject can move out of the beam of the light. If the motivation is carefully planned, the camera can be panned off into a dark area or moved behind a dark object. This device was used by Olivier in the film "Hamlet." Another variation on this is to have an actor walk directly into the camera until he blocks out all the light. Whichever of these devices is used to effect the fade, it is usually effective to use the same thing in reverse for the fade-in of the following scene.

THE DEFOCUS TRANSITION

The defocus transition is akin to a dissolve and is used for somewhat the same purposes. The effect is simply that the picture becomes blurred, then clears up again, and a new picture is revealed. Some directors reserve the defocus for a transition backward through time and signify a flashback by this means, while an ordinary dissolve is used for time lapses in the forward direction. This device is particularly useful when the sequence it introduces is led up to by an actor thinking, or falling asleep, or passing out. It is not necessary to use the full transition; simply a defocus and a dissolve to the next picture are often just as effective, and there is a shorter period of eyestrain for the viewer.

Making a defocus transition requires a little coordination between TD and cameramen. First you ready the camera which is not yet on the air with the order "Ready Two out of focus." When the moment arrives for the transition, give the next three cues in rapid succession: "Out of focus One. Dissolve to Two. Into focus Two." It is assumed that the cameraman on No. 1 will refocus his camera again without being told, as soon as you are through with the effect.

VISUAL CONFUSION OR INTERFERENCE

Almost anything which fuzzes up or confuses the picture can be used very nicely as an alternative to the dissolve. It is best, of course, if the first appearance of the effect is motivated in some way. People walking in front of the camera, fire, smoke, water, etc., in front of the lens—whatever is at hand will do. The Flexitron, an electronic special effect (page 289), with its wavy distortion is sometimes used. These special transitions are rarely utilized because they take time to rehearse and execute properly. But remember that the transition device may arise directly from the special effects within the show. Anything which confuses the picture will find its use somewhere as a transitional effect.

THE WIPE

The wipe is a cinematic transition in which the new picture starts as a small area and grows until it covers the entire screen. Film wipes can be made in a great variety of patterns, and new ones can easily be devised to suit special purposes. The simplest is the plain horizontal wipe. Several types of simple wipes can be done optically by shutters and masks in front of the camera. These will be discussed in Chap. 13. A wipe transition between, for example, two title cards is not to be confused with a pull-off or slide-through, which is a bodily movement of the title in front of the camera. In the true wipe, two cameras are used (or two stages of an effects machine), and everything is stationary. The only thing that moves on the screen is the line of demarcation between the two pictures as the area of one grows larger and the other smaller.

No standard connotation was ever found for the wipe in motion pictures. It is very rarely used in dramatic films, finding its greatest value as a decorative device to dress up industrial films, film commercials, and the like, which depend on surface devices for their visual interest. A wipe is sometimes used to lead into a split-screen effect. A man starts a phone conversation. On the opposite side of the screen a wipe begins, which proceeds far enough to reveal the party at the other end of the phone. When the call is over, the second picture wipes back out again.

The variety of transitions and effects which can be produced without special technical preparation depends on the flexibility of the available switching equipment. The following chapter will describe the standard switching systems which are to be found in most of the television studios and will indicate the usual things that a switching system will be called upon to do.

7

Television Switching Equipment

There is considerable variation in design between the different switching systems put out by manufacturers of television equipment. General engineering departments of the major networks, and many independent stations, have designed and built their own systems. All these permit the operator to fade to black, lap-dissolve, and superimpose. Not all switching systems, however, will permit complicated effects such as cutting to a superimposure or cutting away from a superimposure to a shot on another camera. Not all will permit the operator to preview a superimposure before he puts it on the air. Before discussing specific equipment, however, let us consider the standard requirements of the studio switching system.

PREVIEW SWITCHING

It is always a great risk to put anything on the air without being able to watch it right up to the moment of the switch. Every picture must be previewed somewhere before being switched onto the air. Not all picture sources which go to make up a program have their individual monitors in the control room. Incoming lines from projection rooms, remote locations, network feed, etc., are regularly used. A preview monitor is generally provided on which any of these may be shown. A special switching system controlling only the preview monitor (a single row of buttons) is necessary.

Some switching systems make it possible to use the master monitor for previewing these incoming lines. This is a poor practice, however, since it sacrifices the master monitor during the time another channel is being previewed. It results in a type of previewing which amounts to only a quick glance at the next picture, and it certainly is not desirable for best programming results.

DISSOLVES

A switching system must also be designed to fade channels or cross-fade them so that dissolves, fades, and superimposures can be accomplished. There are three common ways to design a switching system to do these things.

Mixer type of switching system. The first system provides each channel with a separate gain control and runs them all together into a mixer, just as the outputs of many microphones are mixed in an audio console.

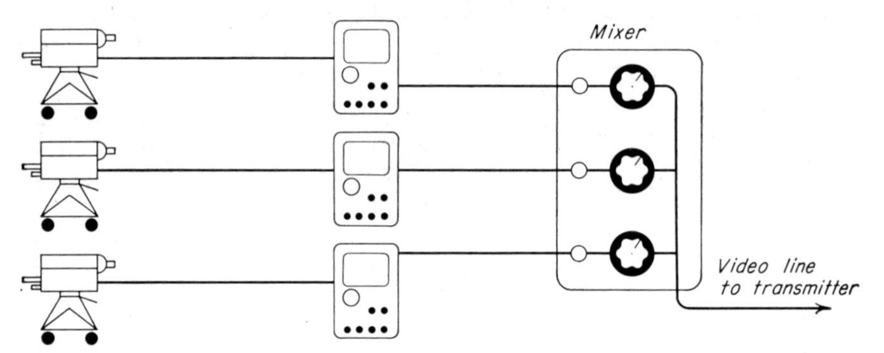

Fig. 7–1. Mixer type of switching system.

The signal from each source is collected by a common "bus," or copper bar, and this then feeds the program line. This kind of switching system may have separate switches, as well as separate fading controls. The old Mt. Lee studio of KTSL had such a switching system, built to the studio's own design. It had seven positions for fading, but no switches. Instantaneous cuts had to be approximated by very quick dissolves. The Du Mont "mixer" is a switching system of this general type; it provides for only four channels but has switches and a number of additional features and refinements.

Dual fading-bus type of switching system. The second type of switching system provides two basic master channels which feed through two fader controls. They are usually termed "channel" or "fading bus" *A* and *B*, and all the video channels which feed into the switching system can be punched up on either one.

Only one of these two channels is used when straight switching is desired: the fader control for the channel being used is left open, and the fader control for the other is closed. If you have been using bus *A*, for example, and wish to make a dissolve, first punch up the camera you will

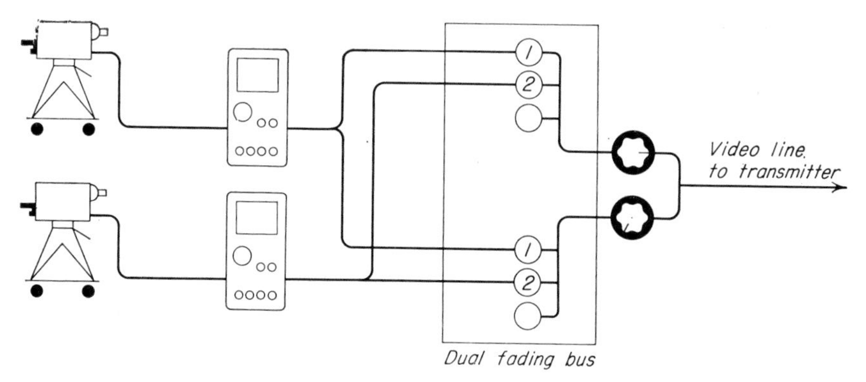

Fig. 7–2. Dual fading-bus type of switching system.

dissolve to on bus *B;* then simultaneously fade out bus *A* and fade in bus *B*.

Three-bus type of switching system. The third system has three master channels, two of which are for fading and dissolving, as just described, while the third is intended for straight switching. The program-switching bus has an extra button marked *E* for *effects,* through which the com-

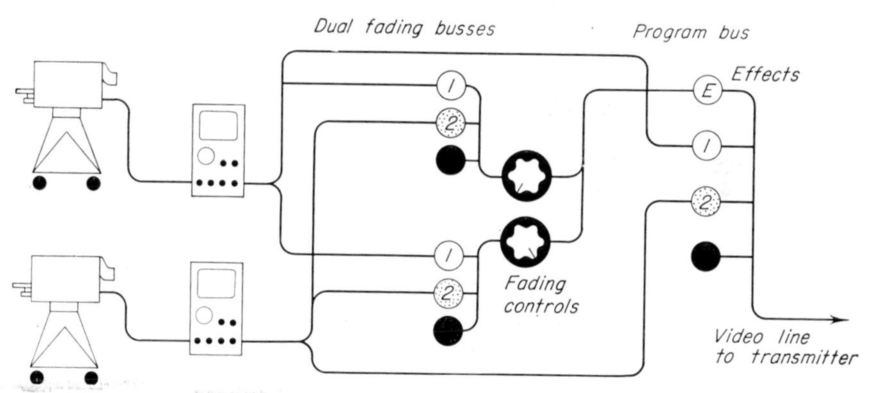

Fig. 7–3. Three-bus type of switching system.

bined output of the two fading busses must feed. Whenever dissolves or superimposures are desired, this button is pressed and the two fading busses are operated exactly like a two-bus system. The three-bus method permits switching to a superimposure or switching away from a superimposure to a single camera.

A STANDARD STUDIO SWITCHING SYSTEM

The example in Fig. 7-4 is a dual-fading-bus system with two banks of push buttons each controlled by a fading handle. The combined output of the two fading busses is the program line. The two fading levers can either work separately to fade out one bus and fade in the other or, clipped together, will operate simultaneously for lap dissolves.

In Fig. 7-4, the two rows of buttons are connected to the two fading busses. The white row may be faded by the white handle, the black row by the black handle. Above the two rows of switches is a row of tally lights that show which channel is on the air.

Straight switching between cameras can be done with either bank of push buttons, provided that the fading control for that particular bank is open. The signal from camera 1, in other words, is carried to *both* white

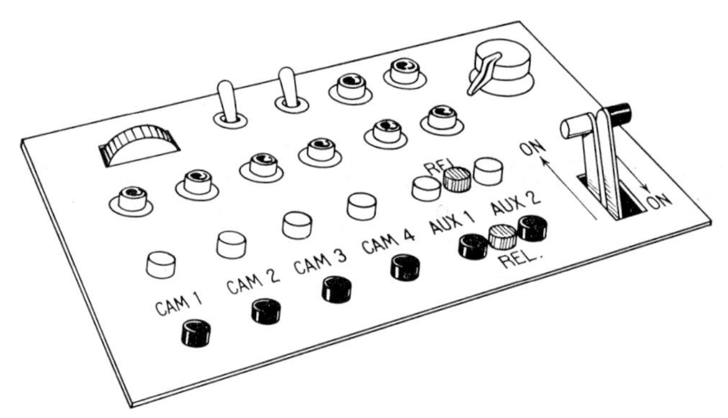

Fig. 7–4. RCA studio switching system.

button 1 on the white row of buttons and to black button 1 on the black row. When white button 1 is punched, the signal goes onto the white bus and through the white fader control, if that control is open. If a dissolve is desired to, say, camera 2, button 2 must be preset on the black row (since the black fading control is closed, nothing happens to the program line). When the moment for the dissolve comes, the white bus is faded out and the black bus is faded in. The two fading levers work in opposite directions; that is, the "on" position for the white handle is at the top, and the "on" position for the black handle is at the bottom. Thus, at the beginning of the dissolve, both levers will be at the top, and so it is possible to work them with one hand and simultaneously fade one picture out and fade the other in (there is a spring clip with which the levers can be fastened together).

Fades. The fade-out–fade-in effect can be done in two ways. The first is "dissolving to black." Punch up the "rel" (release) button on the opposite bus and bring both handles down (or up) together. Then punch up the next camera on the original bus and move the handles back again.

The second method involves separating the handles. If the white bus is carrying the signal, bring only the white handles down for the fade-out. Fade in when ready by bringing the black handle down. This method is considered better practice because all buttons can be preset; only the handles are used at the time of the effect.

Superimposures. The halfway position in a dissolve is a superimposure, and the handles may be left in the midway position if desired. Each camera is then at half brilliance. This does not always make the best superimposure, however. Sometimes it may be necessary to superimpose a ghost onto a scene, for example, without making any change in the tone of the scene itself. In this case the two handles are separated, and the second one is faded up to the desired brilliance without changing the first.

Cutting to or from a superimposure. It is not intended to be possible, in a switching system composed of two fading busses, to tie up both in a superimposure and then switch to another shot. There is nothing left to switch to; everything is in use. If another camera were punched up on either of the fading busses, the new picture would simply take the place of one of the other camera signals within the superimposure. One of the cameras must be lost from the superimposure before straight switching can be done. The same is true in getting into the superimposure. A straight shot must be taken first and the superimposed picture added; the two cannot appear at once. Technical directors with skill and ingenuity have discovered ways, however, to operate this equipment and effect a cut to a superimposure or away from a superimposure to a single shot.

A practical problem like this sometimes arises. A girl enters a room, sees a ghost, and speaks to it. But the ghost must be *in* the room as soon as we see it. We must then cut away from the room-and-ghost shot to a single shot of the girl as she speaks.

One method of doing this is as follows: Camera 1 takes the girl as she enters the door, camera 2, the room, and camera 3, the ghost (an actor in another set, brightly lighted against a black background). Camera 1 is on the air. If No. 1 is punched up on, say, the top row of buttons, punch it up also on the bottom row and set the handles halfway. Half the camera 1 signal is then coming through one fading bus and half through the other. Now place one finger on button 2 in the top row and a second finger on button 3 in the bottom row, and press them both at once.

This produces a superimposure which is the mid-point of a dissolve. To cut away from this superimposure back to camera 1 again as the girl speaks, simply press both camera 1 buttons at once.

A second method allows one signal to be made stronger than the other. Preset the black row of buttons with no signal. (This means punching up either the "rel" button or a dead channel.) Set the black lever to whatever position was found to be best in rehearsal. When the time comes, simultaneously punch camera 2 on the white bus and camera 3 on the black. To cut back to camera 1 from this, simply punch both camera 1 on the white bus and the "off" button on the black bus.

Dissolving to or from a superimposure. The only way this effect can be accomplished is to punch up two cameras on one of the busses. This results in half strength for each picture, but a dissolve can then be made to the other bus, either to a third channel or to another pair of channels (dissolve from super to super).

Note that when No. 1, for example, is on the white-bus, feeding program line, and No. 1 is preset on the black bus, there is no effect. If No. 1 and No. 2, however, are preset on the black bus, the level of the program picture drops. If No. 2 and No. 3 are preset on the black, there is no effect. Experimentation with the equipment itself will make this clear.

THREE-BUS SWITCHING SYSTEMS

The three-bus type of switching system is more common than any other in network studios. Figure 7-5 shows a typical example. Instead of having a row of tally lights above every row of buttons, a plastic button is used which is in itself a light, going on as soon as it is punched.

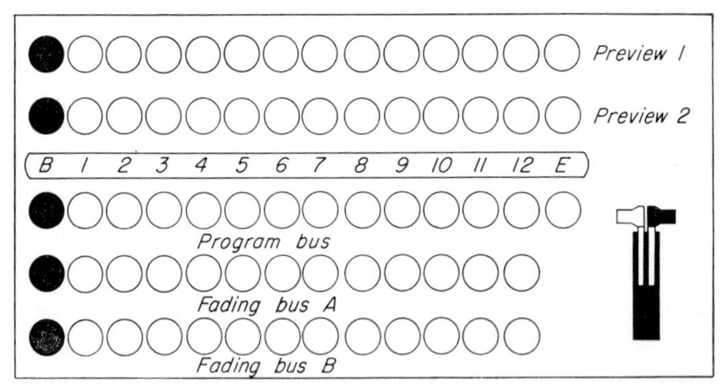

Fig. 7–5. Typical three-bus panel. Release off, or black, buttons at far left of each row are used for dissolving to black.

The advantage of having three busses in the switching system is that you can cut to or from a superimposed effect. The last button on the program bus is a special button labeled *E* for effects. A glance at Fig. 7-3 will reveal that when the *E* button is punched, the output of the fading busses goes out the program line exactly as if it were a two-bus switching system. Like any other punch button in the straight switching line, the *E* button flies out as soon as another button is punched, thereby cutting out the two effects busses entirely. In this condition the switching system is operating as a single-bus type, with no fading or dissolving facilities. Although the effects busses are not feeding the program line, their combined output can still be *previewed* by punching up a similar *E* button controlling a preview monitor. Two separate single-bus switching systems controlling each of two preview monitors are provided at the top of the panel. Thus it is possible to preset a superimposure, look at the effect, get just the right adjustment of strength from each signal, correct each cameraman's framing, all just before the effect is used. To cut to a superimposure, simply press the *E* button in the program bus. To cut away from it again, punch another button on that same top line, and the *E* button will fly out.

The usual method of operating this type of switching system is to use it like a two-bus system most of the time. Straight cutting is done on one of the fading busses so that a dissolve can be quickly preset and made with little advance warning.

It is only in the case of a special requirement such as a cut to a superimposure or the need to preview a super that the straight-switching bus is brought into operation. Regular use of the program bus is undesirable. If the TD is operating on the program bus when the director suddenly calls for a dissolve, he must go through several motions to make ready. To begin with, he must bring the fading busses into operation. To do this, he presets the same channel that is on the air on one of the fading busses, sets the correct handle in the "on" position, and punches the *E* button. No effect will be seen, and he is now ready to preset the other fading bus for the channel he will dissolve into.

FIVE-BUS SWITCHING SYSTEM

Some effects which are occasionally very useful, especially in musical shows, cannot be achieved readily on any of the switching systems described so far. None will allow you to set up a superimposure, preview and check it, and then *dissolve* into it. Only the single-bus mixer type will allow you to dissolve *within* a superimposure so that one of the two pictures gradually changes. Only the mixer type will allow a triple superimposure, or allow a TD to dissolve from one super to another.

To give a few examples, in a song about memories the director may want to superimpose a man's thoughts in one portion of the frame. If he can dissolve within the superimposure, the memories can slowly change during the song. A much more common example is the case where the director will dissolve between title cards which are superimposed on a live scene. A dissolve to or from a super is a natural transition and would be found useful in a great many instances.

A switching system capable of all these effects was first built in the CBS studio in New York for the "Fred Waring Show." It was designed by Bob Banner, the director, and Al DeCaprio, the TD of the show, and was built by General Electric.

This type of switching system contains five busses, one for straight switching and four for effects busses, in two pairs, each with its two fading handles (Fig. 7-6). The output of each pair of fading handles goes

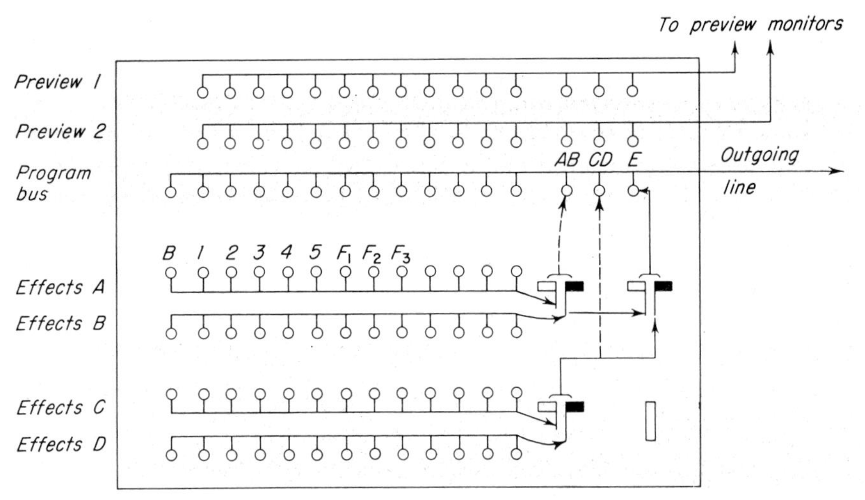

Fig. 7–6. Special five-bus switching system built by CBS.

to one of a pair of master fading handles, which in turn feed to a master *E* button on the straight-switching bus. Each of the effects pairs has its own subsidiary "*E*" button so that the master faders can be bypassed if desired. In normal operation the *E* button is punched and the master handles at right are placed in the down position. Then effects banks *C* and *D* are used exactly as a two-bus switching system. The second pair of effects busses is used only when a dissolve to a super or another of the special effects mentioned above is desired. In this case one super can be on the air and another set up and previewed at the same time. If a dissolve from super to super is desired, this can be done with the master fading handles, fading out one pair of busses and fading in the other. The program bus is used when a cut to or from a superimposure or other effect is desired. Another advantage of this type of switching system is that a superimposure can be faded out through the use of only one fading handle. (With the two- or the three-bus type, two controls must be used.)

PRESET-BUS SWITCHING SYSTEM

Probably the most advanced American switching system design is in use at NBC. The NBC switching system is similar to the five-bus system described above, but differs in the addition of a "preset" bus and a "switching bar" (Fig. 7-7). One pair of effects busses is located on the inclined panel at the top, a second pair flush with the desk top just below, each with its pair of fader handles, and just below this the program bus. The lowest bus (nearest to the operator because it is the one most used) is the preset bus, and below this, nearest of all, is the cutting bar.

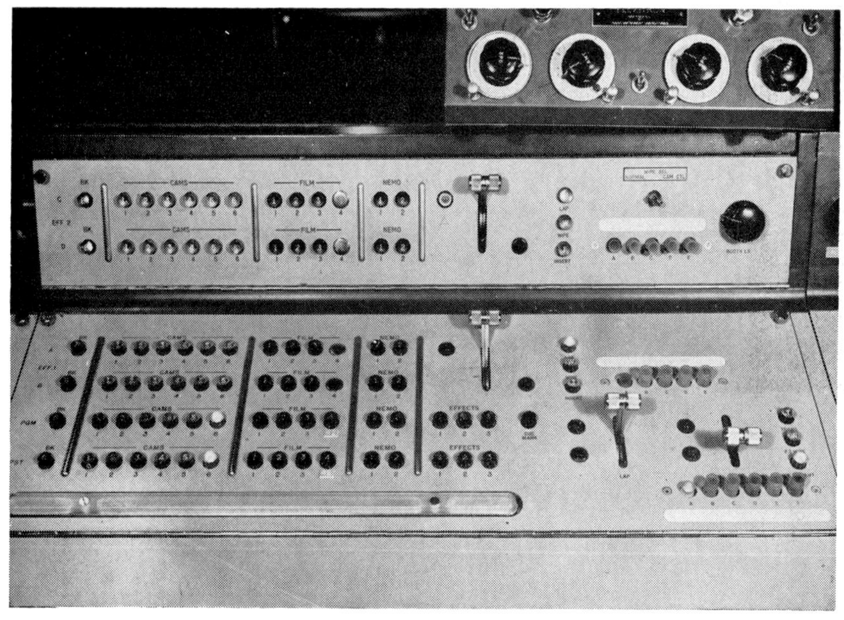

Fig. 7–7. NBC switching system. See description in text. The four black knobs, upper right, are not part of the switching system; they are controls for the "Flexitron" effect (see p. 289).

As in any of the switching systems described above, straight cutting can be performed by punching the buttons in the program bus. In addition, this switching system provides for presetting cuts, just as dissolves and fades are preset. In normal operation the TD will use this feature and preset each cut by punching the necessary button on the preset bus. Then, on the director's cue, he will make the actual take by striking the cutting bar at the bottom with the thumb, just as the spacing bar on a typewriter is operated. He will resort to direct cutting on the program bus only when the cuts come so rapidly that there is not enough time to preset. The presetting of cuts is an extra operation, but it greatly reduces operating errors. One of the most common hazards in switching is that under the excitement of the show the TD's fingers perspire and will occasionally slip off the buttons. There is also the possibility of error at the time of switching. The theory behind the principle of presetting in any equipment is that all complicated switching, setting, adjustments, etc., are made at relatively calm times in a production, when the mind is able to double check the operation. Only the simplest actuation is performed on cue under the excitement of the moment, when there is time to act but none to think.

Another useful feature of this switching system is that the preset bus has its own "memory" and automatically presets the channel which was last on the air. For example, let us say the TD is cutting between two cameras, an extremely common situation in any type of television program, with camera 1 on the air and camera 2 preset for the next take. As soon as the cutting bar is struck, putting camera 2 on the line, the preset bus automatically presets camera 1. It is necessary to punch the preset bus only when a new picture source is to be used.

The major advantage of the NBC switching system lies in the ease of making dissolves. The two pairs of effects busses are not used in the simple dissolve; instead, the same preset bus is used, but instead of striking the cutting bar, the TD operates the handles just to the right of the preset bus. It makes no difference which position these handles are in—a movement of the handles in either direction fades out the channel on the air and simultaneously fades in the channel which has been preset (the dissolve effect). Thus most of the operation of this switching system is done with the preset buttons, the cutting bar, and the dissolving handles at the right.

Effects may come from three sources, indicated by the three effects buttons on the program and preset busses. Effects button 1 provides the output of the nearest pair of effects busses (directly above the program bus); effects button 2, the output of the top pair; and effects button 3, the output of the fourth pair of fader handles shown at the far right of the switching panel. Each of these effects sources can be preset or punched up directly on the program bus.

All the effects described in connection with the five-bus system are possible here. For example, a dissolve from a super to a super would be performed in the following manner. The first super would be set up on effects busses *A* and *B*, and effects button 1 would be lighted on the program bus. Then the second super would be set up on effects busses *C* and *D*, preset by punching up effects button 2 on the preset bus, and dissolved in by moving the main dissolve handles. A quadruple super could be achieved by stopping this dissolve halfway, and adjusting any handles independently as desired.

Previewing a super is automatic, since whatever channel or combination of channels is set up on the preset bus is immediately viewed on a preset monitor fed by this bus alone.

The consideration of even more complex switching arrangements than those described above will lead us into the area of electronic special effects which is discussed in Chap. 15.

8

Technical Limitations and the Production Problems Involved

DEFECTS AND SPURIOUS EFFECTS IN THE IMAGE-ORTHICON TUBE

When the conditions of subject or lighting cause contrast range to be extreme, today's image-orthicon tube will exhibit certain strange effects. The viewer may see a black halo around bright objects, for instance, or streaks across the picture in line with the slats on venetian blinds, or a ghostly repetition of a bright object just beside it on the screen. These are called spurious effects and are due to "secondary emission"—uncontrolled electrons flying around inside the camera tube and landing in strange places on the target plate. Some other effects are functional defects within the particular tube and may show up worse as a tube becomes older. These will be discussed first.

DYNODE SPOTS

Sometimes tiny spots of light are visible which stay in the same place on the screen even when the camera pans, and disappear only when another camera is switched onto the line. These are called dynode spots, because they originate in the multiplier section of the IO tube, toward the back where the returning beam jumps from dynode to dynode, increasing in strength. Dynode spots are present in all tubes but are considerably worse in some. If the scanning beam is thrown slightly out of focus, these spots can be made to disappear, but at the expense of good resolution over the rest of the picture as well.

IMAGE RETENTION

The image-orthicon tube has an unfortunate tendency to retain an image that has been held on it too long, especially if the scene has considerable contrast. A cameraman who has held his camera poised on a title for a few moments at the opening of a show often finds the lettering remaining on his picture long after he has left the title. This is particularly noticeable in an older tube.

Sometimes strange effects result from image retention. An actor will move in front of a background, for example, which has become "burned into" the television tube; and both the image of the actor and the background behind him will be seen. One can see through him like a ghost. The author once used a very old tube for rehearsal purposes which had such a bad case of image retention that it remembered everything it saw. When an actor who had been seated was asked to stand, there were two actors on the screen, one sitting, and one standing. Then, if the actor moved again, there were three.

When a tube has developed a burnt-in image, it can be erased by exposing the camera to an even, bright surface. Sometimes a cameraman will pan his camera back and forth across a bank of fluorescent lights. Accepted procedure is to illuminate a blank card or sheet of white paper and let the camera rest on it for an hour or more depending on the severity of the condition. A small flashlight can be used directly on the photocathode for this purpose and is standard equipment in many mobile units.

ORBITERS AND ORTH-SAVERS

Movement of the image on the target of the image-orthicon tube, even when imperceptibly slow and slight will effectively prevent burn-in. This can be achieved by (1) movement of the scene, (2) movement of the camera, or (3) movement of the image inside the camera. A common problem is the test pattern on which a camera must often rest for long periods during technical adjustments. The author first saw scene movement used to solve the burn-in problem in 1953 in the TV studio in Zurich, where the engineers had provided the test pattern with a motor drive to keep it in constant orbiting motion.

Slight panning and tilting by the cameraman is, of course, standard procedure, even when the camera is on the air. In 1958, however, orbiters were developed to perform this function without moving the camera or the scene, but applying movement directly to the image within the camera tube. There are two ways in which this can be done: (1) optically, thus achieving a movement of the light image on the photocathode of the IO tube, and (2) electronically, achieving movement of the electron image on the target within the tube.

The Orth-Saver is an optical device which can be added to almost any camera. It consists of a special lens turret powered by four synchronous motors which actually move the camera lens in a slow imperceptible orbit (orbiting, not rotation). The RCA color camera is equipped with a wedge prism behind the lens which is slowly rotated, thus displacing the image in a slowly changing direction, now up, now to the side, now down. RCA monochrome cameras are equipped with an electronic orbiting device, an extra coil of fine wire on a cylinder surrounding the image (front) section of the IO tube. Slowly changing voltages in various parts of the coil displace the electron image within the tube and achieve the orbiting effect.

The introduction of orbiters substantially increased the useful life of image-orthicon tubes. Tubes which before had to be discarded because they burned in too readily could be used with good results for many additional hours.

HALO

A particularly bright highlight will cause a black flare to develop just around it (Fig. 8-1). The greater the contrast between highlight and

Fig. 8–1. The effect of halo around an extremely bright highlight. A small image-orthicon ghost is visible just beside the candle flame.

background, the darker and more extensive this halo will be. Unfortunate effects sometimes result from this defect, though at times the results are pleasing. Halo can be minimized to a certain extent by careful camera adjustment, but only a very close control of highlights and brightness range within the scene can eliminate it.

IMAGE-ORTHICON GHOST (IMO GHOST)

When a particularly bright object is seen against a dark background, not only is halo visible around the edges of the light area, but a ghostly repetition of the object is visible, displaced slightly on the screen. A title with white lettering on a black background will often display this effect. The farther the object is to the right of the screen, the farther the ghost is displaced upward to the left. Toward the left of the screen the ghost image is displaced progressively farther downward and to the right. In the center of the screen, however, there is no displacement, and hence no visible ghost. Placing such a bright object in exact center screen, then, is one solution to the problem of IMO ghost. A reduction in contrast range, either by darkening the object or by lightening the background, is a better measure.

CLOUDING

Another spurious effect is noticeable when large, dark areas are included in the same scene with white areas of high intensity. The dark area does not stay dark but clouds up in the center in a manner which resembles lens flare in a film camera. If the light tone is kept down to no more than five times the shadow intensity, clouding will not be a serious problem.

STREAKING

This effect is noticed when strong horizontal lines appear in the scene, especially if they contrast strongly with the rest of the scene. A white or a dark streak appears across the picture in line with these horizontal shapes. This is due to the line in the scene falling exactly along the scanning lines of the tube (Fig. 8-2). If the camera angle is changed so the contrasty lines in the scene fall at even a very slight angle to the horizontal, no one scanning line will be following them very far and no streaking will result. A better solution is to note beforehand any hori-

Fig. 8–2. Streaking caused by white venetian blinds.

zontal set elements which may cause streaking and make sure these do not contrast too greatly with the rest of the scene. A tan venetian blind, for example, will look the same as a white one on the screen and will be much less likely to cause streaking, even when perfectly horizontal in the picture.

PRODUCTION PROBLEMS ASSOCIATED WITH COLOR RESPONSE

A bright color carries a strong hue to the eye because it reflects one predominant wavelength of light, whereas a dull or in-between color is often a composite of many wavelengths distributed throughout the spectrum. If this predominant wavelength is in the blue or in the red (at either end of the spectrum), it will sometimes elicit a different response from different camera tubes. A red dress has looked dark in one camera's picture but has come out a perfect flesh tone in another, providing a startling undressed effect. Designers have usually avoided reds and blues; and some have painted their sets in monochrome, either in shades of some single color or only in tones of gray. When this was done, there could be no possible difference in color response, even between badly matched cameras, and the designer could always know exactly how the set would look on camera. Even though current tubes have a panchromatic response, this is still a good method of working. Very few designers or scene painters, however, derive much enjoyment from working in monochrome.

Systems of color analysis always recognize three qualities to every color: hue, intensity, and tone (or value). Hue is what we usually mean when we say "color," i.e., red, green, blue, etc. Intensity is the brightness of the color (bright red, red, dull red, etc.). For each intensity of each hue there is then a full scale of tones ranging from the lightest tint to the deepest shade (pink, red, maroon, etc.). There is an almost infinite variety of colors which the eye can detect and which an artist or designer might decide to use in front of a television camera.

In black-and-white television we must ignore the hue. Whether a color happens to classify as a green or a red will make very little difference since the television tube will turn them all into monochrome anyhow, in the same shades as they appear to the eye. The intensity of the color can also be ignored. If all other factors are constant, a bright red will look exactly the same as a dull red on the television screen. This leaves only tone to be considered. If we can determine by looking at a color just what its tone is, we shall know how it will look on the television system.

Colors can sometimes be deceptive. An artist may use two colors which contrast with each other, not in tone, but only because of their difference in hue. On camera he may be surprised to find both colors registering with the same tone of the gray scale, so that any pattern or picture which depends on a contrast between them disappears entirely. Oranges and grapefruit are of different hue but very close to the same tone, and the oranges must often be made up with a darkened wax to give them a contrasting shade. Sometimes the colored labels and wrappers of commercial products register poorly when seen on camera. Some studios make photostatic reproductions of them. Whatever the color response of the photostat paper may be, at least the producer can see the effect in black and white beforehand and retouch if necessary, knowing that the black-and-white photostat will not suffer any great alteration of tones when it is seen on camera.

It is difficult to look at a color, forget its hue and intensity, and see only its tone. Squinting at it will help. Perhaps the best way is to compare it with a scale of gray tones (Fig. 8-4) and see which it most closely resembles. Lay the scale against the color, and you will find that you can eliminate very quickly the grays which are lighter or darker in tone. This will leave one or two grays which are doubtful. As you squint at the gray scale, the boundary between your color and one of the grays will appear less distinct. The two will seem to "run together." This means they have the same tone. Calibrate your color according to the gray-scale number. This is the shade it will probably appear on the television system (provided, of course, that the camera tube is giving standard panchromatic response).

CONTRAST RANGE AND THE GRAY SCALE

There is a much more serious limitation to perfect performance of the television system than unbalanced color response, lack of sensitivity, or any of the spurious effects. How a performer will look on television, how a fabric or a paint will show up depend more on the tonal response of the television camera than any other factor. When the camera is pointed at a scale of grays, it will not register the same series of tones as are seen by the eye. There is a distortion of the gray scale. Briefly, it may be said that the lighter tones of the scale are condensed together and the lower tones also are compressed. Light tones all seem to go white, while dark tones tend to appear black. It is a rare camera indeed which can register all 10 tones of the gray scale. More often only 7 are visible, the other 3 looking like their adjacent tones. It has been found that tones from the central portion of the gray scale are reproduced more or less faithfully, and the best studio lighting and set design is directed toward keeping the important tones of the scene within this middle range. Lots of fill light is necessary on the set so that the shadow tones will not be too black. Film made specially for television use is photographed with rather even lighting and printed soft so that there is not too great a contrast range for the television system to handle. Night scenes on film are notoriously bad: all the shadows go pure black and an exaggerated contrast results.

The limited tonal range is further reduced by the characteristics of the home receiver. The great majority of television receiver tubes are not capable of showing a greater range of contrast than 20 to 1. The tone of the screen when the receiver is turned off is the darkest black that the receiver can show. The brightest tone is usually twenty times brighter than this. Under ideal room-lighting and operating conditions a television receiver tube will show a range of 40 to 1, which is the range usually encountered in 35-mm projection on the theater screen. The human eye, however, is capable of seeing at least a 100-to-1 contrast range in an actual scene. It is evident, therefore, that certain tones (details within a shadow area or variations within a light area), although visible as distinct tones to the eye, and possibly also to the camera tube, will exceed the contrast range of the receiver tubes and go either pure white (the lightest receiver tone) or pure black (the darkest tone). If every tone in the original scene falls within a 20-to-1 range, however, the scene will be more faithfully reproduced on the receiver screen.

THE GRAY SCALE

Figure 8-3 is a 10-step scale of gray tones varying within a 20-to-1 contrast range. This represents the range of tones which ordinarily can

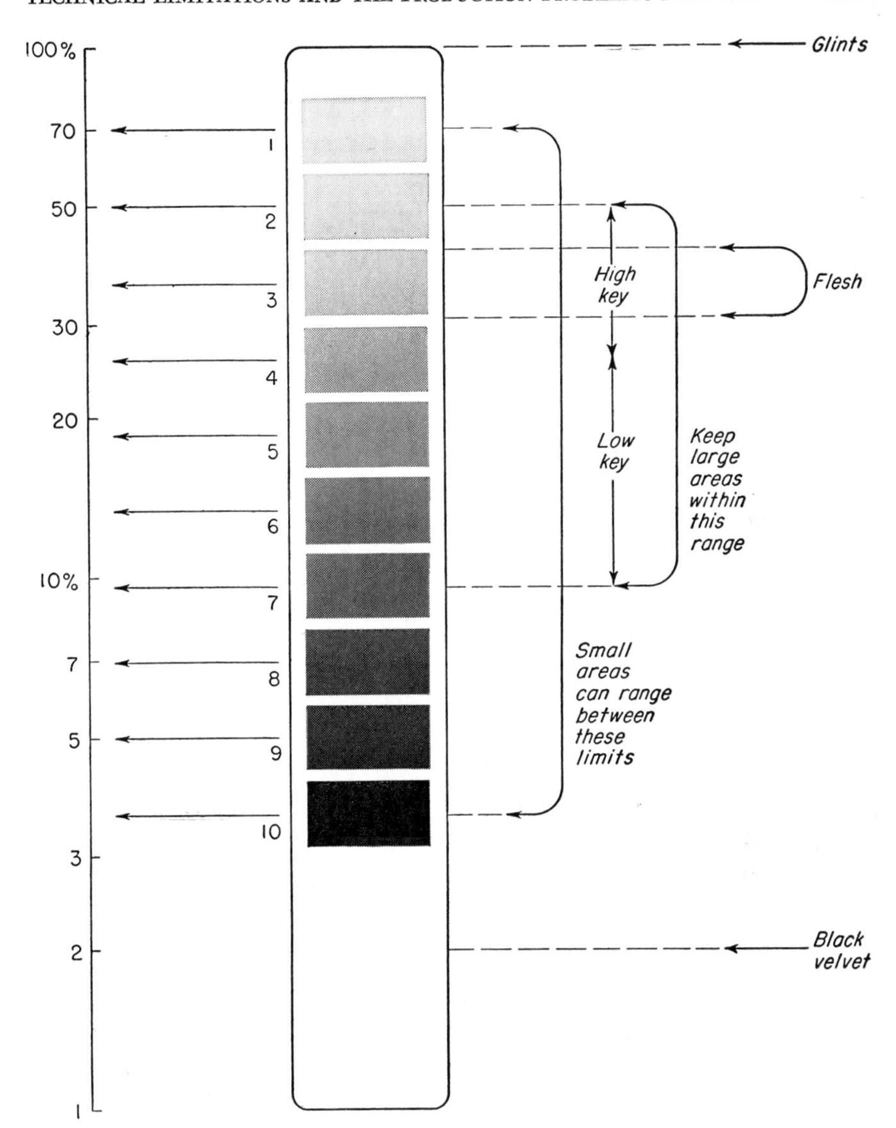

Fig. 8–3. Ten-tone gray scale calibrated in per cent of reflectance. Note that the reflectance scale is logarithmic (10 per cent is the halfway point). This is due to the human eye. A small increase in light will make the difference between two dark tones (just as a single candle will illuminate a dark room), whereas it takes a much greater increase in light to make the difference between two light tones. (Information for above chart from Richard S. O'Brien, CBS.)

be used on television. Tone 1 is not pure white, but it will appear pure white on the television screen. Likewise tone 10 is not a black, but it will appear black on television. The full range from tone 1 to tone 10 can be used if the lightest and the darkest of these tones are confined to small areas. Any large area of the screen, however, must be kept within a more limited range. It should be borne in mind, of course, that a close-up will enlarge an otherwise small area. Clothing worn by performers will often fill a large area of the screen in close-up or medium close-up and should be considered in the same way as large painted areas of the set.

Tones are measured here in terms of per cent of reflectance (scale at left side of chart). Merely a measure of the reflected light from a tone is not enough, since the brighter the illumination on the tone, the higher this measurement would be. Per cent of reflectance, however, will be the same in any light. A comparison of these per cents of reflectance figures will provide a quick measurement of the contrast range between any two tones. Tone 7, for example, at about 10 per cent reflectance, is one-fifth the value of tone 2, which is measured at 50 per cent reflectance. The contrast range between them, therefore, is 50 to 10, or 5 to 1.

A SIMPLIFIED GRAY SCALE

Although the 10 tones described above might be resolved by a good television system operating under optimum conditions, most television systems are incapable of this range. As tubes age, they tend to have a shorter gray scale. The control-room picture will often show no more than seven or eight tones, including black and white. Two or three of the tones on a 10-tone scale may look the same as the next lighter or the next darker tones beside them. This will be most likely to happen at the top or the bottom of the scale.

If this shortening of the gray scale is visible on control-room monitors, what will be the ultimate effort on the home receiver? It is not likely that the picture will be improved after transmission and reception; if it is changed in gray scale, it will certainly be for the worse. Many viewers set their contrast controls too high and inadvertently shorten their receiver's gray scale. The tendency to do this is particularly strong when there are other lights in the room which wash out the dark tones on the receiver screen. Furthermore, it is logical to assume that almost any home receiver will produce a poorer picture than a control-room monitor, even in top working order. A $200 set cannot be expected to perform like a $2,000 monitor which is serviced daily by expert technicians.

Accordingly, if seven or eight tones are visible on the control-room monitor, five or six may be all that a large percentage of home sets will show. In order to be perfectly safe, a five-tone scale can be chosen: an off-white, an off-black, and three grays—dark gray, medium gray, and light gray. If the television artist restricts himself to the use of these five tones, he will be perfectly sure that the tones he uses will be distinguishable on every receiver screen. If he tries to use more tones, a pattern or lettering composed of two adjacent tones is likely to disappear completely.

Another type of gray scale, devised by the author, is shown in Fig. 8-4. This scale is arranged in two rows of five tones each. This makes it into

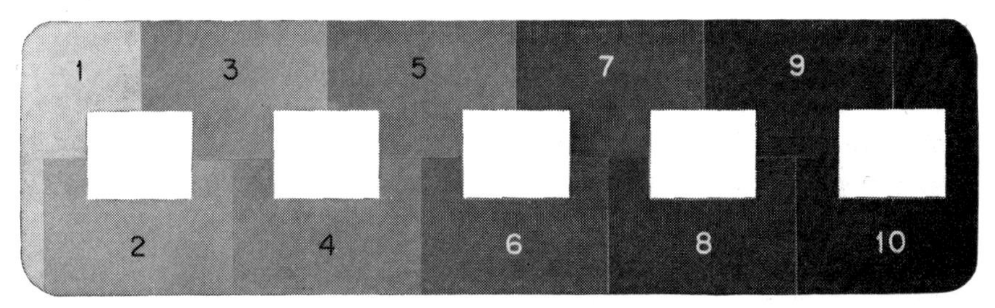

Fig. 8–4. Bretscale. Reproduction shows all tones too dark. Tone 1 should be off-white.

two 5-tone scales, one a step lighter than the other. The TV artist may choose either of these scales and, as long as he stays within it, will run little risk of losing one tone against another.

This scale may also be used in checking the tone of a fabric or a prop to determine whether it will be visible against the background with which it will be used. So long as the two tones are separated by two or more steps on the scale, they are sure to show a contrast between them. One should be careful, however, about using No. 7 drapes against a No. 6 wall, for example, or a No. 2 bathing suit on a No. 3 model.

THE CAMERA AS A MEASURING INSTRUMENT

With the development of the highly stable 4½-inch image-orthicon cameras, there has been a growing trend to use the camera as an objective measuring device. CBC practice is an example: The camera is lined up on an EIA logarithmic gray scale chart. This chart displays simply two 9-step gray scales running in opposite directions, one with black (3 per cent reflectance) at the left, the other starting with white (60 per cent reflectance) at the left (chart contrast range is 20 to 1). The chart is illuminated to the mean front-light level of the set, the target setting is adjusted and locked, and the lens aperture is also set and no longer touched. Then lighting adjustments are made so as to give a proper waveform on the oscilloscope.

DC RESTORATION

Control-room monitors and all good-quality video receivers are provided with a d-c-restorer circuit, which for reasons of economy is eliminated from mass-produced home receivers. The presence of this circuit assures that blacks are always presented as black and whites always look white no matter what the relative amount of black and white in the picture may be. A producer may achieve an effective shot; he places the performer in a small pool of light against a black sky with a scattering of twinkling stars—relative areas of black to white: 50 to 1. On his control-room monitor, with d-c restoration, the producer sees a beautiful velvety black tone. However, when this unbalanced scene reaches the home receivers which have no d-c restoration, the background is presented as a dirty gray. The opposite will happen when the predominant area is white: the white tone will appear gray. Since the broadcaster, to be realistic, must design his sets and lighting so his picture can be seen properly on the existing home receivers, he has no choice but to balance carefully the areas of dark tones against those of light. The Canadian network applies the following rule of thumb: in "limbo" or "cameo" shooting (black backgrounds) at least 50 per cent of the picture should be visible material. Such a picture will look the same on the home receiver as it does on the control-room monitor. A good practice, of course, is to provide an un-d-c-restored monitor on which the producer can check his pictures. In local stations an off-the-air monitor (usually a small home receiver) serves this purpose.

PRODUCTION PROBLEMS CONCERNED WITH TONAL RESPONSE

Technical men in Hollywood say that 90 per cent of the motion-picture business is concerned with the actor's face. Make the face look right, and the picture is acceptable. Miss out on proper rendition of the flesh tones, however, and no matter how perfect every other detail may be, the picture is rejected. This is just as true of television. The reflectance of the human skin is in the neighborhood of 30 to 40 per cent. This is seen by the eye as a relatively light tone which under proper illumination can show highlight areas of considerably higher value. The variations of tone in the face, however, are subtle. The lighting man tries to keep these tones as close together as possible, knowing that beauty and glamour are easily lost if there is too much contrast between highlight and shadow. Any rendition of the face which exaggerates the tonal range will bring out wrinkles, undesirable forms, harsh edges, etc., which make any woman look ten years older. This is the effect that has given television the reputation of being merciless to the human female.

(The same effect is not so damaging to the male visage, since a little added harshness often brings out lines of strength and virility.)

The important thing to note, however, is that the ability of the television camera tube to resolve the subtle face tones and reproduce them without exaggeration depends on *the other tones within the same picture.* If the performer wears a white dress or even a white collar and tie, the face can suffer. A recent television show was rehearsed without all the props; it looked fine in rehearsal, but when the show went on, it appeared that one of the acts involved drawing pictures on an easel. The easel was brought on stage complete with a large pad of white drawing paper, and when the performers stepped in front of this, their faces went pure black. To avoid experiences of this nature, the engineering staffs of the networks have worked out rules for staging practice as a guide to the producers and directors of the shows.

According to CBS, large areas of the set or of any particular picture (such as the dress or the background in a head-and-shoulders close-up) should be kept within a limited range. Small areas can exceed this range and appear as maximum black or up to as high as 70 per cent of total reflectance (off-white). Large areas should be kept within a middle range. From step 2 to step 4 (Fig. 8-3) is a wide enough range for the usual high-key scene. In the case of a low-key scene (dimly lighted interiors or exteriors at night) the reflectance of large areas should be between step 4 and step 7. If the scenery for a low-key scene is painted these dark tones to begin with, the low-key effect can be achieved without having to cut down on the studio light (with consequent deterioration of the camera signal).

In respect to small areas of the scene, these may range the entire length of the 10-tone gray scale (from 3½ per cent, maximum black, to 70 per cent, maximum white). They may not exceed this range without causing spurious effects, but since they are small and not likely to become a very large portion of a close-up scene, they do not have to be kept within the limited range which is allowed for large areas. White shirts and handkerchiefs are small areas of even a close-up scene, but these must be specially treated, or they will reflect too much light. Starched white cloth reflects 90 per cent of the incident illumination, which puts it way above step 1 on the gray scale. Not only will it come out pure white, but it will bloom and cause halos and affect the tones of the face nearby. If the performer wears a colored shirt or a white shirt dyed a light blue or yellow, it will have a lower reflectance (equal to tone 1 on the television gray scale) and still look pure white on the television screen.

If dark clothing *must* be worn, the only thing to do is to keep the background low in tone. This will reduce the contrast range by holding everything else down to accord with the one thing (clothing) which cannot be altered.

The highlights caused by shiny or white props on the television set are a frequent problem. White refrigerators and kitchen equipment, shiny metals or polished surfaces are encountered every day. If these objects are not treated, halo will result, as well as other undesirable effects. A shiny black object is worse than a shiny light one, since the range between highlight and body tone is greater. Automobile advertisers usually prefer to display light-colored cars for this reason. Aside from this choice of the tone of the object, highlights can be handled either by cutting down the reflectance or by softening the light. Softening the light means eliminating all spots, open floods, sometimes even fluorescent tubes from the studio lighting.

Lowering the reflectance of a highlight can be achieved by one of several means. When the object itself is white and its regular reflectance, irrespective of highlights, is already too much for the television gray scale, it must be repainted. Refrigerators and other white kitchen and laundry appliances have commonly been painted with a light gray or yellow water-color paint which is washed off again if necessary. The interiors of these subjects are sometimes shown but do not have to be painted, since they usually receive so much less light. CBS uses a canary-yellow mixture of clear shellac colored with dry pigment for this purpose. This can then be washed off with alcohol and will hold up a little better than water-color paint. A permanent coat of flat paint is of course best.

HIGHLY REFLECTANT OBJECTS

When the surface of an object is shiny, light sources reflect almost as they would in a mirror; an image of each light is seen. This is called *specular* reflection. Usually this can be overcome by dulling the surface, by spraying on wax, soap, or some similar coating. Shiny oilcloth has been sprayed with a solution of shaving lotion for this purpose. A solution of epsom salts and stale beer is a standard (one tablespoon of epsom salts to one cup of stale beer). Mirrors are treated in this fashion so that they will still look like mirrors but will do a poor job of reflecting objects or lights. The solution is sprayed on thinly while the mirror is lying flat, and it is then allowed to dry before the mirror is used. Clear liquid wax is often sprayed onto shiny objects to cut down specular reflection. White china teacups have been rubbed with lipstick on a rag. Spirits of camphor and sour milk have also been used to take down shine. Pressure cans of Krylon dulling spray or Marshall's Pre-color are the handiest to use.

Occasionally one will encounter the need to televise shiny objects which cannot be specially prepared to reduce reflectance. Jewelry and musical instruments appear in many shows; sometimes silverware must be shown in close-up. Silverware is an almost impossible subject to light by ordinary methods. At CBS a method was worked out in connection

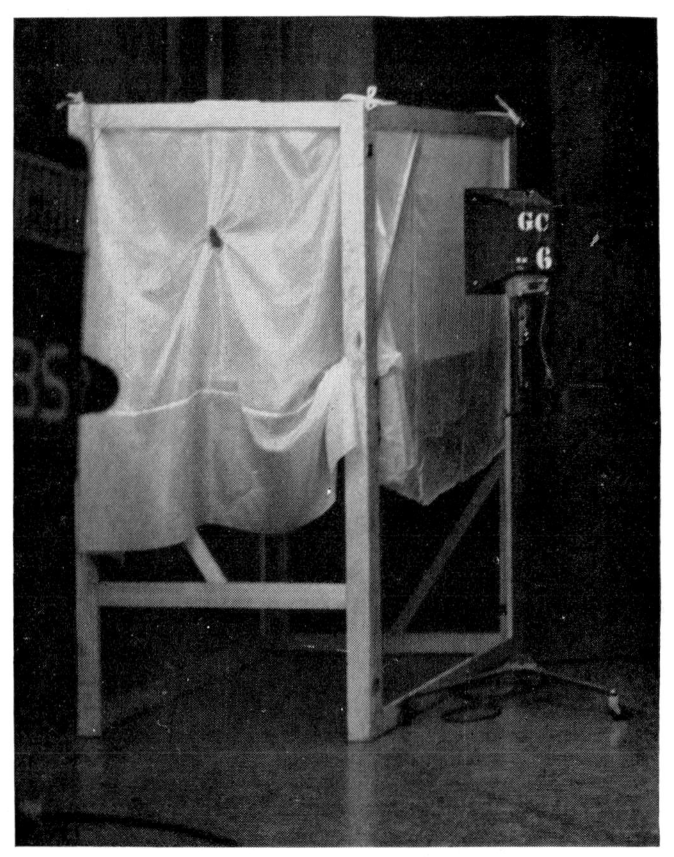

Fig. 8–5. Tent for lighting silverware. Used for commercials on CBS program "Silver Theatre." (Courtesy of CBS.)

with the live commercials for "Silver Theatre" which involved the use of a method known to film production but rarely used on television, the method of tenting. A canopy of silk or muslin is built entirely around the subject with the exception of an opening for the camera on one side, and all lights are directed at the tent from the outside (Fig. 8-5). This produces the ultimate in soft, diffuse lighting, since the whole interior of the tent acts as the light source. The silverware does not lose its gleam, but there are no brilliant highlights to cause halo and tonal distortion.

The proper lighting is a very important factor in keeping the contrast range of the picture within the necessary limits. Subject contrast can be controlled by keeping the reflectance of objects and surfaces within the proper range of the gray scale, but lighting contrast can upset this if not properly employed. If dark objects are dimly lighted and light objects brightly lighted, for instance, the range of tones can be easily increased far beyond the capacity of the television system to reproduce them well.

LIMITATIONS OF THE PICTURE AREA

Another serious limitation of television transmission is the loss of picture area around the top, bottom, and sides of the screen.

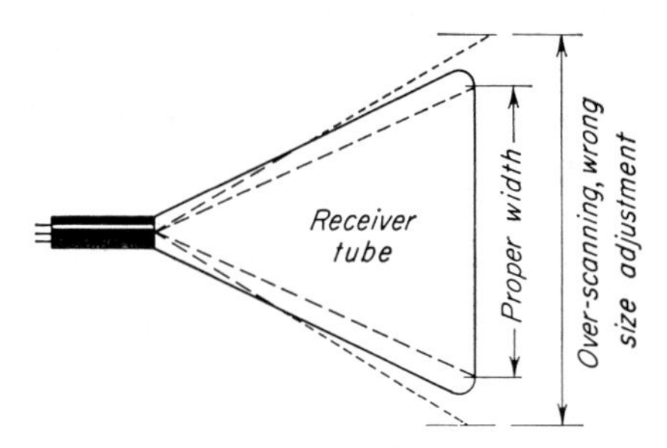

Fig. 8–6. When the height and width controls on a receiver are set for too wide a sweep, the beam will strike the sides of the tube and only the center of the broadcast picture will be seen.

The height, width, and centering controls on a television receiver are usually adjusted only by a more or less competent serviceman, but on many sets they are not too well hidden, and the owner of the set may alter them from time to time. The result is that a certain proportion of sets are out of adjustment in regard to picture size. This maladjustment is usually made in the direction of overscanning of the receiver tube, since the results of underscanning are much more noticeable (Fig. 8-6).

Several formulas have been worked out for determining the area of the picture which will always be visible, even on poorly adjusted or circular screen receivers. This area will be referred to as the "safe title area." Subject matter which is considered absolutely essential (such as the commercial message or an object of importance to the plot) must be kept within this area. The total original picture is called the "scanned area."*

* The scanned area is also called picture area, camera field, transmitted area, or exposed area. The safe title area is known in some stations as the essential area, lettering area, copy area, or usable area.

The border area, which when added to the safe title area makes the scanned area, may be called the "supplementary area." Information supplementary but not essential to the picture may be included in this region.

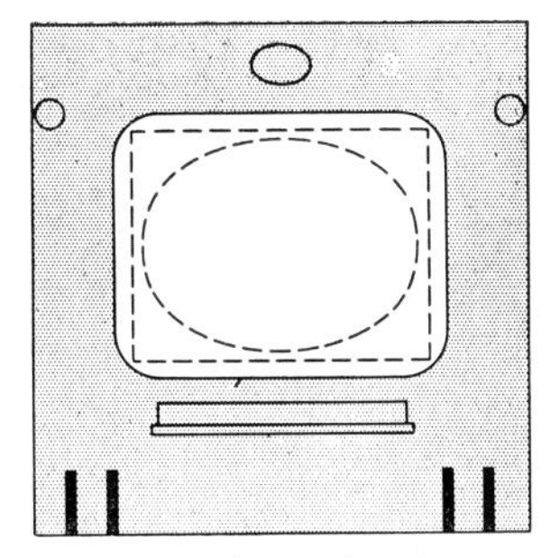

Fig. 8–7. CBS monitor overlay indicating areas of picture loss.

CBS television has approached the problem in a logical way. A celluloid sheet, outlined in an oval shape, is laid across every monitor and camera view-finder screen. The cameramen call this the "ellipse of essential information" (Fig. 8-7). It comprises slightly over half the total picture area.

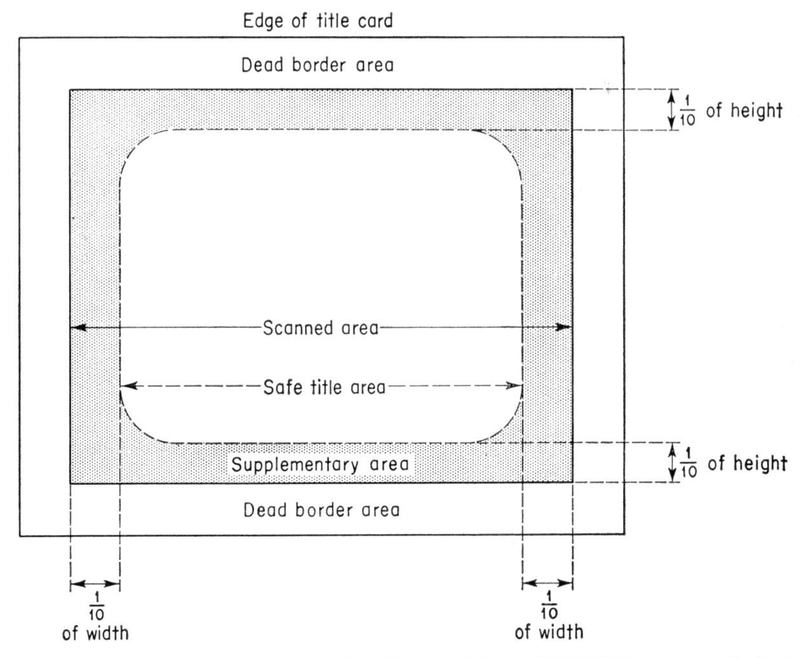

Fig. 8–8. Method of determining safe title area. From SMPTE Recommended Practice (RP8), established May 7, 1961.

LIMITATIONS OF THE VIDICON TUBE

For the first few years of vidicon camera use, vidicon tubes were considerably less sensitive than image-orthicon tubes and required something like four or five times the amount of light if the same *f* stops were used. Of course, large *f* stops were possible on the shorter vidicon lenses without losing depth of focus, so vidicon studio light levels were rarely higher than two or three hundred foot-candles (at a lens setting of *f*/2.8). This applied to such tubes as the 6198 and 7325 vidicons. As the tubes were improved they became more sensitive, until vidicons such as the 7226 were able to equal or exceed the sensitivity of the original image-orthicons (but not, of course, the more recent models).

The vidicon exhibits no halo, IMO ghost, or clouding, yet has much the same limitations as the image-orthicon with respect to contrast range and gray scale. The contrast range which the vidicon can accommodate is somewhat smaller than that of the image-orthicon, a limitation which shows up particularly in respect to studio lighting. When vidicon cameras are used, the range of contrast between key light and fill light must be held carefully to a 2-to-1 ratio, whereas with IO's this range has been known to go as high as 9 to 1 for special low-key effects in network studios without too much trouble with spurious effects.

The vidicon camera will exhibit one disturbing fault, especially when the target voltage is set high, as in the case of low light levels. This is known as "smear." When a contrasty subject moves across the frame (as a blonde against a dark curtain, or white letters against black moving up the screen), the subject seems to leave a trail behind it. Smear can be reduced by lowering the target voltage but often at the expense of a proper gray-scale reproduction.

9

Graphic Materials

Anyone who produces television shows will find sooner or later that he must have a rather intimate knowledge of the many contributory fields. One of these is graphic art. Every show uses some kind of graphic materials, if it be no more than opening title cards. Some news programs and documentary shows have built the major part of their programs around such things as maps, graphs, charts, drawings, still pictures, and various kinds of simple animations. Commercials, particularly those which are produced on film, lean heavily on graphics for this visual material.

The simplest and most common graphic element is the title card. It is traditional to begin a film with a series of titles, and until rather recently Hollywood producers have tried to outdo each other in lavish production of this opening title sequence. Many of the early television productions tried to follow this tradition, but the rehearsal of complicated openings took entirely too much time. Sometimes half a director's rehearsal would be devoted to his opening and closing sequences—out of all proportion to their importance to the show as a whole. The simplest, quickest, and most straightforward entrance into a show has come to be accepted as best in television. Within practical limits, however, a great deal can be done to enrich a show through the opening titles. Style and design of lettering, for example, can do much to set the mood.

There are two basic ways of using a title, and of course innumerable variations within each and between the two. The first method is to show the title as a card, frankly, and nothing more. This is as far as possible from the motion-picture tradition. The most striking example was the opening of the "Garroway at Large" show, where a hand simply hung the title cards on the wall.

The other method is to disguise the method of production so that the title becomes, not a title card picked up by the camera, but simply lettering appearing on the screen. When the letters are superimposed on a background scene, this method is most effective. When the titles are changed by dissolving, either between cameras or between two stages on a projection machine, rather than leafed over or slid bodily in front of the camera, the edges of the cards are not seen and there is no clue as to their actual size.

Sometimes the titles can be integrated with the live action of the opening scene, in which case they may not be title *cards* at all. Byron

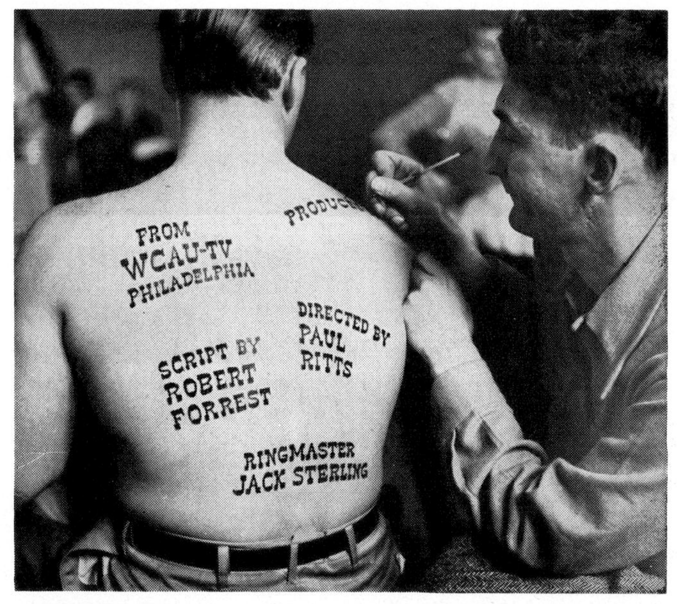

Fig. 9–1. Some productions have found unusual ways of handling titles.

Paul opened his CBS production of "Carmen" in this way, with titles in the form of bill posters on the walls of the exterior set. Figure 9-1 illustrates an unusual method of handling closing credits on the CBS-TV show "Big Top."

When it comes to still pictures, either art work or photographs, it is much more difficult to use them frankly as pictures on cards. There is an element of illusion about a picture. There is much less, of course, in the case of a still picture than in the case of a film, but some illusion is still there. Perhaps you have seen a shot where a camera dollied up on a painting in a frame: while the picture frame is visible, the picture is only a painting; but when the camera comes close enough to lose the frame, the picture (if the technique is a realistic one) suddenly imparts an illusion. It begins to have depth. Objects assume their full and natural size. One almost expects them to move.

This illusion of reality is further enhanced if the camera then dollies in on the picture or pans across it, or both. Carl Beier first demonstrated this magical effect at CBS in 1945 when he set up large Breughel prints and explored them with the camera. As the camera dollies in, it seems to pass foreground objects and to go beyond them, actually carrying the audience into the scene. Some very excellent motion-picture films have been based largely or entirely on still pictures brought alive through camera motion. Actually there is no perceptible difference between a pan

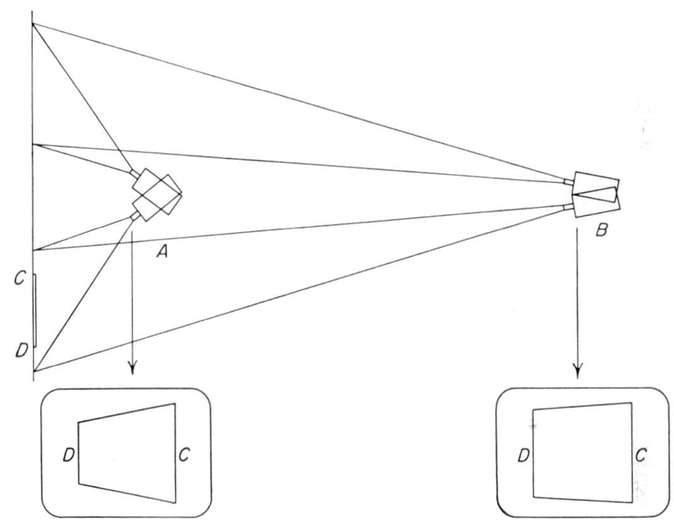

Fig. 9–2. (*A*) Camera in near position with wide-angle lens. Effect of keystoning is noticeable (square or rectangular area takes a keystone shape). (*B*) Camera in more distant position with long lens. There is less keystoning because camera covers the sides of the picture from more nearly a perpendicular angle.

shot across a still picture and a motion-picture pan shot across a static scene. Nothing moves but the camera in either case. When your still picture contains obviously arrested action, however, it is very difficult to make it look like anything more than a still.

Rather large blowups are necessary if the camera is to move around on them. The cameraman will be happier the larger these prints can be made. This will relieve him of the difficult focusing problem when a subject is very close to the lens. An 11- by 14-inch picture is about the smallest that a camera can easily pan around on. Prints 18 by 24 inches or larger are better for this purpose. The cameraman will prefer a long lens (narrow angle) with a distant camera position, rather than a wide angle with the camera close to the print. From the distant position he can pan across a wider arc without introducing distortion (Fig. 9-2).

Still pictures can be cut into live scenes to give the effect of greater space. In one production a couple walked through a zoo pointing at the animals in the general direction of the camera. Each time the actors pointed, a still picture of an animal was cut in briefly, giving the impression that the animals were actually in the set.

If a live shot is to contain no action or camera movement, it can as well be a photograph. Considerable saving on cost and studio space can be

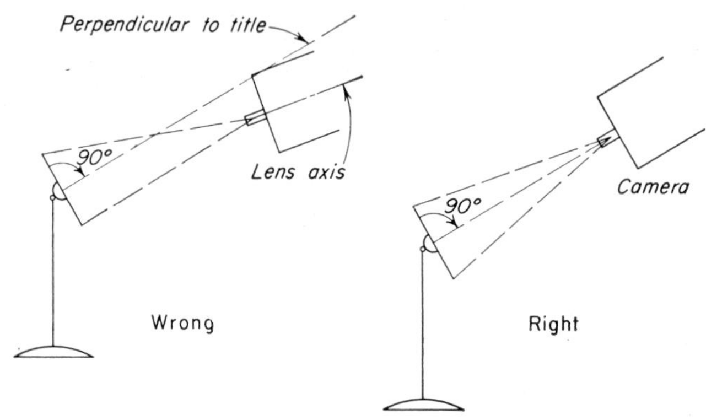

Fig. 9–3. Lens axis must be perpendicular to the center of the title or title will be distorted.

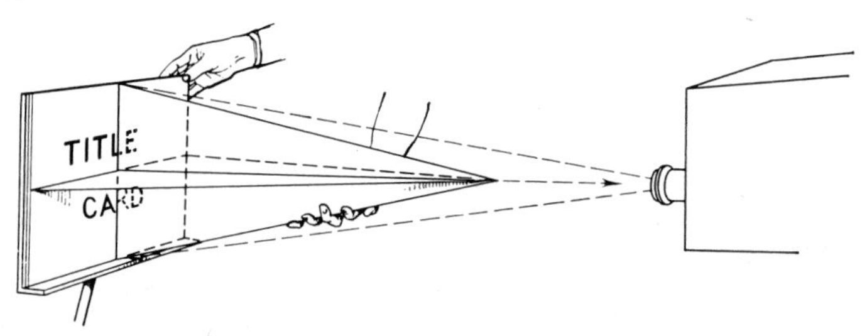

Fig. 9–4. Double T-square device to aid in lining up titles. Known as "Bretzaligner." Can be built of two pieces of cardboard, each notched halfway like dividers in an egg crate.

achieved if objects (such as furniture, household items, etc.) which are for static display are photographed first and the picture used instead of the live shot.

GLARE

In studios where floor lights must be used to illuminate the easels, it is often a problem to eliminate glare from the face of the card. Glare is reflected light which follows the regular laws of reflection (such as the second law, which states: The angle of reflection is equal to the angle of incidence). Apply this to a camera and title card just as though the card were a mirror instead. If it were a mirror, would the camera see the light source in it (Fig. 9-5)?

If all light is kept out of this field of view, pictures framed under glass can be used, but this is impossible in the ordinary television studio. There is bound to be some light behind the camera somewhere, which

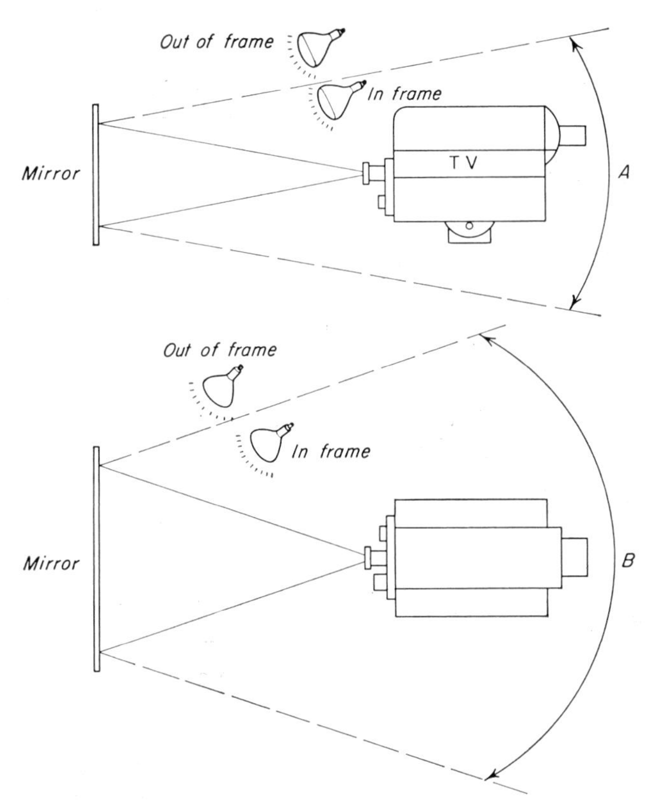

Fig. 9–5. Will lights glare off the title card? Imagine that the title is a mirror, and determine whether or not the lights would be in the mirror's field of view. (*A*) Vertical field of view, (*B*) horizontal field of view.

will reflect in the glass. Glossy prints act like glass in this respect, and it is mandatory to use matte-surface pictures and title cards in the studio. In good opaque projection machines stray light is fairly well eliminated, and any surface may be used. Sheets of celluloid which don't lie flat, however, cause trouble anywhere. Wherever you put the light, if the celluloid bulges enough it will reflect the light somewhere along the surface of the bulge. Marshall's Pre-color spray can be used to give a glossy print a matte surface.

TITLE-CHANGE DEVICES

The dissolve and the cut are natural ways to join titles together but are not very practical for studio use. Two cameras must be tied up on titles, and many studios do not have a third camera which can be readied on the opening live shot. Some method of changing titles in front of a single camera or with a single film chain is more practical for most studios. Listed below are some of the most common means of doing this.

***Fade to black** (**or dissolve to black**).* The title is changed during the dark period. Not recommended, because of the feeling of finality in the black fade. Continuity is lost.

Fade to white. This can be done only in coordination with the video engineer, and is rarely considered worth the trouble involved. The feeling of finality is avoided, however.

Blackout. Some 2- by 2-inch slide projectors include a shutter which momentarily blacks out the light as the slide is changing. This is quicker and hence more desirable than the fade-out.

Defocus. Crank the camera out of focus, pull the card, and crank it in again. This is all right if it can be done quickly, but too long an out-of-focus period is very hard on the eyes. An alternative method to cranking the camera is to zoom the title up to the lens either by hand or on a track, slide the new one in behind the first before you pull it out, and zoom back.

The drop-in and drop-out. Drop titles are generally punched with two or three holes and work vertically on a large ring binder. Drop-in titles have the holes at the top and are allowed to fall into position in front of the camera. Drop-out titles work the opposite way; the holes are on the bottom, and the cards are flicked away so that they drop out of sight, revealing the next card behind. This method may be a little slow and irregular on the beginning of the movement if the operator is not too deft. The drop-in title, also, commonly exhibits an irregularity of motion just at the end of the movement when the eye is trying to comprehend the new title.

The drop-in title has been used by NBC as a standard device in lieu of a better method. Every studio is equipped with special stands called "hods." The hod design provides a sloping top to hold the cards (Fig. 9-6) securely, and the operator moves each one forward on the rings and drops it on cue. The ring binding is superior to the separate-card method since it assures that cards will not be mixed up in order between rehearsal and air. It is routine practice for a director to check the order of his titles just before air time; the author can remember more than once finding separate cards out of order in the last few moments before the start of a show. The drop-card board should be lighted from in front, from the sides, or from below, but not from above or the shadow of dropping cards will precede them. Some hods have their own built-in gooseneck lights.

An engineer at WLWT, in Cincinnati, designed and built a drop-title device which could be mechanically controlled. A large screw with very deep threads holds the top of the cards and slides them forward as it is turned. They are pushed forward at the bottom by springs. As each card comes to the end of the auger threads, it falls out of the shot, revealing the card behind.

Fig. 9–6. Drop-out title in special stand; drop-in title on hod. The hod may be equipped with its own lighting, such as the gooseneck lamp shown.

Calendar leaves are made to drop off the wall, one by one, by mounting the entire pad on two knitting needles which can be withdrawn from the back of the set. As the needles are pulled back, the front leaf, unsupported, falls off. This could probably be applied to title cards as well except that the device is precarious and too fast a pull could easily send two cards falling instead of one. This principle of threading the object on a wire and pulling the wire to release it has been applied also to petals or leaves which must fall from a plant on cue.

Titles which turn like the pages of a book can also be fixed up with wires—in this case, however, wires of a heavier kind. Each "page" is fastened to a separate wire which protrudes through the back of the card. Moving these wires one by one on the back side will leaf over the pages in front (Fig. 9-7).

The pull-off. The pull-off is perhaps the simplest of all title-change devices. You just pull one title off to reveal the next one behind. Both cards must be the same size, however, and in perfect register. Without the ring binder to assure this, something must hold the cards in one place on the easel, or the action of pulling cards off the face may disturb the position of the others beneath. The author developed a card box for this purpose at CBS, deep enough to hold two dozen cards, open at the top and one side. A phosphor-bronze spring at the back of the box pressed the titles up against the front, where they were held by a half-inch rim around all sides. There was enough spring in the phosphor bronze to keep even the last card flat against the front, where it was in the same plane of focus as all those which had gone before (Fig. 9-8). When this device was adopted in the small studio at WPIX, even the supporting easel was

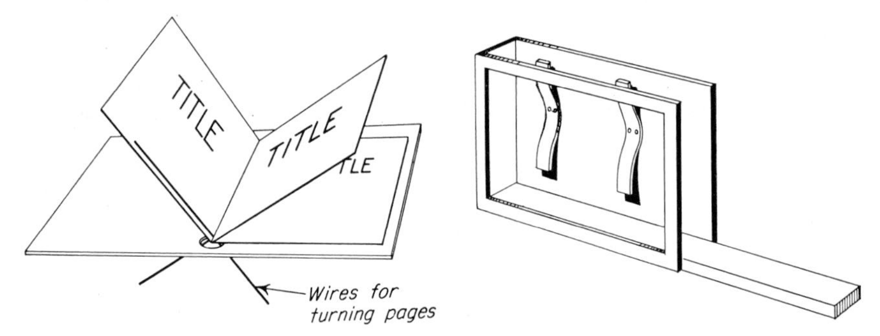

Fig. 9–7. Turning pages. Each page is attached to a stiff wire which is operated from the back.

Fig. 9–8. Card box. Springs at the back force cards against face of box. Extension of bottom prevents wiggle as the cards are drawn out.

eliminated and the card box was fastened directly to the wall of the studio.

The pull-off method is used in certain types of opaque projectors, such as the Multiscope and Projectall, where the slides are placed in the machine in a pack. Since the cards must usually go into these machines upside down and are pulled up, the pull-off gives the effect of the title sliding down off the screen.

In mounting pictures to be pulled off in this manner, be sure that the picture extends to the trailing edge. It is undesirable to see an expanse of white border slide by as the card is removed.

The slide-through. The slide-through is familiar to all who have watched stereopticon slides. One slide seemingly pushes the other off the screen. The slide carrier usually puts a lot of dark area between the two pictures, however. There are slide-through methods for opaque slides and camera cards which can eliminate the border so that one picture is in contact with the next.

CBS once used long slide boards, 6 feet or longer, which could be pushed across an easel. Luckily the studio was large, or the length of boards sticking out at each side of the easel would have used up most of the studio room. Pictures were mounted to the boards, the camera lined up properly on the first one, and then the board was pushed through and marks were established according to the cameraman's direction for each succeeding picture. The slide-through is a simple method of title change, when balop slides are mounted on long strips (described later on page 170).

Most of the 2- by 2-inch slide projectors have a standard slide holder that works from side to side. When slides are changed on the air with these devices, however, it looks like nothing more or less than a lantern-slide projector changing slides. That is enough to disqualify it for use.

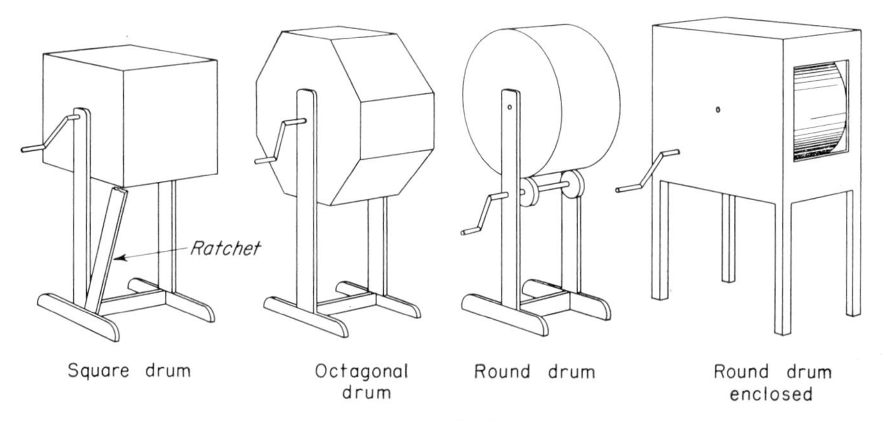

Fig. 9–9. Title drums.

No worse criticism can be leveled at any brilliantly conceived special effect. "What do you think of this idea?" the production assistant asks. "Well," says the director, "you know what it will look like, don't you? It'll look like just exactly what it is." That's all that needs to be said; the idea is dead. But if you ever need the effect of a lantern-slide projector changing slides, you know how it can be achieved.

The drum. For separate titles round, square, and octagonal drums have been used in studios for quick title changes. The round drum must be relatively large in comparison with the framed area, or the curve of the surface will be noticeable. Drums are always used vertically, since the vertical dimension of the frame is shorter and more pictures can be put on the drum when they run this way (Fig. 9-9).

A square drum eliminates the problem of the curve, but only four surfaces are available for cards. Hexagonal or octagonal drums have been built to make space for more titles per drum. These machines are bulky things at best and call for rather careful operation to start and stop them smoothly and accurately. Some kind of indexing device must be devised to stop a drum at the exact point where the next picture is squarely in the frame. A ratchet device which prevents the drum from turning too far until it is released is a good solution. If you try to do it by marks alone, you may find the operator going too far and having to back up to the proper point.

The windmill. This is a variation on the square drum and gives much the same effect. Only four titles can be mounted on the windmill; but, with the proper design, titles can be changed during its operation on the stages which are not before the camera (Fig. 9-10).

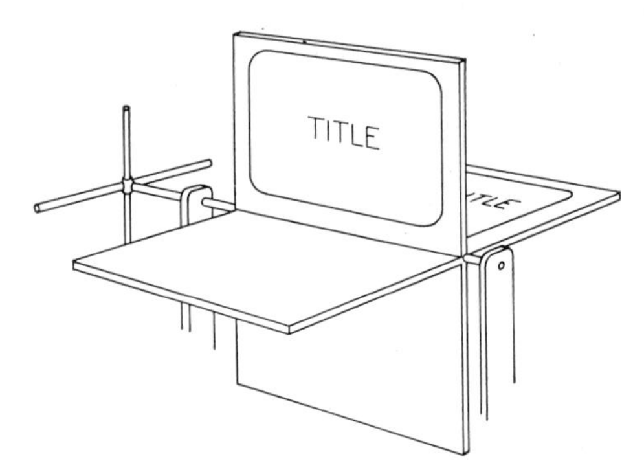

Fig. 9–10. Windmill.

The live-hand change. The subject of title-change devices would be incomplete without a description of the device known as the human hand, appearing before the camera. Some of the most interesting title changes are done by this method. Titles are even written by hand before the camera when all that is necessary is a quick scribble on a memo pad or a scrawl on a blackboard. Any kind of careful lettering, however, will seem to take an interminable length of time on the air.

Bert Gold devised a very clever method of lettering quick titles by working with a single-stroke brush on the back side of a sheet of glass. The formation of a title or a commercial message took a relatively long time at best, however; and it was mostly the fascination of watching the title take shape that made the technique interesting. (Sometimes key letters were left until the last so that the title remained a mystery until the end.)

One of the best title devices in the author's memory was used by Dick Rose to open the Gloria Swanson show at WPIX. Titles were in elegant script on large cards that looked like engraved invitations. They were pictured lying casually on a silver tray, with a gardenia nearby, and a delicate hand reached in with each new card and laid it on the others.

The flipper. This is a derivation of the drum and windmill devices but holds only two cards. It is a two-sided drum. A flipper can be rotated either on its vertical or on its horizontal axis. The author has used the flipper principle for large news maps which could be swung around to show a second map, sometimes a close-up of the first, on the reverse side (Fig. 9-11). In the case of both the 11- by 14-inch flipper and the swinging map, a change could be made on the back side if time were allowed, and a series of pictures could be run. However, at the halfway point of the flip, the cards are edgewise to the camera and don't occupy the entire screen, so that whatever stray studio equipment, stagehands, etc., happen to be standing behind the machine will be seen, if only for the briefest moment, and registered on the eye. A special backing is necessary for these machines; usually a simple curtain will suffice, hung as close to

Fig. 9–11. Vertical and horizontal flippers.

the machine as possible without interfering with the movement of the flipper.

The venetian blind. Titles have been lettered on venetian blinds or specially built gadgets of the same design. A quick change to another title is effected by reversing the blind; and there is a third, though less legible condition, where the blind is left open and a card behind shows through. It is very difficult to disguise the cracks between the vanes, even in a carefully constructed machine; so don't use this device where there is any reason for not wanting it to look like a venetian blind. WSPD put this device to good use in a commercial for selling blinds. Another station uses two blinds; after two titles, they roll the blind up and have another behind for two more titles. A blind with three-sided vanes has been used in display advertising—a field from which many valuable television techniques have been drawn.

The disk. A title or still picture has sometimes been mounted on a disk so that it can be spun around for a special transition. Here, as in all movement, evenness is essential. It will not do, for example, if the operator of the disk can reach only a part of it to turn it and must alternately push and let go for a new grip. There must be either a crank for continuous driving or, what is even better, a heavy grindstone behind the disk to give it weight and balance. The flywheel will keep the movement smooth.

Crawl titles. Titles that crawl slowly up the screen (up because the eye reads down) are familiar in television. Very often an entire series of titles will be lettered on a long strip, which is then fastened to a drum. The crawl is a method of title change similar to the push-through in

Fig. 9–12. NBC crawl-title device. Aperture in box, 7½ by 10 inches. Scanned area, 6 by 8 inches. NBC suggests using a safe title area of 5 by 6 inches.

horizontal movement, but easier to follow, since the eye naturally progresses down.

When a drum is used for this purpose, it must be constructed so that it can be turned evenly. The best drums are motor-driven. If the drum must be manually controlled, gear it down so that it takes several turns of the hand crank to move the drum the height of the camera frame. In this way starting and stopping can be smooth, and irregularities of movement are greatly reduced on the screen. NBC has standardized on the title drum (which they call the "crawl") and equipped all studios with this device (Fig. 9-12). The crawl and the hod have been the only standard devices this network has used.

At CBS in 1945, Chuck Holden built a device he called the guillotine. It was a long, thin board, to which a title could be mounted, with a gear train along each edge, so that it could be cranked smoothly up in front of the camera (Fig. 9-13). A guillotine strip would have to be over 6 feet long, however, to contain as much title as a 2-foot drum. A long, vertical board curved so that every part is equidistant from the camera will give the same result as the camera pans from top to bottom.

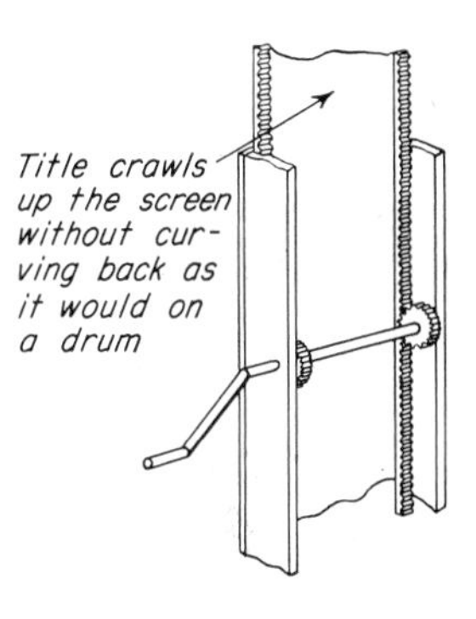

Fig. 9–13. Guillotine.

PREPARATION OF GRAPHIC MATERIALS FOR TELEVISION

Every station has slightly different requirements from the next, both in the manner of preparation of the material, and in the sizes of art work which its particular slide and opaque projectors can handle. The artist should make himself familiar with the requirements of the station (and sometimes even the particular studio of the station) where his work will be used so that these requirements can be met.

FRAMING

When any piece of graphic art is prepared for television use, it is essential for the artist to know the area on which the cameraman will frame and also the area which is certain to be visible on every receiver screen. This problem has been explored in the previous chapter; this section will suggest a simple way in which the artist can quickly determine the safe title area (the area which is sure to be seen on all receivers).

Titles and other art work are usually prepared on 11- by 14-inch cards. A border area an inch wide is allowed around the edges of the card to take care of fingerprints and damage from handling, and the scanned area is established as 9 by 12 inches. The artist draws a line around this area and expects the cameraman to frame up just within this line.

The first step in determining the safe title area is to divide the scanned area into 10 segments (Fig. 9-14). To make sure the safe title area is the same proportion as the scanned area, a diagonal line is drawn from one corner of the scanned area to the other. Where this diagonal line intersects the two outer divisions establishes the corners of the safe title area. The next step is to draw the top and bottom of the safe title area to meet these corners. Some artists have prepared framing guides of card-

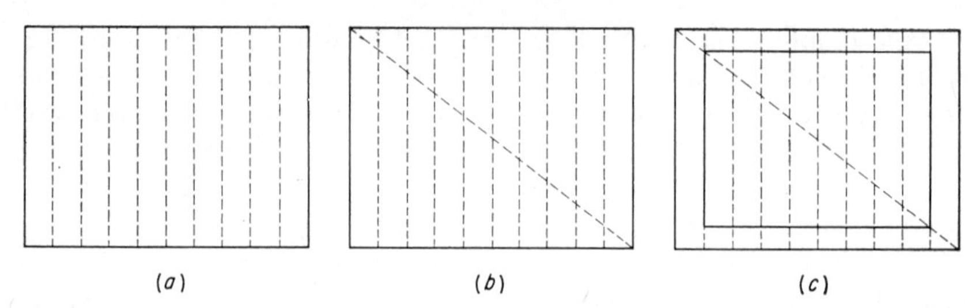

Fig. 9–14. Sherwin method of determining copy (essential) area. (*a*) Total scanned area (dead-border area may surround this). Scanned area is divided into 10 vertical segments. (*b*) Diagonal is drawn from corner to corner to locate corners of the safe title area. (*c*) Top and bottom of safe title area are drawn.

board or heavy acetate to lay over their work. Whatever the size of the art work, however, this method of establishing the copy area can be used: a tenth of the width on each side, and a tenth of the height down from the top and up from the bottom.*

DETAIL

The question of the amount of detail which can be made visible on the receiver screen is an important consideration in television art work. It determines, first of all, the minimum size of lettering. Legibility is not always a matter of size, however. The design of the letters and the tonal relationship between them and the background are fully as important. Furthermore, it is possible to make out details on the screen by close examination which would strain the eyes to continue to look at for any great length of time. The face of a performer is usually the important detail upon which close attention is centered, and one feels a welcome relief when a close-up is taken. No artist would like his work to strain the audience; he wants it to be easy on the eyes. He is obliged, then, to lay out his work in close-ups.

These are the factors that tend to confuse details in television pictures:

1. Soft focus—either optical (on the camera) or electronic (behind the camera) or in the home receiver.

2. Exaggeration of tonal contrast. Spotty pictures are hard to see and are worse when the spots are exaggerated in contrast.

3. The small size of the TV screen in relation to motion pictures. Screens are slowly getting larger. For some time to come, however, a large part of the television audience will be watching on relatively small screens.

* This method of determining the essential area was developed by Ray Sherwin when he was art director at Young and Rubicam.

Determining the degree of detail is a matter of angles. A viewer 6 feet from a 12-inch screen takes in the width of the screen with an angle of view of about 10 degrees. A viewing angle of 10 degrees projected from the eye onto this book at normal reading distance would cover a width of less than 2 inches—almost postage-stamp size. We are working in thumbnail art. Try it some time, when there are visitors at home and you are sitting in the back row of chairs. Hold your thumbnail up to what seems like a comfortable scrutinizing distance, and see if it doesn't just about cover the television screen. This example is not the average; neither is it the extreme. It represents a certain portion of the television audience, a portion which must also read our titles and understand our commercial messages.

Some television artists prefer to sketch things out first in the 2-inch size. In designing a symbol, for instance, which is to appear on a map,

Fig. 9–15. Station title by Tom Nagaele. This composition is acceptable in a variety of framings. (*A*) Picture on control-room monitor; (*B*) framing seen on average receiver; (*C*) framing on poorly adjusted receiver—safe title area only.

they first draw it on a 2-inch map, in the correct size relationship. Naturally, this is working in microscopic proportions. But it prevents the design from getting too detailed. If it can be seen on the sketch, it will come across the screen. Some artists use a reducing glass for this purpose; others just hang the work on the wall and step back across the room.

A simple production aid to assist in determining the degree of detail can be constructed by cutting a window in the end of a small box. The principle is the same as that of the Bretz box (Fig. 5-21), except that in this case the window confines the user's field of view to correspond not to that of a certain camera lens, but to the 10-degree angle of view of a person seated 12 screen-diameters from a TV receiver. Checking TV art work through this viewer forces the user to back far enough away from the graphic to know what it will look like on TV, at least to some viewers.

This is one test for clarity: look at it small. Taken alone, however, this is not enough. Because of the extremely good definition obtainable in steel engraving it is possible to see great detail in a postage stamp without the aid of a magnifying glass. But television does not have that definition. Occasionally a particular camera tube or a perfectly operating system will put out pictures of razor-sharp clarity. But as yet such picture quality cannot be sustained all the time, even by the networks.

The second test for clarity, then, in television art work, is to squint through your eyelashes at the picture. This is a very valuable test. You can get a rough idea of how anything will look on television if you just step back and squint at it. This applies to film, sets, props, even people. Filtering the light through the eyelashes seems to cut down the brightness range that the eye can see. Detail is lost in the shadows; dark tones all go black; fine lines and small print are blurred or lost entirely. If you squint at the picture and still can see it clearly, grasp its meaning, read the lettering easily, then you can be sure the television audience will too.

TONALITY

Closely associated with the limitation on detail which the television system imposes on the artist is the limitation on the range of tone. Sometimes called "values" or "shades," tones range from black to white in what is commonly called a scale of grays. The tone which the television camera sees is not necessarily the tone which the artist intended, however. Several factors may operate to alter it. If facilities are available, the artist should prepare a series of tones of the paints he wishes to use and look at these on the television system at different times and with several different cameras. A discussion of the response of the television system to the tones of the gray scale, plus the pros and cons of using color instead of monochrome in art work, is to be found in the preceding chapter. In a simple way, however, this is what the artist is likely to find when he puts a scale of tones in front of the television camera:

First of all, the number of tones between white and black which the camera can distinguish is limited. The eye can see many variations in tones between black and white. The television system can rarely see more than seven or eight. This range is further reduced by poor reception, so that it is safe to say that a maximum of five tones (including black and white) is sure to be distinguished on all television sets. Any attempt to use an in-between tone involves the risk of its coming out the same as a tone just adjacent to it on the tone scale. If these five tones (black and white and three grays) are standardized to begin with, the artist can be certain that any effect he creates will look very much the same to the television viewer as it does to his eye. On the other hand, if he uses a great variety of tones, or hues and intensities of colors, he will be creating many effects which either will not be visible or may come out entirely wrong when the art work is seen on the television system.

Figure 9-16, a program title, is done in six tones. Note that black and white are used very sparingly, the former only for certain letters and small shadow areas, the latter only for highlights on the clown's face and sleeve and for decoration in the letters.

Fig. 9–16. Program title done in six tones. (By Tom Nagaele.)

MATERIALS AND MEDIA

The television artist works in all media, but tempera is probably the most common. The airbrush is an essential tool in a well-equipped art department. Water color, black-and-white line, and sometimes the medium of collage (pasting up a composite picture) are used. Quite often the artist is called upon to make three-dimensional models, retouch photographs, and make props such as book jackets, posters, etc., for use on the set.

Versatility is important in the television artist; few stations hire specialists. Most small stations can afford only one man, and often he has other duties as well. He must be able to do everything; but most important of all he must have speed. The ability to do things quickly (and reasonably well at the same time) is a quality which is not new in television. From the producer and director on down, no one ever has what he considers adequate time to do a good job. The entire job of planning, laying out, and finished rendering of a series of drawings must be accomplished in a few hours' time.

STYLE AND TECHNIQUE

Television art is closest to poster art in technique. The poster must be seen and understood from a distance; tones and details are designed for their carrying power. The poster must be basically simple and clear,

Fig. 9–17. Effective television art work. Upper left, station closing title used during playing of "Star-spangled Banner," by Tom Nagaele. Upper right, program title also by Tom Nagaele. Lower left, program title by Arthur Rankin. Lower right, program title by Georg Olden.

but it may have further subtleties and finish which reward a closer look. This is essentially the problem in television as well. Carrying power is necessary because of the small screen. Simplification in line, in detail, and in tonality is essential. Simple gradations of tone made with the airbrush are pleasing. A simplified cartoon or poster style of drawing figures and faces lends itself better to television than an attempt to be more realistic (Fig. 9-17).

Some of the best titles used by the network stations are finish-rendered entirely by photography. A photographer specializing in trick effects can take the necessary lettering and, following a sketch of the desired result,

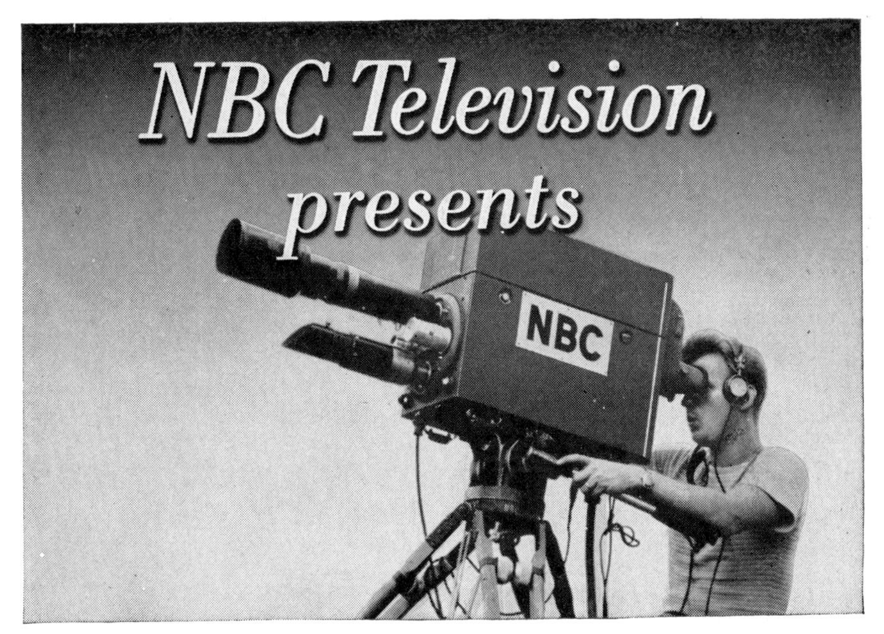

Fig. 9–18. Photographically rendered title. (By Martin Webber, New York.)

produce shadows, tones, gradations, beams of light, etc., which are the same sort of thing that a renderer with an airbrush would do, but smoother and cleaner in appearance (Fig. 9-18).

LETTERING

Lettering is usually a problem in the television station. Although a staff artist can do good lettering, it is probably not his specialty, and it takes him a long time. More complicated alphabets and script are often entirely out of his line. The network stations in New York often farm out difficult lettering jobs to free-lance artists who specialize in this field.

There are a number of short cuts to lettering available on the market today, and one or another of these is to be found in use in every television station. Lettering aids are of several kinds: (1) the mechanical guide with which the artist draws the letter; (2) the ready-made letters (on paper or celluloid) which the artist assembles and fixes to his work; (3) the simplified printing-press devices, with fonts of metal type; (4) the movable type, which is set up and photostated, and (5) the three-dimensional movable letters. These will each be described, together with some other methods of lettering that have been used and deserve brief mention.

Show-card lettering. If the artist has had experience in show-card painting, he will classify as a lightning letterer. His style of lettering, however, will be very simple and not too accurate, but good enough for many purposes. He will choose a thin, flat brush called a single-stroke brush, the width of the letter he wants to paint, and without going back over his work will turn out signs at the rate of two or more words a minute. If an artist has not had show-card experience, however, he will fuss over his lettering and spend 15 or more minutes per word. The result may be much better, but it takes too long. It is much more economical to give him a mechanical aid.

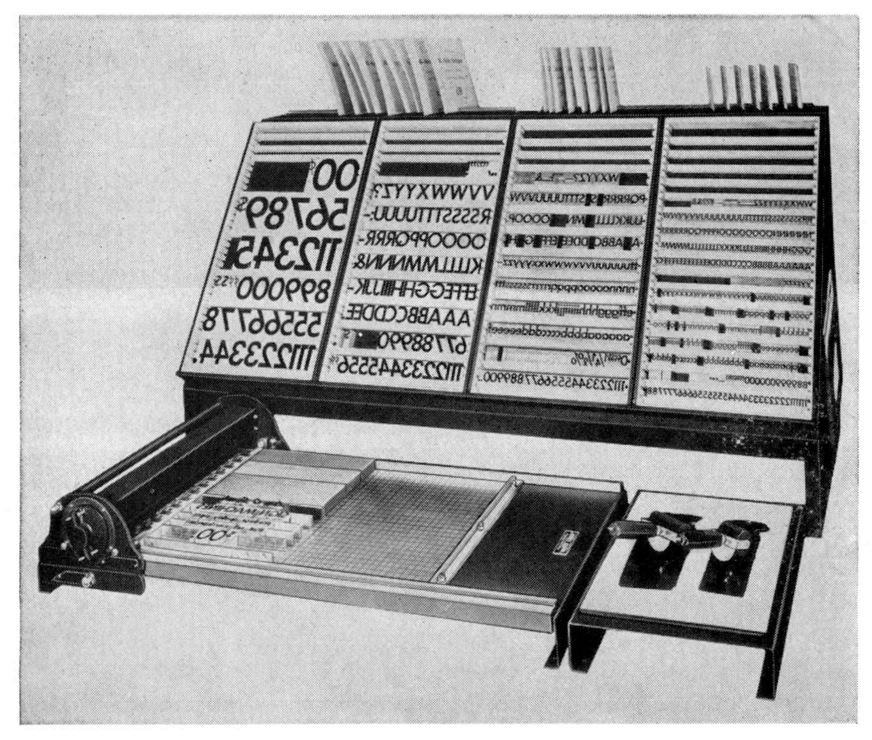

Fig. 9–19. Line-o-scribe machine.

Printer's type. A hand press with a horizontal chase some 14 by 22 inches in size is a common piece of equipment in TV stations. "Line-o-scribe" and "Showcard" are presses of this type. Standard-depth type is set face up, locked in place, and then inked with a hand roller. The card is turned face down, properly centered, and laid against the type. Then the entire chase is rolled through a wringer, so to speak (actually the wringer is generally rolled across the type), and the card is lifted off.

Since such a press takes standard type, the variety of type faces which may be used is almost endless. Several fonts of large-size sans serif letters are generally provided. Standard half-tone cuts, lead castings made for a few cents from newspaper mattes, wood and linoleum cuts may all be used.

Typewriter. A typewriter with oversize capitals (bulletin), another thing which is often found in a large newspaper office, can be put to good use in the direct preparation of titles. The style of type is much the same as that of teletype or news type, which is commonly used in television, and is suitable for purposes associated with news. If the station uses an opaque projector with a 3- by 4-inch stage, even standard typewriter titles can be used for special purposes or in an emergency.

Spaghetti board. This is a derogatory name that production men have given to the black cloth board with movable plastic letters that is used in restaurants for displaying the day's menu. The letters fit into horizontal grooves in the face of the board. WPIX found this very useful in their remotes work when covering harness racing. Before each race it was necessary to give a run-down of the entries, and this could be made much clearer if a list were visible to the audience. Entries were not known far enough ahead to allow an artist to prepare titles; so the production men set up the list on the spaghetti board. It is a quick, simple, and not very elegant method, but it gets a title on the air, even though it may have a cafeteria look.

Fototype: cardboard or acetate. These letters are set up on a composing stick, face down (duplicate letters are printed on the back of each piece). Once they are set in perfect alignment, scotch tape is pressed across them and they can be lifted out in a body, turned over, and affixed to the work. This is all right if the art work has a plain white background. Fototype also makes transparent letters which are set up the same way on a composing stick and can be used on top of any background. Transparent letters are very useful in reproduction. Ozalid, Apeco, and several other machines can make a contact print through this transparent lettering. The manufacturer claims a composing rate of 15 characters per minute for the Fototype composing-stick method, but this does not include the job of spacing and of fixing them to the layout (Fig. 9-20).

Movable type set up and photostated. Bernhard Magnet type is the best example of this method of lettering. Letters are printed on thin pieces of metal and are laid out to form the desired words on a magnetic board. The magnet holds the letters firmly so that they can be lined up and spaced by eye (something that is not so easily done with the kinds of letters which must be stuck down once and for all). Now the board must be photographed or photostated. Since the type is white on black, black-on-white letters result from one shot on the photostat machine. For white-on-black letters, this negative photostat must be printed—a second shot. If care is taken not to jar the board, the let-

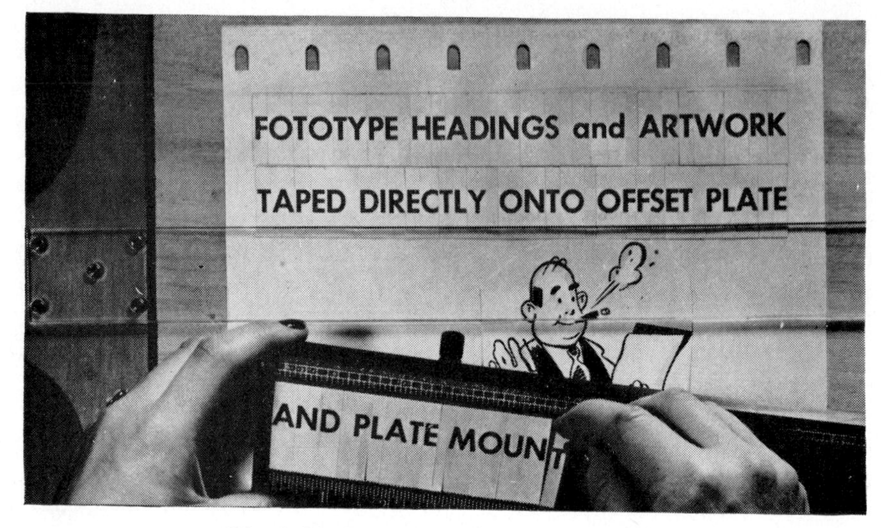

Fig. 9–20. Fototype and composing stick.

Fig. 9–21. Bernhard magnet type.

ters will hold where placed until the shot is made, but it is safer to run a strip of scotch tape across the top and bottom of each row of letters. Slight retouching is necessary on the final print where the edges of the metal pieces may have caught highlights in the photography. Comparatively few alphabets are available, but they are very distinctive and legible.

Ready-made letters. Several makes of ready-made letters are available, some on celluloid, some on paper. They are useful if the lettering is to be reproduced photographically (in the case of slides) or photostatically (the most common method in the case of studio graphics; see page 166). A few examples of ready-made letters are described below.

Wax-coated letters. These letters are printed onto a thin acetate and backed with a layer of wax, so that they can be firmly fixed to a drawing by burnishing the upper surface. But the wax will not hold tight, under any great amount of heat; so the letters cannot be used directly in most opaque projectors. The work is usually reproduced in some way after art type has been used. This allows for retouching the small traces that the edges of the acetate may cause.

A useful type of wax-coated lettering can be transferred directly to the artist's work without cutting or adding unneeded acetate as well. A font of letters comes fixed to the underside of a sheet of transparent paper. After a letter is properly positioned, the upper surface of the paper is burnished and can then be peeled away, leaving the letter attached to the work.

Three-dimensional letters. Mittens letters are the best example of this type. The letters are made of white plaster in very simple block design and can be pinned or cemented to a board. The pins, which are built into the back of the letters, give a false sense of security, however; many of these letters have fallen off and broken from careless handling. The advantage of the three-dimensional letter is that lighting can be used to cast shadows, highlight the edges of the letters, etc.

Embossograph. An example of the simplified printing-press devices with movable metal type, this is perhaps the simplest to operate and is found quite often in television studios. Metal type is set up on a flat surface, lined up, and spaced by judgment and with the help of a centering guide. A sheet of waxed paper of the desired color or tone is then laid face down across the type, and the background card is laid face down on top of that. Now the whole table on which this has been done is slid into a press, and a long handle is brought down to press card and type together. When the card is lifted off, the unnecessary background pieces of waxed paper can be pulled off, the centers of O's and P's removed, and the title has been made. Embossograph type is available in a variety of sizes but in rather ordinary styles. Wherever this machine is used, people complain of the style of titles it makes; yet they go right on using it, because it is so quick and easy for anyone to handle. Background cards of special material are available in a great many loud colors and also in shades of gray, certain textures, and imitation wood.

Embossograph machines are made in three sizes; the largest will make a title 14 inches high, the most useful size will handle a title 8 inches high, and a small desk model is built which is limited to cards no higher than 4 inches. An example of a balop title prepared in this size is shown in Fig. 9-22.

Hot press. The hot-press machine uses regular type in a chase. The type is heated and forms a title in much the same way as the Embossograph, except that the heat sticks the wax firmly without the deep embossing of the edges which is necessary in the former machine, and

Fig. 9–22. Embossograph machine, 8-inch size. At right: 3- by 4-inch balop title made on Embossograph.

Fig. 9–23. Kensol hot-press machine. Standard lead type is locked into chase at right which is attached to head, heated, and brought down onto the card by manual pressure. Opaque roll leaf is laid on top of card and pressed in by the type.

consequently smaller type faces can be used. This is the best and most expensive method of making titles; it is used widely in film production and has been found well worth the expense in network-television art departments, where a great many titles must be turned out (Fig. 9-23).

STILL PICTURES

In selecting still pictures for television, the following considerations must be kept in mind: (1) Is the picture instantly recognizable? (2) Is the subject large enough in the picture? (3) Is the picture pleasing in composition?

The first consideration is mostly a matter of pattern and tone. Hold the picture at a distance, squint at it, or do both, and see if it is going to be confusing on the screen. Sometimes a little retouching or simplifying of the background will make a confusing picture immediately clear. On a matte-surface print a darker tone can be shaded in with a pencil, but on a glossy one, paint must be used, and considerable skill and experience is required. Spray with Pre-color for a matte surface.

The second and third considerations are matters of framing. As applied to still pictures, this is called "cropping." First of all, you attempt to crop the print as far as possible without losing any of its essential parts. You make the subject itself as large as possible in the frame. Of course this can be done only if the picture is to be reproduced to a standard projector size before being used. If the balop size is 8 by 10 inches and the picture comes 8 by 10 inches, there is nothing that can be done in the way of cropping, framing, or altering the composition. You have to trust to the judgment of the printer who has made the enlargements. Luckily the requirements for newspaper reproduction are in most of these respects similar to the needs of television, and good news photos generally make good television stills.

The ability to crop pictures effectively calls for a knowledge of the framing requirements of television and a well-developed sense of composition. A help in cropping is a couple of L-shaped masks which are laid one over the other above the still and can be adjusted to frame a picture in almost any size (Fig. 9-24*a*). However, care must be taken to see that the proportion of the picture stays 3 by 4. Calibrations can be marked on the lower mask: numbered inches on the horizontal, and similarly numbered ¾ inches on the vertical.

The author has devised a sliding frame which can be made small or large and will retain the 3 by 4 proportion at all times. It consists of two cardboard pieces which slide past each other along the diagonal of the frame. Figure 9-24*b* will serve to illustrate how this device (which has

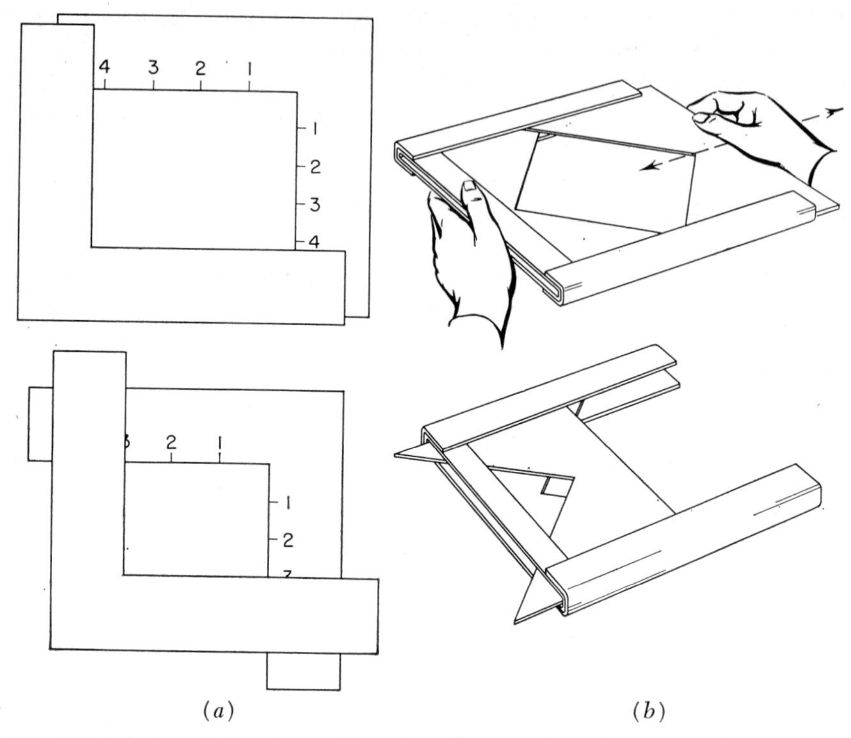

Fig. 9–24. L-shaped framing guides. Bretziframe sliding framing guide. Retains 3 by 4 aspect ratio.

been known as the Bretziframe) can be easily produced with a little cardboard and scotch tape.

REPRODUCTION METHODS (OPAQUES)

The photograph and the photostat are the methods of reproduction most frequently used. Both require equipment that is usually not to be found in a television station; so the work is sent out. This is at very best a matter of hours, more often of days, unless the station has obtained particularly good cooperation. In the interests of time, therefore, much original art work is used on television, especially in the case of news programs. The artist must work to the projector size, however, and he will be happier if the station has a larger size balop. But if the graphics are to be used before the studio camera, they are usually made in an 11- by 14-inch size. The artist will usually prefer to work in this size whenever possible and reproduce small balop prints from this size original.

Photostats are less expensive than photographs but have very definite limitations. The photostat machine is a photographic enlarger which handles opaques instead of transparencies. Whereas in photographic reproduction a transparent negative must first be made, developed, and dried before prints can be turned out, the photostat machine makes a paper negative and prints from that by reflected instead of transmitted light. It is a good idea to find out the enlarging capacity of the photostat machine you will be using. If it can enlarge only two diameters, for example, it may take several steps to blow up a small original to a large-size print. If the original is 4 inches wide, for example, such a machine could make a negative 8 inches wide and a print 16 inches. Another negative would have to be made from this if a larger print were desired.

Pure black and white is the proper material for the photostat, but tones of gray can be reproduced fairly well if they are not too subtle and are confined to the middle range.

Ozalid. The Ozalid machine is a dry-printing contact device, incapable of enlarging, but very useful for some particular purposes in television. It makes positive prints from positive transparencies. The transparent art work and the unexposed paper are fed together into the machine like sheets into a mangle. Developing is done in a few moments by the action of ammonia fumes within the machine, and the finished result is ready immediately.

Apeco. Some stations have used a small machine similar to the Ozalid for the purpose of reproducing art-type titles. The Apeco uses transparencies only and a negative-to-positive process (not positive-to-positive like the Ozalid) so that white on black letters result from the reproduction of art type. It has been used primarily for titles that were to be superimposed.

METHODS OF MOUNTING OPAQUES

Still photographs, photostats, and some art work may not be prepared on heavy enough stock to withstand ordinary handling or even to lie flat in front of the camera or in a projector. This material must be mounted in some way before it can be used.

Stapling. Every television studio has a "staple gun," a machine which drives heavy staples without clinching them on the back side. When pictures are to be mounted on the walls of a set, on particularly heavy board or wood, this type of stapler can be used. For mounting on regular cardboard, an office stapler is best because it clinches its own staples. The "throat" of such a device is limited, however; and it cannot reach very far in from the edge when mounting a small picture on a large board. CBS once adapted one of these staplers with an extra-long extension so that it could reach in about 12 inches. The stapler method of mounting is very crude and may leave bulges and wrinkles which will catch light. It is used only when there is no time for anything else.

Scotch tape. Without the various types of pressure-sensitive tape it is doubtful that the average television studio could function. The author once had fourteen kinds of tape in regular use at CBS. For the mounting of pictures, both the single- and the double-faced tape can be used. The scotch cellulose tape has about the strongest pull. There are some paper-base masking tapes that are very useful, including black ones. Black tape is best around the edges of a picture because if the camera inadvertently shows edges, they are not nearly so noticeable in black as they would be in white.

The double-faced tapes are particularly valuable for mounting, since they do not show at all. It takes a bit of skill to use them without getting all stuck up, but if you turn the picture over and run this tape around the edges and then apply the picture to the board, it will do a pretty good job. Bulging paper will, however, still bulge, since only the edges are firmly held down. If a title must be slid into a machine or pass other titles and obstructions, the double-faced tape is superior to the single type or to stapling, since there is nothing on the face of the card to catch or gum up the motion. Mounting with scotch tape must still be regarded as a short cut, but, after all, short cuts are what television production is made of.

Rubber cement. This is a good method of mounting if used correctly. Putting the two pieces together while the cement is wet makes a temporary bond which can be peeled off again—and which probably *will* peel off of its own accord just about air time. For a solid bond, both surfaces must be covered and the cement allowed to dry on both before the mounting is done. A better job can be done with rubber cement than with any other kind of cement, glue, or paste, and it leaves less of a mess around when it is not handled too carefully. Under great heat, however (and some opaque projectors are not too well cooled), rubber cement will soften and peel off. Scotch cellulose tape is stronger, but for real security there is nothing like stapling.

Dry mounting. This is probably the best method of mounting. It is done in a hot press with a sheet of heat-seal adhesive sandwiched in between paper and board. Sheets of dry-mounting tissue are also sold separately, and one is supposed to apply the heat by ironing the picture on with an electric iron; but this is slow and rather difficult. The Fotoflat dry-mounting press is in use in several television studios. It heats up to around 225°F and makes a quick and perfect job. The Fotoflat heat-seal adhesive will soften if heat is applied again; so it is easy to remove mounted pictures by putting them back into the press. The same thing may happen under the hot lights of a balop, however; if your balop operates at a high temperature, none of the mounting processes so far described can be recommended (Fig. 9-25).

Fig. 9–25. Fotoflat dry-mounting press.

Metal mounts. This category includes the septum, the sheave, the holder, and any other methods of mounting without adhesive. The 8- by 10-inch opaque projector that Paul Adanti built years ago at WRGB used lightweight sheaves with a rolled-over edge, into which the 8- by 10-inch glossies could be slid with a little effort and a lot of finger pressure on the

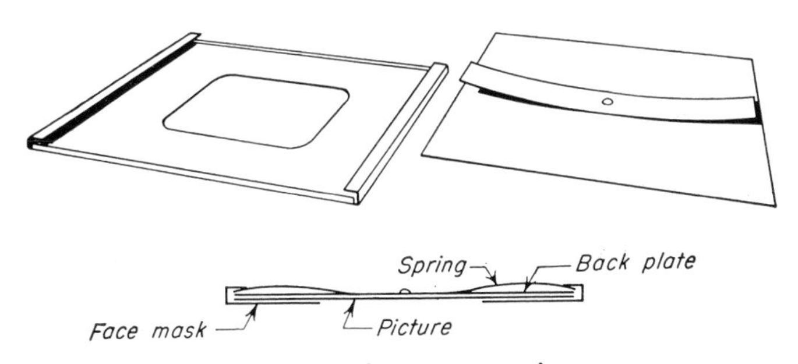

Fig. 9–26. Septum mounting.

face of the paper. It would not have been good for original art work. The advantage was, however, that the print was held firmly by each edge and, in its metal mount, could be handled easily by a machine.

Common are opaque projectors which employ 3- by 4-inch pictures mounted on a long metal strip. The strip is cut out as a face mask, and backing plates are fastened behind each opening. The plates do not come off the strip, however; when released, they spring back just far enough to allow a picture to be slipped in easily and when held down again are then clamped securely by a small turn button at the edge (Fig. 9-27).

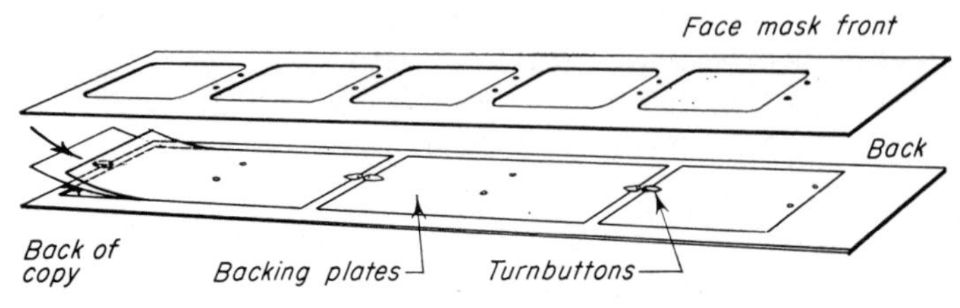

Fig. 9–27. Telop strip mounting.

REPRODUCTION METHODS FOR TRANSPARENCIES

The standard transparencies in television are the 2- by 2-inch slides adapted from school and home use to the television projection room. Some stations are also equipped to project the larger 3¼- by 4-inch slides, which have been standard lantern slides for auditorium use for many years.

3¼- *by* 4-*inch slides.* For projection onto a large screen as in rear projection these slides are best. Because of their larger area, more light can be transmitted, and a bright picture can be produced over a larger area. This advantage is of no particular value in the television projection room, since the light is concentrated onto a small TV tube, and relatively little is needed. However, the larger-size slides fit more accurately into the machine and are more likely to come out consistently straight on the screen. Slides 3¼ by 4 inches are invariably made on sensitized glass, faced with a cover glass, and bound along the edges. The standard scanned area on a 3¼- by 4-inch slide is 2¼ by 3 inches. Accordingly, the safe title area should be about 1¾ by 2⅜ inches.

2- *by* 2-*inch slides.* The 2- by 2-inch dimension of these slides is the outside dimension. The camera field is considerably inside this. The aspect ratio of standard 2- by 2-inch slides is not the 3 by 4 aspect ratio of the television picture (the picture area on the slide is wider in proportion to its height), and a certain amount of picture area must be lost on each side when such a slide is projected on television (Fig. 9-28).

The advantages of the use of slides over filmstrip (described below) is that titles can be used in any order. A station usually keeps a filing box of slides, assigns each slide a number, and refers to it by number on the daily routine sheet. The same feature may be a disadvantage also. There is room for human error in keeping the order right.

The biggest disadvantage of 2- by 2-inch slides is the inaccuracy and variation in their size and shape. A slide which is bound a little too loosely or with a slightly heavier edging tape will ride higher in the projector than the slide just before. Very tiny irregularities will cause it to set at an angle and come out crooked on the screen. This is such a problem that some stations make it a regular routine to check the set of each slide in the few seconds before it is used and relay quick instructions to the projection man to "raise it on the left," "push it a little farther in," or whatever adjustment must be made. It is because the over-all size of

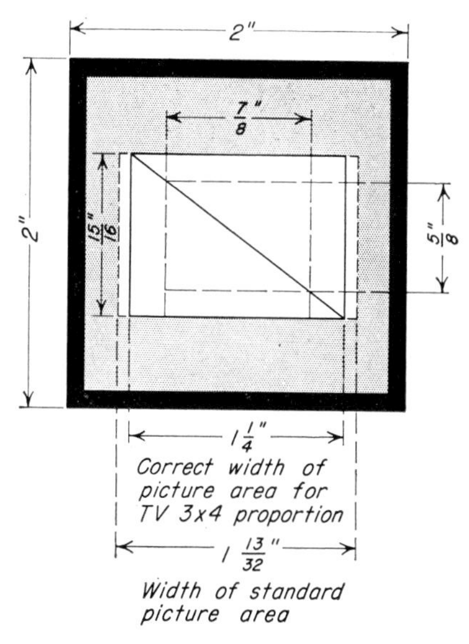

Fig. 9–28. Standard 2- by 2-inch slide with framing dimensions. Picture area for TV means scanned area. The safe title area is figured here on the basis of a ⅙ loss at each border rather than ⅒, making is somewhat safer (see p. 138).

the slide is so small that these minor bumps and thick places in the binding make such a noticeable difference. Each irregularity is enlarged greatly on the screen. The same bumps are not nearly so noticeable in the larger-size slide because they are much smaller in proportion to the slide.

Slides 2 by 2 inches are made in two ways: (1) photographed horizontally on 35-mm film and bound in metal or cardboard holders called "ready-mounts" or in paper holders which are bound between cover glasses; (2) photographed on glass plates and bound with cover glasses like the larger lantern slides. Metal holders for 35-mm film such as those made by Brumberger which simply snap together over the film are fairly accurate and are affected very little by heat.

It is very troublesome for a projectionist to try to use both types interchangeably. They differ in thickness, which is hard on some projectors.

One type of slide may rest in a slightly different plane from the other, with the emulsion either a little closer to or a little farther from the lens, and this may require refocusing of the projector.

A photographer with limited darkroom facilities may turn out satisfactory 2 by 2 slides if he approaches the problem as a precision job and devotes great care to centering the picture on the slide and binding the cover glasses together smoothly. There are a number of short cuts to slide making on the market, metal holders, cardboard mounts, etc., which should be looked on only as emergency possibilities. These devices will mount and center 35-mm minicamera film, and slides can be made with any type of 35-mm minicamera. These mounts are relatively inaccurate, however, and the film may curl; so the best way to make a slide is to photograph the picture on a 2- by 2-inch glass plate and bind a cover glass to it. There are many kinds of binding tape on the market, some of which are likely to soften when hot. This leaves a sticky deposit in the projector gate, which makes slides work badly, especially in automatic projectors. Since it is very difficult to distinguish the sticky from the nonsticky tape, manufacturers recommend the use of Slide-ease. This is a sealer compound which does not become tacky or sticky under heat, stiffens any material which is treated with it, and seals the slide against dust and damage. A thorough discussion of the techniques of slide making is to be found in the "Kodak Data Book on Slides."

35-*mm filmstrip.* Filmstrip projectors, long in standard use as visual aids in education and selling, have found a place in television also. The filmstrip is made on 35-mm motion-picture film, but the film runs vertically through the projector, not horizontally, as it does in 35-mm miniature cameras. Thus the camera field is smaller than it is on the 2- by 2-inch glass slide (approximately ⅝ by 13/16 inches).

The great advantage in the use of filmstrips is that the pictures cannot get out of order. Of course, the order cannot be shifted either, short of cutting and splicing the film; and splices are likely to catch in a stripfilm projector unless they are very carefully made. Picture change is by a rapid pulldown to the director's cue "Flip it." This is not unnoticeable on the screen, but neither is it particularly objectionable. WPIX produced a still-picture news show twice daily by this means over a period of several years.

16-*mm filmstrip.* The Dunning Animatic is a very precise machine which makes the pulldown so quickly that it appears to be instantaneous. This has been found to be of great value both in the projection room and for studio use. Some stations have acquired the equipment for making the 16-mm filmstrips which this projector uses.

10

Projection Equipment

The present chapter will deal with the types of equipment used for the integration of film and slides (either transparent or opaque) into the television system. The same equipment is sometimes used for the pickup of small objects of shallow-depth dimensions, since the optical system involved allows for no great depth of focus.

The term "projection" is applied mainly because, at the outset, projectors of various types were adapted to the TV system. Each, of course, included a lens, and an image was truly projected through this lens to the TV pickup camera. Had the lens been attached to the camera instead, the process might not have been called projection.

The principle is the same, of course, whether a camera alone or a projector and camera are used to pick up the image. A slide or object is illuminated; an image of the subject is formed by a lens on the camera tube. The "flying-spot scanner" principle of slide projector, however, differs from the above, since a camera is not used as the pickup device; instead an inexpensive photoelectric cell is involved. This method is described at the end of the present chapter.

The standard pickup camera in use in TV projection is the vidicon, which began to supersede the iconoscope during the early '50s. A TV camera used in this way (see Fig. 1-3) is known as a "film chain" or "film-pickup camera." The vidicon film-pickup camera is usually quite small (some are only a few inches on a side) and carries a single lens. No further controls are provided unless it be a scanning reversal switch (see page 285) and/or a polarity reversal switch. When this latter switch is thrown to reversal position, it will cause negative films or slides to appear as positives on the screen (and vice versa, of course).

Before going into detail regarding the various types of projectors, let us consider briefly the operational practices involved.

The integration of "residue" is a very important part of TV production, since it is the short commercials and spot announcements between programs which support the commercial TV station. Some advances are being made in the development of automation equipment to perform this production task. At the present writing, however, it is the local station TV director who must with considerable skill cue films, live or taped announcements, change slides, and operate the switcher, running one commercial or station promotion announcement smoothly into the next with split-second accuracy lest the rigid starting time of the following network program catch the last commercial before it is over, force him to cut the end of one or the beginning of the other, and in either case incur a rebate to the advertising agency involved.

REMOTE CONTROL OF PROJECTORS

Since the small station must operate with a limited staff, as much control of the projectors as possible is usually given to the director, or to the TD where a TD is used.

Although "start" and "stop" buttons are available for the projectionist on the film projectors themselves, these are almost always duplicated in the control room and a remote switch is provided on the projector with which the projectionist can give the TD control. The usual setup provides a ready light on the switching panel, which lights up when the projectionist has punched the remote button and indicates that the film is threaded up and ready to roll. On the cue "Roll film" the TD punches the "start" button, and the projector begins to turn. Then a third step is necessary before the picture is actually on the air. If there is only one film chain and it is already on the line, with a slide or film from a second projector, a change-over must be effected by operating the dousers. These are small shutters which slide across the light beam. If two film channels are involved, it is simply a matter of previewing the upcoming picture and putting it on the line by switching to it at the proper time.

At one station an opaque and two transparent slide projectors were set up on one film chain. The TD's control panel for this assembly is shown in Fig. 10-1. Three tally lights at the top keep track of which of the three projectors is operating. The two rows of numbered lights at either side indicate which slide position is in place for projection. The same numbers are repeated on the machine itself so that the projectionist can put the proper slides in their assigned positions. For simplicity in operation all even-numbered positions are on one projector, and all odd-numbered positions are on the other. The slide-change buttons advance a projector one position and work only on the projector which is off the air. A toggle switch (center) makes the change-over from one slide to another. Since only one projector can be on at a time, a special super button will add the second projector for as long as the button is held down. All transitions are instantaneous, however, and there is no provision in this control setup to allow a fade, a dissolve, or a slow superimposure.

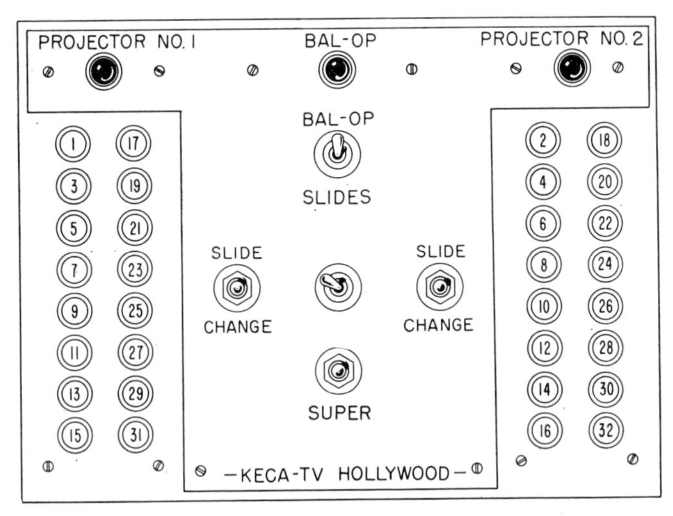

Fig. 10–1. Remote control panel with tally lights showing which slide is in place in each projector.

MULTIPLE USE OF SINGLE FILM CHAIN

Film-pickup camera chains are expensive, and every station has devised some means or other to associate the maximum possible number of projectors with each camera. If the station can afford only one film-pickup camera, there is then no way for the control room to preview an up-coming picture from one projector if another is in operation. A second camera makes this possible and also ensures against loss of program due to equipment failure. In such a case if there is a 16-mm projector and a 2- by 2-inch slide projector on each camera channel, the station will be able to continue programming even though one film chain is out of order. The optical device which allows several projectors to be fed to a single film-pickup camera is called a "multiplexer."

MULTIPLEXERS

When the standard film chain changed from the iconoscope to the vidicon camera, the design of multiplexers changed basically as well. The iconoscope film-pickup camera used no lens; an opening in the camera cover allowed the various projectors to shoot in and focus their images directly on the mosaic (plate) within the camera tube. Several projectors could be fed in from slightly different angles (Fig. 10-2) and a great variety of optical systems were devised to make this possible.

The vidicon film-pickup camera, on the other hand, is equipped with its own lens. This will be of the necessary focal length to focus on a "field lens" part way between camera and projectors. Each projector is

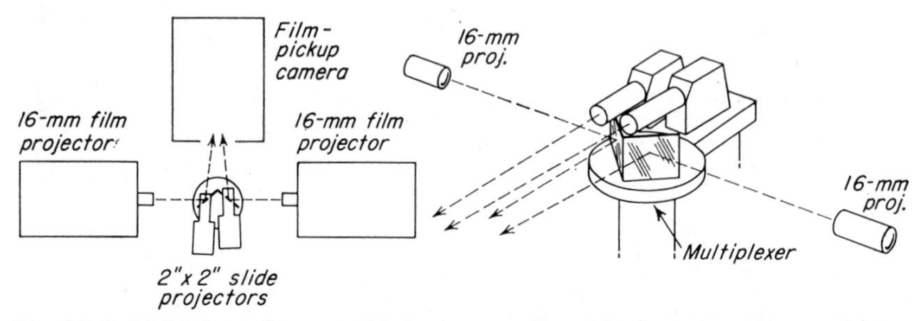

Fig. 10–2. Multiplexer for use with iconoscope film-pickup camera. Four projections are imaged on camera tube, each one slightly off camera axis, causing unnoticeable keystoning.

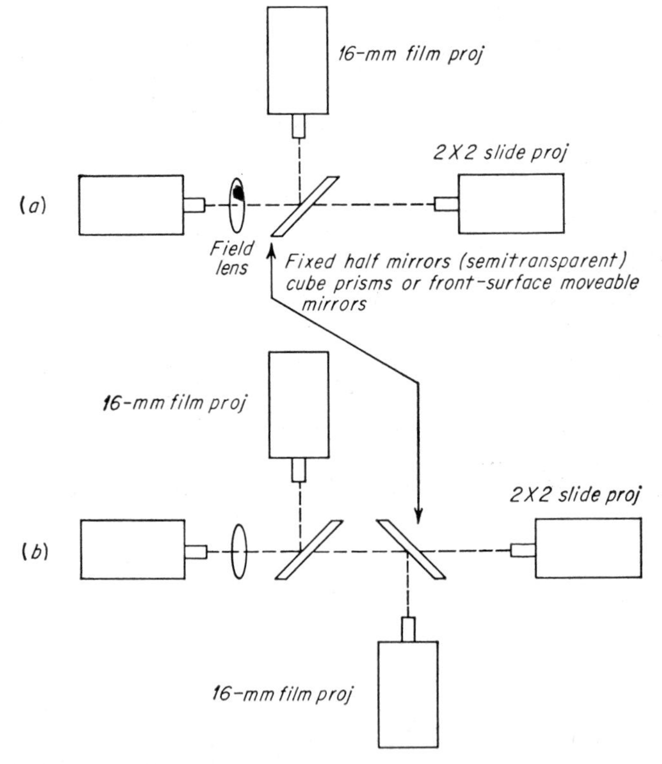

Fig. 10–3. Simple multiplexers. (*a*) A two-input, one-output multiplexer. (*b*) A three-input, one-output multiplexer.

then also focused on the field lens and the system is in focus. Since each projector involved must be on the optical axis (i.e., directly in line with the camera lens), it is not possible to feed in two or more projectors from slightly different angles. Figure 10-3 diagrams simple multiplexer designs for a vidicon film chain. In this example, beam-splitters are used; it is possible for one projector to project straight through the beam-splitter while a second projects by reflection from the side. Control of

Fig. 10–4. RCA multiplexer with cover removed, showing cube prisms. Slide projector at left projects through both prisms. Film projector at back is reflected by inner surface of left-hand cube. Right-hand cube provides for another projector position on near side. A 45-degree mirror between the field lens and the camera, a second field lens, and a front surface mirror provide another projector position at the near side of the camera. This is a four-input, one-output multiplexer.

projection must be through the dousing of projection beams; if all projectors are opened at once, all will superimpose their images on the TV camera when the beam-splitter method is used.

A beam-splitter may be a semitransparent mirror (see page 197), or it may be a cube prism as shown in Fig. 10-4. The cube prism is simply a beam-splitting surface sandwiched between two solid blocks of glass so that it traverses the resulting cube at a 45-degree angle.

An alternate method uses front surface mirrors (see page 207) in place of beam-splitters. Since these are solid mirrors, it is not possible for the

Fig. 10–5. Mechanism of the RCA TP15 multiplexer, an example of the four-input, two-output type. Mirrors hinge down for almost instantaneous change-over.

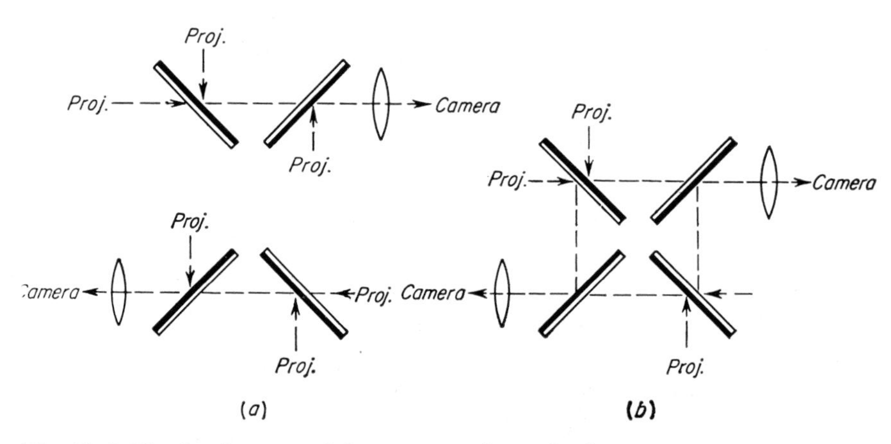

Fig. 10–6. The development of the more complex multiplexer. Two 3-input, 1-output multiplexers (*a*) facing in opposite directions are combined (*b*) to make a 4-input, 2-output multiplexer.

in-line projector to project through the mirror, and one or more mirrors must be mechanically moved during the change-over from one projector to the next. A typical though somewhat more complex multiplexer with movable front surface mirrors is shown in Fig. 10-5. With this design two film-pickup cameras can be set up so that either one can receive a picture from any of the four projectors which can be set up around the multiplexer (see Fig. 10-6).

TRANSPARENT SLIDE PROJECTORS

Of the several sizes of transparent slides used in various projection applications, only one has been adopted to any extent in television, and this almost universally. It is the 2- by 2-inch slide, sometimes known as 35-mm, because 35-mm film exposed in minicameras can be inserted in a great variety of special mounts to make a slide of this outside dimension.

Specially manufactured projectors have been available in the 3¼- by 4-inch (lantern slide) size, notably the General Electric, but have tended to be less and less used, especially since the replacement of the iconoscope by the vidicon as the standard film-pickup camera.

A single slide projector does not lend itself to smooth TV programming. Slide change can be accomplished only by moving the slide on

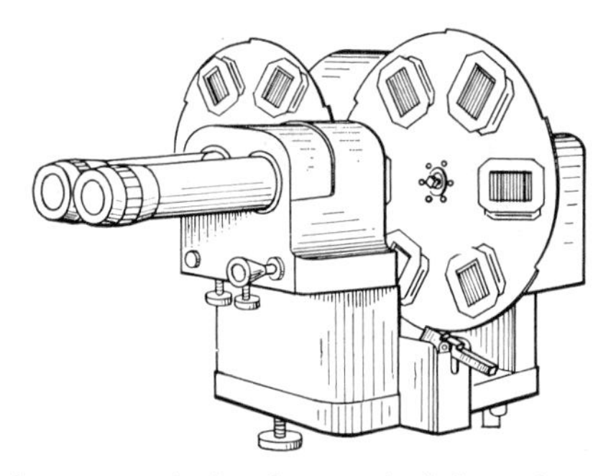

Fig. 10–7. Gray Telejector, a dual 2- by 2-inch slide projector holding 12 slides.

the air or by going to black between slides, an interruption at best. Thus it is common practice either to mount two standard projectors together as a pair or to employ one of the specially designed TV projectors which are really twin projectors with two stages (although a single lamp and optical system may be employed). Such projectors can be loaded with from six to fifty slides in each of the pair; some have detachable magazines which can be loaded before they are on the projector. With several magazines, one for each evening's programming, some stations avoid the largest part of slide loading. The illustrations accompanying this chapter present examples of several types of dual projectors used in TV production.

OPAQUE PROJECTORS

The simple name "balop" has come into general use in referring to any of the various types of opaque projectors or to the slides and art work prepared for them. It derived from a standard Balopticon (initials BAL for Bausch and Lomb) which CBS had adapted for television use in 1939. Just as all cameras are not Kodaks, all opaque projectors are not balops unless usage makes them so.

A balop consists of two parts—a stage suitably illuminated and a lens in such a position that it can project an image of the stage onto the tube in the pickup camera. Most balops include at least one mirror somewhere

Fig. 10–8. RCA TP7 slide projector, a dual 2- by 2-inch slide projector utilizing one light source and one projection lens. Magazines hold total of 36 slides.

in the system, usually just before or behind the lens. This saves space, since the balop stage does not have to be vertical and in a direct line from the camera. When the mirror reflects a horizontal stage, there is an added convenience in operation since cards and objects will be held on it by gravity and it can be used for many purposes that a vertical stage cannot.

Before opaque projectors were specially manufactured for TV, a great variety of classroom opaque projectors were adapted for use with the iconoscope film-pickup camera. One such single projector was adapted for continuous showing of slides by removing the regular stage and substituting two sets of tracks, one above the other. A card could be inserted in the top set of tracks, and then pulled out to reveal a second card just below it in the second level. A third card could then be pushed in above, the bottom card changed behind it, and so forth.

Fig. 10–9. Beseler OA4 opaque projector adapted for television. Optical system has been doubled back on itself to conserve space. This machine handles a picture size of 8 by 10 inches.

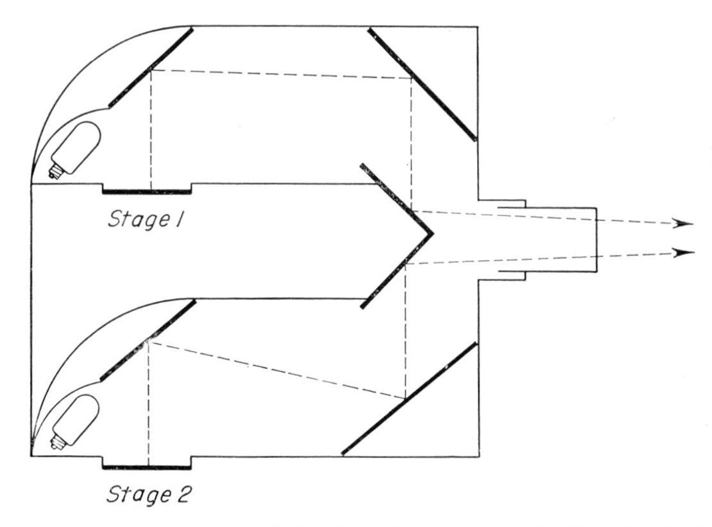

Fig. 10–10. CBS two-stage balop built from two standard Beseler OA2s.

The next step was to combine two of these machines into a two-stage balop (Fig. 10-10). This projector will permit dissolves or cuts as well as fades to black between slides. Some have been adapted to perform simple wipe effects. When the iconoscope film chain was standard, projectors with dual lenses were possible, each projecting into the camera from a slightly different angle, not great enough to cause "keystoning." The vidicon camera, however, with its own objective lens focused on a field lens in the multiplexer, requires that all components of the optical system be strictly on the optical axis. Thus both stages of a dual projector of any sort must utilize the same lens.

A typical balop is the two-stage Telop made by the Gray Company. One stage is fed at the top of the machine and faces downward, while the other faces up from below. Both are mirrored to project through a single lens. Card size is 4 by 5 inches, with a picture area of 3 by 4

Fig. 10–11. Four-stage Telop; third and fourth stages are vertical at back.

inches. Lights on the two stages are controlled by dimmers, the control handles of which work in a manner similar to that of the two-bus switching system handles described in Chap. 7. When the two handles are moved as one, one stage fades out as the other fades in. When they are split in one direction, a superimposure can result; in the other, both stages can be faded completely to black.

TELEVISION FILM-PROJECTION EQUIPMENT

Sixteen-millimeter film is universally accepted as the most practical for television use, and all TV stations anywhere in the world, to the writer's knowledge, are equipped with film projectors in this size. The networks and a few of the larger independent stations have also installed 35-mm (standard theatrical size) film projectors.

Whereas 35-mm film has noticeably better quality on the TV system, especially as far as the sound track is concerned, most films for television use are released in 16-mm prints. The cost of postage is much reduced, of course, and if the local station goes into the production of its own film commercials and newsreels the cost of equipment and film stock is very much less in 16-mm. Historically there is another reason for the preponderance of 16-mm film in television. When television began, all 35-mm film was made of nitrate stock. Highly flammable, this film stock was required by local fire laws everywhere to be stored in fireproof vaults and handled in special fireproof rooms, and it could not be carried by messenger on bus or subway. It was thus most inconvenient to use.

The writer first saw an 8-mm projector adapted for television use in 1958 in East Berlin, the purpose being to provide for the use of privately owned and amateur footage. With the advent of high-quality 8-mm sound film, some TV stations in this country have installed 8-mm equipment and begun to cover news events with this much less costly medium. KPHO-TV, Phoenix, was the first to begin this trend. It is expected that 8-mm will find increasing applications in television production.

THE SYNCHRONIZING PROBLEM

If a motion picture is projected onto a screen and this image is picked up with an image-orthicon camera, a picture containing considerable flicker will result. A vidicon camera will show almost no flicker. A standard motion-picture projector may indeed be projected directly into a vidicon camera and, with proper optical adjustment, result in an acceptable transmission of film images. The problem involved in the use of the image-orthicon is that of synchrony. A motion picture is a succession of still images following each other at the rate of 24 per second. Television, on the other hand, scans a series of still pictures and presents them on the viewing tube at a different rate. These rates vary according to the various world standards: in Europe with 50-cycle electric current the frequency of TV frames is 25 per second. In America with 60-cycle current the frequency is 30 frames per second.

The Europeans have no film-synchronizing problem: twenty-five frames per second is so close to twenty-four that they simply run all film on TV at twenty-five. Thus each frame of film is scanned once and everything is in perfect synchrony.

With the 30-frames-per-second (60-field) standard, synchrony is not so easy. Obviously there are not enough film frames to project one for each TV scanning: there will have to be some doubling up. The answer was found in projecting a film frame once for each TV *field*. A field, the reader will recall, is half the duration of a TV frame, and consists of a scanning of all the even-numbered or all the uneven-numbered lines in the 525-line picture. There are sixty fields per second. The twenty-four frames of film can be distributed evenly over these sixty fields by projecting the first film frame twice, onto two successive TV fields, the next film frame three times, the third twice, the fourth three times, and so on. Twelve of the frames are projected twice each, making 24 TV scannings, and the intervening twelve are projected three times each, adding 36 more for a total of 60. Figure 10-12 shows this relationship over a period of 1/6 second.

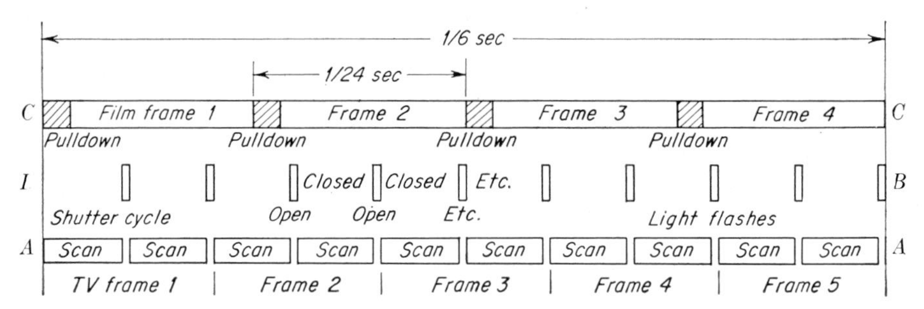

Fig. 10–12. The synchronization problems between film and TV. A typical method of fitting 24 film frames into 30 television frames. (The above chart shows four film frames and five TV frames, since 1/6 second is covered.)

The vidicon camera tube does not require such accurate synchronizing (although for optimum performance it is considered desirable), because of the slow decay nature of this tube. An image formed on the vidicon tube does not immediately disappear, even after several scannings, leading to an undesirable "smear" effect if the condition is extreme. In the case of film, therefore, synchrony is not important since the tube will retain an image for scanning no matter at what point in the scanning cycle it may have arrived.

In Fig. 10-12 row *A* represents the television scanning system. The retrace time during which the scanning beam moves back to position to start scanning a new field is indicated at the end of each 1/60 second. Row *B* represents the shutter-timing pattern of a television film projector in which the shutter is designed to project light in very short bursts every 60th of a second during the TV retrace periods. Row *C* represents the operation of a special type of TV projector with a regular pulldown cycle, using a much faster pulldown than ordinary projectors employ. This design is possible with 16-mm projectors because of the light weight of the film which must be moved.

An example of another solution is found in the Bell and Howell CBVM (a modified JAN). The shutter in this machine opens 120 times a second (standard projectors are 48- or 72-cycle). This means that each frame of film is projected five times. Since the total light-application time dur-

Fig. 10–13. RCA 16-mm television film projector.

ing a given TV field is greater than 30 per cent of the field's duration, the necessity of synchronization of film pulldown with the TV scanning rate is eliminated. Referring to the chart (Fig. 10-12), there is no need in this projector for any particular relationship between rows *A*, *B*, and *C*. The pulldown times could fall at any point in the TV fields and frames without affecting the picture.

THE FLYING-SPOT SCANNER

An alternative method to the vidicon film chain for the pickup of films and slides is the flying-spot scanner. A scanner is like a projector in reverse. Instead of a light projecting an image *out* of the machine onto a TV tube, in the scanner a TV tube (kinescope type) projects its light *into* the machine, through the side or film and onto a photoelectric cell which is positioned much as though it were a projection lamp. The illuminated raster of a cathode-ray tube is really just a tiny spot sweeping back and forth and, because of persistence of vision and the decay time of the phosphor coating, looking like a series of horizontal lines. At any given moment, then, the light which is "projecting" the slide or film onto the photocell consists only of a tiny spot. As this sweeps across the slide, it passes through to the photocell according to the density of the emulsion on the slide. The photocell then, just as in a sound-film projector, passes an electrical signal which varies as the light that falls upon it. Thus the slide is scanned by the light itself, a much simpler method than the usual means of pickup where an image of the slide is scanned inside a camera tube. Not only is the flying-spot "camera" less expensive (no camera tube required), but the results are superior in matters of gray-scale rendition and tolerable contrast range.

11

Mirrors and Prisms

Perhaps the most useful single device in the field of special effects and illusion is the mirror. Almost any kind of television production requires some understanding of the properties of mirrors and how they can be used. The effects that can be achieved with mirrors will be discussed first, after which the properties of mirrors will be briefly outlined.

HIGH-ANGLE SHOTS

Figure 11-1 illustrates a common use of the mirror in television studios. The mirror reflects a top shot of the subject which could otherwise be obtained only by positioning the camera above the set. A "virtual" camera position is obtained. The direction of the camera view has been changed by the mirror. If the viewer does not know a mirror has been used, he will think the camera is actually placed above the set.

This is one aspect of the mirror's effect: the mirror seems to transport the camera to a different position. In other cases the change seems to have happened to the subject instead, and a virtual position of the subject is obtained. You can think of it either way. In this particular example the subject is seen in mirror image walking on the wall, which is impossible. So the eye believes instead that the camera has assumed a high position.

To determine which end of the subject will be up, in Fig. 11-3, simply trace out the top or the bottom edge of the camera's field of view. The bottom is shown as a dotted line in the accompanying diagrams. The subject's feet are closest to this bottom line, and his head is closest to the top line; hence he is not inverted. Left and right appear to be reversed, however, and the subject seems to hold the cane in his left hand instead of his right. It is only the *actor's* right and left that are reversed, however; camera left and camera right remain the same. In a direct shot the cane would be on the camera-left side of the man; in the reflected shot the same is true: the cane is camera left of the man. Camera left is still camera left.

Taking advantage of the mirror's property of creating a virtual camera position, the camera can apparently be placed in impossible positions. Two examples from field pickups will explain this. The camera setup

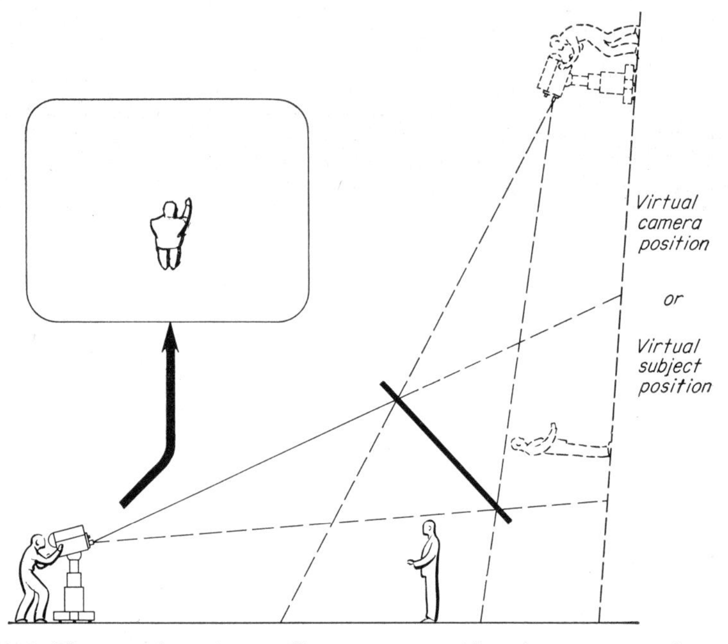

Fig. 11–1. The use of a mirror will seem to put either the camera or the subject in a different position, whichever seems most logical. In this case it is the former.

for hockey at Boston Garden had to be so close to the press box that a shot of the commentator was not possible. To solve this problem, the staff installed a mirror in a spot where the commentator was visible and gave the camera a more advantageous apparent position. The mirror shown in Fig. 11-2 is on a swivel so that it can be set at any angle.

Figure 11-3 illustrates some other methods of using the mirror for the effect of a top shot. A single mirror between camera and subject will give the camera a high-angle shot, but the image will be upside down. This can then be righted by the use of an image-inverter prism (*b*) or by the use of another mirror (*c*).

Fig. 11–2. When the camera can't see the subject directly, a mirror can make it possible. (WNAC-TV, Boston.)

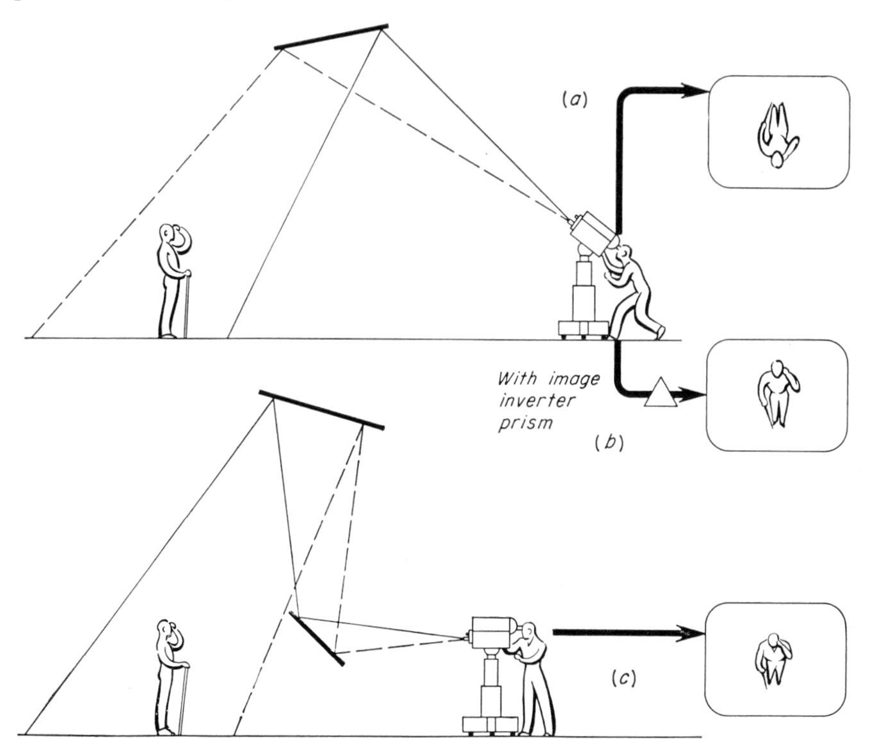

Fig. 11–3. Some other methods of using an overhead mirror for a top shot. (*a*) Single mirror, (*b*) single mirror with image inverter, (*c*) two mirrors.

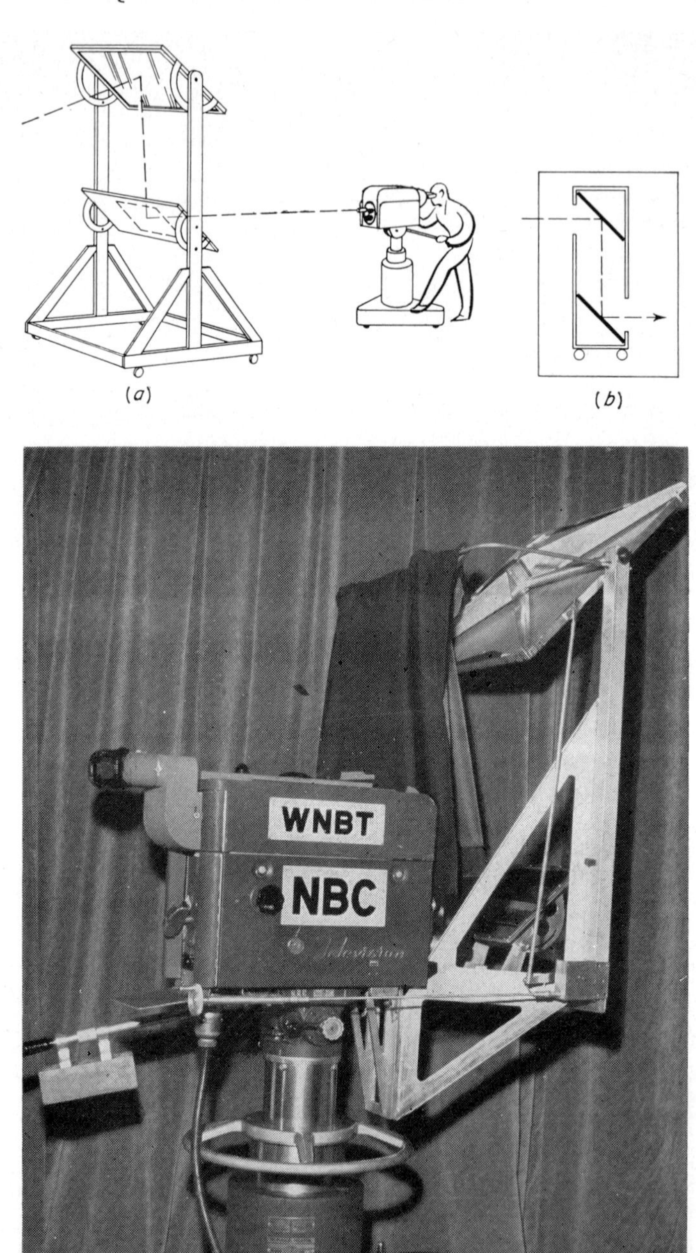

Fig. 11–4. Studio periscopes (*a*) for high-angle shot, (*b*) for low shot, (*c*) with adjustable top mirror attached to NBC camera.

Fig. 11–5. Above, top-shot periscope in use on CBS show. Below, mirror on floor in NBC's "Cameo Theatre" reflects top shot from mirror on ceiling.

THE PERISCOPE

The two-mirror method illustrated in (*c*) has been incorporated into large periscope devices where both mirrors are adjustable and the entire unit can roll quickly into place and be removed after it has been used (Fig. 11-4). In the top photograph in Fig. 11-5 the still photographer has pointed his camera into the lower mirror of such a pair, showing the reflection of the larger mirror above and also, over the top of the small mirror, the actors as they appear from standard camera height. The lower photograph shows a different way of mounting the mirrors; the lower

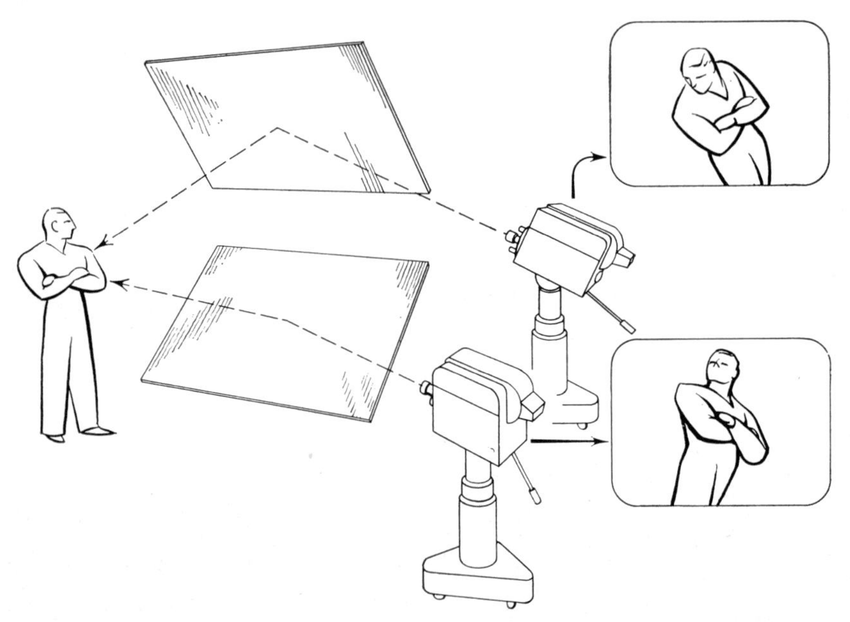

Fig. 11–6. When the mirror is placed to the side of the subject, with its surface out of the vertical plane, a canted image will result. See Chap. 4 for other ways of obtaining a canted shot.

mirror is flat on the floor, while the upper one is suspended from the ceiling. It will be noticed that a microphone-boom problem develops when a top shot is used. The camera cannot pan very far, either, without panning off the mirror, unless a very large mirror is used.

WPTZ in Philadelphia was probably the first station to use this device in a production of "The Medium." The effect of a high top shot down through a skylight was obtained, and the window mullion bars were made by sticking black tapes across the face of the upper mirror. Some studios have installed permanent mirrors on the ceiling above the permanent sets for kitchen shows, demonstrations, etc., so that a camera may use a top shot whenever desirable without special preparation. This particular use of the single mirror is quite often seen in television: a group of people stand in front of a fireplace, for example, looking up at the family portrait. Out of camera range above the portrait is a mirror; and a second camera, side by side with the first, shoots into this mirror, for a shot of the group from the portrait's point of view. The only trouble with this shot is that stage left and stage right are reversed. Whereas the girl was on the stage-right end, for example, in the mirror shot she appears to be stage left. When there is a group such as this in which left and right make a difference, the single mirror shot may look wrong. If only one person is involved or a subject in which the left and right elements are similar, this reversal will not be noticed.

REFLECTION EFFECTS

Sometimes a show will call for the effect of a reflection in a woodland pool. This is best achieved by a large mirror which is covered by a half inch or so of water. An electric fan can be used to ripple the surface of

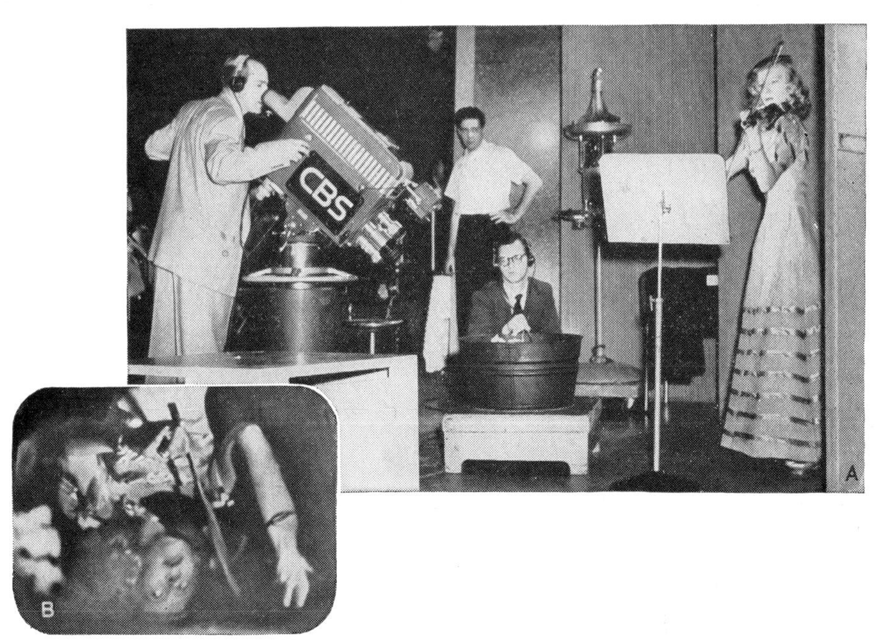

Fig. 11–7. Washtub used for reflection effect on Fred Waring show. (Courtesy of *Popular Science*.)

the water or, if this is too noisy, a stagehand, well off-camera, can disturb the water with the end of a stick. Sometimes water alone will create this effect without need for a mirror beneath it. Figure 11-7 shows an ordinary washtub of water being used for a reflection effect. The inside of the tub must be painted black in this case, however, or its image, somewhat out of focus, will be superimposed on that of the girl.

An old photo trick to create the illusion of reflection in water is to put a small mirror just beneath the camera lens. The drawing in Fig. 11-8 indicates the kind of shot which this trick will produce. The mirror must be held parallel to the optical axis of the lens and placed just as close to the center of the lens as possible without interfering with the picture or cutting out any light. If the lens is stopped down to a small

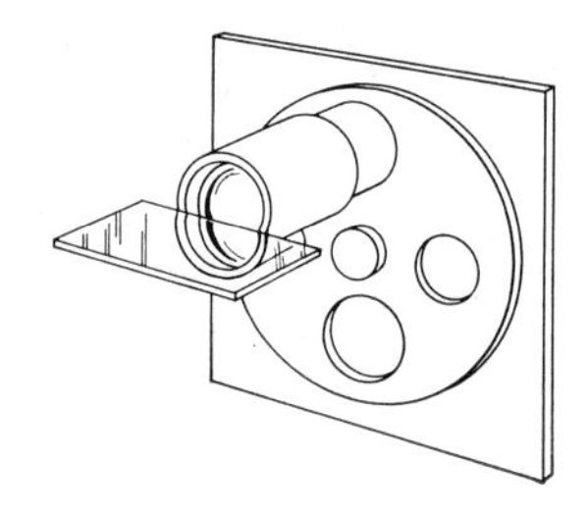

Fig. 11–8. Use of a small mirror beneath the camera lens for reflection effect.

opening, the mirror may be placed as shown in Fig. 11-8 without blocking out light.

SPLIT SCREEN AND WIPE

A large mirror has been used for the split-screen effect, set at a 45-degree angle to the camera and extending only halfway across the frame. Thus the camera sees half of the image by direct viewing, the other half reflected. Two ends of a phone conversation can be shown at once in this manner (Fig. 11-9).

The mirror will have a sharp or a soft edge, depending on how close it is to the camera. If the mirror is very close to the lens, it will be well out of focus and one scene will seem to dissolve into the other along a border area up the center of the screen. If the mirror is as close to the subject as possible, it will be more nearly in the plane of focus and the edge will be sharp.

The method of getting into and out of an effect smoothly is important to consider at the time the effect is being planned. In the case of the phone conversation the split screen might appear in a direct cut after a single shot of the person making the call. However, if the mirror or the camera moves, a wipe effect can be obtained. This can be very smooth: an actor picks up the phone and dials a number; then a wipe begins at the opposite side of the screen and moves in far enough to reveal the party at the other end of the line as he answers the phone.

The mirror may be put on tracks and effect the wipe by sliding into the scene. This requires accurate tracks, however, both at the top and at the bottom. The mirror must be held solidly and kept moving in exactly the same plane. If it should tilt ever so slightly, the reflected image would ride up or down on the screen. Sliding a mirror can be done more easily when it is small and light, although the smaller the size of the mirror (and the nearer to the camera), the greater the accuracy of movement which is required (smaller irregularities are enlarged on the screen).

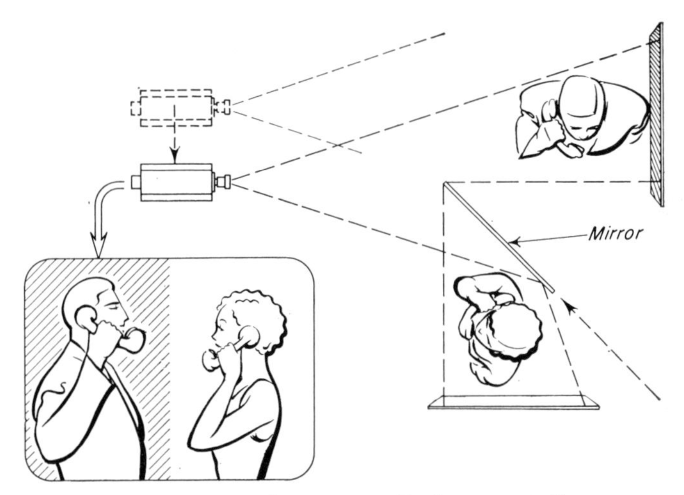

Fig. 11–9. Split-screen effect done by a mirror. Dash arrows indicate two methods of wiping in the reflected image: trucking the camera and sliding the mirror.

SUPERIMPOSURES AND GHOSTS

A superimposure effect is the appearance of two images on the screen at once. To do this optically with only one camera, the camera must see two things at once and in the same place. A plain sheet of glass will permit this, since it will both transmit the image of the scene behind it and reflect a scene which is to the side. Reflections from glass in windows or picture frames are often a problem on the TV set; but in this instance the mirror property of clear glass is put to good use. This is the method of the old "Pepper's ghosts" illusion, known almost as far back as the manufacture of plate glass. The real actors were seen on Pepper's stage through the glass; the ghosts were reflected from the wings (Fig. 11-10).

This method of producing ghosts is used frequently in motion-picture production because the final effect can be watched and the coordination between live actor and ghost can be accurately set during rehearsal. It has one big advantage for television, which is that the camera can move freely without changing the relationship of live actor to ghost. As long as the positions of the actors and the glass stay the same, it does not matter from what angle the effect is viewed. The usual method of producing ghosts on television requires the superimposing of two cameras. Whereas this is much simpler than installing a large sheet of plate glass, both cameras must be motionless during the superimposure. If either

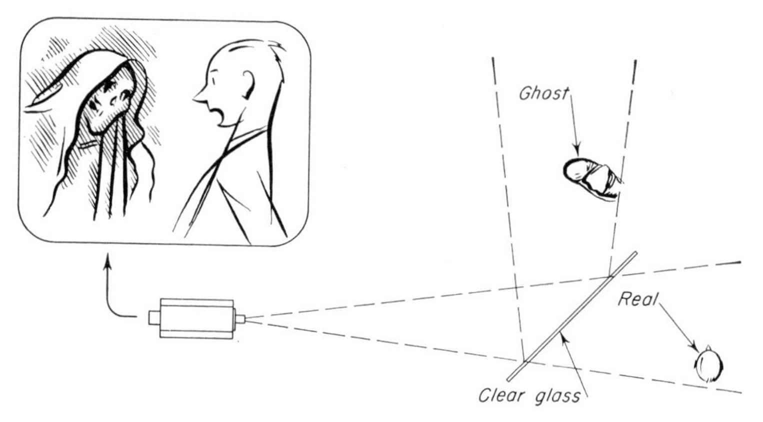

Fig. 11–10. "Pepper's ghosts" illusion—reflection from sheet of glass.

camera should move, an unnatural floating effect of the ghost is seen which can easily spoil the illusion.

If the large sheet of plate glass is impractical, a small sheet of glass closer to the camera can accomplish the same purpose. This can be mounted either in an effects box on the front of the camera or on a floor stand separate from the camera itself. Lining up the camera on the shot is greatly simplified if the glass is separate from the camera; if the two are connected, the actual position of the camera itself will determine the relationship of live actor to ghost and this position may take considerable time to find. Also if the glass is attached to the camera, the camera must be absolutely rigid throughout the effect.

The effect of sliding the mirror to produce a wipe can be applied here. If the glass which is reflecting the ghost is slid away (and kept accurately in the same plane), the ghost will be wiped out of the shot. If the glass is moved from its original plane, hinged up or swung out like a door, the ghost will be seen to move bodily or float within the scene. This can be useful if the movement is smoothly controlled.

A sheet of glass at a 45-degree angle to the camera will reflect only about 15 per cent of the light from the ghost. Of the light from the transmitted scene about 85 per cent will reach the camera through the glass, a similar 15 per cent having been reflected off the back side. The reflected ghost, therefore, must be very brightly lighted in comparison with the transmitted scene in which he is to appear, or he will be only faintly visible.

TRANSPARENT MIRRORS

A more even balance between transmitted and reflected light can be obtained with a transparent mirror. This is a standard item, available from glass manufacturers, but expensive in comparison with ordinary mirrors. It is sometimes called a half-silvered mirror.

Transparent mirrors have sometimes been called "one-way glass." This is a confusing term and leads people to believe that there is something about the glass which prevents light from going through in one direction while allowing it to pass in the opposite direction. This is entirely untrue. When such glass is installed in the police line-up, in hospital observation wards, or for photography with a concealed camera, the person under observation sees only a mirror because all the light is on his side of the glass. The observer on the other side remains hidden as long as he remains in the dark. If the lights should change and the lighted room become dark and the dark room lighted, then the erstwhile observer would find himself revealed to the person he was spying on, while he himself could see only an ordinary mirror.

The transparent mirror has found valuable use in television in the construction of multi-stage balops or shadow-box devices for the handling of graphic materials on the studio floor. Control of lights on two or more stages, in the manner of the telop (Fig. 10-11), will make optical dissolves, wipes, and superimpositions possible through the use of only one camera. The various types of shadow boxes utilizing these mirrors will be described in a later part of this chapter.

PROPERTIES OF MIRRORS

There are two laws of reflection which govern the action of mirrors. The second law is the more familiar and can be explained more easily before the first. It states that the angle of incidence is equal to the angle of reflection.

This means simply that a ray of light bounces off from the mirror surface at the same angle that it came in from. The angle is measured between the ray of light and the normal (perpendicular) to the mirror surface (Fig. 11-11). Instead of speaking of a ray of light, we can apply this rule to the line of sight from the camera to the object. By changing the angle of a mirror in front of the camera, the camera will be able to see in different directions (Fig. 11-12). Swinging the mirror during the shot will give the effect of panning the camera. Notice how more mirror is necessary when the camera shoots into it at a flat angle

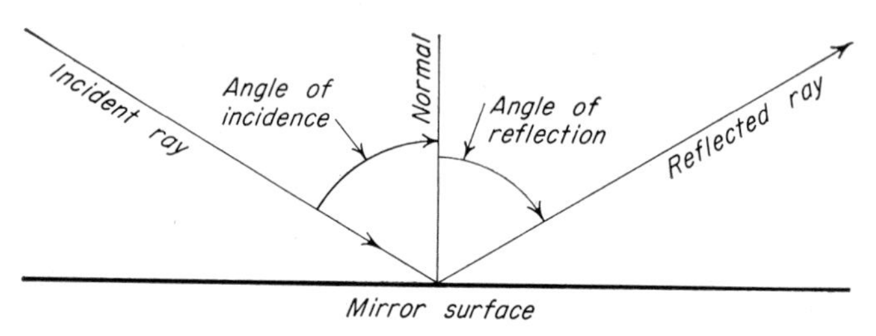

Fig. 11–11. The second law of reflection: Angle of incidence equals angle of reflection.

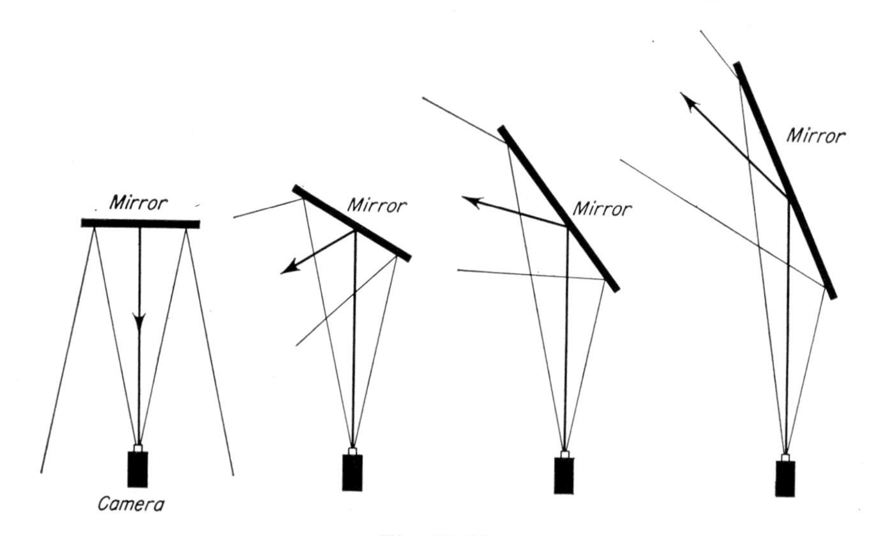

Fig. 11–12

The first law of reflection states that the incident ray, the reflected ray, and the normal to the surface lie in the same plane. There is a symmetrical triangle formed by the imaginary lines between camera, mirror, and subject; and the normal to the mirror surface bisects this triangle. Figure 11-13 applies this to the tilted mirror, which is used for the canted-camera effect. It explains why the image is low when the mirror is tilted back and high when it is tilted forward.

In shooting a picture through a mirror, the cameraman *does not focus on the mirror.* A plane mirror gives an illusion of position; it makes the

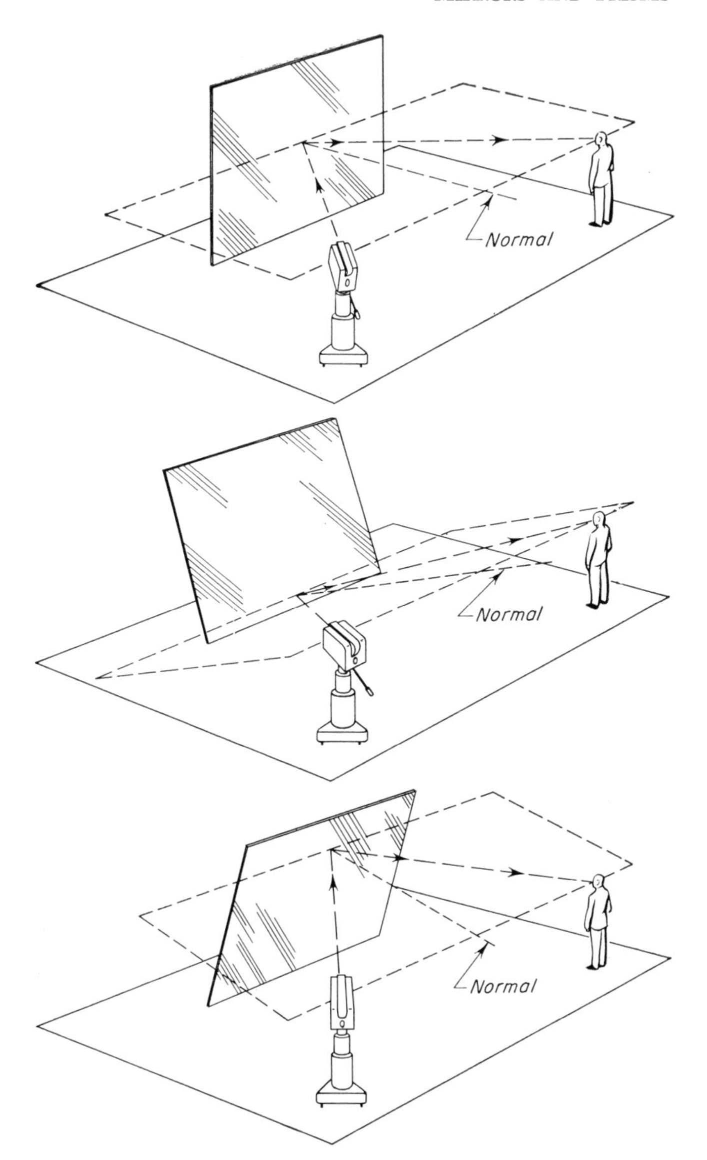

Fig. 11–13. The first law of reflection: The incident ray, the reflected ray, and the normal to the surface lie in the same plane.

subject seem to be in a different place from where it is. It does not bring it closer. The mirror is intermediate between camera and subject. If you focus on the mirror, the subject will very likely become fuzzy. All that will be seen clearly will be the dust and fingerprints on the mirror surface. Focus the camera always on the subject, just as though there were no mirror. The distance from subject to camera is the total distance the light must travel to get there.

IMAGE INVERSION

There are three methods of turning a picture upside down: the mirror, the prism, and the electronic method of reversing the scanning in the camera. Naturally they can each be used to erect an image. If a mirror, placed where it will give a desired camera angle, also gives the undesired effect of image inversion, this can be corrected by any one of the above methods. The use of a second mirror has been described. An image-inverter prism is in many cases simpler to use.

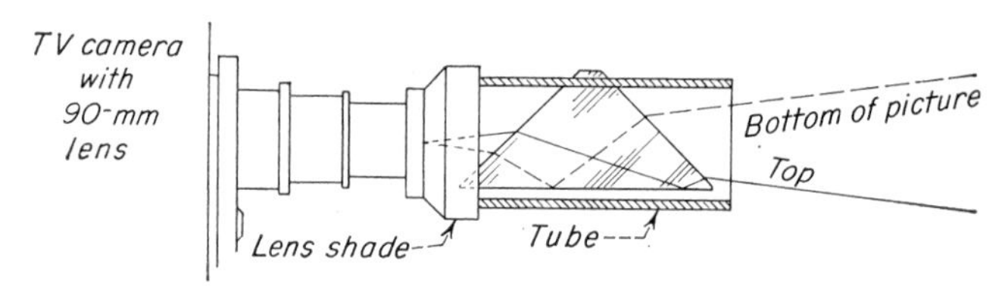

Fig. 11–14. Image-inverter prism.

The image-inverter prism is a right-angle prism of a rather large size, a "porro prism" or a "dove prism" (Fig. 11-14). It can be mounted in a tube which is fastened to a regular lens shade. The lens shade carrying the prism is screwed onto the front of the lens when the effect is wanted and does not interfere with the functioning of the other lenses on the camera.

If this prism is placed on its side and the camera directed toward a scene, an erect image will result, but reversed from left to right just like the image in a single mirror. As the prism is rotated, the scene rotates in the camera's view, until with 90 degrees of prism rotation the scene has completely turned around (180 degrees) and is upside down. It is still seen in mirror image, however, just as it would look in a single mirror held above or below the camera.

The rotation of this prism can be accomplished by hand, either by the cameraman himself (if he locks his camera controls so that he can move around to the front of the camera) or by an assistant. The engineering department at NBC devised a better means of controlling the rotation of effects on the front of the lens by the method used in controlling the Zoomar lens, a rod through the center of the camera turret shaft (Fig. 11-15). A simple gear system on the prism mount makes it possible for the cameraman to rotate a small crank at the back of the camera and turn the prism around with quite an even motion. Other prism effects, which are described later, can also be used with this rotating device.

The show "Tom Corbett, Space Cadet" put the image inverter to very good use. When the space ship had suffered the failure of its artificial gravity apparatus, the crew had fun for a few installments walk-

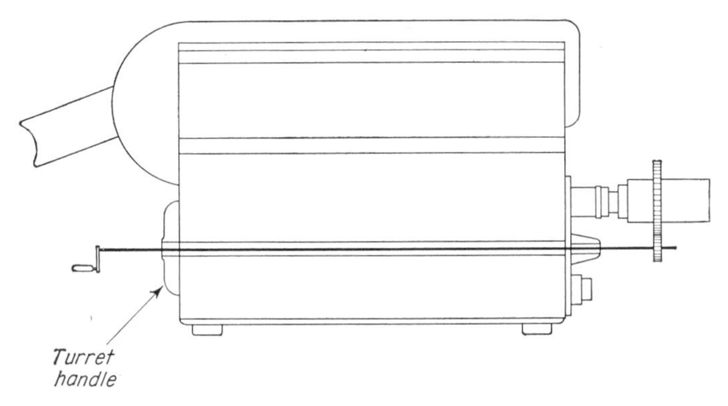

Fig. 11–15. Control for rotating prism from rear of camera.

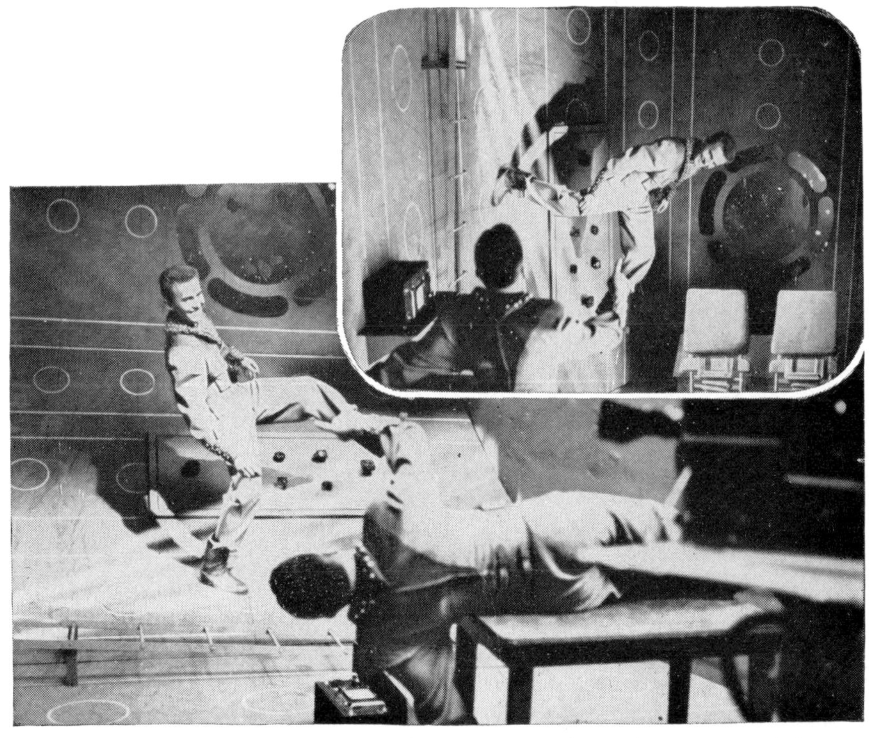

Fig. 11–16. Example from "Tom Corbett, Space Cadet," showing use of image-inverter prism to give illusion of actor walking on wall.

ing on the walls and ceiling. A special set was built for this effect, lying on its side, so that the actors could really walk on the wall. Then the set was erected by means of the prism. An actor in the foreground (Fig. 11-16) who was supposed to be standing vertically and talking to the man on the wall was placed horizontally on a table in front of the camera. The use of the image inverter reversed left and right, and since this was undesirable, electronic scanning reversal was employed to correct for it. This meant, oddly enough, that the prism was first set up to give an inverted picture; then this was righted by scanning reversal so that a straight shot resulted, everything right side up and right way to. Then 45 degrees of rotation of the prism produced the sideways shot.

If a prism of the type described is not available, the same thing can be done by a series of small mirrors. Simple image inversion can be accomplished by three mirrors as shown in Fig. 11-17. If these are mounted so

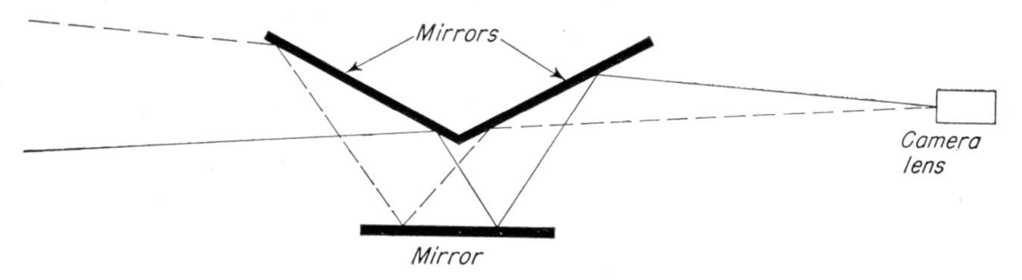

Fig. 11–17. Simple image inverter made with three mirrors.

that they may be rotated, the image can be placed at any angle or rotated just as it may with a prism.

If four mirrors are used, the image is fully corrected just as it is when seen through two mirrors. The four-mirror system is thus superior in this respect since both the prism and the three-mirror method reverse the image and require the cameraman to pan or tilt in the opposite direction from that he is used to. The four-mirror image inverter was first used on television in 1947 by Karl Weger at WPTZ on the Ted Steele "Piano Patter" show. The same man is responsible for the three-mirror method and is credited with the later introduction of the image-inverter prism into general use. The mirrors, each only 2½ by 3 inches in size, are arranged in the manner shown in Fig. 11-18. When rotated about the proper axis, which is also shown, the image will turn through twice the angle of rotation of the mirror assembly (similar to the prism). The mirror system is inferior to the prism because of the greater light loss from all the reflecting surfaces, but it has one advantage. Four mirrors, like two mirrors, correct the image, and a reversed picture does not result.

Two right-angle prisms instead of two pairs of mirrors can be used. This is the principle used in the erecting systems of prism binoculars.

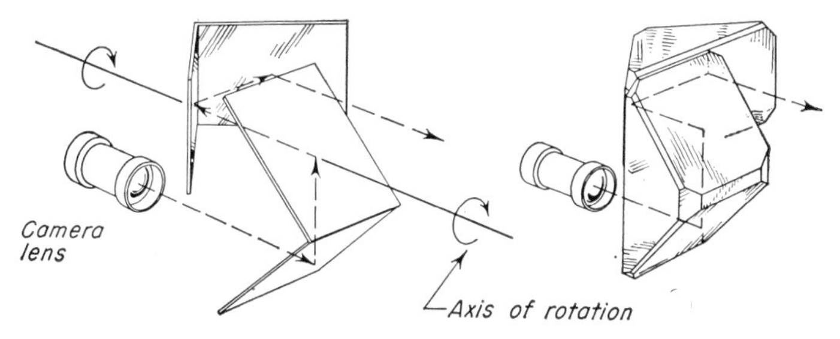

Fig. 11–18. Image inverter made with four mirrors. Right, with porro prisms.

Fig. 11–19. Typical canted shots for dynamic composition obtained with image inverter.

Two pairs of right-angle prisms used in this way are called porro prisms. The only difference is that if prisms are used, a rotation of the system will not rotate the image—the picture remains inverted. The image can be righted only if one of the prisms is rotated against the other.

MULTIPLE-IMAGE PRISMS

A type of prism which produces a multiple image has been used in motion-picture work for many years and has made its way into television.

Effects such as that in Fig. 11-20 can be obtained with almost any number of images if the proper prisms are set before the lens.

If these prisms are rotated, the images will revolve around each other, like a side view of the seats on a ferris wheel, remaining upright all the

Fig. 11–20. Camart Optical Effects Unit attachment for multiple-image prisms.

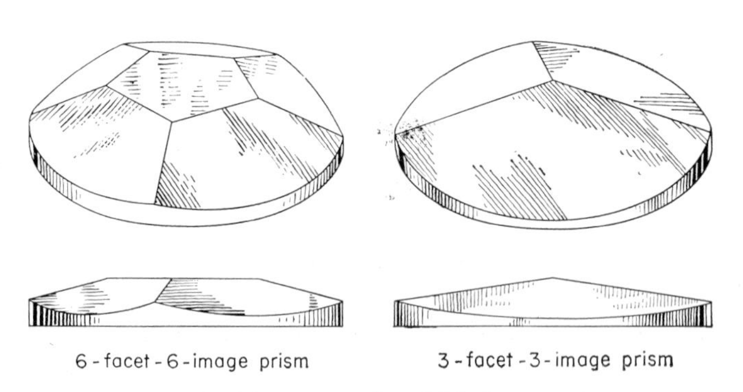

Fig. 11–21. Two types of multiple-image prisms.

time. The NBC rotating-effects gadget (Fig. 11-15) will take multiple-image prisms and rotate them smoothly from the rear of the camera. The prisms involved in these devices are relatively simple pieces of glass on the front surface of which several facets have been ground (Fig. 11-21). The number of facets determines the number of images.

THE KALEIDOSCOPE

One of the special uses of mirrors or prisms is in the design of a kaleidoscope. The kaleidoscope, as anyone will remember who has ever taken a child's toy kaleidoscope apart, is essentially a pair of mirrors between which the eye looks at a subject. Since the subject is reflected and re-reflected in these mirrors, a beautiful, symmetrical pattern of many radiating segments is seen.

The first projection kaleidoscope was designed by Bill Eddy at NBC in 1939 and was used to project moving patterns on the film-pickup camera. Patterns were drawn or photographed onto a strip of 35-mm film which was then driven horizontally through the picture at a steady rate. A long, V-shaped prism was used (rather than two mirrors). The pattern was centered, not in the middle of the screen like a rosette, but at the bottom of the screen, so that only a half-rose pattern like a rising sun was seen. Highly imaginative production techniques were used, and the patterns were synchronized to music and were even used as semiabstract transitions between scenes in dramatic productions.

Bill Eddy has since marketed a simplified version of this kaleidoscope through his Television Associates Inc. This device uses a circular disk to carry the pattern, turning so slowly that it takes three minutes for a complete rotation. There can be no actual synchronizing with music, however, but the eye is quick to note chance relationships between picture and sound, and with almost any music the viewer gets an illusion of synchrony although none is planned.

A kaleidoscope was used successfully on one occasion as a decorative *lei* to surround a singer on the "Garroway at Large" program. Built by the cameraman, John Casagrande, this kaleidoscope was fastened to the lens of the television camera, which then was focused on the far end of the kaleidoscope (a few inches from the lens), and pointed toward some suitable source of illumination for transmitted light. Since a full rosette was wanted in this case, the apex of the two mirrors had to be centered in the frame. This meant that the kaleidoscope had to be mounted on the camera at an angle (Fig. 11-22). The center of the rosette was made black, and a small close-up of the singer was superimposed over this area from another camera. The changing patterns originated from the traditional bits of glass, which tumbled about as the kaleidoscope was rotated.

WPTZ in Philadelphia fascinated viewers watching musical shows and interludes by a device they simply called the "whirligig." Accurately synchronized to whatever music was played, a wiggling, jumping pattern in a rosette shape made endless fascinating gyrations on the screen. A conspiracy of silence kept viewers (and the staff of other Philadelphia stations) in a quandary for months. Spies sent into the WPTZ studio on trumped-up business returned with no information on the new invention, having seen nothing but the usual studio equipment: cameras, mike boom, and test oscilloscope standing in the corner. Had they examined the oscilloscope a little closer, however, they would have noticed that

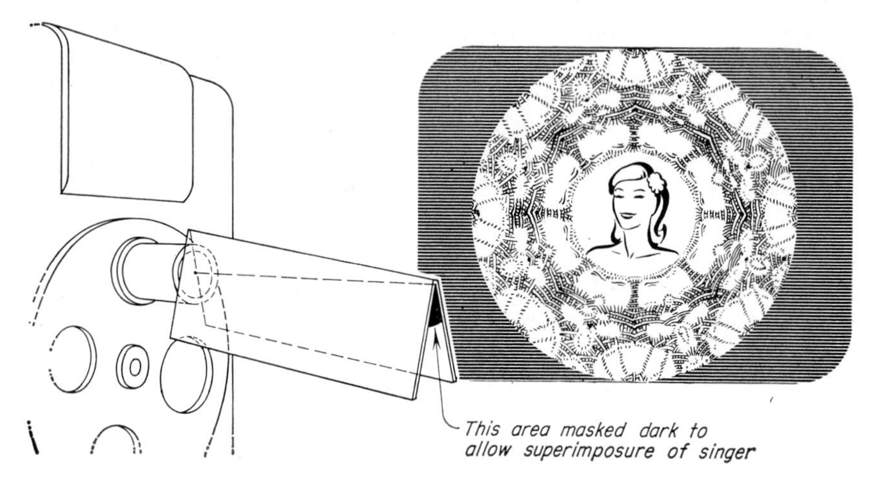

Fig. 11–22. Kaleidoscope used by NBC on "Garroway at Large."

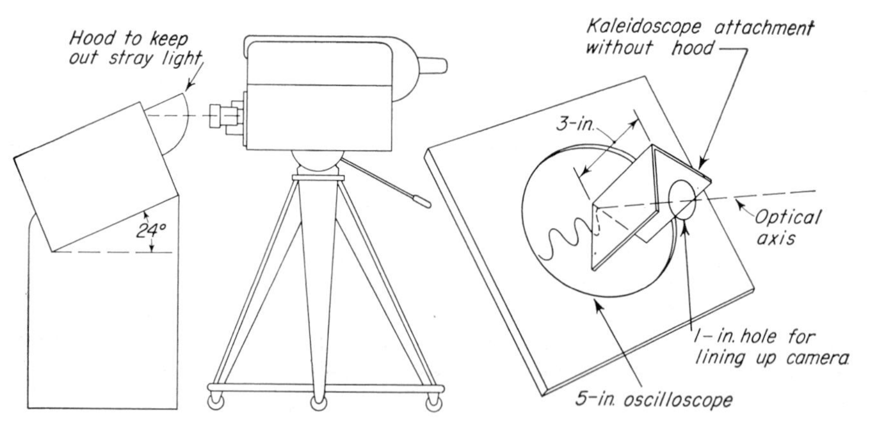

Fig. 11–23. WPTZ Whirligig.

Karl Weger had been at work and had built a kaleidoscope onto the front of it (Fig. 11-23).

An oscilloscope, as the reader may already know, is a testing instrument which when fed by an audio signal transforms the sound vibrations into a visible wave pattern which is seen as a green wiggling and jumping line. The camera, looking between the mirrors of Weger's kaleidoscope, saw only a portion of this line multiplied into a rosette. Since the television audio line was fed to the oscilloscope, the moving line synchronized perfectly with the music because it *was* the music, in a visual form.

A large-size kaleidoscope may be made of two pieces of ordinary mirror 3 or 4 feet long and perhaps 14 or 18 inches wide. There is nothing critical about the dimensions. Face the two mirrors together and simply tape them tightly together along one side. The mirrors can then be opened like a book; the extent to which they are opened will determine the number of segments in the resulting rosette. Twelve is a pleasing number; for this result the mirrors will have to face each other with a 30-degree angle between them (360 divided by 12). A slightly larger angle will result in eleven segments, a smaller angle in thirteen, etc.

This type of kaleidoscope is very useful for many purposes, since any object, prop, graphic, or the hands of the operator himself can be used to create fascinating geometrical designs which can be manipulated to music. The mirrors are solidly mounted so the camera lens can look into them as nearly as possible from the apex of the two mirrors. Fabrics of various kinds, open lace-work of any material, and especially leaves, ferns, and other natural objects create the best effects. Light may be used from the front or from behind the objects. Experimentation will unfold endless possibilities for the visualization of music. For example, a typical three-minute recording can be accompanied by a fascinating three minutes of changing visual patterns simply by moving the album cover about in contact with the ends of the kaleidoscope mirrors.

Whatever is to be used in a kaleidoscope must be in contact with the ends of the mirrors, or the reflected pattern will not be symmetrical. The right-hand mirror will reflect a different scene (to the left, beyond the kaleidoscope) from the scene reflected by the left-hand mirror. Thus a kaleidoscope cannot be used on a studio scene and produce a symmetrical pattern. However, if the studio scene is first fed to a studio monitor and the kaleidoscope is brought into contact with the monitor screen, a rosette pattern can be created from any live subject. The protective glass must be removed from the monitor so the mirrors can make contact with the TV image. Camera 1 can then concentrate on a picture of the hands of a pianist, for example. The studio monitor is fed camera 1's picture only instead of the program line. Then camera 2 lines up on the monitor through the kaleidoscope mirrors and picks up a moving, dancing rosette changing in perfect rhythm with the music. Arms, shoulders, any part of the performer that is moving will thus produce a rhythmically matched visualization for the music.

If kaleidoscopes for this purpose are made from metal instead of glass (photographer's ferrotype plates are ideal), a clearer reflection will result. Ordinary glass mirrors give a double image which is more noticeable when it is small. Front-surface mirrors are used in all devices mentioned above when the mirrors are less than about 18 inches wide.

12

Composite Shots and the Illusion of Space

Television studios are usually much too small for the kind of production they are expected to provide. Quarters are badly cramped where cameras should have free play and flexibility, and sets often look small and confined when they should have a more spacious look. There are

Fig. 12–1*a*. Set by James MacNaughton for a production of the "Paul Whiteman Revue." This high-angle photo reveals painted perspective in several areas of the set. (Courtesy of *Life Magazine* and copyright by *Time, Inc.*)

Fig. 12–1*b*, *c*. Camera-level photos of same set show painted perspective from the proper point to give the intended illusion.

some productions, however, of such gigantic scope that even the largest television studios do not provide enough space. In these productions the designer often creates the feeling of endless space. Backgrounds go back to infinity; the great outdoors is reconstructed in the studio.

James MacNaughton and Bob Bright consistently achieved these effects in designing the "Paul Whiteman Revue." Realistic or stylized, the backgrounds were always vast, giving a feeling of space almost unlimited. The designers of this production achieved their great feeling of space with properly designed sets and painted backdrops and did not resort to the "trick" effects of process photography (Fig. 12-1). Smaller studios, however, will have greater need for these illusions, all of which have found frequent use in motion-picture production.

ARTIFICIAL PERSPECTIVE

The tricks that the artist uses to create the illusion of depth in a two-dimensional drawing are centuries old. They constitute the art of drawing in perspective. When perspective painting was added to the stage, it had to be combined with three-dimensional actors, props, and scenery. No matter how well the artist created his illusion of depth on the two-dimensional backdrop, if it did not fuse with the three-dimensional elements of the stage it was not a successful illusion.

Depth on a painted backdrop was never wholly successful in the theater because the audience had to view it from so many different angles. Designers compromised, of course, and gave the better-paying patrons in the orchestra seats the benefit of a good background illusion, banking on the "willing suspension of disbelief" to keep the balcony customers happy.

Theoretically, the perfect fusion of foreground and background design is possible for only one spectator position. An exception is the diorama and habitat groups at the natural-history museums, which create wonderful depth illusions for a great range of viewing positions in front of the glass. One advantage that the diorama has over the stage is that it can have a curved backdrop, while the stage drop must be flat. Furthermore, the natural-history exhibit will rarely attempt architectural subjects where straight lines in the foreground must match with lines on the background painting.

For a foreground construction and a background painting to combine and give the illusion of a single scene, *the perspective of the two must match.* A simple example is a road running from the apron back to the drop and continuing on the drop far into the distance (Fig. 12-2). The viewpoint must be right, or the perspective will not match. First of all the height from which the real road is seen and the height from which the painted road is depicted must be the same. The eye level of the painting must be at the eye level of the observer. Since the horizon is always at eye level, we can put this another way and say: The horizon of the picture must coincide with the real horizon. Since for the people in the top balcony eye and horizon level is well above the proscenium arch and for those in the pit it is about stage level, it is never possible to give everyone a perfect match in perspective.

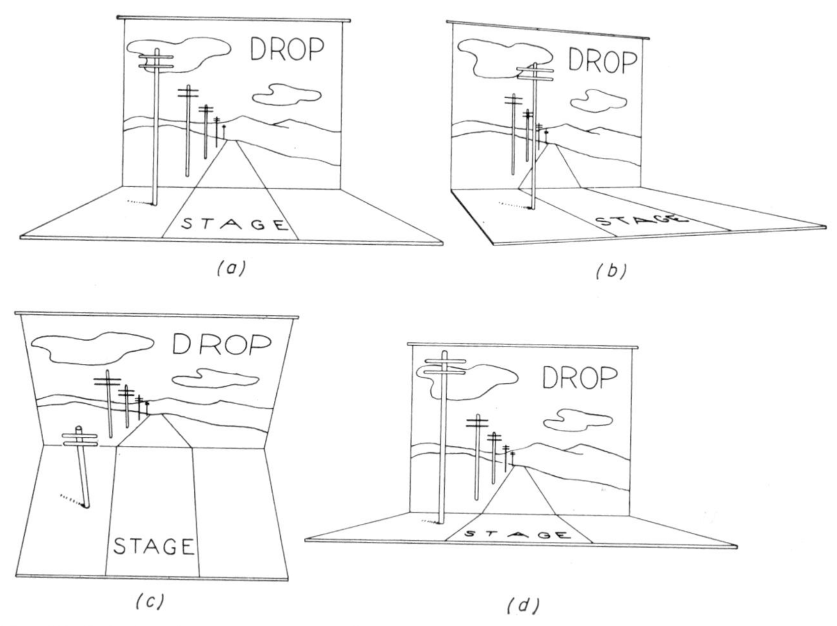

Fig. 12–2. Painted perspective in the drop will match the actual three-dimensional construction on the stage only if seen from the correct point of view (*a*). In (*b*) the illusion is lost because the viewpoint is too far to the side; in (*c*) too high; in (*d*) too low.

When only one camera is involved instead of an auditorium full of spectators, the problem is greatly reduced. The horizon line on the painting is drawn at camera height. The camera may not move very far, however, without spoiling something. Other cameras from different viewpoints cannot be used except for such close shots that the matching between foreground and background does not show.

These considerations are most critical only when architectual forms with straight lines are used. If there are no straight lines or architectural planes which must carry through, the perspective can fail to match exactly without being noticed.

PAINTING THE FLOOR WITH ARTIFICIAL PERSPECTIVE

Since the floor of a television studio is seen a great deal, especially in long shots, it constitutes background for the shots just as much as the vertical flats and drops. Only in the larger studios, usually, is there enough budget to afford floor painting, or enough time when the studio is not in use. Some studios have laid ground cloths to protect the original floor surface; others have laid sheets of masonite for a painting surface. In either case the covering cannot be removed or replaced

Fig. 12–3. MacNaughton-decorated floor.

between rehearsals, and the floor painting must remain after the show until the floor is washed or a new design is put on it.

The significant thing about floor painting, however, is the opportunity for forced perspective. James MacNaughton, dean of television-set designers, has been the foremost proponent of this technique. His floor designs usually contain straight lines running from the camera into the "distance," or they may contain design figures which by virtue of their change in size will seem to dwindle in the distance.

It is usually quite difficult to make a perfect match between floor and drop; most designers provide a ground row to disguise the break, or the change in perspective, between the two. This allows a greater freedom of camera position and movement, but there are still certain limitations. The perspective can be painted for only one camera position. Of course, cameras may be used freely all over such a set in any desired direction as long as they do not show the floor. But shooting backward or across the design will make the floor look very peculiar. It may even stop looking like a floor and take on the appearance of a wall instead (Fig. 12-4).

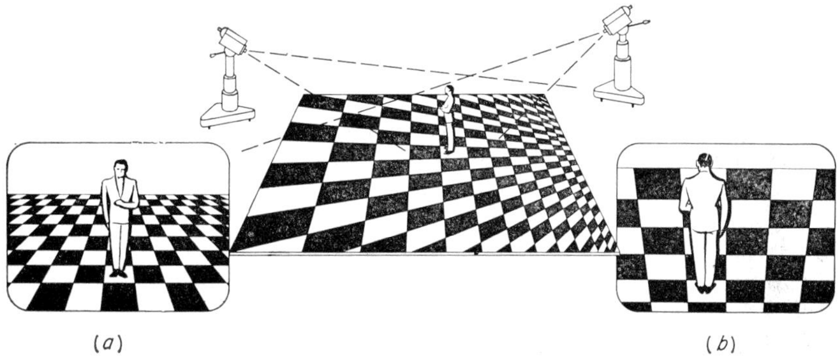

Fig. 12–4. Forced perspective seen from correct angle of view (*a*) and from the opposite angle (*b*).

Fig. 12–5. The illusion of space obtained by building sets in forced perspective.

THE GLASS SHOT AND THE CUTOUT

The glass-shot method of creating the illusion of space is very old in the motion-picture art. It consists in painting the background of the shot on a sheet of glass in front of the camera instead of on flats or drops behind the actors. The camera takes in the glass painting, shooting directly through certain clear areas of the glass to photograph live action in the distance which appears to be in the foreground of the finished shot. This method was widely used in photographing large exterior sets and often saved greatly in construction costs, especially when the large parts of buildings could be painted on the glass. A similar method made use of a cutout board instead of a sheet of glass. The portions through which live action was to be seen were open instead of being clear glass. It must be noted, of course, that foreground action (Fig. 12-6) cannot appear *in front of* background painting. If backgrounds are to be seen behind the actors, such as the doorway and steps in Fig. 12-6, a portion of a real background must be built and made to blend into the glass painting.

Fig. 12–6. Motion-picture glass shot.

An accurate match between foreground live action and background glass painting can be achieved only by very careful camera placement. A great deal of time was always consumed by the motion-picture camera crew in getting their camera and painting adjusted correctly. This careful adjustment is necessary only when actual backgrounds must blend with painted backgrounds on the glass. If the glass should contain *foreground* elements only (trees, archways, a theater proscenium, etc.), there would be no such critical problem of camera placement.

Fig. 12–7. NBC gobo, a two-dimensional cutout containing foreground elements of the composite scene.

It is largely in the creation of foreground rather than background that the glass shot has been used in television, and it is usually the cutout method rather than the glass sheet that is used. The use of the technique for foregrounds eliminates the necessity for exact camera placement and makes it possible to focus a television camera quickly on the effect. The use of the cutout instead of the glass eliminates the hazard of reflections, which is always present when the position of camera or lights may vary slightly between rehearsal and air time. NBC has standardized on 20- by 30-inch and 30- by 40-inch cutout boards (called "goboes") which are mounted in front of the camera on simple H stands (Fig. 12-7). An effect is sometimes wanted where the camera dollies in toward the gobo until the cutout area fills the screen and the gobo has disappeared. This might be used for the effect of dollying through an archway or through a door. As the camera moves forward, the area of live action seen through the cutout widens very rapidly. If the live portion is supposed to look like a two-dimensioinal picture on the cover of a magazine or song sheet, the camera may not dolly forward without immediately revealing that the two elements of the picture are in separate planes. A zoom lens, however, will allow the camera to move into a close-up of the "picture" without widening the field of view through the cutout.

After the camera has moved up to a close-up of the cutout area (either by dollying or by zooming), it is often desirable to clear the gobo so that the camera will have freedom of movement. This can be done easily if the gobo is made in two parts and supported by two H stands, one on either side. It is then necessary only for the stagehands to pull the two stands away, and the camera is free.

Karl Weger invented a derivation of the glass shot which he called "Studio Z." It eliminates any depth-of-focus problems and at the same time permits the camera to dolly forward and back freely without the

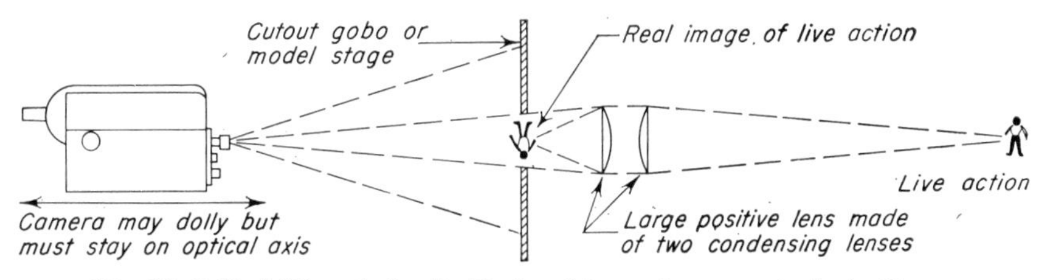

Fig. 12–8. Karl Weger's Studio Z, the ultimate in matte (gobo) effects.

difference in size between the live action and the gobo painting becoming obvious. In this method the live action is imaged onto the same plane as the gobo by means of a positive lens (a pair of large condensing lenses) behind the opening (Fig. 12-8). The lens behind the cutout has its own depth of focus, and there is a certain limitation involved here, but as far as the television camera is concerned, it need focus only on the gobo and the live action will also be sharp. Of course, the additional lens must be large enough to cover completely whatever door, arch, or window opening is provided in the cutout.

The image formed by a positive lens is inverted, as shown in Fig. 12-8. When this device was used on WPTZ in Philadelphia, the gobo was also turned upside down, and then both were erected by means of an image-inverter prism on the camera lens.

A better method is suggested by the inventor in his patent disclosure, which utilizes a system of three mirrors (see Fig. 11-17) placed behind the special large lens, between it and the live subject. This will allow the gobo to remain upright and simply erects the image of the live action.

THE MATTE SHOT

Matting is a method of making areas of the picture black. It involves placing a shutter of the correct shape in front of or behind the lens to block off the desired areas.

This is often used in television to combine two portions of a scene so that they can be shown simultaneously on the same screen. A pitcher winding up, but watching out of the corner of his eye, is shown in fairly close shot in the upper corner of the screen, while a similarly close shot of the runner leading off first base is placed in the opposite corner.

Lens turret matting. The simplest way to matte out a portion of a shot is to turn the camera lens turret so that the lens is no longer directly in front of the tube. Part of the scene will then be cut off by the body of the lens turret and will appear black on the screen.

If the turret of one camera is off-set to the left and the turret of the other is off-set to the right, the black area of each picture will coincide

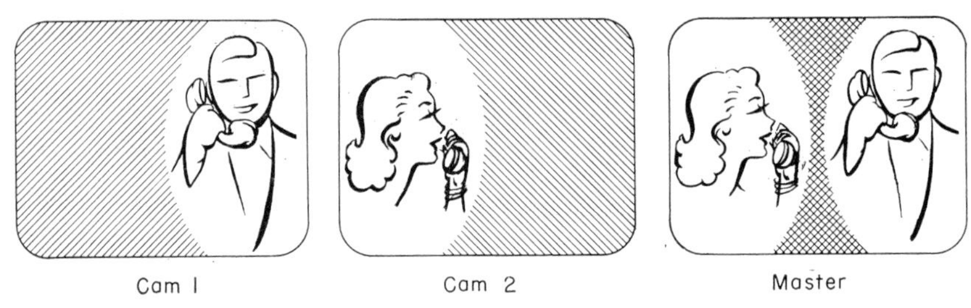

Fig. 12–9. Matting by off-setting the lens turret. The two cameras are superimposed for the composite effect shown at right as it is seen on the master monitor.

approximately with the picture area of the other and when the two are superimposed there will be no ghosting. The effect is not exactly a split screen, of course, because the edge of the black area is out of focus and soft and has a curved shape—oppositely curved in the two cameras so that it does not match (Fig. 12-9). A fuzzy strip of black or of overlapped pictures will be seen across the center of the screen. This is not necessarily a disadvantage, however; sometimes the area of demarcation is quite desirable.

The position of the tube in the television camera will make a difference in the split-screen effect. In the RCA camera the tube is centered, and the top lens is the taking lens. As the turret is turned, the direction of motion is an arc across the width of the picture. Thus an off-set position will produce a roughly vertical edge. The Du Mont camera, on the other hand, mounts the tube in the lower right-hand side, and the turret turns in an arc which goes diagonally across the end of the tube. An off-set turret will accordingly produce an edge which is roughly diagonal (Fig. 12-10).

The cameraman will find that as he turns the turret to an off-set position, the picture will move bodily off the screen. If he wants to keep the

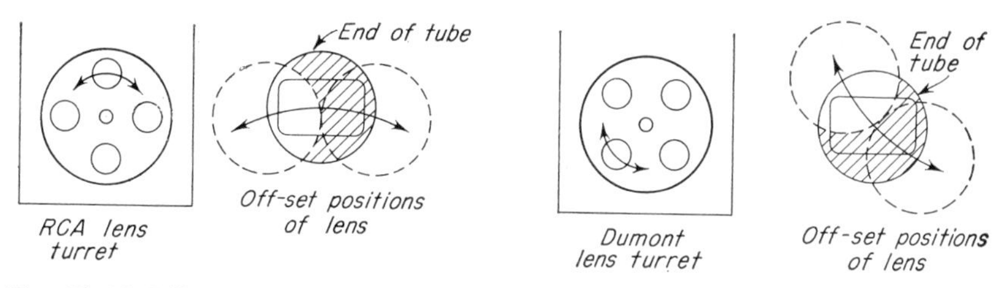

Fig. 12–10. Effect of off-setting the turret on two cameras with different positions of the taking lens.

subject in the same position in the screen, he will have to pan the camera as he turns the turret. This is difficult to do smoothly, but it produces a nice effect. As the actor picks up a phone, for instance, a dark area appears on the far side of the picture; and as it grows, the other camera, previously made ready with the opposite off-set, is dissolved in. The person answering the call on the other end of the line appears as he is picking up the phone. At the end of the call the reverse procedure can be followed. Both actors put their receivers down, the cameraman on the first camera turns his turret back and pans the camera to keep the subject stationary, and the second camera is simultaneously faded out.

A common method of making matte shots in motion pictures is to fix to the front of the camera a matte box in which cutout masks can be inserted. The matte box also serves as a sunshade over the lens and is used for a great variety of filters and diffusing materials which are a part of motion-picture photography (Fig. 12-11). Simple matte boxes have

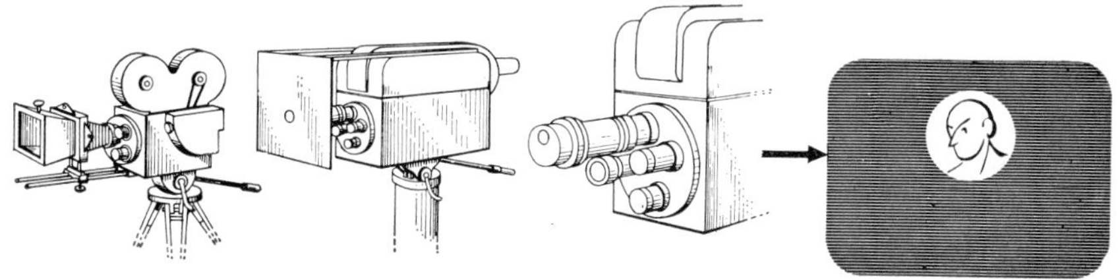

Fig. 12–11. Mattes attached to the camera.

been used on television cameras, but the large rotating turret with its long lenses makes it difficult to design a permanent matte box.

There are many kinds of mattes besides the simple half mask. A matte may take the form of a vignette, allowing the camera to show only a small circle of picture. This might be used for the old motion-picture vignette effect to show what the actor was thinking about, in the upper corner of the screen. The device has been so frequently revived in television that it has almost lost its corny flavor.

REAR PROJECTION

Much experimentation has been done in the use of rear projection in television. The process has great possibilities which, after the solution of a few basic problems are certain to be realized. Several new developments in screens and projection equipment have come out of the experimentation to date, innovations which may well find application in the motion-picture field as well. Whereas the prime purpose of rear projection is to create the illusion of space by producing a composite shot, the process has many other advantages and there are frequently other purposes behind its use, as the following sections indicate.

STILL BACKGROUNDS

Through the projection of slides, static background scenes of many different kinds are possible. Unless the background contains objects which naturally would be in motion, a slide will look as realistic as a motion picture. When motion pictures are projected on a large-size screen, the slightest weave or jump becomes noticeable. In the case of static scenes, slide projection is frequently preferable.

Rear projection of stills has been used to create the illusion of great depth or space (outdoor backgrounds which go far off into the distance) or interiors, such as those of cathedrals, which could not be constructed in the studio. The technique has also been used to create backgrounds which could as well have been built or painted, but would have cost a great deal more. Certain natural subjects, such as rocks and foliage, are very difficult to paint, and photographic backings must be used instead. Photomurals are quite expensive, especially when solidly mounted for use on a television set. The only cost for new backgrounds when rear projection is used, however, is the small transparent slide.

Sometimes a projected background need be only a few feet square, such as an exterior seen through a window. If such a projection is to play an important part in the story, however, it must look realistic and this requires that it be kept some distance behind the window frame. Different areas of the exterior scene will be revealed as the camera looks through the window from different angles, and movement of the camera will cause a realistic movement of the background scene behind the window frame. This will all be minimized if the backing is too close. Furthermore, if the camera takes close-ups at the window, the background will appear in close-up as well, unless it is considerably farther back. This applies to shooting against any "distant" background; if actors are to be seen in close-up, they must be far enough ahead of the backing so that distant objects will not look surprisingly close.

The perspective of background and foreground must match in a rear projection shot, or the effect will be unreal. This is the same problem that was described in connection with painted backdrops. The eye level of the background must be camera level (Fig. 12-12).

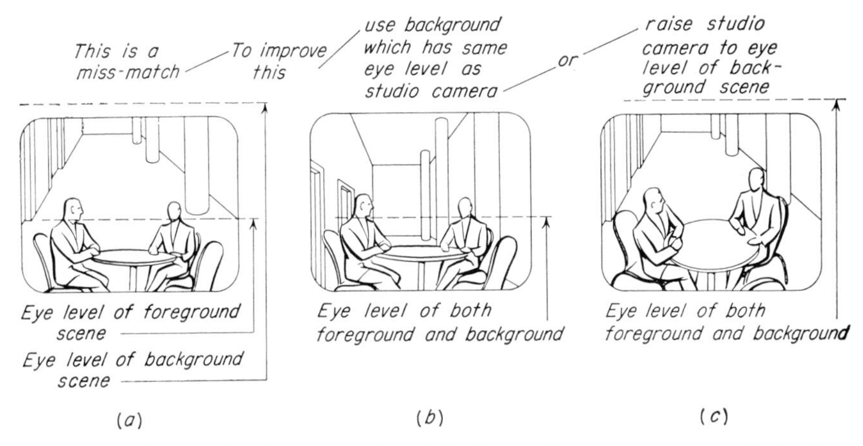

Fig. 12–12. Perspective in rear-projected background scenes must match the foreground. In (*a*) the two do not match; (*b*) and (*c*) indicate two solutions to the problem.

Movement in rear projection stills. A moving background can be produced with a long slide which is slid through the projector aperture. In the CBS show "Mr. I-magination," a background slide of trees and telephone poles was slid through the projector, and Paul Tripp's train appeared to be in motion. In many instances only a simple panoram motion is called for, and such a slide usually will serve the purpose better than a motion picture. Because the slide is larger than the motion-picture frame, it allows more light to reach the screen. A motor drive is necessary for these long slides, since irregularities in manual operation show up greatly exaggerated on the screen. The Trans-Lux projector incorporates this feature.

THEATRICAL EFFECTS PROJECTION

Effects projectors have been familiar equipment for many years in the theater (Fig. 12-13). A large circular slide is rotated through the projection opening, and a 2,000- or 3,000-watt spotlight provides the light source. Stage-lighting companies like Kliegl and Century in New York keep libraries of these effects slides for rental or purchase. It is possible to get anything from fleecy clouds to fire, smoke, and demons ascending out of hell (an effect which the Roxy Theatre used every year for their Halloween show). The slides are circular (about 2 feet in diameter), but the projector aperture is the standard 3¼- by 4-inch lantern-slide size. The slides are disks of mica, to withstand the heat, and designs are hand-painted on them in the type of paint that is used for frosting light globes. The turning mechanism, whether motor or clockwork, can be set

Fig. 12–13. Century effects machine. Circular effects slide rotates by motor drive. This particular projector will take a 1,500- to 2,000-watt bulb.

for a wide range of speeds. Effects projectors are used very often in the New York stations. Most cloud effects are produced with these machines, either by rear or by front projection. They are superior to film in several respects: (1) projection is continuous without the problems of using a film loop, and (2) a better projection is usually possible because more light can be thrown on the screen. The slight arcing effect due to the circular motion of the slide may sometimes be undesirable on a large projection.

MOTION-PICTURE PROJECTION

With rear-projected motion pictures, the possibilities of effects are greatly expanded. Backgrounds containing action, often very distant action, can be produced. Street scenes and landscapes with figures or vehicles in motion are possible. One production used the rear screen for a very realistic scene of two people on a bicycle as they crossed the entire length of the Golden Gate Bridge. The people were in the studio, pedaling a stationary bike, while the background film was a shot which had previously been taken from a slow-moving car crossing the bridge.

Sometimes an endless loop of film is used instead of a reel in the ordinary manner. A loop may be of any length. A special continuous reel is used which will wind up film on the outside of a roll and unwind it again from the inside. The advantage, of course, is that special timing is not necessary. The director is never afraid that his background film may run out before his shot is completed.

The point at which the loop is joined, however, must be very carefully chosen, so that a jump in action is not discernible. For example, one rear-projection scene showed people crossing a street, and each time the "join" came around, a car suddenly disappeared from the foreground and three people miraculously appeared in its place.

"Hot spot," "fall-off," and length of throw. The light which carries the images of a background projection must pass through a translucent screen. If this were a perfectly clear screen, no image would be seen, but only a bright point of light from the projector lens. This is because the camera would be seeing the direct rays of light from the projector. If the camera should move, this same bright spot would be seen in another part of the screen. The screen is designed to diffuse the light, however. The direct rays from the projector, instead of all passing through in the same direction, are reflected in many directions. The "hot spot" is reduced in intensity. A perfect diffuser would deflect just as much light in one direction as another, and no hot spot would be seen.

But no existing screens can attain this ideal. The most intense transmitted light is still the direct ray. This means the camera will see a bright area in line with the projector. In television this hot spot very rarely shows up. However, a concomitant effect, fall-off of intensity around the edges of the screen, is a constant problem.

In Fig. 12-14 three rays of light are illustrated, and the relative intensity of the diffused light in various directions is shown by the length of the arrows. It can be seen that a camera placed perpendicular to the screen sees a maximum of illumination in the center of the screen and a minimum along the edges. If the camera were to move to a side position, the near side of the screen would then appear brightest and the intensity would drop off progressively across the screen.

In motion-picture studio practice both the hot spot and the fall-off problems are countered by an extremely long projection throw. The projector is placed at least five times the width of the screen behind it, and usually much more than this. The advantage is that the direct rays from the projector come to the screen in a more nearly parallel position, and the angle to which they must be bent to reach the camera lens is less. Hence there is better illumination around the edges of the shot and less fall-off.

In television, such space is unheard of. The studio is lucky that can allow a space equal to twice the width of the screen for the projector behind it. An ideal relation would be a ratio of only 1 to 1: a space

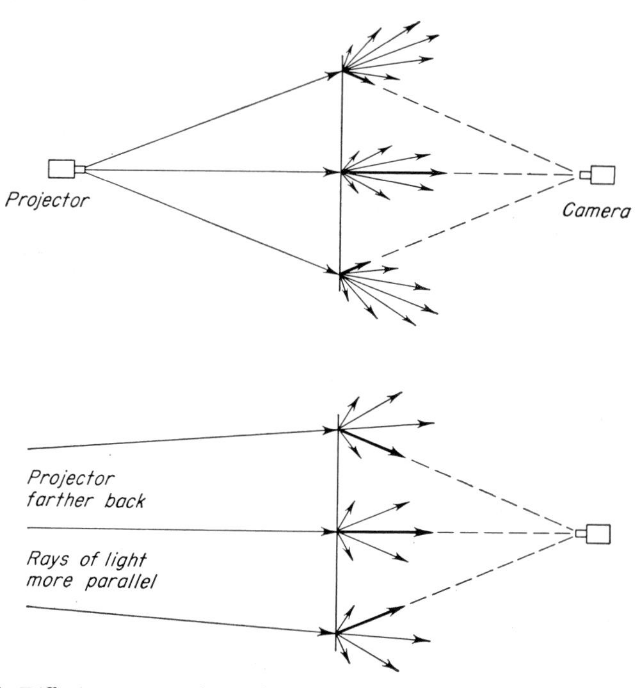

Fig. 12–14. Diffusion pattern from three rays of light, one central and one at each side of the screen. When the projector is close to the screen, the sides of the picture are dark; when the projector is farther back, the screen is more evenly illuminated.

equal to the width of the screen allowed behind it for projection. Figure 12-15 shows how this wide angle of projection differs from even the widest angle that is ever used in motion-picture rear projection.

The front-light problem. The lighting of foregrounds in front of rear-projection screens has always presented a problem, since the light must not be allowed to fall on the screen. The darkest tone it is possible to achieve in the rear projection will be the tone caused by reflected light on the front of the screen. Whatever tone the screen assumes when the rear projection is turned off will be the darkest black of the projected picture. This is often quite light, and rear projection is frequently unconvincing because of its grayish tone.

In order to keep lights off the screen, only side, top, or back light can be used on the actors, unless they are considerably forward of the screen. This leads to a contrasty style of lighting, which is even more difficult for a grayish screen to match. Front fill light, so important in television,

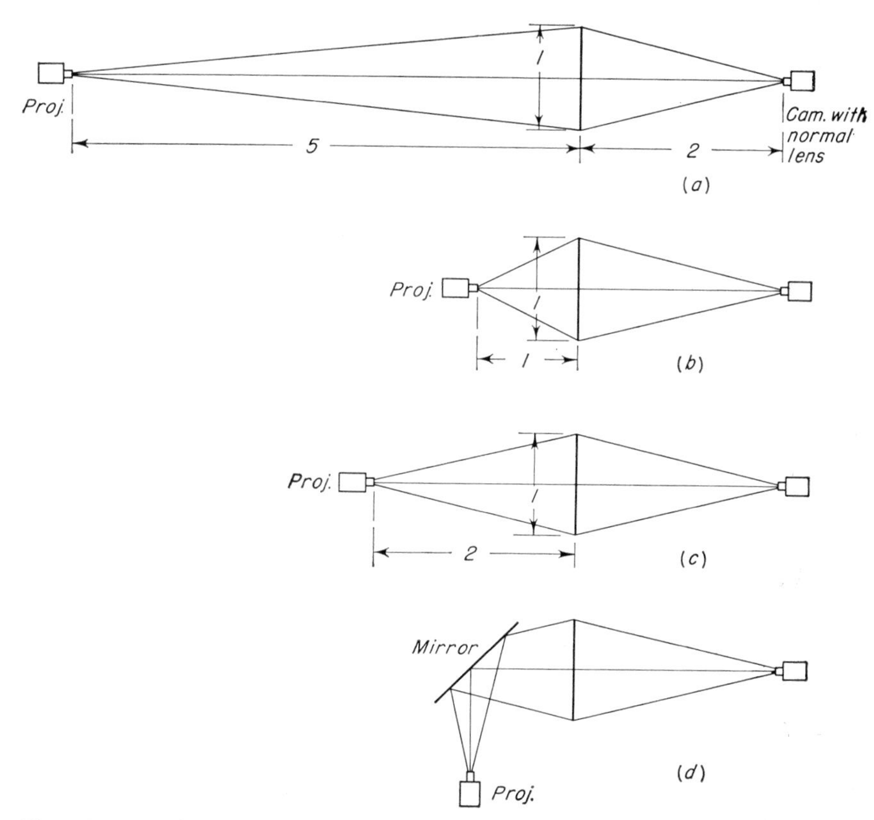

Fig. 12–15. Relations of camera and projector to process screen. (*a*) The most extreme conditions to be found in motion-picture rear-projection practice. Most motion-picture rear projection is done with a much longer projection throw and with a longer-than-normal camera lens. (*b*) A 1-to-1 ratio of projection throw to screen width is the most desirable condition in the television studio owing to the limited space available. (*c*) A 2-to-1 ratio is more commonly used and gives better results. (*d*) Sometimes this length of throw can be obtained, even though the studio is small, by using one or more mirrors.

must be very sparingly used. Even when direct light is kept from falling on the screen, there is enough reflected light loose in the room (ambient light) to illuminate the screen to a certain minimum shade. Light reflects off the foreground objects onto the screen, and it is very difficult, with standard white screens, to make the blacks come out black. A black screen was devised to solve the spill-light problem. Transmitting almost as much light as a white screen, it absorbed front light and reflected very little.

Sometimes such a short throw and wide screen are used in television that the illumination falls off to practically nothing along the edges of the screen. On a white screen the edges then come out the minimum milky gray, which is the darkest the screen can get. The black screen, however, falls off to pure black, which is much more noticeable. A compromise has been effected, and manufacturers now provide blue screens which both absorb some of the front light and do not exhibit excessive fall-off around the edges.

PROJECTION SCREENS

It is not always necessary to use the commercial rear-projection screens for every television need. Quite often the size of the screen is small, fall-off is no problem, and a number of cheaper materials can be used.

The simplest of these is tracing paper or cloth. Oiled canvas has been used for this purpose also. Care must be taken in the selection of screen material, especially in the case of very small screens, to make sure the grain of the material does not show. If the grain of cloth, for example, should exceed the resolution of the projected image, this would cut down on the quality of the picture.

A fairly good screen can be made from white koroseal (the material from which raincoats are made and which is found in most department stores). The material comes in a 48-inch width only and must be butt-spliced to make wider screens.

Al Jenkins has experimented with sheets of white latex, 0.0064 inch thick, and says this material gives a very brilliant transmission and is very inexpensive. However, it is not permanent and is likely to soften and rot after a few months' time.

REAR-SCREEN PROJECTORS

The larger the screen, the more projected light is necessary to illuminate it properly. This problem was faced in motion pictures and solved by projecting with three carbon-arc projectors at once. The "triple-head" projector used three identical films. The two side projections were reflected from a kind of multiplexer, while the middle one projected directly. Perfect register was necessary. The combination was in some cases built into a permanent booth and in others mounted on a movable base so that it could be used in different parts of the studio. Such an arrangement is considered economically impractical in television, and the problem must be solved by a single projector.

It is difficult to get an accurate estimate of the exact amount of light which should be transmitted through a screen in order to equal studio illumination in front. With night scenes, of course, the background can be much darker than the foreground and can exhibit considerable fall-off

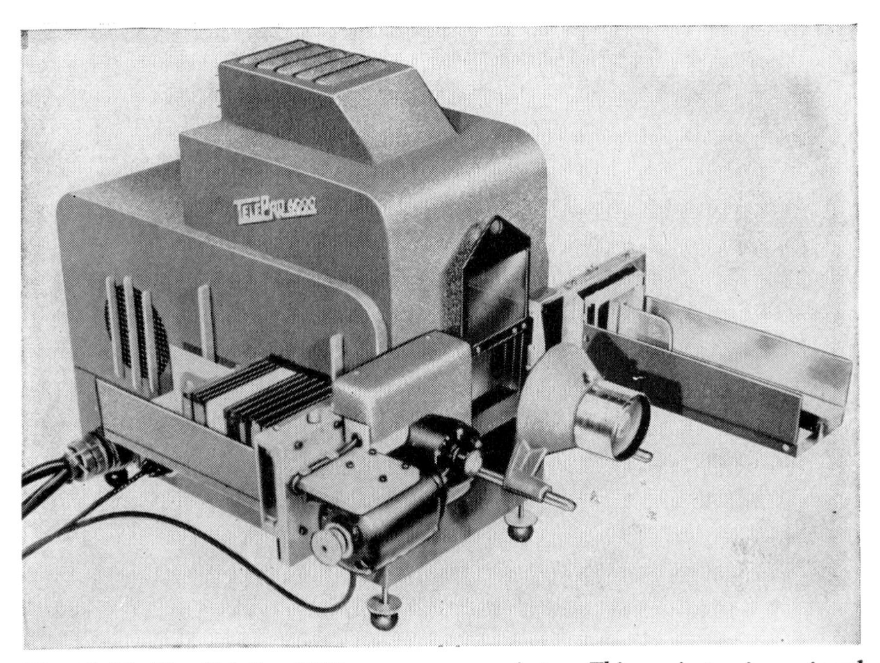

Fig. 12–16. The TelePro 6000 rear screen projector. This projector is equipped with an automatic remote-control slide changer, takes a maximum of sixty-five 3¼- by 4-inch slides (including Polaroid transparencies), and changes slides in ¼ second without black screen interval. Auxiliary slide holder (center, above projection aperture) allows single slides to be inserted manually at any time during slide sequence.

without being objectionable. Other factors such as size of screen, density of the slide, the kind of studio lighting being used, the angle of the camera to the screen, etc., also break in.

Some studios have estimated there should be 90 foot-candles transmitted through the screen. Others, using a lower studio light level, figure only 20 to 40. In terms of light *quantity* (measured in lumens), this amounts to 20 to 90 lumens per square foot. That is quite a range. The most valuable expert advice obtainable is simply to put the slide in the projector, illuminate the screen, and see how it looks.

According to the lowest of these estimates, the "TelePro 6000" which delivers 6,000 lumens through a 3¼- by 4-inch slide could cover a screen 15 by 20 feet in size. According to the highest estimate on the illumination level needed, a 6,000-lumen projector could put 90 lumens on each of 66 square feet (1 lumen per square foot of light equals one foot-candle of light intensity); 66 square feet means a screen about 7 by 9 feet. The manufacturer of the TelePro 6000 suggests a maximum screen size of 9 by 12 feet.

The problem of getting enough light through the slide is much greater when 16-mm film is used because of the much smaller area of the film. A carbon arc will provide plenty of lumens and when used in a still projector will cover almost any screen, but such a projector must be attached to a vent pipe to carry off the fumes, and this greatly limits its flexibility.

FRONT PROJECTION

For the station with limited space and facilities a little experimentation with the method of front projection is highly recommended. Karl Weger at WPTZ, with a relatively small studio, used front projection in preference to rear projection. According to Weger, "the only thing which rear projection can provide that is not also possible with front projection is the ability to place action close to the screen. This, however, is not a disadvantage in the case of front projection because the effect of separation between the actor and his background heightens the illusion."

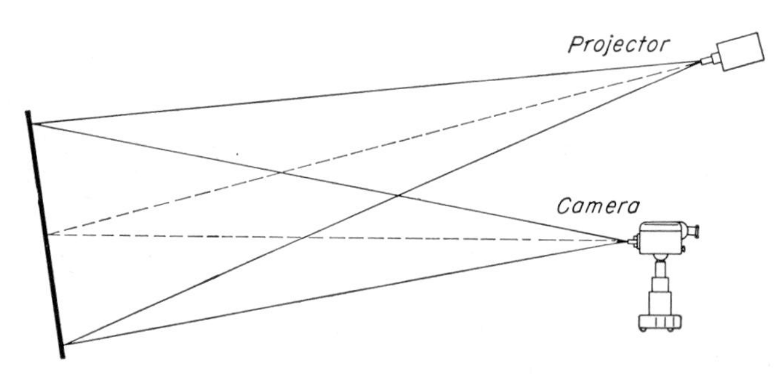

Fig. 12–17. Front projection from overhead with tilted screen.

Front projection does not require an expensive screen; almost any fairly light surface will do, although regular white rear-projection screens can be used for front projection. Front projection is not subject to hot spot or fall-off unless the camera is shooting from a relatively extreme angle. The projector is best placed above the cameras, shooting down at an angle over the actor's heads. The projector should be as far away as practical, at least as far as twice the diagonal of the screen. Projectors usually have a shallow depth of focus, and if it is not possible to keep both the top and bottom of the screen sharp in projecting down at an angle, it is possible to tilt the screen up a bit so that it is perpendicular to the projector (Fig. 12-17). The angle of projection and the position of the screen in relation to the projector should be standardized, and if necessary the slides which are prepared can be predistorted. If the angle of projection, for example, causes the lower part of the background picture to appear larger than it should on the screen, the slide can be made (with special photographic methods) to be distorted in the opposite manner so that the lower part of the picture on the slide is smaller than the upper part and an undistorted projection will result.

SHADOWGRAMS

Another method of still projection is based on the point-source lamp. Western Union has developed a ziconium arc lamp in which the light source is a tiny crater a few hundredths of an inch in diameter. Such a lamp will project an image of a transparency without a lens system at all. It is best described by first discussing a familiar theatrical projector, the Linnebach lantern.

The Linnebach lantern consists of a large box or hood containing a small-filament incandescent lamp. The front of the box will take a large celluloid slide at least 1½ by 2 feet in size. A shadow of this transparency is cast on the screen. As with any shadow, it will vary in size directly as the distance of the screen from the projector and inversely as the distance of the light source from the transparent slide.

This machine is usable in the theater only for soft or distorted images, since it cannot be sharply focused. A shadow, as anyone knows who has made shadows on the wall with the light of a candle, becomes softer the larger it is made. And the same simple experiment will show that a tiny candle flame throws a sharper shadow than a large light bulb, and the shadow cast by a lamp that is covered by a shade is so soft as to have very little form at all. That is why the lamp in a Linnebach projector must have the smallest possible filament and why the inside of the hood is painted black. The ideal light source for the Linnebach would be a point having no size at all. All rays of light would then emanate from one point, and the shadow would be as sharp as the image on the transparency.

With the new concentrated arc lamps, this is now possible. This light source is almost a point. A sharp projection is possible without a lens and in any size, depending on how close to the lamp the transparency is placed. It may be set at an angle to the axis of projection without the edges going soft, as they would in an ordinary lens projector. This means that angle projection is possible. Old-style Linnebach lanterns are commonly used in this manner in the theater, shooting up or down at the screen. As long as the transparency is kept parallel with the screen, there will be no distortion of the image (Fig. 12-18). Angle projection is

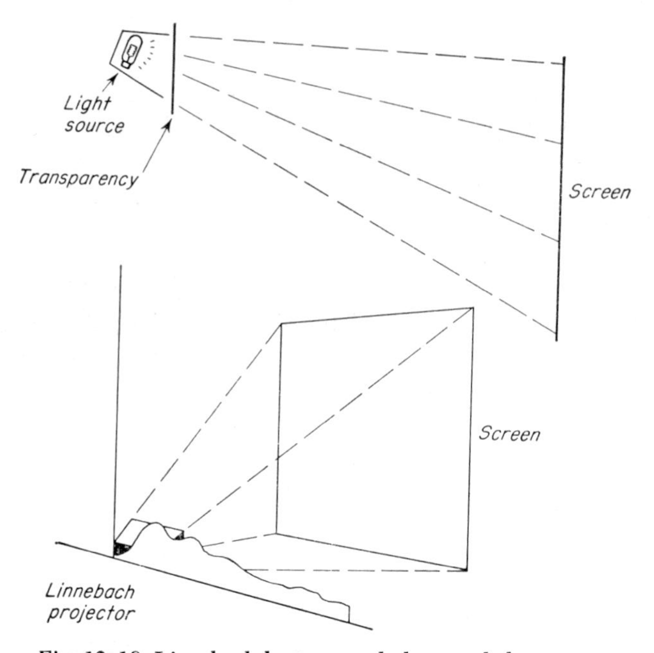

Fig. 12–18. Linnebach lantern used above or below screen.

no advantage in television rear projection, since the angle with which the projected rays would strike the screen would be too great. The entire screen would exhibit the fall-off usually noticeable only around the edges. For front projection, however, angle projection is a great advantage in television. It is possible to place the projector above or to the side of the screen and hide it from the camera.

PROJECTION OF SHADOWS

The distinction should first be drawn between a shadow, or shadowgram, and a silhouette. The latter is not the product of projection, but an illuminated object seen against a lighted background. It is usually made by keeping a performer in the half light in front of the lighted set or in front of a rear-lighted translucent screen. The silhouette can be sharper than the shadow since the camera can focus directly upon the performer.

Shadows may be large or small, sharp or soft-edged, strong or weak, natural or distorted. They may be produced by a moving or changing light source and thus become moving or changing shadows. The shadow may be produced by placing a performer between the light source and a wall surface, so that the shadow is cast upon the wall. Or the performer may work behind a translucent screen so that the shadow is projected onto the screen and seen from the reverse side (Fig. 12-19).

Fig. 12–19. An episode in a CBS drama told with shadows cast on a rear-projection screen. Actors work between projector and screen. Note that hot spot and fall-off actually enhance this style of production.

The size of a cast shadow made by either of these methods is inversely proportional to the distance of the subject from the light source.

$$\frac{\text{Size of shadow}}{\text{Size of subject}} = \frac{\text{distance of shadow}}{\text{distance of subject}}$$

The size of shadows can very easily be plotted on paper if the position of the light and the size of the performer are known (Fig. 12-20).

Sharpness of the shadow is dependent on the size of the light source and the distance from subject to screen (Fig. 12-21). A large source of light (say a floodlight with a diffusion screen in front of the bulb) will cast a soft-edged shadow. This is because light emanates from many sources. A shadow cast by light from one side of the lamp, for example,

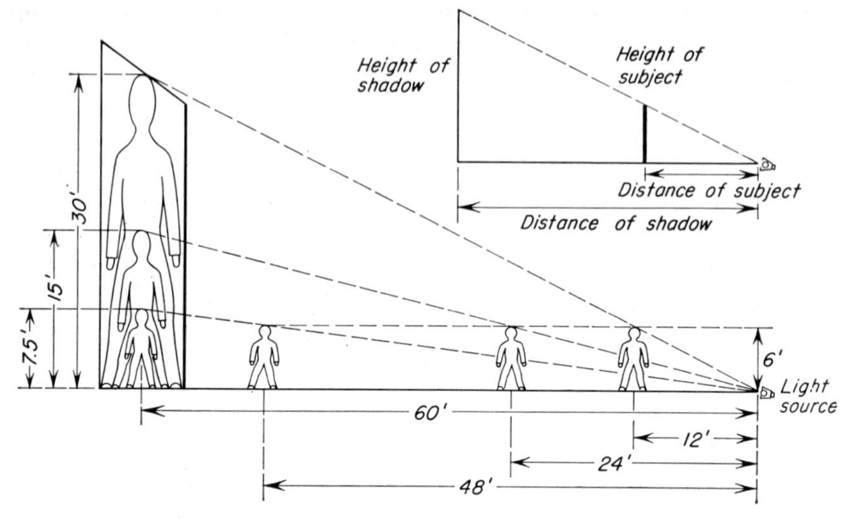

Fig. 12–20. Size of shadow varies inversely as distance of subject from light source.

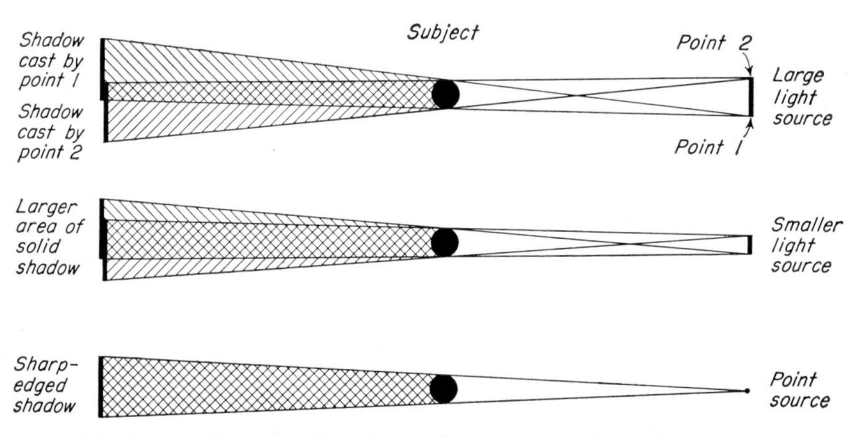

Fig. 12–21. Sharpness of shadow is determined by size of light source.

Fig. 12–22. Wide-angle shadows, like pictures through a wide-angle lens, exhibit exaggeration of depth.

is partially wiped out by light coming from the other side of the lamp which can "see" around the corner of the subject a little farther. In astronomy these shadow and half-shadow regions are known as the umbra and penumbra.

A distorted shadow will result if the surface on which the shadow is cast is not perpendicular to the source of light. The larger shadows illustrated in Fig. 12-22 are distorted to a certain extent, since the top of the wall is considerably farther from the light than the bottom. If the surface is of an uneven shape, the cast shadow will be distorted in an irregular manner.

13

Special Effects with Graphic Materials

Where special effects are concerned with graphic materials, they may be either optical or mechanical. Usually the purpose is to invest the graphic subject with some kind of movement so that it develops or animates on the screen. Some of the optical devices are simply complicated methods of handling graphic materials, changing titles, etc., a subject which was discussed in Chap. 9, Graphic Materials, but which will now be explored further.*

THE TWO-STAGE SHADOW BOX

A shadow box is a title device containing two stages for titles or pictures. A transparent mirror is placed at a 45-degree angle between the two stages so that the camera may see either one stage or the other or both at once in a superimposition according to the illumination of the stages. Figure 13-1 illustrates a simple device of this type. Each stage is a card box. The mirror is sufficiently silvered to reflect and transmit equal percentages of light from the two stages. When the lights are dimmed down on stage *A* but are full up on stage *B*, the reflected image of *B* is seen (left and right are reversed because it is a mirror image). When *B* is dimmed down and *A* is full up, the transmitted image of *A* is seen. When both stages are illuminated, a superimposition results. This device permits one to run a series of stills or title cards with dissolves between them, entirely by optical means, only one camera being neces-

* The reader is warned that many of the devices described herein are covered in the patent art and commercialization may be subject to royalty.

sary. A method of shielding the lights must be devised so that when a stage is dark and cards are being changed in it, light from the other stage does not leak over and dimly reveal the motion. The most serious fault of this device, aside from the space it takes on the studio floor, is that every other card or picture must be prepared in reverse so that it may

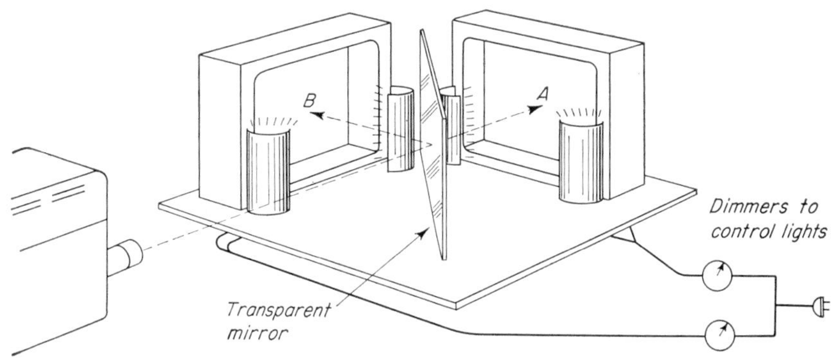

Fig. 13–1. Two-stage shadow box.

be seen properly in mirror image; the cards are thus not interchangeable between the stages.

THE TWO-MIRROR SHADOW BOX

If two mirrors are employed instead of one, the reflected image can be corrected by the second mirror and cards can be used in either stage interchangeably. A shadow box of this type was built by the author at CBS in 1940; it had two mirrors and a total of three stages (Fig. 13-2*a*). Cards used on stage 3 were reversed (since the image of that stage was reflected only once), but stages 1 and 2 were interchangeable. The third stage was used primarily for rear-lighted cutout animation (to be described). All manner of materials were used on the two main stages: drums for continuous movement, slide-through effects, three-dimensional objects, and working models. The stage could be taken away and the operator's hand or face inserted instead. A particularly startling effect was obtained by having the operator look through a mask which revealed only the eyes and then slowly superimposing this very accurately over a portrait. The moving eyes made the picture seem to come to life. Another advantage of a machine with three stages is that two of the stages may be superimposed and then dissolved out together as a third stage is dissolved in. In a two-stage machine one part of the superimposure must first be lost and that stage changed before a dissolve can be made to another subject.

A wipe can be installed in a shadow box by one of two means. If the semimirror is replaced by a plain mirror, dissolves are no longer possible, but sliding the mirror in and out will produce a wipe.

A second method might be called the "focal plane shutter" method. A sliding black shutter is installed just in front of each of two stages.

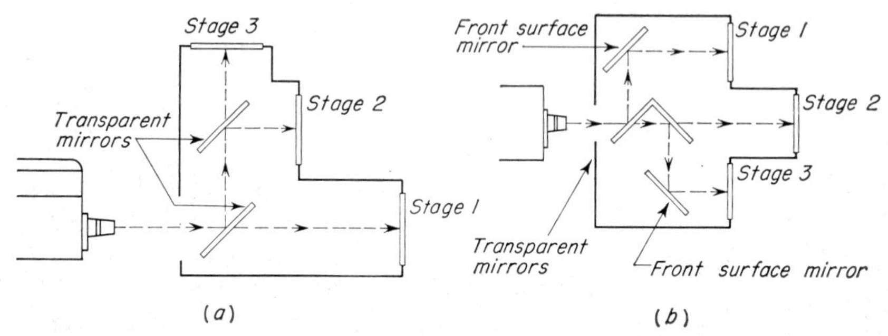

Fig. 13–2. Three-stage shadow box. (*a*) Two stages correct; one reversed. (*b*) Alternative design; no stages reversed.

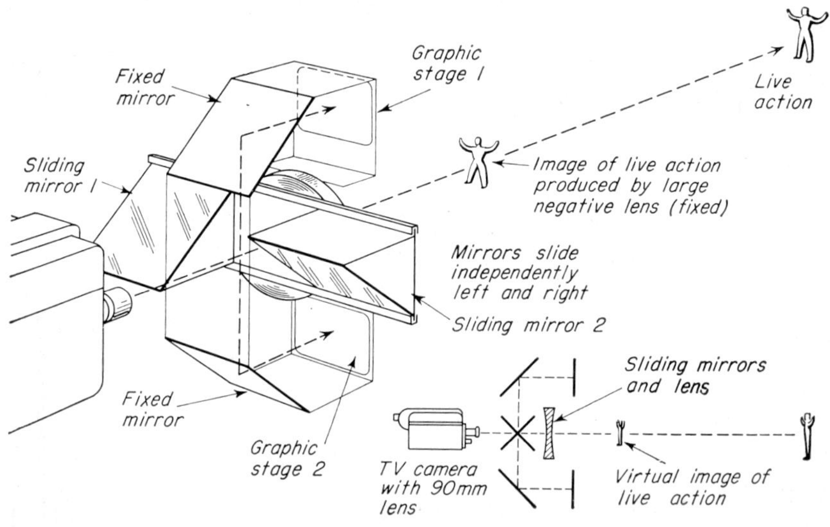

Fig. 13–3. Combination of shadow box and live action with mirror wipe. Designed by Karl Weger.

These two shutters can be ganged together in such a way that while one stage is covered the other is revealed, and vice versa. The trailing edge of the first shutter is accurately registered with the leading edge of the other. The wipe may be a vertical line moving left or right, or a horizontal line moving up or down. A shutter of either of these types with a diagonal edge will produce the effect of a diagonally moving shutter.

Since these shutters are in the plane of focus (they are placed just in front of each stage), the wipe will have a sharper edge than will the sliding-mirror wipe where the edge of the mirror must be some distance from the focal plane.

OVERHEAD TRANSPARENCY PROJECTORS

Standard equipment for visual instruction in the classroom, the overhead projector has found interesting applications in television. The main feature is the large, open horizontal stage.

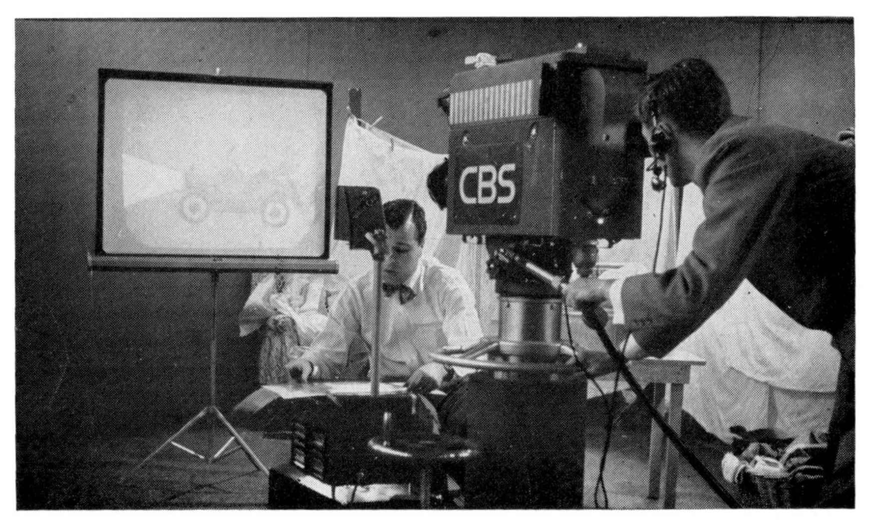

Fig. 13–4. Overhead transparency projector in operation. (Courtesy of *Popular Science.*)

The horizontal stage makes it possible for the operator to write or draw on the focal plane. The light originates below this stage, and a shadow of the writing is projected on the screen. Of course, the shadows of pencil and hand are also visible. Additional elements in a drawing may be made to appear suddenly by hinging "layovers" of celluloid and flopping them down quickly onto the stage. Each layover may have further layovers hinged to it. Ingenuity has found numerous ways to utilize this machine for interesting presentation of graphic materials. It is projected onto either the front or the rear of a screen, where the studio camera picks up the image. A program called "Toon-a-vision" was built around this machine and the effects that it can produce. A small transparent screen was built into the rear wall of the set on which cartoon stills were projected. These were given a feeling of animation by quick overlays of dialogue balloons or additional elements of the cartoon. Parts of the drawings done on separate celluloid sheets could be moved across the backgrounds (background showed through foreground objects, of course, since both were transparent). Silhouettes could be moved anywhere, but figures done in line drawings could not cross background lines or these would show through the figures.

A 12- or 15-point celluloid is the best material for this machine; the lighter 10-point animation celluloid does not flop down quickly enough. Cel-flex or other celluloid paint must be used. (This paint is flexible and will not crack off.) Half tones are made by wiping on the wet paint. Line drawings are made on one side of the cell, and the half tone is

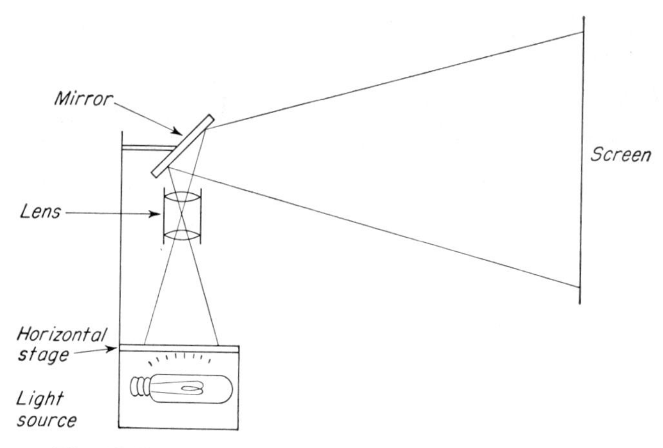

Fig. 13–5. Diagram of overhead transparency projector.

wiped in on the other. Excess half tone which extends beyond the lines can be picked off with a damp brush. White tones or lettering can be made in the half-tone area by the same process.*

The Cellomatic projector is a double overhead projector which, in addition to the various effects listed above, can provide wipes, dissolves, and superimposures between the two stages. It is possible through the use of mattes to insert areas or produce split-screen effects. An iris has been added to each stage for an additional transition effect.

MYSTERIOUS WRITING

One of the most interesting special effects is the mysterious appearance of writing or lettering without pencil or hand being visible. The author

* The firm of Howell and Reagin, artists, do most of the work with this machine in New York, and the author is indebted to Tom Howell of this organization for the above data.

will describe three methods of doing this, one of which utilizes back light and two illumination only from the front.

A carbon-paper scratch-off process. This involves back light and can be done on the Vue-Graph projector. As a pencil writes on the rear side of a special carbon paper, the opaque carbon is removed and a white line appears on the screen. Shadows of pencil and hand may be cast on these lines, however, if care is not taken to keep away from areas which are already drawn upon.

Ink from the back side. If a relatively thin paper is used and a thin and penetrating ink, black ink can be made to soak through from the

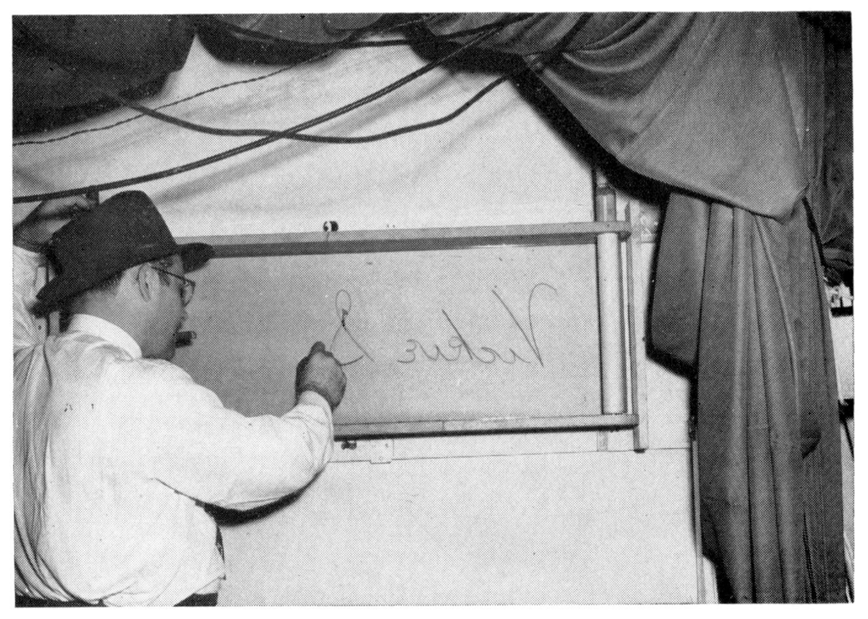

Fig. 13–6. Chuck Holden writing from behind the set on the ABC show "Stop the Music."

back side. The artist ordinarily uses a "fountain brush" for this purpose.* Chuck Holden, ABC production manager, was the first to develop this method on television at WCBS-TV before the war. He built a vertical stage, using newsprint paper which was supported on the front side by a sheet of glass. In Fig. 13-6 he is applying the same technique in the production of "Stop the Music." The name of the contestant answering the phone is mysteriously written out on a small panel behind the MC. Whoever writes out the name, however, must be an expert at writing in reverse.

* Fountain pen with a piece of felt for a point.

A further development of this technique was made at WSPD-TV in Toledo. In this model, the Telescriber (Fig. 13-7), a horizontal stage was used, and the camera picked up the image by means of a 45-degree mirror below. This allowed the operator to work right way to. White wrapping paper was used in rolls and was pulled through the stage sandwiched between wide areas of felt, which held it securely enough so that the pressure of writing would not bulge down the unsupported center portion of the paper.

Fig. 13–7. WSPD-TV mysterious-writing machine, the Telescriber.

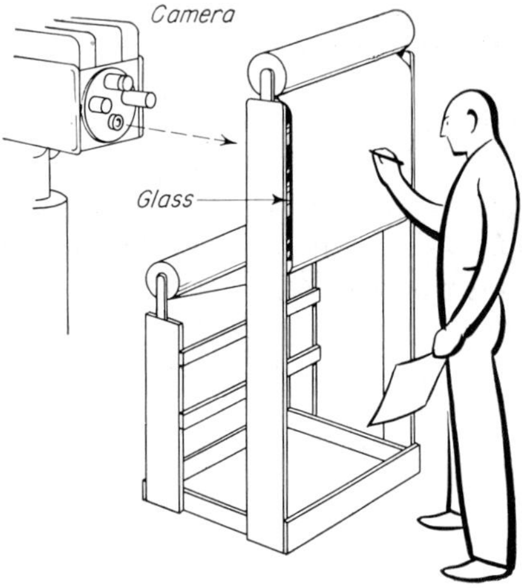

Fig. 13–8. WWJ-TV mysterious-writing device.

Front-lighted ground glass. Ground glass, matte celluloid, tracing cloth, or layout paper will serve as the material on which this type of writing can be done. A white chalk or other soft crayon is used from the reverse side. All light is applied from the front. The hand must be gloved (as described later in this chapter in the discussion of the Bretzicon), and all but the point of the crayon must also be black, or it will show. The white chalk, as it is applied to the back of the translucent material, reflects the front light, and the letters come out white against a dark background.

A black crayon may also be used in this method to achieve a black-on-gray as well as a white-on-gray effect. The black pigment absorbs some of the front light, which would otherwise be reflected back by the diffusing material.

TELEVISION ANIMATION

The term "television animation" is meant to exclude animation which is produced on film. Many of the techniques described below can be utilized in film production, especially when the producer is cutting corners in the attempt to produce on a low budget. However, the technique which is basic to almost all film animation, stop motion, cannot be used in live television. Stop motion has been demonstrated, using video tape instead of film, but only by splicing on every frame. The following sections will describe devices which have been developed to produce at least the simpler types of animation without recourse to the stop-motion technique.

Stop motion, the reader will recall, is the process of shooting a motion picture in separate frames, one or two at a time, and changing the drawings or the position of "moving" objects between exposures. A tremendous amount of art work is necessary when so-called "full animation" is done—12 to 24 drawings per second of finished film—even though all parts of the picture are not repeated in every drawing. Only the moving parts of the picture are redrawn every frame, and since the drawings are done on celluloid, they can be laid over other drawings which carry the static elements. Sometimes as many as 10 or 20 layers of cells are necessary for very complicated animation, and multiplane animation stands allow foreground, background, and middle-background cells to be placed on separate planes, each of which may have its own motion or animation.

MANIPULATION

In the most straightforward method the performer simply adds picture elements by placing them on the picture or moves models or other objects by hand. This simple technique lends itself very well to the actuality and immediacy of television.

The old flannelgraph technique, known for years to sidewalk audiences of Salvation Army sermons, has been reborn in the television studio. The background of the picture is made of cloth, preferably velvet or flannel, and the picture elements are drawn or cemented onto "velour paper" or ordinary sandpaper. (Velour paper is coated with flock, feels like cloth, and can be purchased at most art stores in a variety of colors.) The speaker need only place the cutout against the cloth and it will catch and hold there even in a vertical plane. A picture can be put together piece by piece; it may be a simple two-dimensional design; or it can be drawn in perspective.

A variation on this technique was used by the author at CBS in 1941. Arrows and other symbols were placed on smooth-surfaced maps and held by masking tape. A piece of heavy double-faced tape was attached to the back of the symbol (or if only single-faced tape is available, a circle of tape fastened to itself and flattened out will do almost as well). In utilizing this method of visualizing the news, the newscaster stood before the map, with the various symbols in the order of their use spread out on the table before him.

POP-INS AND ONE-STEP ANIMATION

The instantaneous addition of new elements to a picture is one of the simple effects of animation. This can be done very easily in film by stopping the camera and adding the new element to the picture. In live television, of course, other means must be found.

One way to achieve this effect is to cut from one picture to another, identical with the first except that it includes a new element. If the two pictures are in perfect register, there will be no change at the time of the cut except that the new object will "pop in." Since perfect register cannot easily be accomplished between two studio cameras, this effect is used only where a station has a multiple-stage projector, either slide or opaque, and the two stages involved can be in perfect alignment.

The illusion of a simple type of motion can be achieved by cutting back and forth between two pictures in this manner. The action of pumping up a tire, for example, can be shown in two stages, with the pump up and with the pump down. Rapid cutting between the two stages will keep this one-step animation going as long as desired.

The above is an optical effect when done in a shadow box or projector, since it depends on controlling two images by light and mirrors. Pop-ins may also be done entirely mechanically in front of a television camera. A drawing is done on celluloid, and the additional element which is suddenly to appear is drawn separately on a card, which is then placed behind the first. A shutter of the same material as the background of the second drawing is placed between the two, covering the new element. As the shutter is pulled out (Fig. 13-9), the new element is revealed. This

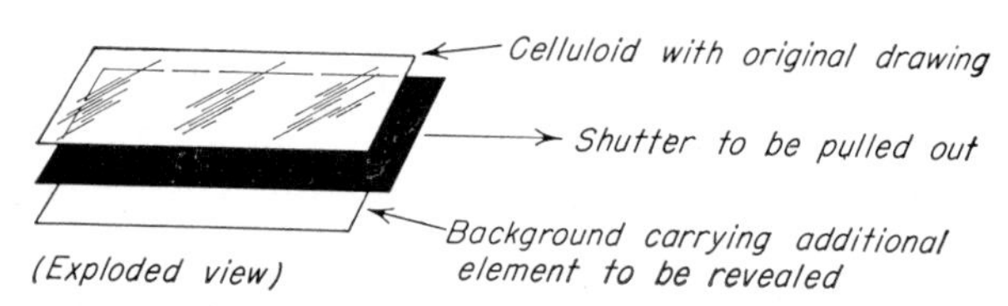

Field 13–9. Method of making new element of the picture pop in by quickly pulling the shutter that covers it.

is known as the "pull-out" technique. If the shutter is a heavy material (black paper, for example), the edge may catch the light and show as it is being pulled out. To avoid this, use a piece of matte celluloid for the original (front) drawing. As long as the picture beneath is held tight against the ground surface, it will be seen clearly. There should be just enough diffusion to disguise the edge of the shutter. Heavy tracing paper, layout paper, or architect's tracing cloth can be used for this purpose.

The pull-out may be used for one-step animation if the first stage of an action is drawn on the shutter. When the shutter is suddenly jerked out, there is a split second of blurred motion and the eye is left with the subject in another position. Since the picture on the shutter moves bodily away, it gives a momentary sensation of directional movement. If the direction of shutter movement is the same as the direction of movement in the animation, this will add realism to the effect. The eye will inter-

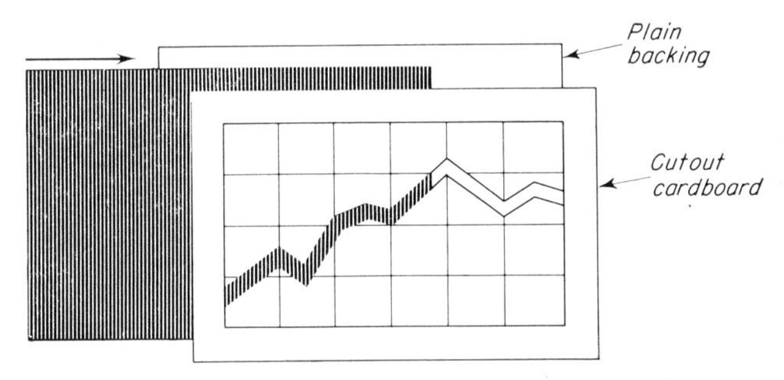

Fig. 13–10. One method of making a graph line slowly grow.

pret the sudden shutter movement as a transitional movement of the object from one position to the other.

Another means of achieving one-step animation is to draw both stages of the action on the same card, but in different colors. In operation, the camera is successively blinded to first one color, then the other, with the result that it sees two pictures alternately on the same card. The Dr. Jekyll–Mr. Hyde make-up change has been achieved by this technique.

Two methods can be used for blinding the camera to first one color and then the other. Either the light on the subject can be changed in color, or filters may be rotated in front of the camera lens. Spectrolite, a commercial process that has been used in some television stations and in the production of filmed commercials, utilizes the changing light. The colors chosen for this technique are usually red and blue since they are widely separated in the light spectrum. It is possible to find a red-light source (or filter or pigment) which contains no component of blue, and vice versa. Thus when the red light is on, all blue portions of the art work appear black. (Blue pigment absorbs all but blue light, and since there is no blue light on the subject, there is nothing to reflect.) Red portions of the drawing, however, reflect a maximum of light, take on the same shade as the background, and disappear from sight. The background shade (usually a neutral gray) is carefully chosen to reflect the same amount of red light as the red pigment and the same amount of blue light as the blue pigment. Where this technique is not entirely successful, the trouble is likely to be found in this pigment-to-background match.

If red and blue filters are used in front of the lens, the subject is then illuminated with white light (which has the same amounts of red and blue in it). A red filter will turn the blue pigment black and make the red invisible. A filter wheel will make a continuous effect possible. The filter need not necessarily be placed in front of the lens, however; it may be a sheet of gelatin, for example, used in place of the usual opaque shutter in a pull-out. Whichever technique is used, its success depends on very careful matching of pigment to background and of light or filter to both.

SIMPLE MOVEMENT

The most obvious method of injecting movement into a graphic is to rig up cutouts and added portions with levers and other manual controls so that they can be moved from outside the borders of the picture. A man's jaw may work up and down, a figure may bow and straighten up again, a golfer may work his club. Chuck Holden devised many such cardboard animations at CBS-TV before the war. One of the best of these portrayed the action of pumping up a tank of air. As the operator worked the pump up and down with one hand, he lifted a shutter to expose more and more of the tank with the other.*

The growth of a line on a graph may be shown by first preparing the graph by cutting out the line from the front card on which the lines of the graph are drawn. This is then backed with the same material, so that unless the front card is particularly thick the line will not be seen until a black (or white) shutter is pushed in. As an alternative, the shutter may be the same material as the front card and pulled out to reveal a background of some contrasting shade.

By far the most successful and the most complicated animations of the mechanical type are the work of Joe Fox at WTMJ-TV in Milwaukee. These were not used before a studio camera but were worked instead on an open-stage opaque projector in the projection room. The stage is horizontal, and at convenient table height, but upside down to the operator. With space above and to all sides of the stage, it was possible to pull things across, hinge frames of celluloid or cardboard cutouts to lay

* Joe Ferrier, at WNBW in Washington, has made his "Ferriergraph" animations familiar on many NBC network programs.

over, and manipulate with considerable freedom. In a short paper distributed by WTMJ-TV to interested people in the industry, Joe Fox describes some of the effects as follows:

> The simplest animations are those in which a message is obscured, or revealed, through a sort of wipe, done with a sliding panel. This can be elaborated into a whole section of the card moving into or out of the picture, carrying the message. The effect of this is to show the letters alone moving into the picture. Further, a glass strip or cellulose acetate sheet may be used, so that the letters move in or out over other parts of the card. The next development is to move a message or picture in or out by means of what we call a drop-over. This is an opaque card, or a cardboard frame holding a plastic sheet, hinged to one side of the picture-area rectangle, and allowed to fall into the picture. . . . Further development in animation is introduced with the use of panorama fields moving behind carefully cutout windows. We use endless belts of some material like strong, flexible paper, or black cloth, fixing them so that they pass over pivoted rollers on either end of the card. . . . One of our cards uses a belt of this type to show coal sliding down a chute into a basement window of a house.

Figure 13-11*a* shows a card designed to promote a program which this station was carrying. It is appropriate for a large number of television programs. The card showed two hands struggling over a knife. As the

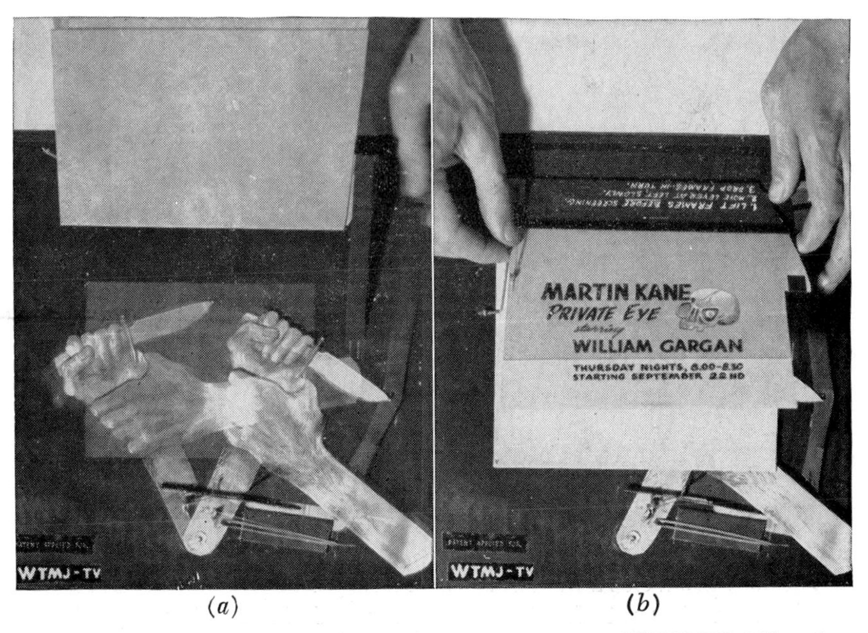

(*a*) (*b*)

Fig. 13–11. Joe Fox animation for program announcement, WTMJ-TV, Milwaukee. (*a*) Hands struggle; hand with knife wins. (*b*) Frames carrying lettering are dropped in.

operator worked the proper lever, the hand with the knife was pushed back until it reached the far left side of the screen. At that point a rubber-band mechanism was tripped, and the hands flew back again to the starting point. Since the knife blade disappeared off-screen, the effect was that it had ended up in someone. Immediately following this a series of cardboard frames (Fig. 13-11*b*) were dropped over the picture, falling quickly enough to seem like instantaneous cuts.

A somewhat more complicated animation is illustrated in Fig. 13-12. This was used as a spot commercial. The audience saw first of all a hopeless pile of junk. The script read "If your car looks like this, bring

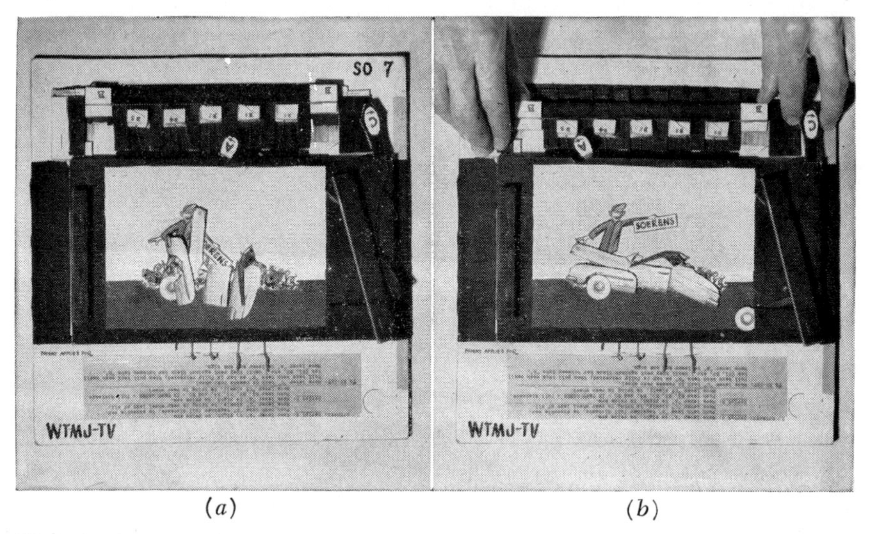

(*a*) (*b*)

Fig. 13–12. Joe Fox animation for local commercial spot. (*a*) "If your car looks like this," (*b*) "bring it to us and we'll make it look like this!" Parts rotate to make new car.

it to us [the little man's arm was raised at this point to display the advertiser's name] and we'll make it look like THIS!" At this point the operator pushed forward on tab *B*, and the parts of the car spun around and reassembled into a new convertible, complete except for rear wheel, which was added a moment later as a delayed "joker" by means of lever *C*. The man's arm was raised and lowered by means of lever *A*. Complete instructions for operation were attached to each animation; these are upside down in the illustrations since the operator worked the card from the top edge.

Another Joe Fox animation showed a magic carpet leaving an Arabian roof and floating out of sight, to reappear again in the distance, going the other way. Another showed a football player making a place kick from the finger of the holder. The picture showed the kick (with arms and legs flying high) and the ball sailing into the distance between the goal posts. When the author held this one in his hand and asked Joe how it was accomplished, he himself couldn't figure it out but had to take the animation apart to determine just what levers released which watch springs, rode on what cams, etc.

Joe has found that simple animations take about half a day to produce, complicated ones perhaps two days in all. Considering that this is only one man's time and no further cost is involved, this method compares most favorably with other methods of producing spot commercials. Only one essential requirement must be met: the station must have a man like Joe Fox on staff.

WIPE-IN, OR GROWTH, OF LINES, AREAS, OR SYMBOLS

The pull-out device, described earlier in this chapter, lends itself very readily to the wipe-in effect. The simple graph (Fig. 13-13) is a good

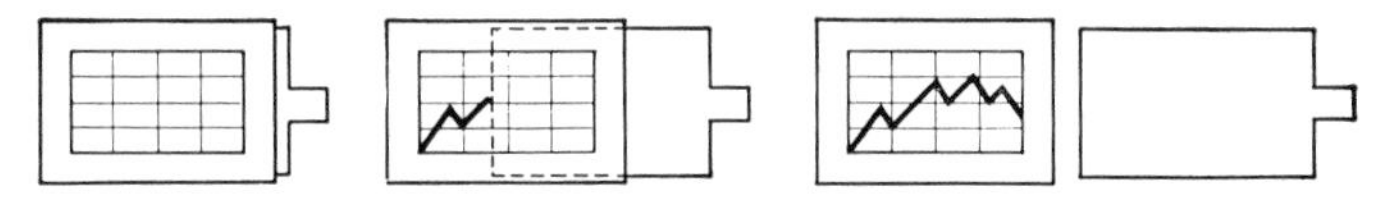

Fig. 13–13. Pull-out technique applied to growth of line on graph.

example. The only animation required here is a slow growth, or wiping in, of the line on the graph. This may be done in one of several ways.

The subject (line on the graph) may be dark and the background light. The original crosslines of the graph are painted on clear or matte celluloid which becomes the front leaf of a pack. Just behind is a shutter of the same paper as the background, and very thin so that the trailing edge is as unnoticeable as possible. And behind this is the background with the subject to be added painted on it. As the shutter is pulled away, the line of the graph slowly grows. If this line is on a piece of clear celluloid instead of on the background card, another shutter may be placed behind it, which when pulled in turn can add further elements to the picture. The same technique can be used with the reverse tones; the subject may be light and the background dark.

Paint against paint. Still another method involves preparing the line of the graph in advance by painting a background tone on the back surface of the front cell everywhere but where the graph line will be. The line is left clear celluloid just as it will be when the animation is complete. When the cell is laid in contact with a shutter which has been painted with the same paint, there will not be even the thickness of a piece of celluloid to reveal the edge of the prepared area. Paint is in direct contact with paint. If the shutter is painted with two shades of paint, the appearance of the contrasting shade as the shutter is pulled will wipe in the line of the graph. This same technique can be used to wipe in letters or irregular areas or, with a rapid pull of the shutter, to make an element suddenly pop in.

Rear-lighted cutouts. It is often necessary to devise a means to animate an arrow which grows by wiping in from tail to head (Fig. 13-14). The

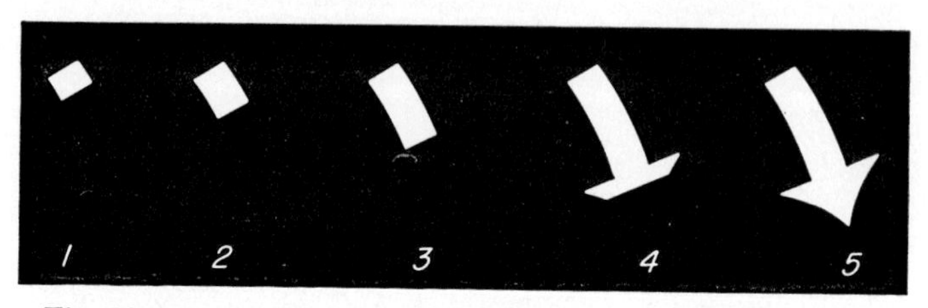

Fig. 13–14. Successive stages in wiping in a rear-lighted arrow.

base map on which the arrow is to appear is done on thin paper such as newsprint, and the arrow is cut out of a sheet of cardboard which is then placed just behind the map. An even illumination of considerable intensity is provided behind this, but the arrow is prevented from showing by a small, opaque shutter laid across it. As the shutter is pulled away, a white arrow is wiped in (Fig. 13-15).

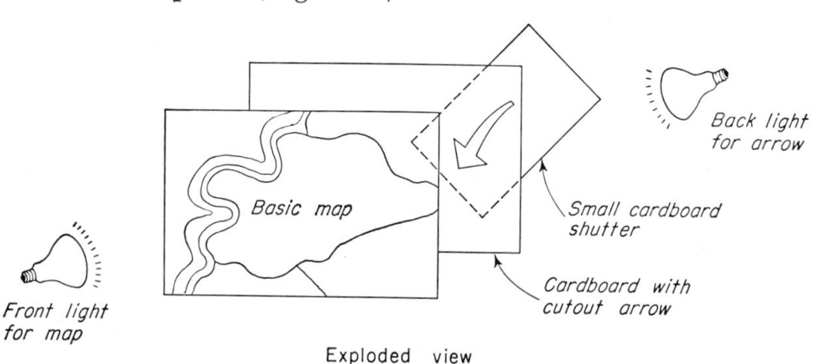

Fig. 13–15. Method of wiping in rear-lighted arrow.

When Chuck Holden first devised a machine for this at CBS in 1941, he used a vertical stage about 24 by 32 inches in size, with a spot on a floor stand for back light. With the vertical stage, shutters had to be fixed tightly to the board by scotch tape until they were operated. Further development of this method has shown that a horizontal stage of considerably smaller size is more practical. The horizontal stage is viewed from beneath by means of a 45-degree mirror (Fig. 13-16).

The front map and the cardboard backing with cutout symbols are of course fastened securely together, either by stapling or cementing one to the other or, as in the case of the original Holden animator, by stapling both into a wood frame of 1- by 2-inch material. The wood frame made it possible to handle the animations and place them in position easily. A sheet of glass was placed on the front of the stage, against which the map was held. In the horizontal device the same sheet of glass is used, which

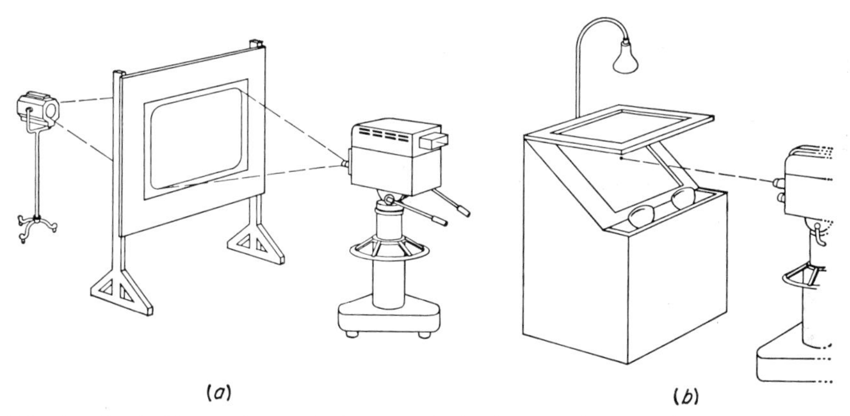

Fig. 13–16. Holden animator (*a*) as originally built with vertical stage, (*b*) with horizontal stage similar to Bretzicon.

in this case provides support for the hands or arms of the operator if he should rest them on the stage during operation.

It was found that a good many symbols could be revealed, either by wipe-in or by pop-in on the back of such an animation, provided that it was not necessary for the operator to reach across an already uncovered area. In such a case he might shadow symbols on the map and cause them to disappear again. A long, thin line that twists and doubles back on itself cannot be made to grow by pulling off a shutter, and the mere fact that it is cut out of the cardboard may weaken the latter and cause it to start to fall apart (Fig. 13-17). Occasional bridges of transparent scotch tape across the cutout channel will hold it together without being visible. The line can be covered by a long piece of opaque scotch tape, which when pulled off will wipe in the most convoluted line.

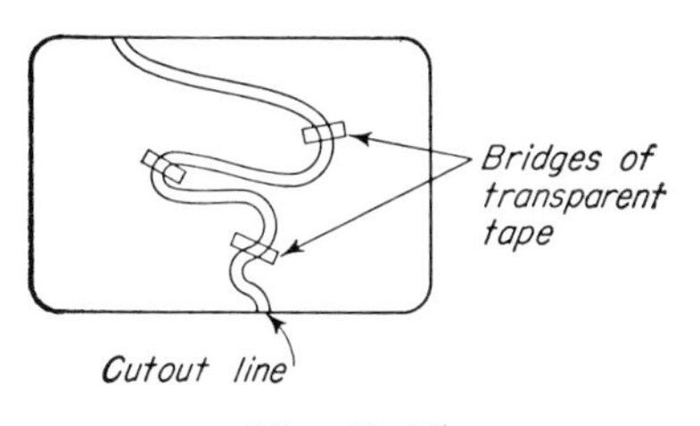

Fig. 13–17

BODILY MOVEMENT

One step nearer to full animation is the technique of moving objects bodily across a background. It has been found in the development of new techniques of film animation that such simple bodily movement can have considerable charm and thus can replace the much more costly full-animation techniques. When this method is used in film animation, at least the cost of art work is saved, although the photography is usually done by stop motion as always. Since, in this technique, an object does not change shape as it moves, realistic figures may look wooden when moved in this manner but *stylized* figures fit in with it very well. The simplest and commonest object that will require bodily movement is an arrow. It is clear that if this movement is to be flexible and free, it must be done by the hand of the operator. The problem is to devise a way to move these objects by hand without the hand itself being visible.

The rear-lighted animator described above is limited in the kind of movement it can perform. If an arrow is to move bodily from one side of a map to another, it must be cut out of a piece of cardboard sufficiently large to provide a shutter both before and after the arrow has been moved (Fig. 13-18). Of course no other symbols could be revealed

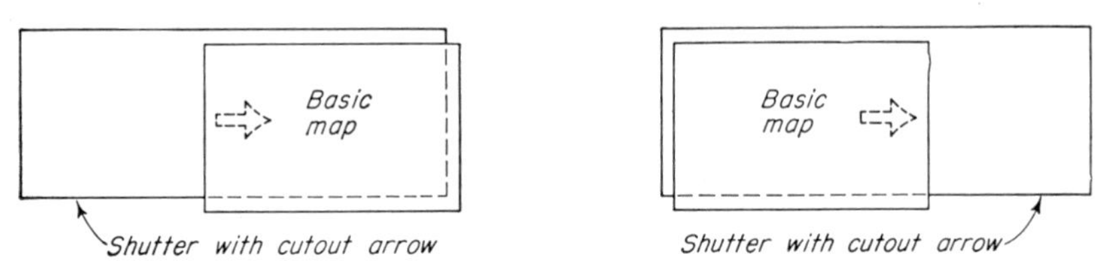

Fig. 13–18. Bodily movement of rear-lighted arrow.

in proximity to the arrow, or they would have to be cut out from the same piece of cardboard and, if revealed before the arrow, would have to move along with it across the map.

The most complicated animation of this type that the author ever devised represented the sinking of a battleship (Fig. 13-19). The ship

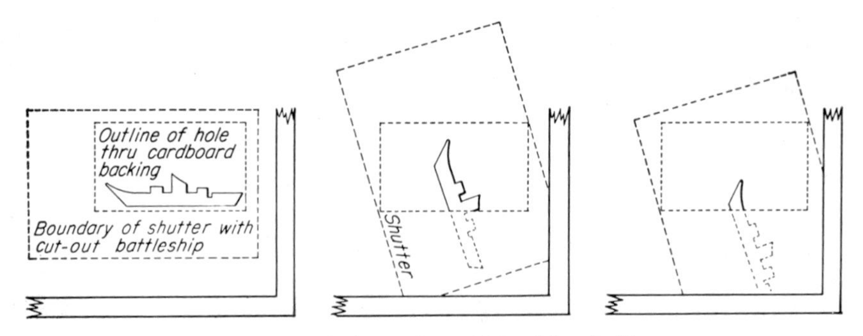

Fig. 13–19. Sinking of rear-lighted battleship.

itself was cut out of a small piece of cardboard which was then laid over a hole cut into the main cardboard backing. The ship could be moved around a little as long as it did not disappear behind the edges of the background hole. When it was to be sunk, it was simply rotated so that it passed stern foremost slowly down behind the bottom edge of the hole.

An obvious method of moving symbols or figures is to build them out of iron or steel and control them with magnets from behind the card on which they are placed. A children's show called "Magnitoons" used this method for telling stories on a long series of programs on WABD in New York. Cartoon characters moved around on graphic backgrounds, were jiggled to indicate when they were speaking, and were occasionally provided with a little articulation so that arms, feet, or a lower jaw could move separately. The "Magnitoons" operators worked behind vertical screens to control the figures used in these programs (Fig. 13-20). There

Fig. 13–20. Magnitoons magnet board as used on Bob Emery's "Small Fry."

have also been horizontal-stage magnet boards, the most ambitious undertaking of this type being the huge terrain model the Army constructed for training purposes, where dozens of operators moved around underneath a large relief map, each controlling a separate truck or tank. The greatest problem in magnet control is to make it possible for the operator to watch what he is doing, since he must work from the back side of an opaque board.

BRETZICON ANIMATOR

The Bretzicon was the first animation machine, to the author's knowledge, which was built with a horizontal stage. (A 45-degree mirror beneath the stage reflected a vertical image for the studio camera to focus on.) This machine made possible the bodily movement of white objects across a picture or map, limited articulation of figures, plus a combination of many of the other animation techniques which have been listed above. The pull-out technique was originally developed as part of the functioning of this machine. A front diffusing sheet (layout paper, tracing cloth, or matte celluloid) is the basic requirement. All light is from the front. Since the stage is horizontal, a number of symbols can be placed on it at one time and will stay in place of their own weight without having to be held.

When front light is cast on a translucent surface such as frosted acetate or the others just described, anything black behind it will not be seen. A black-gloved hand, for example, is invisible. A white object, on the other hand, such as a white arrow cut out of cardboard, will reflect the front light brilliantly when brought into contact with the back surface of the diffusion sheet. If it is lifted away from the surface, it becomes fuzzy and, if taken far enough back, will dissolve away. It is thus possible to put a suitable handle on a symbol (such as an arrow, a ship, or

Fig. 13–21. Bretzicon in operation at CBS in 1945. Operators are Dorothea Claras and Henry Cassirer, subsequently chief of "CBS Television News."

an airplane) and move it anywhere and in any manner over the surface of the map. This complete freedom was very important in animating war strategy, when last-minute news stories left little time to prepare the animation of military developments. Further, this flexibility in operation opened a wide field for creative effort. Manual skill was very important, and there was found to be a great difference between a good and a mediocre animator operator.

Figure 13-21 shows the Bretzicon as it looked in operation except that a camera was not in position in front of the machine at the time the picture was taken. Two operators are working one animation, a method which was necessary when as many as four symbols had to be moved independently at the same time. If a group of symbols were to be moved together (such as a string of airplanes or ships), they could all be painted on one black card and slid along by hand against a guide.

Fig. 13–22. The author demonstrating with a small Bretzicon model.

One of the most complex animations performed by this method illustrated an interview with Bill Offenhouser about his new method of mosquito control. He described how a female mosquito was captured and a recording made of her mating call. Then he described how this was amplified and played over a loudspeaker in a mosquito swamp, attracting all the male mosquitoes for miles around. As they approached the source of sound, they were sucked into a crematorium and disappeared. To animate this story, an articulated mosquito was built which could flap its wings (by two-finger control) and hover around in front of the loudspeaker. To illustrate the sound radiating from the speaker, the rotating

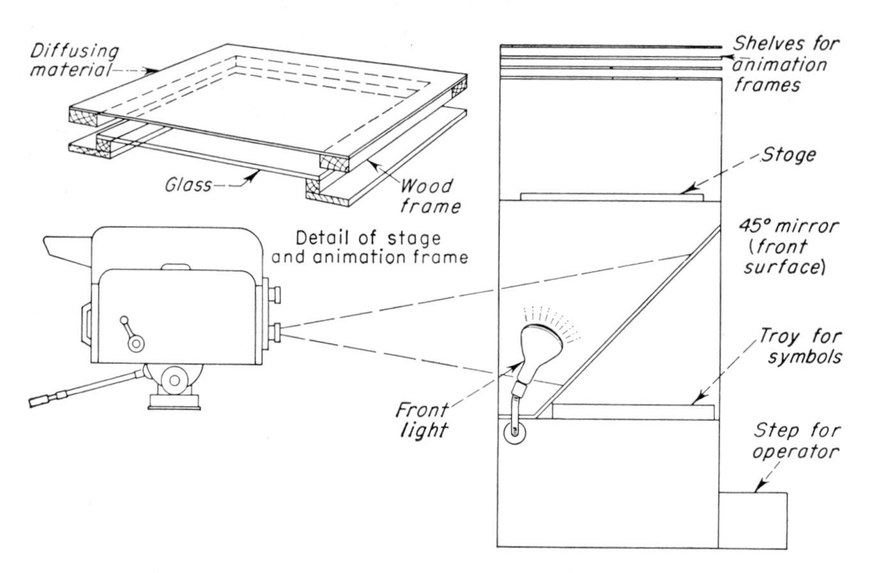

Fig. 13–23. Diagram of Bretzicon.

spiral device was used to indicate flow (Fig. 13-24). The spiral was painted in white on a black card, and a shutter with the proper opening was placed between it and the back of the picture. Thus only one segment of the spiral could be seen, and as it was rotated, the lines in this segment seemed to move outward from the center. This spiral and shutter assembly had to be removed from the back of the animation before a mosquito could fly across the same area, and this was done by simply folding it back on a scotch-tape hinge. The mosquito was flown in, buzzed around a little with a stylized flapping of wings (to the accompaniment of appropriate sound effects), and then entered into the loudspeaker. His wings folded, and he descended into the region of electric coils. Here the mosquito was deftly replaced with a tiny pile of ashes which continued on down to disappear into a garbage can at the bottom. The disappearance was effected by a kind of wipe-out. The symbol was moved behind a piece of black paper (the edge of which could not be seen) which covered the lower portion of the animation up to the top of the garbage can.

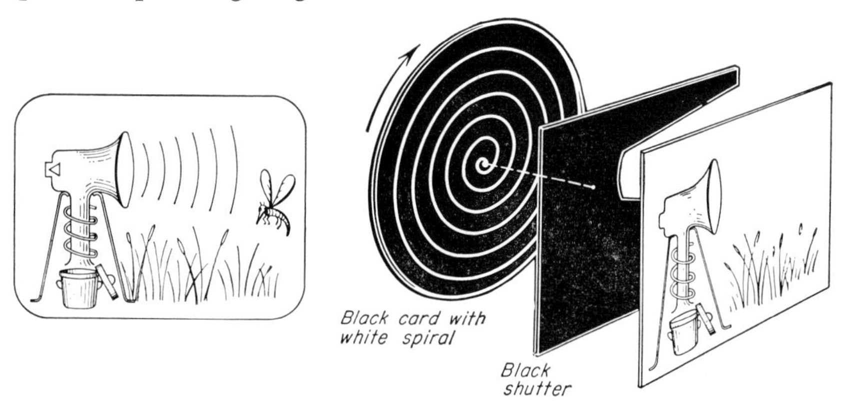

Fig. 13–24. Mosquito animation done on Bretzicon.

It was found that symbols had to be weighted or they would be subject to a lot of unintended movements as the operator took hold of them or let go. Light cardboard symbols were much more manageable if a short piece of ¾-inch iron rod were fastened to the back. This served as a weight as well as a handle. When an animation required a battle line to bulge and change position on the map, a flexible and weighted cord was devised. A thick piece of white cotton cord would have looked as well but would not have formed itself into any desired shape and stayed there. We finally obtained strings of BB shot sewn into cloth for weighting the hems of dresses. Two or three of these strings wound with a heavy white yarn gave the required effect.

14

Studio Effects

The field of special effects referred to here as "studio effects" includes everything from representing rain, snow, fog, and so forth, to the preparation of imitation food which will not disintegrate under the hot lights. There are many techniques listed in this chapter with which the author has not had personal experience although they have all been used in television or motion pictures. The reader is advised to experiment thoroughly with these effects before counting on them for program use. His experiments may reveal other and better ways of achieving the desired result.

SNOW

Snow has usually been simulated with bleached cornflakes or white confetti, either of which can be obtained from supply houses in New York or Hollywood for this specific purpose. For a light powder snow, rough unfinished Pablum has been extensively used. It is usually superior to any other powder since it is nontoxic if inhaled, although there are some performers who will be found to be allergic to it. In one snow number on the Fred Waring program 500 pounds of Pablum was used, calling for the services of six stagehands to scatter it down. Snow has also been simulated by chopped chicken feathers, unroasted potato chips, borax flakes, and soap flakes.

John Demott at CBS has simulated a swirling blizzard of snow with chopped feathers and two electric fans blowing from opposite sides of the set. Feathers are used for a swirling snow rather than paper or breakfast food because they are light and blow around much more easily. The two fans must not blow into each other, but past each other, so that eddies will develop between them. The trouble with feathers, however, is that they don't know when to stop swirling; after a heavy snowfall in one set, occasional snowflakes may be seen drifting through interior scenes in other parts of the studio.

More recently a new snow material has come into use—a light plastic fluff which looks and falls exactly like snow, even in the closest shot, and has no toxic or allergic effects on anyone. It is expanded polystyrene, obtained as a by-product in standard plastics manufacture.

The best method of scattering any of these types of snow is to construct a "snow bag" (Fig. 14-1). This is usually made from a piece of

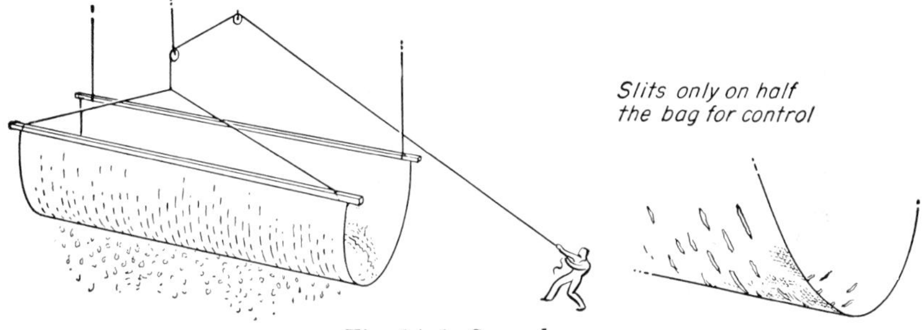

Fig. 14–1. Snow bag.

light canvas fastened at each end to a batten and suspended by the battens above the set. The canvas is cut up with innumerable slits 2 inches long and about ¼ inch wide. One end of the bag is held stationary, and the other is gently raised or lowered. As soon as the bag is touched, snow will begin to sift through the slits in the canvas and the amount of snowfall can be controlled by the degree of agitation. The higher the snow bag is placed, the more even and realistic will be the result. It is also safer; if a lump of snow should fall from the end of the bag, it will be somewhat broken up by the time it gets into the picture. Some snow bags have been made by splitting the bag into ribbons and relying on the spaces between ribbons to sift the snow down. This is not too safe, however, since large amounts of material can sometimes pass through such long slits, whereas the 2-inch slits will never let too much go through.

Snowdrifts in a set may be built up out of wood frames covered with chicken wire and plastered with newspapers dunked in gelatin glue. The papier-mâché should then be covered with old canvas, which can be painted with scene paint plus asbestos powder.

RAIN

Rain can best be produced by using real water. Water is cheap and plentiful and gives a very good illusion of rain. It makes a mess on the studio floor, of course; and if anyone lives downstairs, it is recommended that some means be used for containing it, once it falls. John Demott usually spreads a large tarpaulin with a raised edge. When the show is over and he has an inch or two of water to get out of the tarp, he throws a few wheelbarrow loads of dry sand onto it, lets the sand soak up the water, and shovels it out.

Sometimes a good illusion of rain is obtained without any actual drops falling. If the lighting is right, the sky is dark, possibly with clouds scudding across it, and a little glycerin is put on people's clothes, hats,

Fig. 14–2. Overhead sprinkling system provides rain for a Dinah Shore number on her NBC program.

or umbrellas to give them a wet shine, the effect will definitely be that of a rainy day. Actually, one has to look very sharply in the usual slow drizzle to see raindrops falling anyway. The feeling of rain is conveyed by the surfaces of things. It is only in a sudden summer shower that raindrops are really visible. Most of the methods that are used for producing a shower of rain make the drops too large to be real.

The set should be specially painted to give a wet effect on things. Demott suggests spraying over the regular scene paint with thin varnish or a solution of 1 pint of LePage's glue to 1 quart of water. Only the areas which require a damp appearance need to be so treated. This will both darken the area and give it a wet and shiny surface. Props can be sprayed with common drugstore glycerin, which is then allowed to dry.

Motion-picture rain is usually produced by crisscrossing the top of the set with water pipes which have very tiny perforations on the top side. When the pressure is turned on, the water sprays up from these holes, strikes a deflecting plate, and falls in an even spray. Large amounts of rain, such as this, are seldom necessary in a television set. The perforated pipe is sometimes used above a window or along the edge of a roof, provided that there is some way of catching the water when it falls. A canvas "soaker hose" is often used instead of a pipe.

A group of sprinkling cans fastened to a rack so that they can all be tipped at once will usually give rain for long enough to satisfy most requirements. If other equipment is not available, a single sprinkling

Fig. 14–3. Sprinkling cans ready to provide rain.

can may be used close in front of the camera lens. The actors don't get wet this way; they have to be made up with glycerin instead. But the raindrops, large to begin with, come out gigantic. Still it looks like rain.

The most satisfactory water device is a complete circulatory system, sprinkler, collecting pan, and pump, so that the rain may be kept going for as long as necessary. The collecting pan must be a "fur-lined bathtub" (hair felt will do) so that noise is eliminated. A pump capable of several gallons per minute at about a 10-foot head should be used. The pump and its electric motor must be built into a soundproof box. Austin Huhn constructed these rain units in many sizes, including one in which the rain curtain is only about 3 feet square for use as a gobo between camera and scene.

For the studio which does not wish to use real water, Austin Huhn has recommended superimposing a Rain Glamé, a long mat woven of ⅛-inch cellophane strips and run downward in front of the camera on a standard title drum. According to this expert, superimposing rain of any kind is generally superior to trying to do the effect in front of the camera which is shooting the scene.

Bill Healton at NBC in Chicago has simulated rain very successfully with thin (¼-inch) cellophane strips hanging from a batten. This method is for use behind a window when the camera is inside looking out. If the light is just right, gentle movements of the batten will cause highlights to run down the cellophane very much like drops of water running down the windowpane.

The lighting of falling rain is very important if it is to be seen at all. It must be lighted from the side, and always with a hard light. A fresnel spot with the lens removed will provide a good light source for this purpose. John Demott has used a little blue ink in the water to make it pick up the light better. Some have used condensed milk for the same purpose.

FIRE

Fire regulations prevent television studios from using open fire with quite the same freedom which is possible on the motion-picture set. Small amounts of fire are used in torches or braziers, provided that extinguishers are kept ready. If a large fire is needed, sometimes a small flame close to the lens will seem to be enveloping the entire scene. If open flame cannot be used, flames on film can be superimposed. Theatrical-effects projectors can project flame effects on a background screen if the fire is to be in the background, or foreground projection can be used in the manner of the motion-picture glass shot. A fire in a fireplace can be simulated by pieces of silk or paper in an updraft. But this cannot be shown in close-up, or the illusion will be lost.

Small open flame. Canned heat or alcohol flames are best for a small flame near the camera. The flames won't show up very well, however, unless a little salt is put into the fuel. The yellow sodium flame shows up much better. When a small fire is used close to the lens or a film of flames is superimposed, the individual flames may look very large and it is hard to make the fire seem to be coming from the set in the background. Since the source of the flames is below the bottom of the screen, they will appear to pass across all the objects in the picture instead of beginning somewhere among them. If a lot of smoke is released in the set, however, this method can still give a fairly good illusion provided that it is not on the screen too long.

Projected fire. Projected flames can be classified into two types, foreground and background. In the case of the background fire seen through a window or in the distance, either front or rear projection can be used, depending on the space allowed, with the appropriate type of screen. Theatrical-effects projectors achieve a fire effect by rotating two sheets of irregular glass at different speeds in front of the light beam. If the fire is projected too large, however, it may fail to give the effect of distance because individual flames will be too big.

Foreground flames can be projected by the same machine on a sheet of glass in the manner of the motion-picture glass shot. The glass must be

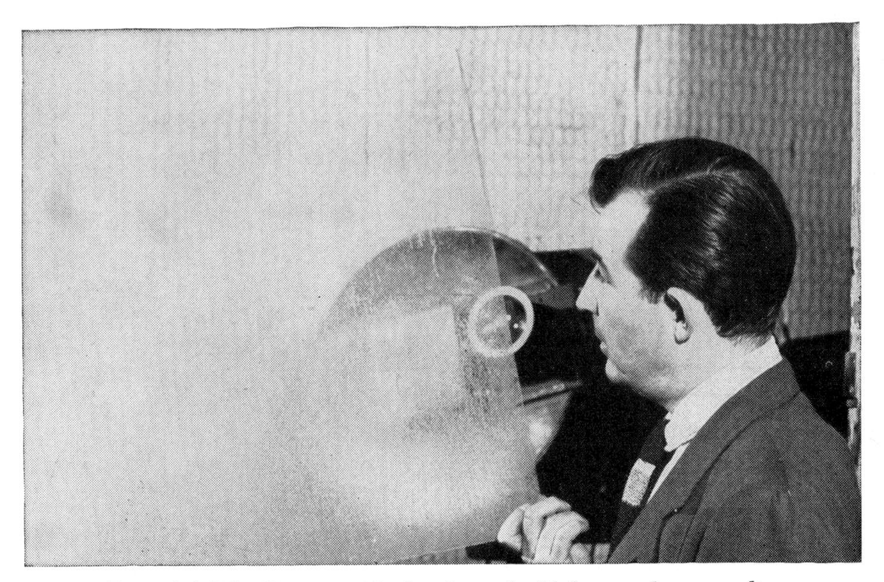

Fig. 14–4. John Demott with glass frosted with beer and epsom salts.

clear if the background scene is to show through it; yet it must be frosted in some way if anything is to be projected upon it. John Demott solved the problem on a CBS show by spraying the bottom portion of the glass with a solution of stale beer and epsom salts. This created a dense frosting which graduated into clear glass in the upper part. Since the frosted glass was close to the effects projector, the individual flames were relatively small in size and gave a better illusion of originating within the set than if an alcohol flame had been used (Fig. 14-4).

Fireplace fire. The fireplace fire is created by implication better than by direct creation. If you can get around showing the fire itself and produce the illusion by creating a flickering fire*light,* the audience may feel they have seen a fire, even though you have not shown them actual flames. Methods of creating firelight are outlined in Chap. 18 on Television Lighting, under "Special-effect lighting."

If real fire cannot be used, paper or cloth flames blown up by an electric fan or the convection from a few hot lamps is convincing enough in a long shot, but this must be very well done to stand even a medium close-up. If a little smoke is added, the effect will be improved. A shot which enlarges the fireplace to even a quarter of the screen width is likely to give away the effect, however. Beware of close-ups on all standard theatrical effects; they are made for audiences that watch the show entirely in long shot.

SMOKE

Smoke and fog are similar in some respects, and sometimes both can be created with the same material if it is used in different ways. Realistic smoke is usually thick and billowing and moves rather rapidly across the screen, especially if it is in the foreground of the shot. There have been many unfortunate attempts at fog which more closely resembled the above description of smoke than the low-lying, evenly distributed haze which characterizes fog.

The easiest method of making smoke is to use liquid titanium tetrachloride. When this liquid is poured out and comes into contact with the air, it gives off thick white fumes. The more air is blown across it, the more smoke is produced. If a small amount of localized smoke is needed, a rubber bulb can be attached to a length of ¼-inch rubber hose and the chemical is simply poured into the bulb or hose. In the CBS show "Mr. I-magination" a small locomotive was equipped to emit puffs of smoke when the engineer squeezed a rubber bulb in the engine cab. Titanium tetrachloride fumes, although not toxic, are extremely irritating and will cause actors to cough; so it is best used only in small amounts.

John Demott has suggested another method of smoke production. A solution of saltpeter in water is prepared, 3 parts water to 1 of saltpeter. Thin rags are dipped in this solution and then allowed to dry. If the dried rags are spread out on a board or piece of tin and ignited, they will smolder and give off a thick smoke, the amount of which can be increased by adding more thicknesses of rag.

Special "smoke candles" are available in Hollywood which when lighted with a match will glow like incense. Austin Huhn obtained more smoke from one of these candles by putting it into a can to which a bellows was attached and blowing the smoke out as from a beekeeper's smoke pot.

The hot plate is a useful piece of equipment for smoke production, and there are several materials which when heated on a hot plate will give off smoke. Bill Eddy mentions asthma powder, a vegetable preparation, which emits a thick cloud of whitish-yellow smoke and creates a minimum of ill effects among the studio personnel. Powdered charcoal, he goes on to say, can be added to this after it is ignited to produce a black smoke. Common bath salts will produce smoke. Probably the best, however, is a smoke powder made from incense and ammonium chloride.

Chuck Holden had success with a chemical method of making smoke. In this method three 2-gallon bottles with two-hole stoppers are used, as shown in Fig. 14-5. Air is pumped into the first bottle, containing hydrochloric acid. The acid fumes are thus forced into the next bottle,

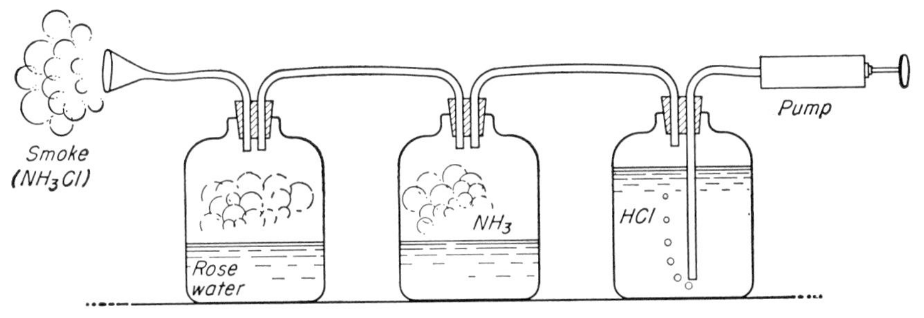

Fig. 14–5. Generator for ammonium chloride smoke.

which contains ammonium hydroxide (or ammonia). The fumes pass on through the neutralizing solution, and a thick white smoke (ammonium chloride) results. The acrid smell of this is greatly reduced by passing it through a third bottle of rose water before it is used on the set.

Another and totally different method of creating the effect of smoke has been mentioned earlier in connection with snow, rain, and fire—photographing the effect on film and superimposing it over the scene. If milk is poured into a tank of clear water and the camera shoots the action in slow motion and upside down, the billowing of the milk downward will look like smoke in the air billowing upward. For black smoke, ink or black water-color paint can be used.

The most controllable smoke effect that the author knows was developed by Bob Banner for his use on the Fred Waring show. This device was known as a "smokehouse" because the smoke was entirely contained (Fig. 14-6). One camera poked its lens through the drapes that formed the sides of the house, and the smoke picture that it picked up was superimposed on the other camera's shots. This is an extremely desirable method for a musical show, where throat irritation may ruin a singer's performance. Titanium tetrachloride, dry ice, or any other smoke producer was placed on a tray at the bottom of the unit, and the resulting smoke was illuminated by a thin wedge of light coming through a single slit in the side. This meant that the camera could focus on this fixed distance and all illuminated smoke would be in this plane of focus. Any degree of agitation could be achieved simply by moving the curtains which comprised the sides of the box. Other openings in the curtain were also provided through which air or more smoke could be blown into the chamber to provide a great variety of smoke effects. If the smoke should

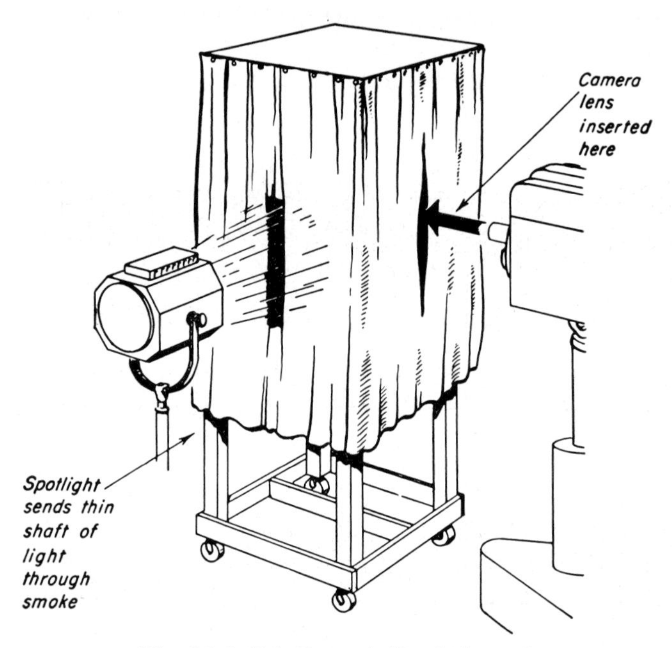

Fig. 14–6. Bob Banner's "smokehouse."

become too thick, the top of the unit could be removed and the smokehouse quickly cleared.

NBC built a smokehouse of a somewhat different design; a glass-walled box about 3 feet high and 4 feet wide and about 1 foot in thickness. This is used in front of the camera in the manner of a gobo.

FOG

Dry ice is a common material for creating fog and smoke. Real fog is produced in large quantities by this method, and breathed without discomfort. Dry ice is frozen carbon dioxide; when the substance thaws, it skips the liquid state and goes directly from a solid into a gas. This lowers the temperature of the surrounding air, and any water vapor that may happen to be present condenses into a cloud. The more humid the air, the greater the condensation; so the best smoke is produced when the dry ice is placed in water or when humid air or steam is blown across it. Boiling water must be used, however, or each piece of dry ice will simply freeze the water around it and seal itself into a chunk of ice. Some studios have created ground fog by keeping a series of pails heating on hot plates until the water boiled, then dropping dry ice into the pails and

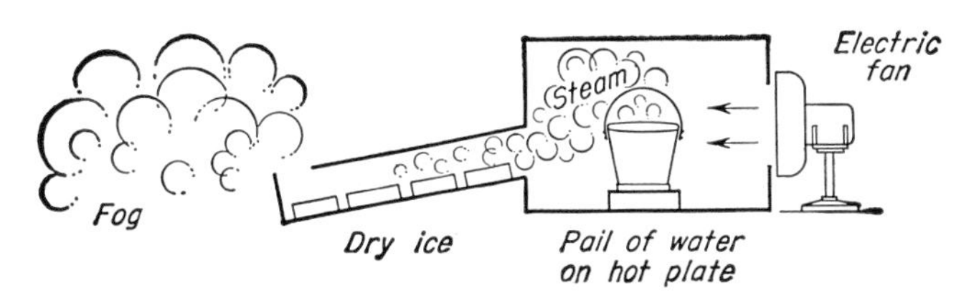

Fig. 14–7. Simple fog machine. Boiling water creates steam which is blown across dry ice to condense into fog.

setting them around at strategic places in the set. Such a pail will boil out great quantities of low-lying fog for a minute or so until the water cools down, at which time it must be replaced by another pail if the fog is to continue.

Fog on the motion-picture set is usually produced by atomized oil. This is known as crystal oil in Hollywood—castor oil without the smell.

Light mineral oil has been used in oil-spray machines in New York television studios. Atomized oil will hang longer in the air than the fog created by dry ice. The latter will eventually evaporate, whereas the oil merely settles. Actors may find their hair and clothes a little greasy from this settling, but aside from that there are no adverse effects. A large paint-spray machine is used for laying the fog. Oil painted onto a hot plate with a paintbrush gives off vapors which are then blown over the set by an electric fan. Wherever smoke and fog are to be lying in layers, the studio must be cold and the floors must be wetted down.

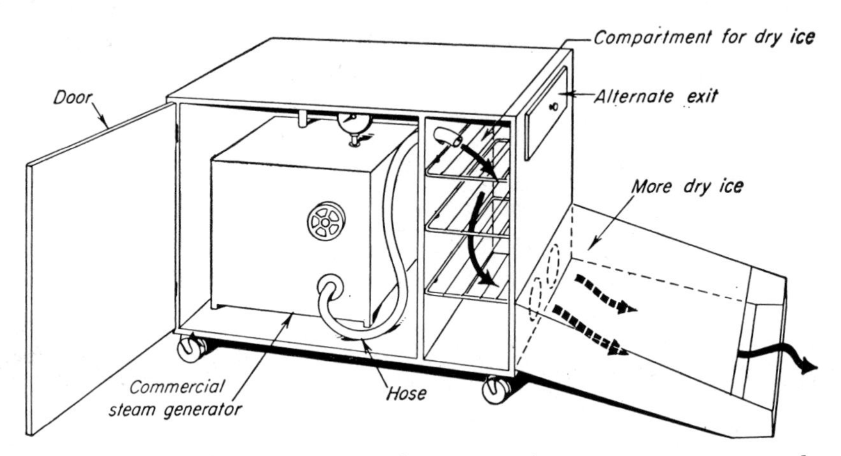

Fig. 14–8. Improved fog machine with commercial steam generator to produce greater quantities of steam and hence fog.

Certain risks are undertaken when fog is produced in the television studio. Each of the following misfortunes has occurred at one time or another when fog was attempted: (1) The fog may be altogether too dense so that the scene is practically invisible to the television camera. (2) It may so fill the entire studio that interior sets will also be permeated with it, and there will be as much fog inside a house as there is outside. (3) The fog material may be irritating to the actors and make them cough (as when titanium tetrachloride or other fumes are used in large quantities). (4) Although a small amount of movement is desirable, the fog may swirl and billow too much and look like smoke instead. (All four of these faults were combined on one unfortunate program when the special-effects man spread titanium tetrachloride around with great enthusiasm.) (5) The fog may be too thin, may lie too low, or may evaporate too fast so that an insufficient effect is obtained.

All these troubles may be avoided if a fog filter is used over the lens of the camera. The "American Cinematographer Handbook" lists fourteen different kinds of fog filters used in motion-picture work, manufactured by George Scheibe or Harrison and Harrison. Lacking any of these, a very thin net or scrim can be placed in front of the lens. Some people have sprayed wax on a sheet of glass or clear plastic to make a fog filter. If several such diffusers are used, one can be moved against the other to create a moving or drifting effect. The filter method sacrifices one characteristic of fog, however, which is the swirling movement often seen, especially when someone walks through the fog. This can be simulated, however, by a small amount of smoke picked up by another camera and superimposed, provided that the movement is not too fast. Another possibility is to generate a small amount of $TiCl_4$ smoke just in front of the camera lens.

The Mole-Richardson Company has produced several models of commercial fog makers which run from a small hand unit that sprays a special "fog liquid" from a 4½-gallon tank (Fig. 14-9) to a senior model

Fig. 14–9. Fog Maker machine produced by Mole-Richardson.

using a 55-gallon drum, capable of creating an ocean fog over a large area or the effect of large volumes of smoke issuing from the windows of a burning building. A dry-ice cooling unit can be attached to one of these models to cool the fog so it will hug the floor and swirl around people's knees or ankles as they walk through the set.

BREAKAWAY GLASS

Panes of glass which can be broken without danger of cutting the actors can be obtained in Hollywood and New York. Heretofore made of sugar, breakaway glass is now made from resin. Of course if the glass does not have to be broken by an actor's fist but is hit by a hammer or other heavy object and there is no particular danger, regular glass can be used and will create its own sound effect. Breakaway bottles are also made of sugar or plaster, which is then painted to represent glass.

BREAKAWAY FURNITURE

To make a chair which will hold together until it is sat in or until it collides with someone's head, cut the chair in pieces and then peg it together with matchwood or small dowels of balsa. First mark the chair for cutting, and then drill holes across the cuts. After the cuts are made,

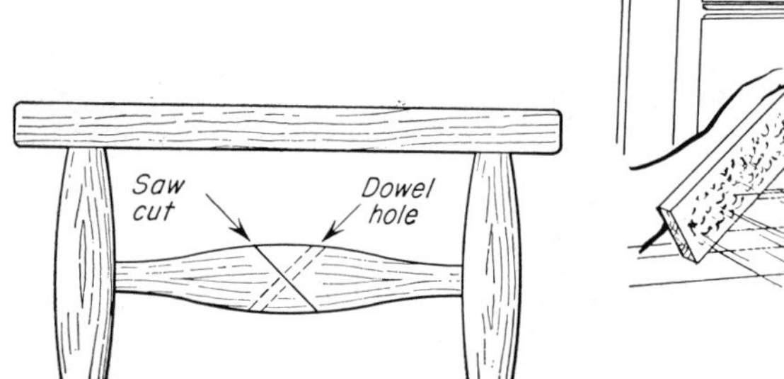

Fig. 14–10. Method of preparing breakaway furniture.

Fig. 14–11. Rubber-cement cobwebs.

the parts can be held together again by tiny dowels, which are all that really break when the chair goes to pieces. The strength of the chair can be controlled by the size and strength of the dowel sticks; balsa is the weaker of the two materials. The chair may be broken in rehearsal and pegged together again in a few minutes' time (Fig. 14-10).

COBWEBS

A simple way to make cobwebs is contributed by Chuck Holden. Two flat sticks are held together with a thick layer of rubber cement between. As they are pulled apart, long streaks of the partly set cement are stretched between them, which can then be laid across windows or bric-a-brac. Liquid plastic can be used instead of rubber cement if desired (Fig. 14-11). These cobwebs, like those made by any other method, are made much more visible and realistic if they are liberally dusted with talcum powder.

A standard cobweb machine can be made by attaching a small can to the face of an electric fan. A cover is placed on the can and held with a center screw so there is a narrow crack all around its edge.

Fig. 14–12. A cobweb spinner made by Mole-Richardson shown in operation.

Rubber cement in the can seeps out the crack and is blown forward in long threads which catch onto whatever they touch.

Fig. 14–13. Dinah Shore with NBC bubble machine.

EXPLOSIONS, FLASHES, AND PUFFS OF SMOKE

Magnesium pills and lycopodium dust are the usual materials for these effects. A lycopodium burner for flash-fire effects is illustrated in Fig. 14-14. A lighted wick or can of sterno is placed in the center, and a sudden puff into the air hose will blow the lycopodium powder up through the holes, where it will immediately burn in a flash of flame.

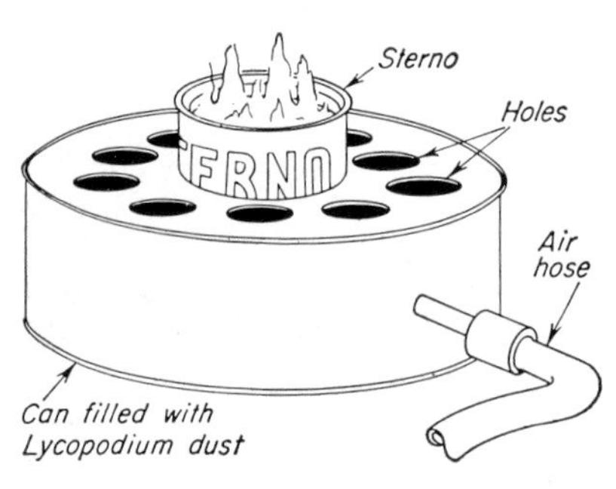

Fig. 14–14. Lycopodium-dust flash pot. (After Eddy.)

Figure 14-15 illustrates two methods of preparing magnesium flash powder for studio use. A 3-ampere fuse is opened up and without destroying the fuse wire is filled with photographer's flash powder. The fuse can then be screwed into any ordinary electric socket, so long as it is horizontal. When the circuit is closed, the fuse will immediately blow and the magnesium will go up in a puff of white smoke. The second method shown is capable of a bigger effect and is somewhat safer to use.

It is a good plan to check local fire regulations before attempting any

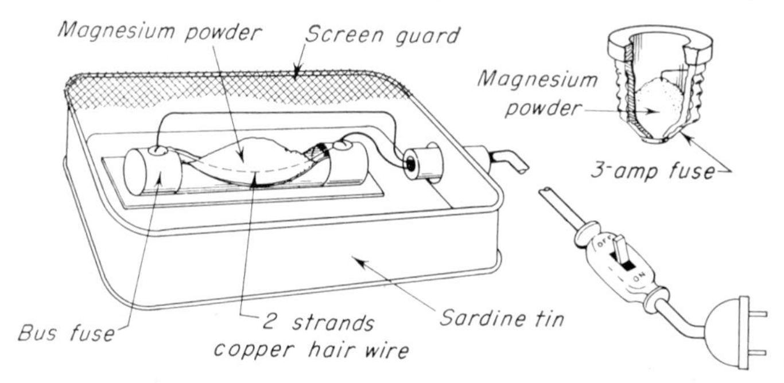

Fig. 14–15. Two ways to prepare magnesium-powder flash pots.

fire or explosion effects in the studio, and extreme caution should be exercised in their use at all times.

GUNS

Gunshots in television are usually handled by the sound-effects man, who coordinates, more or less, with the actor as he points the gun and pulls the trigger. Sometimes a special effect is required, however, where a gun actually spouts smoke or flame. A toy gun on the market, the Roy Rogers Smoker, which simulates a 45-calibre revolver, can be used for this purpose and altered to look like other types of guns by cutting off some of the barrel. The Smokers are equipped with milk of magnesia powder, which can be made to give off more smoke by the addition of common cornstarch. A smoking gun barrel may be simulated by cotton soaked in saltpeter, a method described earlier under "Smoke." A Buck Rogers flame gun was once constructed with flashlight batteries and a thin-wire coil which would heat red-hot when the current flowed, and was then loaded with magician's flash paper.

MISCELLANY

Following are techniques used to obtain some of the more commonly used studio effects:

Water droplets (that don't evaporate): Glycerin—use for raindrops, tears, etc.

Dewdrops on flowers: Spray flowers with water containing a little ink—the droplets will be more visible.

Icicles: Strips of cellophane dipped in melted paraffin and gasoline.

Soapsuds: For large amounts of suds, fill a milk bottle one-quarter full with powdered soap or detergent, and add same amount of hot water. Then drop in a few pieces of dry ice. Take cover.

Blood and gore: Ketchup; chocolate sirup; or whipped cream with vegetable dye and copper filings or tobacco.

A shot in the head: Special-effects man uses a peashooter from off stage loaded with a gelatin capsule containing vegetable dye. Or actor holds chocolate capsule in his hand and claps his hand to his head; when he takes it away, blood is visible.

Aging clothes: Put rocks in the pockets; dampen and hang overnight; rub with beeswax for shine.

Flying bullets: Drill holes in set, and put corks in them from behind. Pull corks for effect. Machine-gun holes can be made to appear by pulling scotch tape off series of prepared holes from the back of the set and letting back light shine through.

Breaking vase or windowpane: A mousetrap is mounted beneath the vase or window and released by a hidden wire.

Falling petals: Petals are held on plant by threading them with a thin wire. As wire is pulled out, petals will fall.

Pots steaming or boiling: If the studio stove does not function, put dry ice into pots containing hot water. Don't close any such pot tightly, or a tremendous pressure will be built up.

For methods of making food look more appetizing (though less edible), the author is indebted to John Demott and Jim Furness for the following suggestions:

Beer: A pinch of sodium bicarbonate whitens the froth.

Coffee: At normal strength coffee often looks too black. A very weak coffee will look better. A little dry ice in the bottom will keep it steaming.

Butter: Butter will look better if mixed with a little margarine coloring.

Milk and cream: There is not enough difference between the tones of milk and cream to show any difference. Pour off the cream and add a pinch of turmeric (a yellow spice), then gently replace.

Meats: Paint the lean parts with undiluted grape juice.

Grapes: Powder with talcum, hold in front of an electric fan to blow off the excess, and then dip in water.

For substitute foods for use under hot lights, the following may be employed:

Bread: A permanent loaf of bread can be carved from a block of wood.

Fried eggs: Sandwich bread and apricots (substitute colored bread for as many foods as possible).

Ice cream: Mashed potatoes colored with vegetable dye.

Cracked ice in glass: Crinkled cellophane.

Caviar: Buckshot and axle grease.

Wines: Coca-Cola, vegetable dyes in water.

Liquor: Tea.

15

Electronic Effects

The most common electronic effect is the superimposure. Many supers are attempted for no greater purpose than the decorative effect which they achieve. An example is a shot of a violinist on which is superimposed a close-up of the strings of the violin. Sometimes a super will serve to associate two things which are not close enough to be shown in the same shot. A speaker and his opponent listening and reacting to his words can be shown on the same screen by superimposure, provided that the important part of each picture falls on a reasonably dark area in the other. If this is not possible, some form of matting (Chap. 12) must be resorted to.

The most successful superimposures are those carrying meaning which is not present in either shot alone. The whole is thus greater than the sum of its parts. A Philco commercial once superimposed a shot of a musician over a close-up of the speaker of a phonograph. The meaning was clear: This phonograph sounds as though the musician were actually present. Another use of the super is in the realm of fantasy. Ghosts and other supernatural effects are easy to achieve by this means.

Whether the two shots of a superimposure tend to blend together into a sort of composite shot so that they seem to be made with only one camera or whether they remain separate entities so that the effect is only that of two pictures on the screen at once will depend largely on the perspective within the two pictures.

Figure 15-1 illustrates creation of a superimposure effect for a General Electric commercial on a Fred Waring program. A washing machine was shown on the screen, and then the working mechanism of the machine was superimposed to give an X-ray view. The reader will notice, however, in the resultant picture, that the effect is not quite perfect. The sizes of the two pictures seem to match, but the perspective in one does not match the perspective in the other. Note how the camera on the washer is shooting down from a high angle so that the top of the machine is visible. The other camera, however, is shooting level, so that no horizontal planes in the mechanism are visible. Either the mechanism should have been placed on a low stand just as the washer was, or the

Fig. 15–1. The interior of a washing machine is shown in "X-ray" view by superimposure. (From "Fred Waring Show." Photos courtesy of *Popular Science* Magazine.)

camera which took this second shot should have been considerably higher than the other camera.

THE GHOST EFFECT

The appearance of a ghost on the television screen is a relatively easy effect to accomplish, although what the ghost is called upon to do may complicate the problem greatly. Actually it is much easier to do ghosts on television than it is on film, because you can *see* the effect as you do it. This is very important, because inexact register of the two shots might place the ghost in the wrong spot—show him standing through a chair or a few inches off the floor. When this is done in motion pictures, the easiest way is to use a large sheet of glass at a 45-degree angle between camera and scene and image the ghost on the scene by reflecting him on this glass. (This method is described in Chap. 11.) The advantage, of course, is that the cameraman can see the final result at the time of shooting. If he had taken two pictures, one of the scene and one of the ghost, and superimposed by double printing, he would not be sure that the register was correct until the film came back from the lab.

When two cameras are involved in a ghost effect—or almost any other type of superimposure for that matter—the order is given to the cameramen to freeze before the cameras are superimposed; not even the slightest movement of any sort can be tolerated when the cameras are superimposed. The reason, of course, is that the two superimposed shots are supposed to look like one shot. If either camera moves, the ghost will be seen to shift within the set and the effect will be robbed of its illusion. This rule can be broken only if both cameras move in exact synchrony.

The usual practice on ghost shows is to equip one set with a black velour background and a black floor so that only the actor who is to portray the ghost reflects any light. Thus only the ghost is superimposed

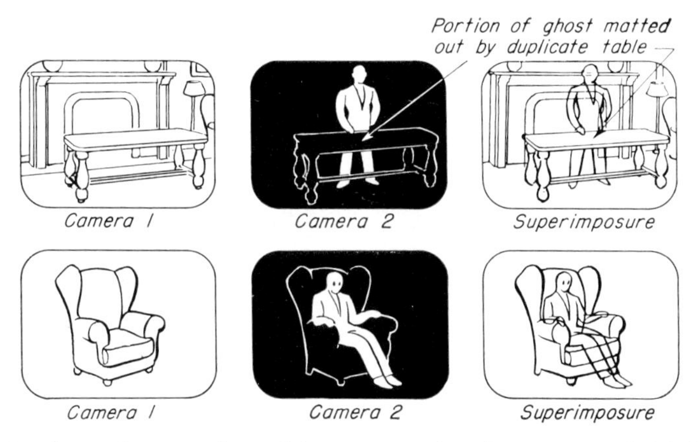

Fig. 15–2. Ghost effect complicated by necessity for ghost to move behind objects in the real scene. Solution is to have duplicate objects (black) in the ghost set.

on the background scene; there are no background areas appearing at the same time.

If the ghost must move around through the set, careful marks must be made on the floor of his black set to represent the furniture of the main set so that he will seem to walk *around* a table instead of *through* it. If he is to go *behind* something, special arrangements must be made. It would not do to see the ghost through a solid table. The ghost will have to be matted out in the part which is supposed to disappear as he walks behind the table. The best way to do this is simply to place a duplicate table, but black, in the ghost set. If this is carefully placed and the position of the camera is marked, it will register with the real table and matte out the ghost in just the proper way.

It was by this method that a ghost was made to sit down in a chair on an ABC show. It was an overstuffed chair, and as the ghost sat in it, a part of him was hidden by the chair arm. The fact that this part of the ghost disappeared made the illusion of his being in the chair complete. The only way this could be done was to seat the ghost in a duplicate chair, which was accurately placed and covered with black velour. The arm of the black chair matted out the correct portion of the ghost (Fig. 15-2).

Whenever a ghost effect is used, the director is never really sure his ghost is going to be in the right place and disappear behind the right objects. Accurate register is possible only if the superimposure can be previewed just before it is used and last-minute adjustments made. Not all switching equipment can allow this to be done.

The positions of actors and furniture are, of course, marked on the floor, as is the position of the camera. The framing of the camera is very important, and this must also be marked. Wax pencil marks on the cameraman's view finder are generally used—just enough to help him register important points in the picture, but not so much that he can't use the view finder during the rest of the show. In the case of Fig. 15-2 it is the top of the table which is particularly critical.

This method of marking view finders, however, is predicated on one assumption—the height and width adjustments on the camera must not be changed. If they are, the view-finder marks will be thrown out. In many studios it is the practice to wait until just before air time before lining up the cameras. If the view finders are to be marked, however, the cameras must receive their final line-up before the marks are made. Before an afternoon's rehearsal is usually too early for this to be done. Conditions within the camera may change so that further adjustments are necessary before the evening show. The best plan is to delay marking the view finders until just before air time, after the cameras have been lined up.

Another problem of the ghost effect has to do with the audio pickup. In most cases the ghost will be conversing with someone. But he will be in one set, picked up on one mike, while the other person is in another set under another mike. The problem is to make the quality of sound picked up by the two microphones match. The quality of the sound a microphone picks up is determined to a large extent by the conditions around the mike. Whether the walls of the set are hard and reflectant or soft and sound-absorbent like the black velour walls of the ghost set and whether the mike is close or far from the source of sound are some of the factors that affect sound quality. The only way to be sure, of course, is to try it and see. If there is too great a difference in sound quality, the ghost illusion will be weakened. This same problem is met in doing two-camera montage or composite shots.

THE FANTASY SUPERIMPOSURE

In the ballet production of "Alice in Wonderland" on "Thru the Crystal Ball," Paul Belanger wanted the Cheshire cat to appear and disappear in a tree above Alice. Arthur Treacher, who played the cat, was placed behind a black flat, cut out so that only his head and arms could reach through. He was made up like a cat, and the rest of the cat body and the limb it sat on were painted on the flat. When this scene was superimposed over the tree above Bambi Lynn, the tree limb with the cat on it matched a limb on Bambi's tree and the cat appeared fairly solid against a dark foliage background. The cat would disappear at will, then suddenly appear again to say something, and disappear again. Finally he was to fade away slowly from tail to head, leaving nothing but his smile. This was a wipe-out problem. Larry Goldwasser, the designer, solved it by providing several stagehands with black velour

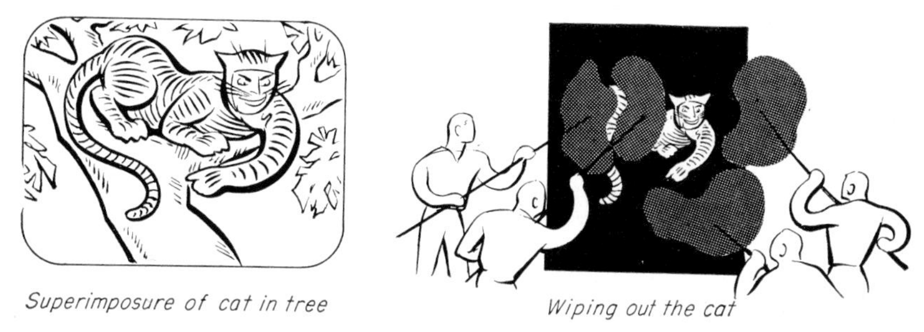

Superimposure of cat in tree *Wiping out the cat*

Fig. 15–3. Fantasy superimposure: Cheshire cat disappears from tree.

shutters of irregular shapes, with which they slowly obscured Mr. Treacher—all but the lower half of his face (Fig. 15-3).

ELECTRONIC WIPE AND SPLIT SCREEN

Optical methods of matting have already been discussed in Chap. 12. *Electronic* matting is also possible, provided that special equipment is installed. If the facilities are available, it is far simpler to make split screens, wipes, and composite shots by electronic means than by any of the optical processes.

Matting can be done electronically by blanking out the scanning beam over whatever areas are to appear black. If, for instance, the first half of every scanning line is blanked out, the resultant picture that the camera makes will be only half a picture—the right-hand half. The left side of the screen will be black. If the reverse is done with a second camera and then the two are superimposed, a split-screen shot will result, in which the line of demarcation is extremely sharp (Fig. 15-4).

If the position of the line of demarcation is made variable, that is to say, if the amount of blanking on each picture is made variable, the same process can make an electronic wipe possible. A wipe-control handle similar to the fading handles on standard switching systems is used, and two wipe busses with two rows of buttons allow the switcher to select the picture which will appear on either side of the wipe. By a simple switch, the same two busses may be used for fades, dissolves, and supers.

Although the simplest wipe is horizontal (Fig. 15-4), a vertical wipe can also be accomplished with the same switching system described above. A second wipe handle controls this effect. If both wipes are made

Fig. 15–4. Electronic split screen used on NBC's "Lights Out."

Fig. 15–5. Wipe control handles on a five-bus switching system. Top: Wipe selector busses with horizontal and vertical wipe control handles. Middle: Two effects busses with dissolve handles. Bottom: Program bus.

at once, the new picture will start to appear along two sides of the frame (top or bottom and one side) and the old picture will dwindle in size toward the opposite corner. As with any wipe effect, this effect can be stopped at any point to create a split screen, which in this case would present an inset picture in one corner of the frame. Depending on the setting of vertical and horizontal controls, this can be any oblong shape and in any corner of the frame.

RCA makes a representative device which can be added to an existing switching system (Fig. 15-6). Other manufacturers incorporate wipe and

Fig. 15–6. A wipe effect with printed circuit attached is selected from RCA kit of 150 types. After removal of selector panel face plate, it may be plugged in to replace one of the 10 now in position.

often electronic montage controls as well in switching systems which can also produce fades, dissolves, and standard supers. A description of the RCA special-effects system will serve to explain the workings of these devices.

To begin with, an extra pair of handles, similar to the fading handles associated with a two-bus switching system, is provided. An effects pattern selector panel gives the operator a choice of ten different kinds of wipes, which can be selected by push buttons. Each of the ten wipe circuits is printed on a small card, and may be inserted into or removed quickly from the selector panel. A total of 150 different effects can be obtained on these cards and inserted into the selector panel. This includes all manner of wipes, split screens, picture insets, block, wedge, circular and multiple-frequency patterns. An example of a multiple-frequency effect is the familiar venetian-blind wipe where the new picture originates in many horizontal lines across the picture, which then proceed to widen until they meet and the new picture is complete.

ELECTRONIC MONTAGE

The electronic composite shot is a comparatively recent development in television. Patents on various methods of combining foreground figures in the studio with film or still-picture backgrounds were registered for twelve or thirteen years before anyone had the time to build any of this equipment and make it work. A pioneer experimenter was Wayne R. Johnson, chief engineer at KFI-TV in Los Angeles, who early in 1950 demonstrated this effect to the Society of Motion Picture and Television Engineers. A background scene coming from a slide in the projection room was combined with an actor in the studio performing against a white backdrop. The actor appeared to be part of the background scene.

Subsequently several stages of improvement raised the electronic montage closer to perfection; "Chroma-Key" applied the basic principle to color-television production and the CBS "VideoScene" added a method of controlling the movement of both cameras simultaneously.

The mechanism with which the electronic composite is produced is briefly as follows: an area must be blanked out of the background scene, which is the exact shape of the foreground actor, and changes from frame to frame as the actor moves. It is clear that only the outline of the actor himself can provide the right signal for blanking out this complex area. Figure 15-7 indicates how this blanking signal is obtained. A bridge is taken off the camera signal. (A bridge is an amount of signal too small to affect the main current on the program line but capable of being amplified to amount to a very close duplication of the same signal.) This control signal is now reversed in polarity and saturated black so that a silhouette of the actor, pure black and white, results. This then is used as a blanking signal.

When this signal is added to the regular blanking pulses which the background camera receives, a blank (dark) area appears in that camera's picture which changes shape as the foreground actor moves about. From then on the effect is easily produced by simple superimposure of both cameras through the regular switching system.

A second method of doing the same thing involves the use of an electronic switch (a vacuum tube, not a mechanical switch in the ordinary sense). The same silhouette picture "keys" or controls it. As the scanning beam (Fig. 15-8) moves across the white background of the control picture, the switch is set to feed signal from the background camera. When the scanning beam in the control camera encounters the black

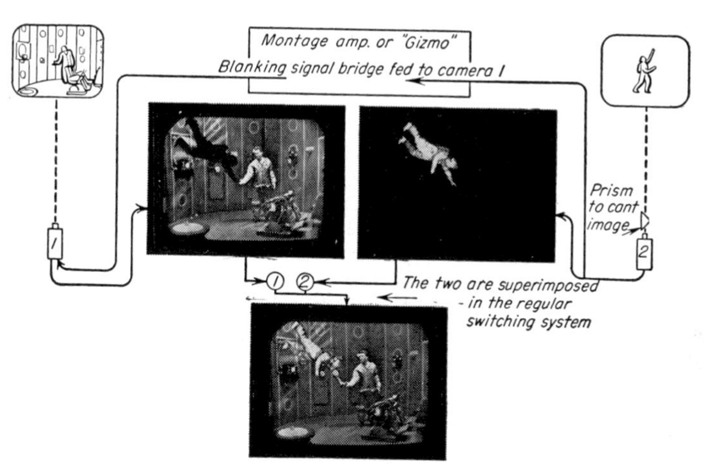

Fig. 15–7. Diagram of the Gizmo, first montage amplifier in regular broadcast use. Designed by Rolf Drucker, David R. Fee, and George Gould for use on "Tom Corbett, Space Cadet." Photos taken off control-room monitors.

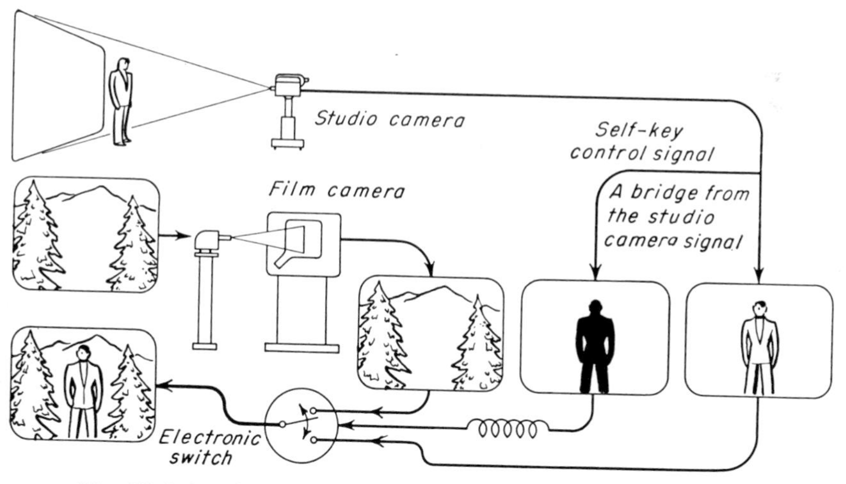

Fig. 15–8. Simplified diagram of a second type of montage amplifier.

figure, however, the resulting change in current triggers the switch and it immediately shifts to feed signal from the foreground camera. The electronic switch must work at least twice on every scanning line, more than 1,000 times in $\frac{1}{30}$ second.

The control, or "key," signal which operates the electronic switch need not necessarily come from either camera involved. A third camera may originate the control signal, which then proceeds to switch signals from foreground to background picture according to the shape of some

Fig. 15–9. Keyhole area used as control signal to make composite of two pictures.

subject which is in neither picture. The key picture, for example, may be a silhouette in the slide projector (Fig. 15-9). The shape of this silhouette will determine the shape of the area which is inset in the montage picture. Moving the slide back and forth in the projector will, of course, move the keyhole across the screen, but the picture which is seen through it will stay in the same position. (The keyhole will pan across the picture seen through it.)

This means that a black-and-white card, moved in front of a control camera or in a control projector, would produce a wipe. The shape of these wipes would be limited, then, only to whatever methods could be contrived to slowly cover a white card with black paper (Fig. 15-10). A photographic iris, placed so that the circle that it makes would appear sharp on the control camera, could key an expanding or contracting circle wipe. A black-gloved hand, thrust in front of the control camera, would key a "hand wipe," brought to its completion when the hand approaches and blocks out the lens.

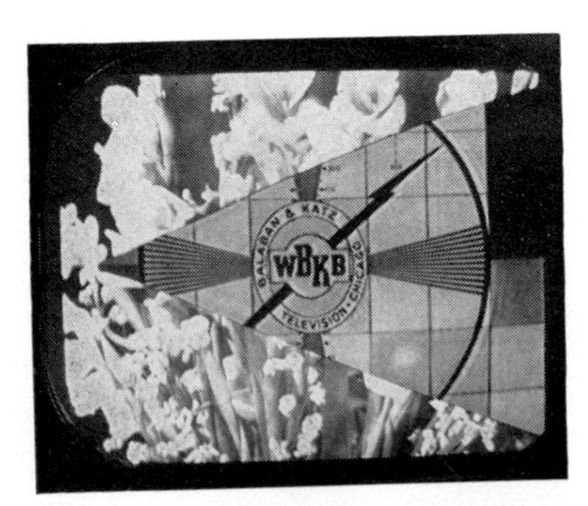

Fig. 15–10. Wedge wipe controlled by a piece of black cardboard of the proper shape moved across the control picture.

Many possibilities of abstract and stylized production present themselves to the imagination. Let us say that a picture of a dancer is used as the control signal. The foreground camera is focused on water, while the background camera is on clouds. The result is a dancer's form made of water, moving against the clouds. Or it might be newspaper dancing on city pavements and walls.

Electronic matting in its early stages exhibited certain limitations. It was found, as with most types of composite shots whether produced by optical matting or by rear projection, that any camera motion spoiled the illusion. Panning, either of the foreground or of the background camera, would make the actor change position in an unnatural way. Only when both cameras were very carefully moved in exact synchrony was the effect convincing. An exception was the effect obtained by dollying in on a foreground subject so long as there was no lateral movement at all, and the background was composed of a distant scene. The result was that the subject increased in size while the background did not, a normal and familiar effect seen whenever an ordinary camera dollies in on a foreground subject against a distant background. Because there could be no other camera movement, actor movement was confined to the boundaries of one static shot.

Another limitation involved the difficulty of effecting a clean separation between foreground and background in the camera recording the foreground action. When the separation depended on differences in tone, the background black and the foreground above black, any black areas in the foreground scene—shadow areas, wrinkles in dark clothing, black eyes on close-up shots, etc.—would cause the background to show through. Comedian Ernie Kovacs once demonstrated a hole in his head by appearing in montage and sticking a circle of black tape on his forehead. Close-up shots were virtually impossible since no performer could open his mouth to speak without the background showing through his mouth.

Subsequent developments have eliminated these limitations for the most part, and although comedians may still have holes in their heads (if they wish), inadvertent bleeding through of the background is much less likely to occur.

CHROMA-KEY

The montage processes described above were not too successful when applied to color television, and NBC devised a method called Chroma-Key for this application. The major contribution of Chroma-Key was that differentiation between foreground action and the background behind it was effected by differences in hue rather than differences in amplitude (darkness or lightness). Blue was used as a background color; nonblue

(*a*)

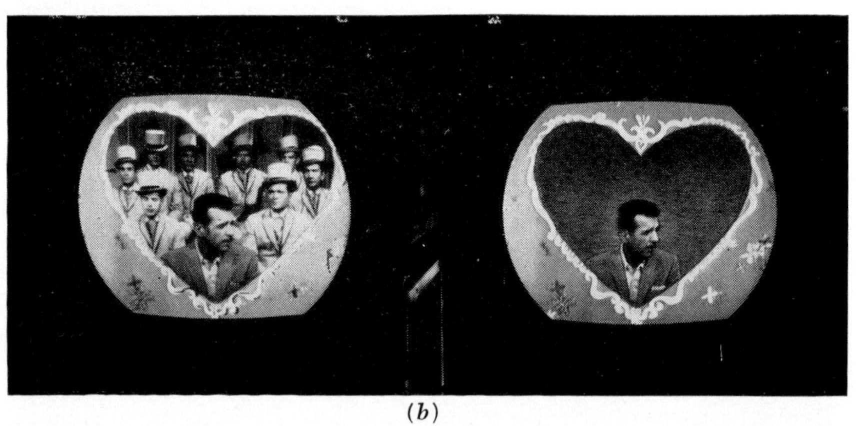

(*b*)

Fig. 15–11. Montage effect done in Chroma-Key on the "Tennessee Ernie Ford Show." (*a*) One camera shoots Ernie behind a heart-shaped gobo, the other frames the chorus. Monitor on left (*b*) shows composite result.

light was used on the foreground. The subject would thus wear any clothing except blue; a patch of blue tape on Ernie Kovac's forehead could still allow the background to show through. Experience has shown that blue eyes reflect sufficient other hues that they do not cause trouble. The reason blue has been chosen for a background color in many of these processes is that this hue is as much unlike the color of flesh as possible.

It is interesting to note some of the production problems involved in the use of this device. While specific to Chroma-Key these problems are representative of the limitations which always accompany a montage process.

The lighting is of course highly critical. No blue light must strike the actors directly, and white light must be kept off the background as much as possible. Because this is not always possible, the background should be painted with a very pure and saturated blue pigment, which has the effect, of course, of absorbing light of all the other hues and reflecting only the blue. NBC has had the greatest success with Idding's Ultra-marine Blue.

If the foreground performer is to appear full length, the floor as well as the background of his set must be painted blue and illuminated with blue light. Full skirts can shadow the floor and cause blobs of foreground to move around in the resulting composite with the performers. Thus side lights and strip lights are very important, so placed that they can flood the floor from an extremely low angle. The size of the set is also limited. NBC recommends a set 12 feet high by 25 feet wide. This is mainly because in a set any larger than this the human figure is too small to key in properly, and slight irregularities in the line of demarcation around the subject, produced in the electronic system, may exceed the width of a wrist or an ankle, and that member may look slightly eaten away.

VIDEOSCENE

The CBS contribution to the art of electronic montage was called VideoScene. The major feature of this process was that it tied together the two cameras involved so they could both be operated by one cameraman. Servo motors linked the pan, the tilt, and the zoom operations and both cameras could work in synchrony, the foreground camera as a master, handled by a cameraman, the background camera as a slave. Thus if both cameras used the same focal-length lenses, almost any type of camera movement could be accomplished without destroying the illusion that the resulting composite picture originated in only one camera. It must be noted, of course, that dollying was still not possible; both cameras had to be statically positioned, and the effect of moving forward or back was achieved by the use of the zoom lens. Automatic servo dollying, a slave dolly reproducing the movements of a master dolly, would still be possible, but might not add enough to the effectiveness to justify the expense.

To obtain a cleaner separation and matting of the foreground elements CBS used a camera with two tubes in the VideoScene process. The slave camera on the background scene could be a standard camera. As with the Chroma-Key process, differentiation was achieved by a difference in hue. White light, containing all colors, was used in the foreground action, while the background was a saturated blue.

In the camera a dichroic mirror divided the light between two camera tubes. A dichroic mirror is coated with a semireflectant surface which will transmit certain wavelengths and reflect others. Dichroic mirrors are used to separate the red, green, and blue components of the light

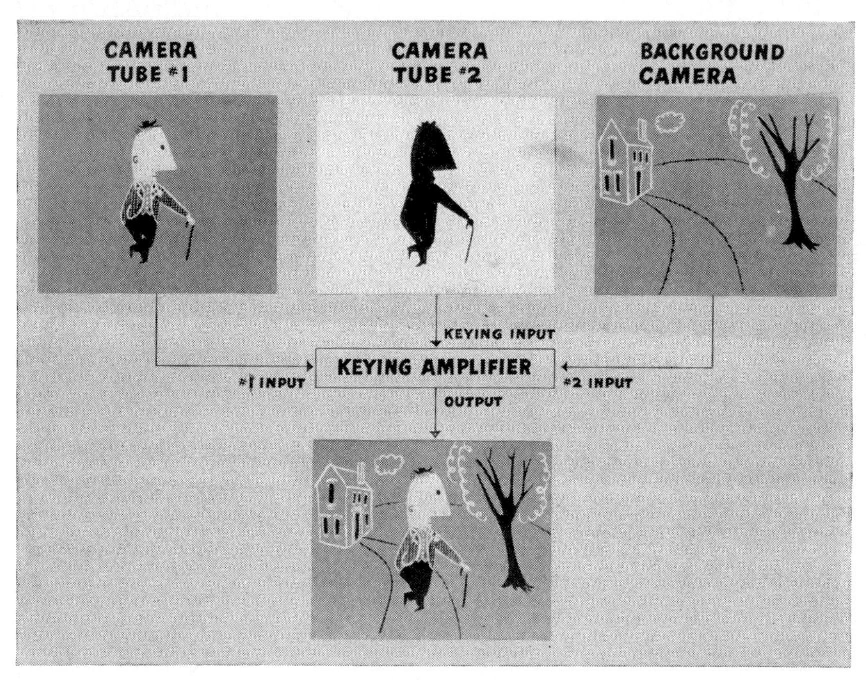

Fig. 15–12. VideoScene technique. The VideoScene camera is an adapted color camera in which two tubes are used. Tube 1 (left) photographs the actor against a special reflective background. The second tube produces a silhouette of the actor. This then becomes the keying signal which controls the electronic switching in the keying amplifier.

entering a color camera, for example, and feed each to a separate tube. The nonblue light entering the VideoScene camera, light which was reflected from the foreground subject, passed through the mirror and formed an image on tube 1. The blue light of the background, however, was reflected to tube 2. Thus to the first tube the background looked black, and to the second the foreground subject was a silhouette. Then the signal from tube 2 was fed into the montage amplifier and served to cut the same silhouette area out of the picture coming from the second camera, the camera which had been focused on the scene which was to appear as the background of the final composite shot. Just as in the original "Gizmo," the foreground shot with the black background and the background shot with the foreground silhouette are combined to create a composite effect.

REVERSAL OF POLARITY

Polarity can be reversed very simply in the television camera. The result is a negative picture: blacks become white, and whites become black. Television film-pickup cameras come equipped with a handy switch for this purpose; a studio camera must have such a switch specially installed. Much newsreel film and last-minute news pictures on filmstrip are projected in negative (so that they can be used immediately without waiting for a print).

SCANNING REVERSAL

Ordinarily the electron gun within the camera scans the picture from left to right, making 525 horizontal passes across it in $\frac{1}{30}$ second. It starts in the upper left of the screen and ends in the lower right. All monitor and receiver tubes do the same. The receiver picture is built up on a fluorescent screen (the inside coating on the end of the tube) by a stream of electrons which moves in perfect synchrony with the scanning beam in the camera—from the upper left of the picture down to the lower right.

If the scanning beam (in the camera) is caused to start at the upper right and end at the lower left instead, the monitors and receivers will have no way of knowing this; they will go right on scanning in the regular way, putting the right-hand end of each line at the left side of the screen, and a backward picture will result. If the scanning beam is made to start at the lower left of the camera tube and work up to the upper right, the receivers will show an upside-down picture.

It is often necessary to reverse left and right scanning permanently in a film-pickup camera when projectors shoot into the camera through mirrors. The mirror reverses the image, and scanning reversal is necessary to correct it again.

Horizontal scanning reversal (left to right) will produce a mirror image of the scene. The subject will look the same as it would in a mirror held at the side of the set or when seen directly through a dove prism. Lettering will read backward.

Vertical scanning reversal (top to bottom) will result in an inverted picture such as a mirror mounted above the set might show or which could be obtained with the image-inverter prism (Fig. 15-13).

Double scanning reversal (left to right *plus* top to bottom) results in an inverted picture which is *not* a mirror image. It is as though the camera had actually been rotated into an inverted position. Stand on your head and look at a shot made by this means, and lettering will read correctly. This will not be true of any other type of inverted picture. If a card is held upside down in front of the camera, ordinary scanning reversal or prism image inversion would turn it right side up again, but it would read backward. Only double scanning reversal (or single scanning reversal of either type plus a prism or a mirror) would achieve a corrected image.

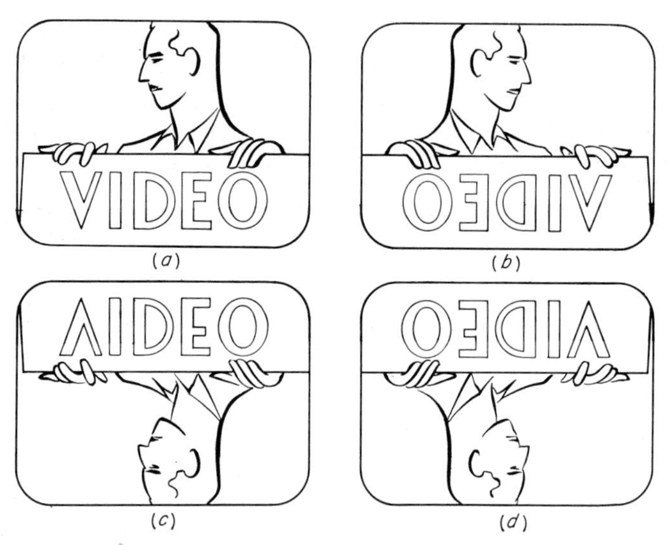

Fig. 15–13. Three types of scanning reversal. (*a*) Straight shot; (*b*) horizontal reversal; (*c*) vertical reversal; (*d*) horizontal and vertical reversal.

Some studio cameras are now provided with scanning-reversal switches. It is a commonly used feature and should be provided on all cameras, whatever their purpose or price. It is a small operation, however, to add vertical and horizontal scanning-reversal switches to almost any camera.

STRETCHING

The controls which regulate height and width of a picture are located on the camera. They are usually regulated only when the camera is lined up and are handled by the cameraman under directions from the video engineer in the control room. They could be handled on the air only if the cameraman locked his camera and did nothing else.

However, purposeful distortion of the picture either vertically or horizontally can often play a dramatic role as a subjective or a fantastic effect. Stretching was first used as an abstract movement by Belanger in visual-music shows on CBS-TV in 1945. The image was stretched and compressed first in one direction and then in the other in time to the music.

Stretching both vertically and horizontally at the same time does not distort the picture but brings the central portion up to full screen size. It is a kind of electronic dolly shot, resembling the effect of the Zoomar lens. An image-orthicon tube cannot be left in this stretched condition for any length of time, however. What is actually happening is that the scanning beam is covering less of the target plate so that a smaller area of the picture is reproduced on the monitor full size. This is underscanning. This smaller scanned area may burn in on the tube, to reappear within the scene whenever the tube is used in the regular way again.

Stretching is sometimes used to correct other distortions in the television picture. When a camera with a long lens is shooting down on a playing field, for example, the compression of depth caused by the long lens has a foreshortening effect and the players look squat and dwarflike. A certain amount of vertical stretching is often used to counteract this effect. CBS adopted a policy of stretching every picture an extra 10 per cent of normal in the vertical direction. This, they feel, improves the look of the video performer and is more likely to result in a correctly proportioned picture on the average home receiver, which is so often stretched beyond normal in the horizontal direction.

IMAGE ACCELERATOR

The image accelerator is one of the electronic controls on the back of the camera generally handled by the cameraman only in removing S distortion when the camera is being lined up. Turning it back and forth has the effect of twisting, or rotating, the picture on the screen, so that vertical and horizontal lines become somewhat diagonal instead. The rotation does not go far enough to make it very useful as an electronic "canted-camera" shot. However, the effect of working the control back and forth will seem to make the room reel and is very good for a subjective shot when a character is losing his senses in some way. On one dramatic show a girl was going out of her head, and two cameras were superimposed, a medium shot of the girl in bed and a close-up of her anguished face. The medium shot was slightly out of focus, and the cameraman twisted it back and forth with the image accelerator for a very successful effect.

BEAM CONTROL

If the beam control on the camera-control unit is turned just a little higher than the proper setting, the picture blooms and turns negative. This effect has been used to simulate lightning or the flash of an explosion.

BLANKING AND PEDESTAL CONTROL

By operating the gain and blanking controls on the camera-control unit, the lights and darks in the scene are properly distributed over the tonal range of the television system so that as few tones as possible go

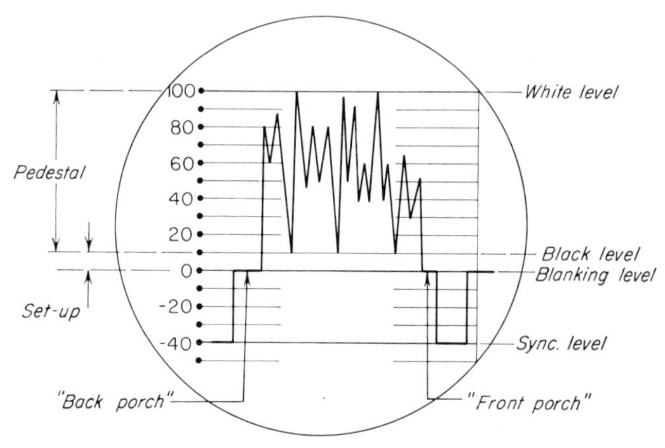

Fig. 15–14. Oscilloscope screen (also called waveform monitor, oscillograph, or C.R.O.).

pure black and as few as possible pure white. The video engineer watches the little green line of the oscilloscope as he does this, because although a monitor picture might be out of adjustment, the oscilloscope always gives a constant measure. When this screen is set for a certain type of measurement, it shows a graph of the ups and downs of every line in the picture, line 1 at the left, line 525 at the right. The level of pure white is generally marked in grease pencil at the top of the scope and the level of pure black at the bottom (Fig. 15-14).

The video engineer will endeavor to keep the ups and downs of the picture within these boundaries. Some of the high peaks should reach pure white, some of the low points should touch pure black, and the majority of the trace should fall between. This area of green "grass" has been known loosely as the "pedestal," since it seems to sit up like a pedestal above the front and back porches and the blacker-than-black sync pulses on either side. "Raising the pedestal" is done with the pedestal control (or blanking control on the RCA field gear) and causes the entire trace to move bodily upward. This, of course, brings more than just the highlights into the white region, and the picture blooms.

Lowering the pedestal brings a lot of intermediate tones down into the black. If the pedestal is lowered way down and the gain control raised so that the highest peaks shoot up to white level, while all else is black, a contrasty picture of pure whites and pure blacks is created. This is sometimes known as "jamming the pedestal" or "saturating black." Some very interesting effects can be created by this method, as, for example, a television version of the effect known theatrically as "black on black," where a dancer robed in black against a black set is invisible to the audience, who see only his partner defying gravity in seemingly impossible feats. Carlton Winckler did a half-hour ballet entirely in this technique at KTSL in Los Angeles, and the effect was striking.

In recent years the networks have devised a circuit which they call the "artificial black level." The addition of this simple circuit to the cameras makes it possible to obtain solid black areas without the necessity of jamming the pedestals to the point where other tones in the picture are affected.

THE USE OF AN AUDIO OSCILLATOR

It has been found that if an audio (regular sound) signal is fed into the horizontal scanning circuits of the camera, a great variety of weaves and wobbles can be induced in the picture. By varying the frequency of the audio signal the picture can be made to ripple in larger or smaller waves. The wave effect can move up the screen or weave back and forth like a water reflection. By slowly varying the volume of the audio signal, the effect can be made to appear or disappear slowly, leaving a clear picture. This has been used for transitions in place of the defocus technique and has many applications in scenes of fantasy, dream sequences, and musical programs. NBC has named this device the Flexitron.

THE MONITOR IN THE PICTURE

An interesting effect is achieved by placing a monitor in the set so that both the live performers and the images on the monitor are visible. By feeding a different picture to the monitor from the one which is on the air we can permit Captain Television to talk with his distant patrol cadets on the screen. Probably a more significant use was found in such shows as Ed Murrow's "See It Now," where films and remote pickups appeared first on the monitor beside him before being seen full screen.

He often carried on an interview with someone in a distant city whose image appeared beside him on the screen.

The monitor should be kept either fully above or fully below the center of the picture. If the camera tilts so that the monitor screen moves from top to bottom of the picture, a shadow edge moves rapidly down the monitor screen. This appears where the scanning lines of the monitor fall into synchrony with the lines of the main picture itself. A separate distribution amplifier and a simple one-bus switching system are necessary to feed a floor monitor a picture other than the one on the program line.

A note of caution should be interjected here, and a plea on the behalf of the belabored engineers whose carefully adjusted equipment is called upon to do the various unusual things listed above. Remember that all camera controls must be accurately readjusted after they have been played with. Sometimes this is possible by accurately marking the dial before the effect is attempted, so that the original setting can be quickly found. These and probably many more electronic effects can be created with the cooperation of an imaginative engineer. Without this cooperation, however, all these effects are better left unattempted.

16

Television Scenery

The primary purpose of scenery in theater or film is the creation of illusion. Since illusion in the theatrical sense (i.e., simulation of a place other than the studio or stage) is necessary to only a part of television programming, it is quite logical that we should find many new ways of using scenery in the television studio and many variations in its use between the complete illusion of the movie set and the complete reality of the "location."

A great many television shows of the panel-discussion, interview, variety, or comedy format take place obviously on the stage or in the television studio, and scenery is used not to create an illusion but merely to dress up what is plainly a functional area. Again, in a show like the classic "Garroway at Large," scenery was used to give complete illusion during musical numbers, after which the camera might show stagehands changing the scenery or Garroway passing by the back of the flats so that the backstage view, so totally shunned in theater and film, contributed greatly to the actuality of the television transmission.

Where real backgrounds are available, they are, in the author's estimation, greatly to be preferred to studio sets. Many production problems are of course intensified outside the studio, but the compensating gain in actuality in many cases well repays what trouble may be involved. Those who have experimented along this line find their budgets considerably eased when "sets" can be borrowed rather than built. This was true in the production of the old "Lucky Strike Hit Parade," which appeared weekly for almost a decade. It was produced in the Center Theater on the largest stage in the world, with center turntable, two elevating stages, and all the finest machinery of the theater. Neither the rotating stage nor the elevating platforms were used more than once in three months. Instead, the producers found countless fascinating locations in and about the theater, from which to stage at least one number each week. The tremendous backstage of the theater was well used, the alleyway outside, the sidewalk and street, the auditorium, balcony, foyer, and long staircases leading to the mezzanine. Productions were done from the roof garden atop the theater, and, in the winter, from the ice rink in Radio City a block away. One imaginative dance number originated from the boiler room in the building's sub-basement.

One network sold a dramatic show and then found to its embarrassment that there was no studio available in which to present it. A fast-thinking executive remembered the mobile-unit equipment housed in a garage across town and the lumber yard next door to the garage. The show's writers went to work on lumber-yard stories, and for the first thirteen weeks each episode took place from location. Both client and audience were well satisfied with the result.

At the other end of the scale is the studio dramatic program which purposely uses no scenery at all. Albert McCleery's "Cameo Theater" type of production left scenery largely to the imagination; the camera concentrated on well-composed groupings of people in which the waist shot, close-up, and extreme close-up predominated. The studio is prepared for a "Cameo Theater" production simply by hanging a dark cyclorama around the studio walls. All the shots have backgrounds of dead black. Some key props may be used, such as a bed for a death scene, or an occasional table and chair. Special effects such as snow and rain may also be used to set the scene.

Considerable space has been devoted in preceding chapters to the special-effects devices which can be used to superimpose or insert backgrounds in a studio scene. Proponents of these "process" techniques commonly predict the elimination of scenery altogther. However, shooting a scene against a rear-projection screen, or in the limited area prescribed by a montage effect, carries with it the same limitations on action, camera angle, and mobility that playing the scene in front of a drop would involve. The camera viewpoint must be pretty well fixed. Only one completely satisfactory shot is possible, and that from a frontal angle and at only one level. Very little freedom of movement is allowed the actors lest they go beyond the camera's range, and no great amount of dollying of the camera is possible without materially changing the looks of the background scene. In addition, a peculiar kind of lighting must be employed for rear projection, since any front light will wash out the dark tones on the screen.

The CBS VideoScene device (see Chap. 15) adds a bit more mobility; the camera can pan, tilt, and zoom as long as it doesn't go beyond the limits of the blue background cyclorama.

THE REQUIREMENTS OF TELEVISION SCENERY

The first requirement of television scenery is that it must be light in weight. Scenery must be set and struck again in the shortest possible time in the television studio, and light scenery, similar to that used in the theater, is necessary. Moreover, the units (such as flats, doors, windows, etc.) must be so designed that they can be put together and taken apart quickly, and here again the theater methods of rope lashing or loose-pin hinges are the most practical for television.

Unlike movie scenery, the television set does not have to pass close inspection in high-definition pictures. For most television purposes stage techniques seem to work fairly well.

SCENERY PERSONNEL

The personnel involved in scenery design, construction, painting, and handling will of course vary greatly from station to station. In a small operation, one man may do the scene designing, construction, and painting, as well as all the station's art work and titles. Of course there are many small stations which do not have anyone on staff in this capacity, and the staff directors design and construct new scenery if any is required.

More often there is an art director who is also the production manager. He designs scenery and art work, as well as directs all the station's production operations. He will then have under him one or more scene painters and graphic artists who actually execute the work he lays out.

In the large-scale network operation there may be many specialists on staff each of whom concentrates on a small aspect of a show's production. Union jurisdictions define the areas in which these people may work, and a member of one local may not do the work which is covered by another union's contract. A network will employ a staff of scene designers, a number of union carpenters in a construction shop, a similar number of union scene painters, and finally a group of union stagehands, including at least one prop man, one stage carpenter, and one electrician in every studio.

Beyond these union classifications the network will employ men with interior-designing background as set decorators; there will be an extensive prop department with personnel in charge of storing and preparing props, renting and buying props, and, of course, handling props during rehearsal and show time. A large number of people in this department will be called "prop shoppers" and will spend most of their time in leg work, visiting pawnshops and antique dealers, department stores and poultry markets in search of the great variety of material required for television production.

METHODS OF USING SCENERY IN TELEVISION

Some of the smaller television stations have avoided the problems of setting and striking scenery by erecting a permanent set and using it for all purposes. There are many kinds of television programs for which the set is only a background, and a little change in draperies, wall decorations, etc., will often allow one set to be used as a background for a news commentator, a children's show, a gardening demonstration, a quiz program, various commercials, and on and on through the studio's program schedule. Usually such a studio will have two or more of these permanent sets so that while one is in use on the air, another can be redressed for the following show. The permanent set is an advantage to the small station for several reasons: (1) It saves time in striking and setting, and the studio may be used for air shows during more hours of the day. (2) It saves having the additional storage space near the studio which is necessary when demountable sets are used. (3) It looks better in some respects since cracks may be covered and it may be built out of heavier material than canvas. (4) It lasts longer than a set which is taken apart and moved in and out of the studio frequently. The usual set can get dog-eared, smudged, and injured rather rapidly if it is frequently moved.

However, the disadvantages of the permanent set are obvious. No matter how the set dressing is changed, every show will have somewhat the same look. Permanent sets are not practical for dramatic shows, except the very simplest type, unless the show is written specifically for the set. This method has been used with considerable success where the sets are not necessarily permanent but there is a limited number of stock units on hand and no budget with which to build more.

When WCAU-TV in Philadelphia did "Action in the Afternoon," a daily live western produced outdoors, rain, snow, or shine every weekday of the year, the stories were written to fit the block-long Western town just outside the back studio door, and the few stock interiors such as the saloon, the barbershop, etc., were left permanently set in the studio.

While only a few of the smallest stations build multipurpose permanent sets, most small studios simplify their setting and lighting problems by establishing permanent *set areas* within the studio. If a studio is, say, 24 by 40 feet, it will be found that each end forms a natural set area, and an occasional shallow set may be placed along the side, but the center area must be kept free for camera movement. When permanent set areas are used, any considerable changing of lights is unnecessary.

When several shows are to take place from one set area during a programming session, the production staff may often resort to a method used in theaters known as "in-setting." The last set to be used is set up around the back of the area and folded back where possible to take up as little space as necessary. Then a preceding set is placed directly in front of it. Sometimes a third set can be placed in front of this. Of course furniture and large set pieces cannot be preset in this manner, but the background flats, which take the most time to erect, can be set long ahead of time (Fig. 16-1). Often the first set at the very back of the studio is a permanent set, used regularly every day, and is never struck.

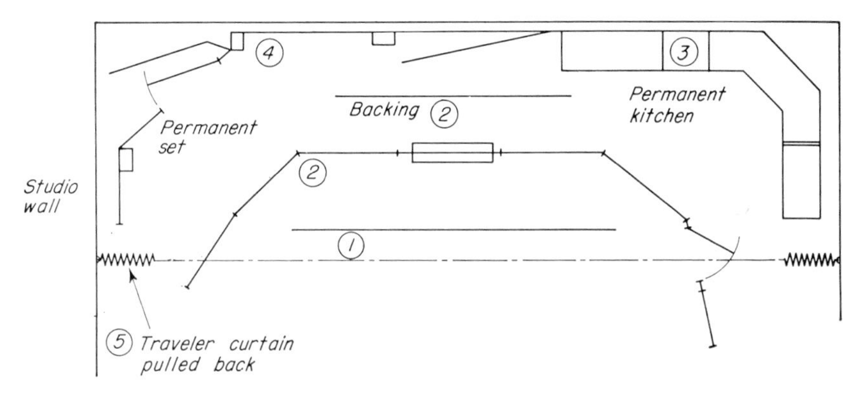

Fig. 16–1. Playing area at end of typical small television studio, showing four sets in place to demonstrate the process of *in-setting*. (1) Roll drop let down for background of show 1. (2) Set for show 2. (3) Permanent set for show 3. (4) Permanent set for show 4. (5) Traveler curtain may be pulled across for still another background.

A permanent kitchen was once part of every commercial TV studio. Plumbing, gas, and current are frequently connected so that the kitchen is fully workable, and other sets are placed in front of the kitchen cabinets when the cooking program is over. Another set which is commonly left permanently erected is the news set, usually only a background to the commentator's desk, with globes, maps, clocks, or sponsor's identification intended as visual interest, while the audience watches the commentator reading from his script. Unless a show is on five times a week, it is not generally considered good use of a small studio's space to leave sets permanently erected. A once-a-week show is almost always set and struck each time unless the studio is unusually large.

In the larger network studios where dramatic shows are produced it is important that the set designer be able to place his sets anywhere in the studio that he desires. This requires resetting of lights for each show, but personnel is allowed for this in the network operation. Usually a full day of a studio's time will be devoted to a half-hour dramatic show, and shows of an hour's duration will more commonly rehearse two and sometimes three days in the studio. The designer's placement of sets usually results in a group of small two- or three-wall sets with the side walls opened out at an angle to allow cameras to shoot in from the sides. These are then placed around the studio walls so that the cameras may have an open working area in the center.

Very often the action of a drama will call for one set to open onto another, such as two rooms, room and hall, or living room and outdoor terrace. Often this requires the sets to be placed in the center of the studio so that the cameras may be operated from several sides. This type of placement allows greater freedom in camera angle, making possible reverse angles which could not be achieved in the usual box set. However, every camera shot is more difficult when the sets are so placed; one camera is likely to show in the background of another's shot, and thorough planning and rehearsal are necessary. Several methods of providing camera access through the back of apparently solid and unbroken sets for reverse angles will be discussed later in this chapter.

STANDARD UNITS OF THEATER SCENERY

The simplest standing unit is the "flat." In the theater these units are constructed almost any height, but many television studios will not accommodate scenery higher than 9 or 10 feet. Whereas the most common width is 4 feet, flats are built of 3-, 2-, and 1-foot widths and occasionally 5 feet 9 inches. Any but the last can be handled by one man. Figure 16-2 illustrates the framework of a common flat and the standard hardware which is attached. The method of lashing it to another flat is also shown. Two flats may be lashed together side by side or with an inside angle (a V shape with the front sides of the flats facing in). If the flats are bent away from each other in an outside angle, a wide crack will result. A 90-degree outside angle is possible, however, by butting the edge of one flat up against the side of the other. All hardware and joinery are generally kept about ⅞ inch back from the edge of the flat to allow another flat to be butted up against it. The two flats are generally nailed together when placed in this way.

There are two common ways of supporting the flat (besides the support it may receive from being lashed to other flats on either side), the "jack" and the "stage brace." The jack is a triangular frame hinged to the back of the flat, then swung out and weighted at the bottom. The stage brace is an extensible stick made of two lengths of 1- by 1-inch wood with a hook at one end to fit into the brace cleat on the flat. The bottom end is usually fastened to a footplate about 18 inches square on which sandbags or other weights may be piled to secure it. Stage counterweights are useful for weighting jacks. They have U-shaped notches at either end, and if two angle irons are attached to the back of the jack, the counterweight may be laid between them and will be held there by the notches (Fig. 16-4).

Loose-pin hinges are commonly used for attaching jacks to flats, holding collapsible platforms together, and many similar purposes. Half

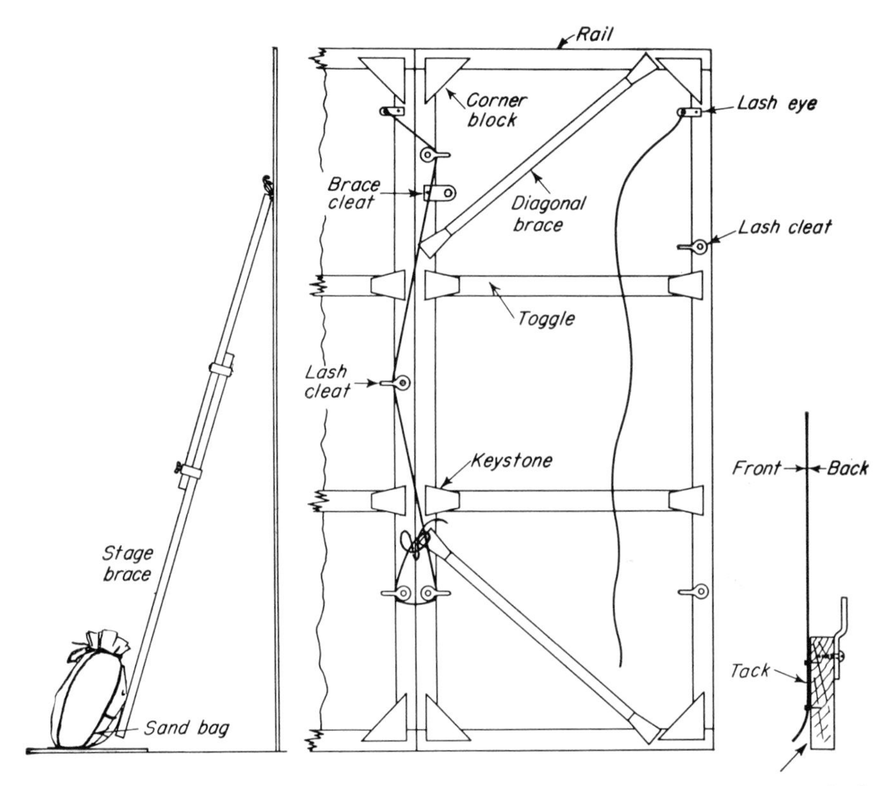

Fig. 16–2. The back of a plain flat, showing frame construction and standard hardware. Part of a second flat is shown at the left to indicate the method of lashing the two together.

of the hinge is attached to each unit; it separates as soon as the pin is withdrawn, and the two pieces can be easily reassembled simply by fitting the two halves of the hinge together again and inserting the pin.

When a door or window is used in theatrical scenery, it is made of two parts, the door or window itself, and a flat into which it is placed. The door or window is known as a "plug" since it fits into a hole in the flat. The door frame and trim are fastened solidly together, and the door is placed in the flat from the front side so that the trim, which extends

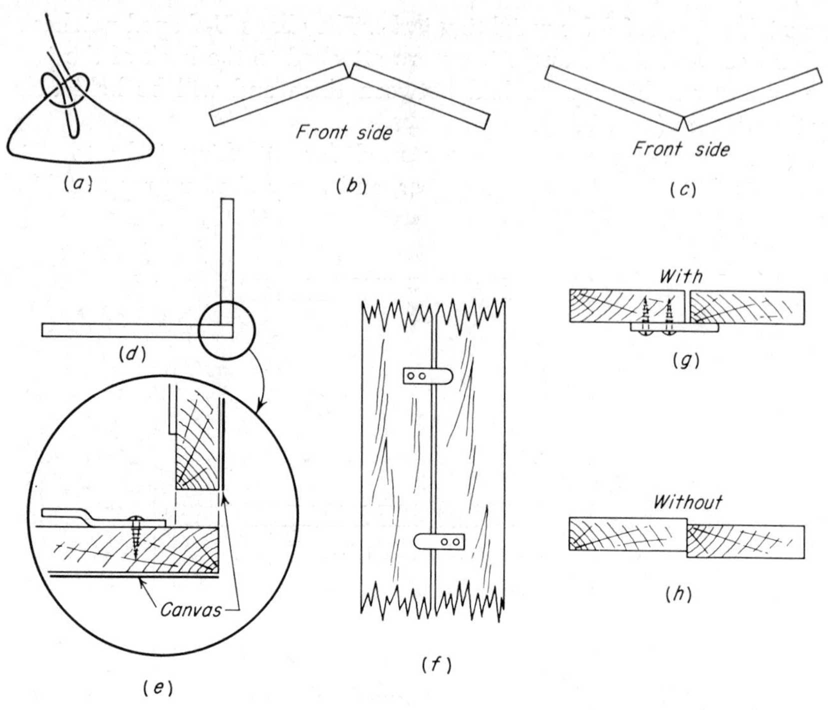

Fig. 16–3. Details of standard set construction. (*a*) Method of tying lash line into a slip knot so that it can be quickly pulled out; (*b*) flats lashed together on inside angle—no crack shows; (*c*) flats lashed together on outside angle—large crack results; (*d*) flats butted together at a 90-degree angle; (*e*) close-up of *d*, showing how hardware is kept ⅞ inch back from the edge to allow for this type of joint; (*f*) stop cleats to keep flats in line; (*g*) cross section of *f*; (*h*) if cleats are not used, one flat may stick out farther than the other, increasing the size of the crack.

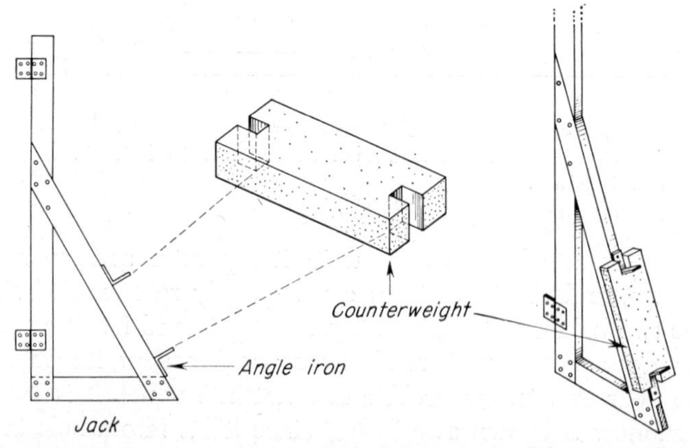

Fig. 16–4. Jack. This unit is hinged to the back of the flat and weighted at the bottom to keep the flat from falling forward. A sandbag may be used or a standard counterweight as shown.

around the door like a flange, is in contact with the face of the flat. Then the door is locked into place on the back side by means of a strap hinge. This simple method of quickly locking things together is one of the most ingenious things in scene construction. A strap hinge (Fig. 16-5) is fastened to the side of the door jamb with the upper half of the hinge free. This is folded up flat when the door is inserted and then bent down behind the flat to hold the door in place. One hinge on each side of the door is sufficient. A window is held in place by the same method. It is known as a "practical" window if it can be opened, "impractical" if it is permanently fixed. Usually only the lower half of the

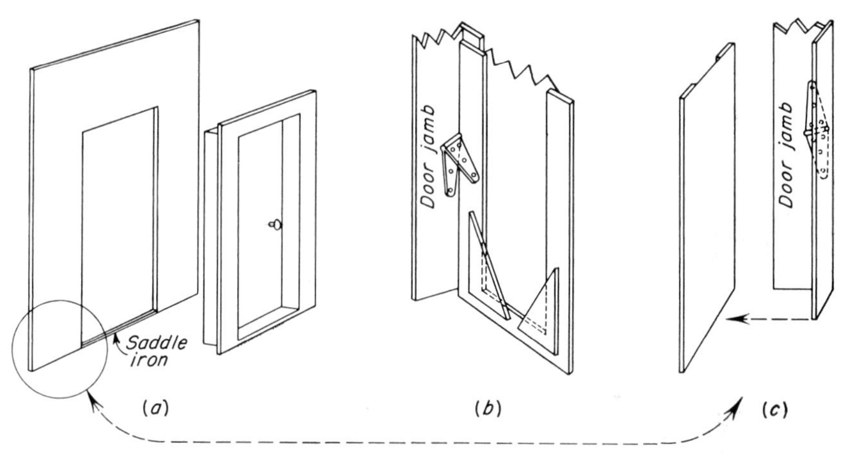

Fig. 16–5. Door flat and door plug, indicating method of securing the plug by means of a large strap hinge.

window (just a frame without glass) is made movable. Fireplaces and bookcases are other examples of plugs which are inserted in special flats.

Besides single flats, there are several types of multiple flats. A "twofold" is composed of two flats hinged together so that they fold inward. They are usually covered by a single piece of canvas, although two ordinary flats may be hinged together and the crack covered. A "threefold" consists of three flats hinged together in the same way. When three flats are hinged together and then folded up for storage, they cannot be folded flat unless an additional member, the thickness of one flat, is inserted between two of them. Figure 16-6 will make this clear. This piece is called a "dutchman," a term which is used for several different kinds of things in scene construction and joinery.

When an outside corner is necessary, a "corner post," or a "return," can be used. This is usually constructed of two narrow flats permanently fixed together at a right angle and covered with one piece of canvas. The return may also be made to hinge like a twofold, but in the reverse direction.

The cracks between flats constitute a problem. Dean Wagner solved it by gluing a gauze dutchman across the crack before painting. A dutchman here is a long strip of cloth. Since the set is usually painted outside

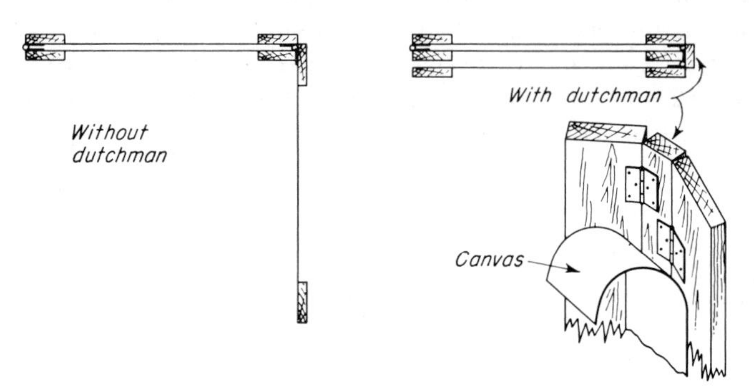

Fig. 16–6. Method of constructing a threefold flat so that it can be folded flat. The wooden dutchman is inserted between two of the flats.

the studio, the dutchman must be carefully peeled off before the sets are erected, and then glued on again when they are in place.

HANGING UNITS

The most common type of hanging unit is the canvas drop. This is usually built out of a large piece of heavy duck fastened both top and bottom to a long stick of 1- by 3-inch lumber called a "batten." Drops in the theater are usually fastened to lines which will pull them straight up above the stage, an operation known as "flying" the scenery; the area above the stage into which the scenery can be pulled is known as the "flies." In television, however, there is rarely enough space above the studio for this purpose—lighting grids and other installations are in the way—and a roll drop must be used instead. This is also theatrical practice in small stages or summer theaters where there is no fly space. The upper batten of the drop is tied to the overhead grid, and the lower batten is allowed to extend 1 foot or 18 inches beyond the drop on either side. When the drop is lowered, a rope is wound several times around each end of the lower batten and led up through a small pulley and over to the side of the stage. As the rope is pulled up, it unwinds from the batten, thus turning the batten and rolling up the drop which is fastened to it (Fig. 16-7).

Another common hanging unit in television is the cyclorama. The cyc is a semicircular or U-shaped hanging which is as high as the studio light grid will permit, covering at least one end of the studio and often three studio walls. If the cyc is made to curve around the corners, the corners of the studio will not be visible in any shot and the apparent studio size is considerably extended.

Cycloramas in television are most useful if they are of the "sky cyc" type, that is, stretched tight instead of falling in drapery folds. The top of the cyc is laced to a curved pipe batten which is fastened solidly to the overhead structure. The bottom of the cyc is also laced to a free curved pipe which is weighted so that it almost touches the floor but

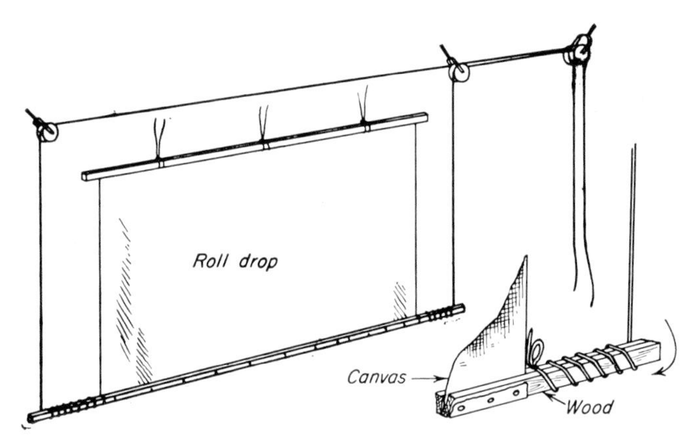

Fig. 16–7. Simple roll drop.

keeps a constant tension on the cyc. The cyc is made of stout duck or linen canvas; if this has to be sewn together to make the necessary width, the seams should run horizontally. Both top and bottom are reinforced and grommeted along the edge. Lacing the cyc is better than tying it since any localized pull which might otherwise result in a wrinkle is taken up and equalized by the entire lacing as it slips slightly through the grommets.

DRAPES

Drapes or curtains are a traditional background for performances on the stage, and drapes hanging in vertical folds are used in television studios for much the same purposes. The author must admit to a prejudice against the use of drapes, probably because of the theatrical implication, which is only rarely appropriate to television. Those who have observed Russian TV have seen much use of drapes, sometimes to the complete exclusion of all other forms of scenery. Russian drapes have been used, symbolically or thematically, to the extent that during intermission periods or preprogram periods a slide of drapes, nothing else, fills the screen. Presumably the theory is that the audience watches the drapes with the same anticipation that a theater audience accords to a closed curtain before a show. The symbol is the more appropriate since most of Russian television is presented in the same formal manner as concerts and recitals are generally handled on the stage.

Naturally those television stations using theaters have inherited all the mechanics of the stage and use almost any type of curtain known to

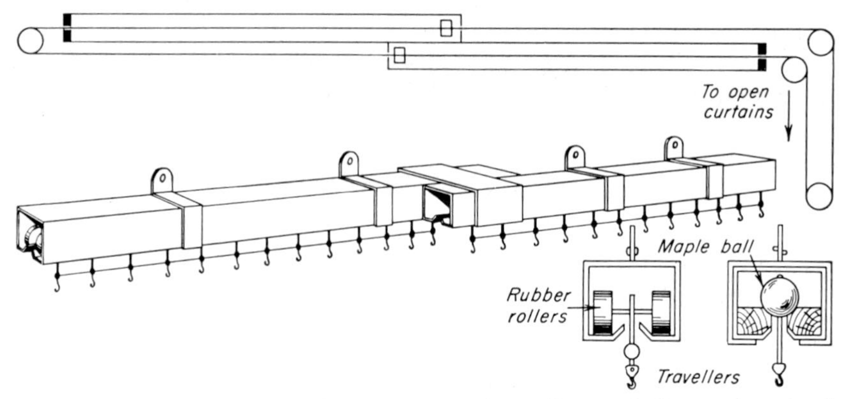

Fig. 16–8. Travelers for traveler curtains. Either rollers or balls may run in the track. One cord moves both curtains.

stagecraft. In the television studio, on the other hand, many of the stage curtains are unusable owing to the elaborate installation required and the lack of fly space. The theater traveler curtain, however, can be easily installed and can be moved from one part of the studio to another without a major rebuilding job, and so has met with wide acceptance. The traveler curtain is a draw curtain made of two halves which can part in the middle. Each half of the curtain travels on a separate track, or traveler, and a single rope or draw line installed as shown in Fig. 16-8 will move them both at the same time in opposite directions. A number of fiber balls or rubber rollers ride in each track, and the curtain is attached to these.

Perhaps the simplest handling of drapes is to fasten them to flats so that they are arranged in neat and permanent folds and can be moved around just like any other units of scenery. The description of screens in a later section of this chapter describes the use of drapes in this manner, attached to folding screens.

BUILT UNITS

A common type of built unit is the platform. Platforms are made in many sizes. Some are mere steps; others are 3 by 6 feet in top area and only 8 or 12 inches high. In these sizes platforms are usually hollow boxes made of ¾-inch fir plywood well strengthened beneath. Since storage space is always at a premium, larger platforms should be made collapsible. This is achieved by building them of two parts, a platform top, or floor piece, and a "parallel" which supports the floor.

The platform top is built so that when it is in place it fits just inside the edge of the parallel and holds it rigidly. The parallel is a light frame, suitably braced, and hinged in a particular way so that it can be folded up with one motion (Fig. 16-9).

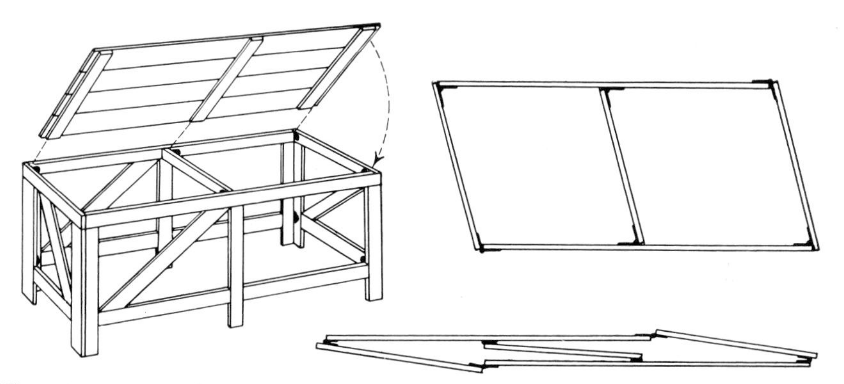

Fig. 16–9. Large platform, built of two parts for easy storage—platform top and parallel. Method of hinging parallel so that it will fold flat is indicated.

Platforms are noticeably hollow-sounding under foot, especially when made of heavy five-ply. This noise can be reduced if the inside of the platform, or at least the underside of the floor itself, is covered with a blanket of hair felt or other soundproofing material.

Other constructed units include steps and columns, as well as various natural forms such as trees, stumps, and rocks. None of these can be made collapsible, however, but must be built up on a wood frame with lath, or with chicken wire if the surface is to be irregular, over which canvas soaked in glue is laid. Detailed instructions for building such units, as well as the other types of scenery here described, will be found in books on stagecraft.

SET PIECES

Set pieces are generally flat and free-standing but constitute separate units and don't fit together with other pieces of scenery like most standing units. A familiar set piece is the ground row—a low, cutout piece made of beaverboard or other stiff material strengthened by a simple wood frame. Ground rows are built to represent walls, flower beds, hedges, etc., and sometimes, a row of distant hills. Some television shows use set pieces against a sky cyc to the exclusion of flats and other scenery.

FLAMEPROOFING

The fire regulations in most cities require any materials that are to be used for scenery to be flameproofed. This can be done by spraying or painting the scenery, either before or after it has been painted, with special flameproofing chemicals. These may be obtained from companies which deal in stage equipment, or they may be mixed at the studio. A flameproofing solution can be made from the following ingredients, which can be found in almost any drug store:

1 lb borax (sodium tetraborate)
1 lb sal ammoniac (ammonium chloride)
3 qt water

SOLID SCENERY

To avoid the drawbacks of frame and canvas scenery, some studios have standardized on a more substantial type built of fir plywood covered with unbleached muslin. The frame of a plywood flat can be built of lighter wood than the canvas flat must have, consisting only of 1- by 2-inch wood turned edgeways. This means that each flat has a 2¼-inch thickness and therefore has considerably greater rigidity than standard flats, which are only ¾ inch in thickness. Instead of being lashed together, these flats are held by clamps or bolts, which makes them somewhat slower to put up. They are also heavier to move than canvas flats.

However, there are several advantages to this design. Plywood flats are flatter; they fit tightly together without noticeable cracks and do not vibrate visibly when doors are opened and closed. Because they are made of harder wood than pine, at least on the face panel, normal battering has less effect and accidents to the face of the flat are not so often fatal. By using casein paint NBC has averaged 100 coats of paint on these flats before they need new muslin.

CARDBOARD AND PAPER

While quality is of primary concern to the network studio, speed and economy are the keynote in the small station. Even standard theatrical scenery has proved too expensive in some stations. WRGB in Schenectady, a station which pioneered in many production techniques, discovered early that large sheets of corrugated cardboard, such as cartons are made of, can find good use in the television studio. This cardboard can be obtained in 4- by 10-foot sheets and can be attached to any flat with a large staple gun. Thus it is possible to leave the flat set up in the studio, paint a new covering for it, and when the time comes to dress the set, take it into the studio and staple it on. When this use is over, the flat itself is undamaged, the cardboard can be pulled off and either stored or thrown away, and the flat is just as it was and can be used for its original purpose again without another repainting. Some stations have constructed their scenery originally from wood frames and cardboard, protecting the edges of the cardboard by binding them with wide (2- or 3-inch) strips of scotch masking tape. Naturally accuracy and realism are not prime considerations when this material is used.

Seamless paper is a very useful material for inexpensive scenery. This paper comes in rolls 9 feet wide and 36 feet long, in a variety of colors and tones of gray, and is obtainable in almost any town in the local display materials house. Seamless paper has been used to create a plain cyclorama background, for floor or ceiling covering, and as a material on which to paint (or draw with chalk) a pictorial backdrop. It is usually stapled against flats, but is often fastened directly to the studio wall. Photographers have long used seamless paper to create a cove background, where one long piece of paper forms both floor and background wall, giving the impression of the subject being in space.

SCREENS

One of the best multipurpose units to have in the small studio is the folding screen. Screens need no jacks, they can be stood up anywhere and handled quickly, and they make excellent backgrounds for the display of products, simple interview or demonstration shows, and many

Fig. 16–10. Screens built and used in studio of WTMJ-TV, Milwaukee.

other purposes. Several types of screens are illustrated in Figs. 16-10 and 16-11.

FLOOR COVERINGS

In many television studios it has been found advisable to paint the floor. A large area of floor space is inevitable in many shots, and the pictures are greatly improved when the decoration of the set can cover this area also. Few small studios have found this possible, since the same floor must serve many programs in a few hours' time, but in a network studio where a day or two is devoted to each production, the floor may well be painted anew each time.

Since most television studios are floored with linoleum, the simplest method of decorating the floor is to paint with water paints directly on

Fig. 16–11. Magnesium frame screens at WTMJ-TV, Milwaukee. Photo shows same type of screen draped and undraped and at different heights.

the linoleum surface. This can then be mopped off with water after the show. Where the studio has a wood floor, paint might be likely to soak into the wood and some kind of ground cloth must be laid down first, just as it is on the stage of a theater. This is usually a heavy duck which is painted and repainted until the paint becomes so thick that it cracks off, at which point it is generally discarded. Some studios have found that the best procedure is to lay down 4-foot squares of hard-surface masonite. This can be painted and repainted even more often than the canvas before it has to be replaced.

BACKGROUNDS

Painted background scenes are an important part of complex television production, although, as indicated in the opening of this chapter, they are only one of many scenery elements and certainly cannot be considered sufficient in themselves. The term "backgrounds" is here used to include canvas drops, already discussed, photomurals, rear- or front-projection screens, painted traveler curtains, and the large, flat set pieces which may sometimes be used in a sizable television studio.

Photomural backgrounds are often used in television studios, and the effect that they create is better than either painted drops or projections. Painted drops are likely to look flat and unrealistic and are usable only where realism is not required. Rear or front projection is likely to be weak-looking and grayish, whereas photomurals under ordinary illumination pick up with good rich blacks and natural tones. Like any photographic material used in television, however, they should be soft in quality rather than contrasty. Hollywood companies which regularly service film studios can supply photomurals as wide as 25 feet and as high as 14 feet. These murals are enlargements made originally on photographic paper and then mounted on heavy duck. They can also be made by enlarging them directly onto canvas which has been sensitized with a photographic emulsion. The latter type stand up much better in use, there being no paper or paint to crack as a result of folding and rolling.

Small studios which use photographic murals have found that a few subjects such as the local sky line, a clouded sky, a wooded exterior with foliage, and perhaps some kind of public building are standard backgrounds that will find many uses.

If the photomural is mounted on flat beaverboard or canvas, it should remain erected permanently, since, as previously noted, rolling the canvas might tend to injure the photograph. When erected, the photomural is often laced to a rigid frame in the same manner as the rear-projection screen and this frame must be braced to a rather wide footing. Photomurals mounted in this way are not economical of studio space. One mural can be mounted on the back of another, it is true, but those which must be stored, if they are of any size, must be stored in the studio, and this takes up needed room.

When the mural has been made on sensitized canvas, however, it may be rolled without danger and handled in much the same manner as an ordinary painted drop, fastened to battens above and below. It has been found cheaper in most cases to have a photomural made than to have a good drop painted, and the results are always more realistic.

The rear-projection screen cannot be rolled but must be stretched permanently on a solid frame (Fig. 16-12). It is subject to considerable danger as sets are moved around in front of it, and its life is definitely limited. The problems involved in the use of rear projection are discussed in Chap. 12. They have by no means been satisfactorily solved for television.

Fig. 16–12. Rear-projection screen laced with heavy rubber bands to rigid frame. (Photo couresty of CBS.)

PROBLEMS WITH EXTERIOR SETS

Scenes laid out of doors pose quite a problem to the set designer, since the simulation of nature with canvas and paint is at best a poor approximation of reality. It is a rare scene painter who can make foliage, and especially rocks, look convincing. The photomural is of course one answer, but flat backgrounds do not entirely suffice, and three-dimentional rocks and trees will always be necessary.

Where large quantities of foliage are necessary, only real foliage can be used, since artificial leaves are expensive and cannot be obtained in large bushes or trees. In using real foliage it is not possible simply to go out and cut a few limbs off a handy tree, since the leaves of most trees quickly wilt as soon as they are cut. Laurel, rhododendron, smilax, water oak, and broadleaved evergreens must be used since they merely dry up without wilting. When no great amount of foliage is necessary, sometimes real branches can be used to which sprigs of artificial greenery have been wired.

Rocks present an unsolved problem in television. There is seldom enough time or budget available to build rocks out of heavy screening and plaster so that they have the proper texture. Such construction would probably have to be done on the set, and the television studio is never available long enough for such an operation. Small rocks are built up in the construction shop, as explained earlier, of wire and canvas, and are light enough to be carried into the studio. However, large rocks must be thrown together in the short studio setup time allowed and seldom look convincing. The folds of canvas are painfully evident, except when a great deal of foliage is used to cover them up. Success has been attained only with stylized rocks and trees which are not intended to look realistic. These are accepted by the viewer as stage sets, no attempt is made to induce him to think of the program as a remote pickup or as a film, and his "willing suspension of disbelief" provides him with a perfectly satisfactory illusion.

METHODS OF QUICK SCENE CHANGING

Beyond the usual method of quick lashing of flats and rolling or flying drops, several television stations have adapted further quick-change methods from the theater which have proved useful in the television studio. Small revolving stages have been tried, where one set is placed on one side of the turntable and a second set on the other. Both have been permanent sets, however, and the turntable has been placed permanently in a certain spot in the studio. A turntable which can be easily reposi-

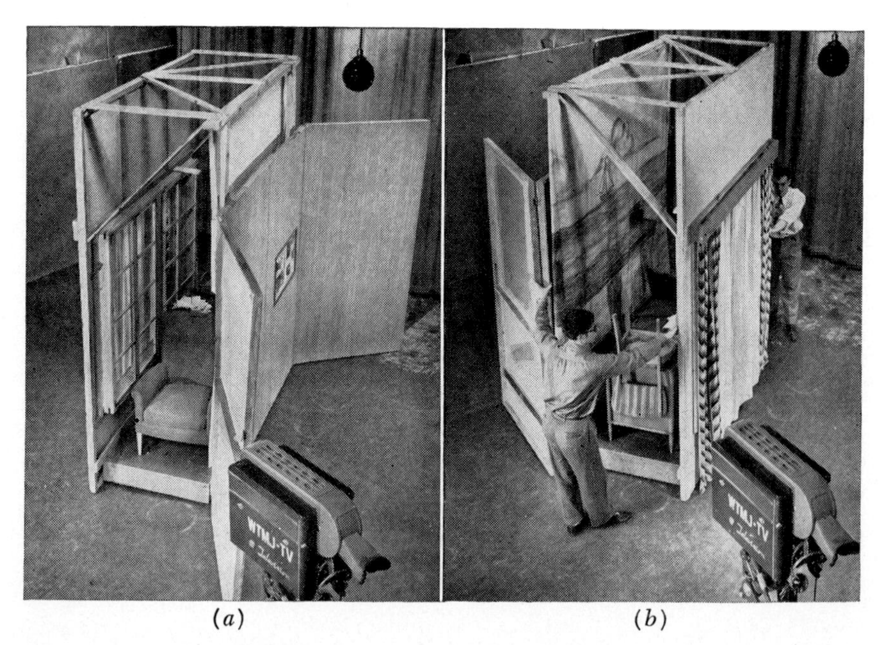

(*a*) (*b*)

Fig. 16–13. (*a*) WTMJ-TV stage wagon carrying two sets. (*b*) stage wagon after being turned around, with another set open and ready to be used.

tioned has never been devised in a size large enough to hold a set. Small turntables have been built, however, out of ordinary platform materials and strong dolly wheels mounted in a circle to run on the floor.

Another method of quick scene change involves the use of castered platforms known as "stage wagons," shown in Fig. 16-13.

TRICK SCENERY

There are many times when the scenery of a television show can play an important part in the special effects which are created. One example is the trick of moving the scenery to create the illusion that the actor is moving. This has been done in the theater by having the actors walk on a treadmill (as in the classic "Green Pastures" scene) while the scenery passed by behind them. Treadmills are not necessary in television, however, since the camera shot need not show the person's feet. One number in the "Garroway at Large" show involved a couple riding a bicycle, and they had to sing an entire song while pedaling along. The bicycle was of course raised slightly off its wheels and supported out of camera range so that the performers were free to pedal, and to give the illusion of movement, various set pieces—trees, bushes, etc.—were pulled through the background of the shot. To give an even greater illusion of reality, one set piece representing a distant hill was moved through slowly while nearby bushes, telephone poles, and so forth, moved by much more rapidly. Another time on the same program a couple were in a carriage which was being rocked and jiggled to indicate movement, while cutout tree trunks and branches were moved through between the camera and the performers.

A thin net or gauze material called "scrim" is used frequently in the theater for special effect and has been utilized in television in much the same manner. Scrim is practically transparent when the lights are kept off it, giving only a slight mistiness to the lighted scene beyond. A certain amount of light on the scrim, especially if it is projected from directly above so that it hits the scrim at the smallest possible angle, will make it give the effect of either a thick fog or an opaque curtain. Designs may be painted on the scrim to be illuminated in this way, and they will disappear entirely when the light is removed. Thus a scene change may be effected by killing the lights behind the scrim while bringing up the lights on the scrim itself. These disappearance and appearance effects are fully as effective before the television camera as they are before an audience. Scrim is generally fastened to battens like canvas drops.

THE ADAPTATION OF SCENERY FOR CAMERA ANGLES

The usual three-walled set, especially if the walls are at right angles to one another, is somewhat limiting to the camera. All shooting must be from the front. When the walls are splayed out, the cameras can get into the scene better and shoot from side angles (Fig. 16-14). The director will often take advantage of a door or window in the set to get his camera even farther around to the side, and occasionally he will find a way to use a camera from the back of the set. In these cases, except for very close shots, studio equipment and miscellaneous personnel are likely to be discovered in the background unless additional flats are put up for protection. A single flat, stood alone in the studio, is known as a "wild wall," and these may be used occasionally in dramatic productions where the sets themselves are not extensive enough.

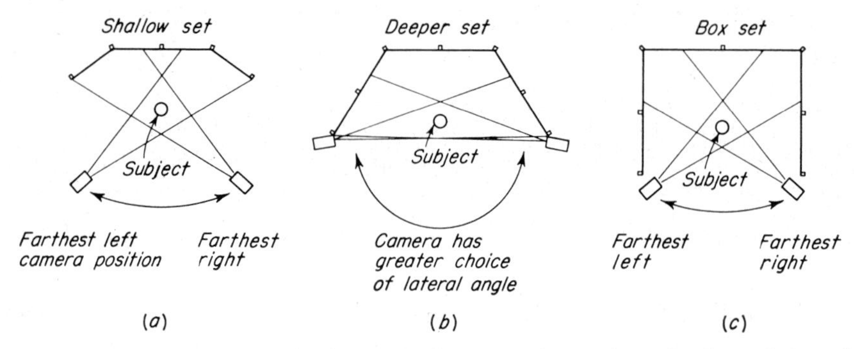

Fig. 16–14. What shape and depth should a simple set have for best choice of camera angles? (*a*) Shallow set limits use of cameras for side angles. If they go too far to the side, they will shoot off set. (*b*) Deeper set allows greater freedom in use of side angles. (*c*) Box set with walls at right angles to back again prevents cameras from moving to the side (unless they go into the set).

Sometimes the designer will fasten a flat with hinges at the far side of the set so that, when it is out of another camera's view, it can be swung out by a stagehand, thus allowing a camera to shoot from a position which would otherwise be inaccessible. Cameras frequently shoot through windows, not simply for window shots, but for various shots of the interior of the room in which the window plays no part. Figure 16-15 shows still another way of making the reverse angle possible. As soon as the fireplace is out of the shot, a panel is raised above it and a camera is able to shoot into the set.

On one occasion a designer was asked to design a nightmare set which would look completely unreal and carry with it the feeling of the dream of which it was supposed to be a part. The designer came up with a set which had no walls. Not unknown in the theater, this was something new for television. Window frames and doors were suspended by wires from the lighting grid, and pictures and other wall decorations were similarly hung from above. A few feet behind the invisible wall was placed a plain cyc to make a simple background. To everyone's surprise the set seemed to have walls as solid as if they had been made out of plywood flats. The background cyc provided a neutral tone which naturally seemed to be the wall.

Moreover, this set was peculiarly fitted for the use of cameras from all angles. There was a 5-foot space between "wall" and cyc in which a camera could move, and it could shoot from any place behind the set.

Fig. 16–15. Camera access through removable panel over fireplace. (Photo courtesy of CBS.)

The only limitation involved here, of course, was that a very carefully worked out camera traffic plan was necessary lest cameras appear in the living-room walls and the set take on a nightmare quality indeed.

THE PROCEDURE OF TELEVISION SCENE DESIGN

The design of a television set begins, in most cases, with the show's director, who visualizes his action and comes to the set designer with a sketch of the kind of set he would like to have. Before the designer can go much further, however, he must know many other things. He must know the general mood of the show and of course its locale and period. Most of this information he can obtain by reading the script. However, the director must have worked out a rough plan of the show's action, the movement of actors both on the air and off the air between sets. The designer will find out whether or not there are any fast moves where an actor must finish one scene and begin the next in another set. Between-scene traffic like this will determine which sets must be adjacent in the studio. Except for this the designer tries to run the sets around the studio in a logical order so that cameras do not have too far to go at any time in the transition between scenes. If there are key shots which the director must have, the designer should know about these also and find out just what kind of reverse-angle shooting the director has in mind so that the necessary camera access and backing can be allowed.

Then the designer must know the studio in which his set is to be erected. He must know the limitations of studio height and the studio areas which cannot be well lighted and which should be used for sets as little as possible. He should know what *else* besides his sets will have to be placed in the studio. Many shows use a live orchestra, and room for it must not be overlooked. A show involving make-up or costume changes during the performance will require two portable dressing rooms on stage, thus further reducing the area of the studio that is available for sets. Last and not least the set designer should remember the sponsor of the show and the agency men who are producing a commercial segment to extol the sponsor's product. Data about the commercial should be obtained as early as possible so that sufficient space can be allowed; otherwise the agency producers will take space arbitrarily and at the expense of the show.

The designer must also consider the throw necessary for rear projection, if this is planned. This will generally be about twice the width of the screen.

After all these requirements and limitations have been considered, the designer must remember the route into the studio and not design anything which is too large to fit into the elevator it must ride in or too long to go around the corners of the corridor leading into the studio. Like the man who builds a boat in his basement and has to tear the house apart to get it out, a scene designer has sometimes had to watch his masterpiece of scene design being cut into pieces to fit into an elevator or eliminated from the show because it couldn't be gotten into the studio at all.

The next step is the preparation of a floor plan and set elevations. The designer will know just what scenery units are in stock and can be repainted and used again, and he will indicate this on the set elevations. Only the construction department will need elevations, but many departments will be interested in the floor plan, including the director himself, and it will be duplicated with many copies.

Floor plans are usually made to a scale of ¼ inch to the foot, and the designer works on printed blank copies of the floor plan of the particular studio he is designing for. Every television studio has its own floor plan

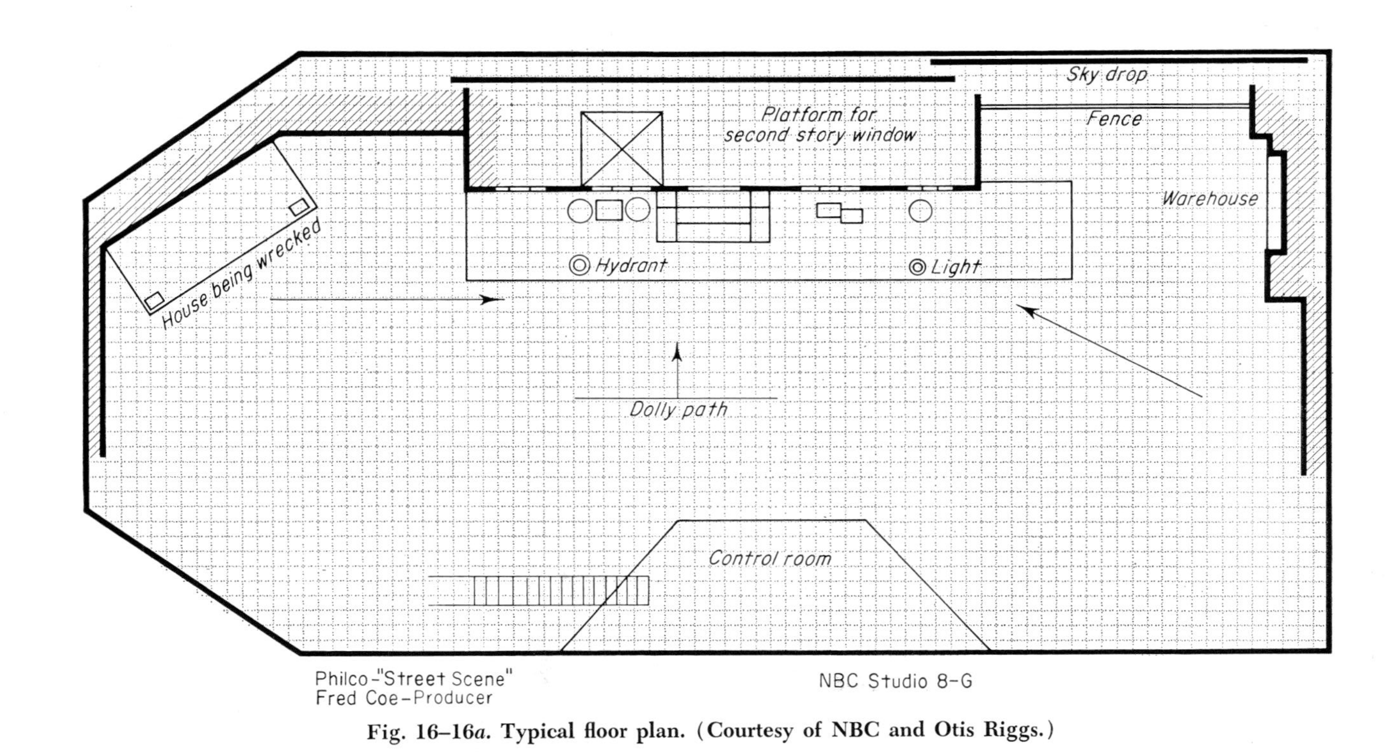

Fig. 16–16*a*. **Typical floor plan.** (Courtesy of NBC and Otis Riggs.)

printed up in quantity for the use of every designer, producer, and director who uses the studio, and it is on this basic floor plan that the designer works. All designers use the same architectural symbols for doors, windows, etc., but they are always careful to write out in detail each dimension and description as well. To illustrate how a studio floor plan looks, a typical floor plan for a television dramatic show is reproduced (Fig. 16-16*a*), along with a photograph of the final set after it was erected (Fig. 16-16*b*).

Fig. 16–16*b*. The finished set as it looked in the studio. Set for "Philco Television Theatre" production of "Street Scene," by Otis Riggs. (Photo courtesy of NBC and Otis Riggs.)

In certain instances when a set is rather unusual or camera and staging problems are anticipated, the entire set will be built first in miniature. This gives the director an opportunity to plan his shots with much greater accuracy and allows him to anticipate many problems of camera and mike-boom traffic before actually starting studio rehearsal. A studio model is especially helpful to new directors no matter what type of show is attempted, and many studios have kept studio models handy, equipped with cameras and mike boom and the standard stock scenery built to scale (Fig. 16-17). If the model studio is built to the scale of an inch to the foot, standard ten-cent-store doll furniture can be used since this is commonly made in that scale. The staff of the "Garroway at Large" show, after the first two years of production, facing ever more complex production problems, finally built a studio model to this scale and found it was a tremendous help in preplanning of the show's production.

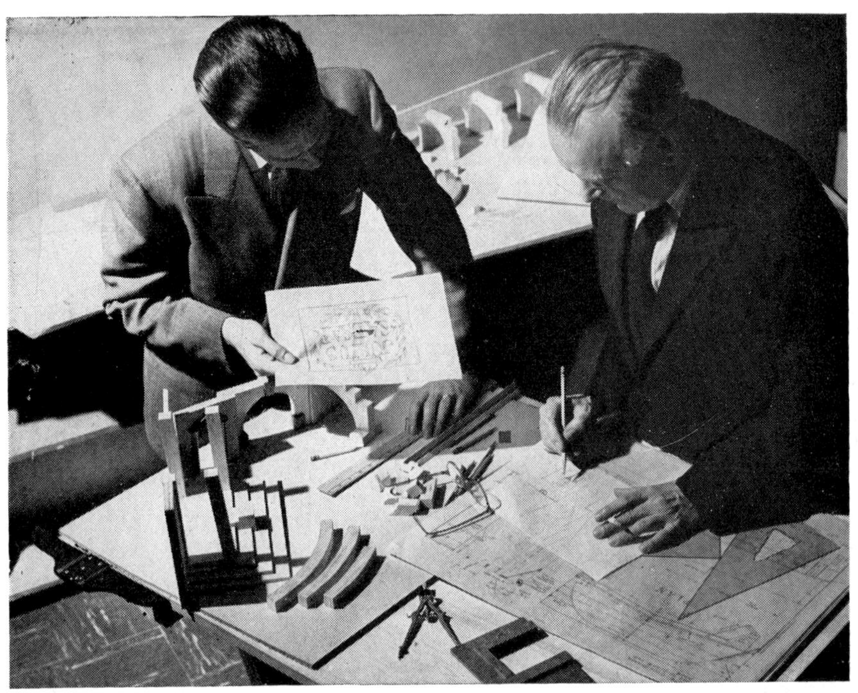

Fig. 16–17. Richard Ryktarick (right), CBS designer, conferring with the director over the set of the "Studio One" production of "Julius Caesar." (Photo courtesy of CBS.)

SCENE CONSTRUCTION

Although some stations have found it necessary to construct sets in the studio itself, this is considered very poor practice and an uneconomical use of highly expensive space. A space at least as large as the studio should be allowed for a construction shop, and it should be close to the studio, if at all possible, to eliminate the time and labor involved in transportation.

A height of 15 feet is usually considered necessary for the construction shop. There should be enough space to make possible a trial setup of an entire set without disturbing other work in progress. Flats are constructed most easily on a bench called a template, just the size of the flat, with a rim around it to hold the lumber in place as the flat is going together. One or two templates of standard sizes will be necessary, and these should be castered so that they can be moved about. Room must also be provided for the operation of several power tools. A large bench saw is mandatory, and if 12-foot lengths are going to be ripped on it at any time, it must be so placed that there is 12 feet of free space both in front of it and behind it. A band saw is often installed, and many shops have a jig saw as well for scrollwork. Racks must be provided along the side of the shop for the storage of lumber and its ready accessibility. Plywood panels, especially of the ¼-inch thickness, should be stored flat, not on edge, to prevent warping.

A very useful tool for cutting out odd-shaped patterns from beaver-board or almost any other material is the Cutawl. This tool has a short, strong knife blade about ⅛ inch in width which is vibrated up and down by the motor. The depth to which it cuts can be regulated, and the entire machine is moved around over the work as the knife is guided

Fig. 16–18. Scene-construction shop, showing jig tables for flat construction. (Photo courtesy of CBS.)

along the lines of the pattern. The Cutawl is superior to a jig saw in several respects. (1) It is portable (weight, 16 pounds) and can be used anywhere. (2) It is moved while the work lies flat and so can be used on work of any size. (3) It can start cutting anywhere; it is not necessary to bore a hole from which to begin. The Saber saw, however, has all these advantages and will probably find more frequent use than band saw, jig saw, or Cutawl, while doing essentially the same work.

Another highly useful tool, which should be as much the property of the scene dresser as anyone else, is the staple gun. Of all tools around the television studio, with the possible exception of the claw hammer, the staple gun is used the most. There should be at least two in every studio. A heavy-duty size should be used when thick material, such as corrugated cardboard, is to be stapled. The staple gun is operated simply by holding it firmly against the material to be stapled and squeezing the handle. A self-contained spring shoots a staple directly into the material. When posters or pictures must be stapled to canvas flats, the canvas will not hold the staple and it must be clinched on the back side. This can be arranged if someone stands behind the flat with a flat piece of iron (clinch iron) for the staple gun to shoot into.

CHECK LIST OF MINIMUM SHOP REQUIREMENTS

For the reader who would like a check list of tools and materials for simple set construction, the following is a short summary of useful items:

Power tools
- Multiplex radial saw (overhead arbor)
- Saber saw

Also useful
- Portable electric drill
- Motor and grinding wheels for sharpening tools
- Portable electric saw
- Drill press

Hand tools
- Crosscut saws (fine-tooth and standard)
- Ripsaw
- Claw hammers, curved and straight claw
- Jack plane
- Block plane
- Keyhole and backsaws
- Brace and set of wood bits
- Yankee screw driver
- Set of chisels
- Set of files and wood rasps
- 2-ft steel square
- Try square
- 5-ft ruler
- Expanding rules

Also useful
- Spoke shave
- Compass
- Soldering iron

Stock materials
- For NBC-type sets
  - No. 1 clear pine 1 by 2 in., 1 by 3 in., 1 by 4 in., 1 by 6 in., 1 by 9 in., and 1 by 12 in.
  - ¼-in. fir plywood—sheets 4 by 8 ft and 4 by 10 ft
  - ½-in. plywood the same
  - ¾-in. plywood the same (plywood can be good one side only for set construction)
  - Bolts of unbleached muslin 72 in. wide
- For frame and canvas construction:
  - Pine strips and boards as above
  - ½- and ¾-in. plywood as above
  - Light canvas duck
- For corrugated-cardboard construction:
  - Pine as above
  - Plywood as above (½ and ¾ in.)
  - Sheets of corrugated cardboard 4 by 10 ft
- Bolted whiting, flake and ground glue, wallpaper paste, shellac, and alcohol

SCENE PAINTING

The carpenter shop is a noisy and particularly dusty place when construction is under way, with sawdust flying around through the air and settling everywhere, and it is no place to paint scenery. Nonetheless some stations have attempted it, having the choice of doubling up on the use of this space or painting in the studio itself. Quite properly, however, a special paint shop should be provided, and here again almost nothing is quite so valuable as adequate space. When flats are painted, it is convenient if they can be laid down flat. When an entire set is painted at once and left for a while to dry, a large floor area is in use. Running water should be provided in the paint shop, as well as suitable cabinets and racks for the storage of paints and brushes. Good scene-painting brushes are fabulously expensive and should be kept under lock and key.

Painting a drop is a difficult task. Even though there is space to lay it out flat on the floor, it is often so large that the scene painter must walk around over it to reach all portions, painting with his brush on the end of a stick. If scenery is to be painted in great quantity, a special *paint frame* is necessary. The paint frame is a wooden framework large enough to hold a drop or several flats at a time, counterweighted and hung vertically against a wall so that it can be lowered gradually through a slot in the floor. By lowering or raising the frame the scene painter can easily reach any part of the scenery he is painting, and large areas of floor space are not tied up. In the large ABC studio in New York, James MacNaughton introduced drops 34 feet high and 100 feet wide. Since there is no suitable space outside the studio for painting drops of this size, they must be painted in place. Instead of lowering the drop on a paint frame, the painters are raised on a motor-driven scaffold. Thus able to reach any part of the work, they paint quietly away during studio rehearsals and turn out at least one such tremendous drop each week. An example of one of these large drops is shown in Fig. 16-19, a set from a production in the "Paul Whiteman Revue" series. This set is also an excellent example of realistic treatment of the floor area.

There is considerable difference of opinion on the question of using color in scene painting. (A discussion of this problem will be found in Chap. 8 in connection with the color response of the television tube.) Some designers work only in monochrome, either in shades of gray or in one color at a time. Most scene painters, however, are used to working in full color and should be allowed to continue to do so if they like, provided that the results on the screen can be controlled. At some stations all scene colors are mixed in standard shades and calibrated against a gray scale so that the designer can specify just which shade he wants and be sure how it will look when it is on the air.

Some painting always must be done after a set is erected. Occasionally something must be redone which does not pick up satisfactorily. Sometimes there is touching up to do where the paint job has been damaged in transit. When the floor is to be painted, it is frequently easier to wait until the set is up so that the total effect of perspective can be perceived

Fig. 16–19. Painted background drop 100 feet wide in ABC Studio 1 for production of "Paul Whiteman Revue." (Photo courtesy of ABC.)

and the floor design most easily matched to the rest of the scenery. Time for this floor painting and time for it to dry must be planned on and allowed before the set is scheduled for rehearsal.

A check list of useful tools and materials necessary for the paint shop is included below:

Lay-in brushes for priming coats
Liners and foliage brushes
Various pails, measures, pots, etc.
Straightedges, lining sticks, and other drawing devices
Stepladders

In regard to scenic paints, Bob Wade, NBC scenic pioneer, has made a very interesting comparison between ordinary scenic paint (distempera) and casein paint, the gist of which is given as follows:

Regular scene paint	*Casein paint*
1. 25 coats maximum.	1. Will take 100 coats before recovering.
2. Former coats of paint soften up under application of new coat.	2. Not soluble in water when dry; hence does not rub up.
3. Must be mixed with animal glue.	3. Mix with water only.
4. Leftovers rapidly spoil as the glue deteriorates.	4. Leftovers are easily mixed with new paint.
5. Drying is uncertain.	5. Rapid drying.

SCENE STORAGE

Facilities for scene storage require further space, and this also has been frequently neglected in the design of television stations. Many stations do all their storing in the studio, a practice which is a very poor use of the studio space except where the studio is larger than the programming needs require.

The "scene dock," a vertical file of flats with their edges facing out so they may be indexed and slid in and out easily, is always necessary and should be fairly close to the studio if frequent use is to be made of the units involved. Many studios use a cart on which the flats can be laid from both sides against a central wall or frame. The network studios handling new dramatic programs daily often erect an entire set outside the studio, then fasten it to wheeled jacks so it can be lifted slightly off the floor and rolled into the studio intact.

Stock items such as flats in modular units are often stored in a building removed from the studio, where they are classified and inventoried. A file listing stock items with photographs or drawings of each is maintained in the art department to assist designers in keeping their set designs within prescribed budgets.

17

Television Make-up

Television make-up has been regarded by many as a mysterious art filled with secrets and special formulas. Naturally this attitude was not discouraged by the cosmetics manufacturers, who brought out special lines of television make-up enough different from their regular products to look impressive. Television make-up men, too, have been responsible for the use of special materials and colors. Actually almost any kind of make-up is usable on television, provided that the right shades are used and it is correctly applied.

The *creative art* of make-up, however, goes far beyond the basic rules for the choice of materials and the techniques of application outlined in this chapter. It is not on the basis of "trade secrets" that the make-up artist establishes himself in the television profession, but because of his creative talent, skill, and imagination. Dick Smith, for example, at the top of his profession, is a sculptor of no mean achievement in the fine-arts field. It is not the purpose of this short chapter to attempt even an approach to the art of make-up, on which several books have already been written. Make-up for theater and for the photographic media is basically the same, differing only in technique and practice. This chapter will attempt to indicate to the reader only when make-up may or may not be necessary and some of the simplest techniques involved in preparing actors for the television camera.

It is not uncommon for people to go before the television camera without benefit of any special make-up at all. If a man, for example, has a light beard, so that his "five o'clock shadow" is not visible to the eye, and he has no skin blemishes or rings under the eyes to conceal, he will probably televise satisfactorily without make-up. The same is true for a woman, who, of course, usually covers up her blemishes and plays down her bad features by her own cosmetics.

In dramatic programs, actors often appear without make-up when a special effect is desired. In crime stories, for example, the director may want the effect of harsh reality or the haggard look that a rough and slightly bearded face will convey. The final judgment, of course, must be made during camera rehearsal, when the make-up man and the director can get a fairly accurate idea of how the actor will look on the air.

PURPOSES OF MAKE-UP

When make-up is used, it is for one or more of several reasons. The first of these is to smooth the complexion, give the person an even, healthy skin tone, and outline and dramatize the features where necessary. No actual changes are made in the face; nature is simply improved on slightly, in the same way in which powder, rouge, lipstick, eye shadow, eyebrow pencil, and mascara are subtly used in street make-up to improve the feminine face.

The second purpose of make-up is also involved in every woman's efforts to make herself more beautiful. This is the *corrective* function of make-up. Broad jaws are made up to seem narrower, small eyes to look larger, long faces to seem not so long, etc., in the attempt to bring each face a little closer to the classic ideal of beauty.

The third purpose it to *correct for age*. Obviously this is involved in the make-up of many actresses except in character roles, since a certain optimum age is implicit in our current concept of beauty. This is a purpose of regular street make-up as well. In the case of actors playing roles in which they must appear many years younger than they really are, the make-up artist must often employ complex methods usually necessary for character make-up only.

A fourth purpose is to make certain corrections to suit the lighting which each particular studio or production may use.

Finally, there is the purpose of creating character. This usually involves changes in the personality, nationality, age, etc. The most involved techniques of make-up are devoted to this purpose and require a highly skilled make-up artist. Very little that is applicable to this function will be described below, and the reader is referred to other books on the subject for the techniques which are involved.

PECULIARITIES OF TELEVISION MAKE-UP

The techniques of television make-up closely resemble those used in black-and-white film photography. They lie somewhere between motion-picture and stage technique, but closer to film than to stage. This is primarily a matter of visible detail. Stage make-up is usually broad and exaggerated, too much so in many cases for the spectator in the first row. Stage make-up will do on television also, provided that the camera does not come too close and the actors are in flat, even lighting. Television theaters (legitimate houses adapted for TV) are usually lighted in this

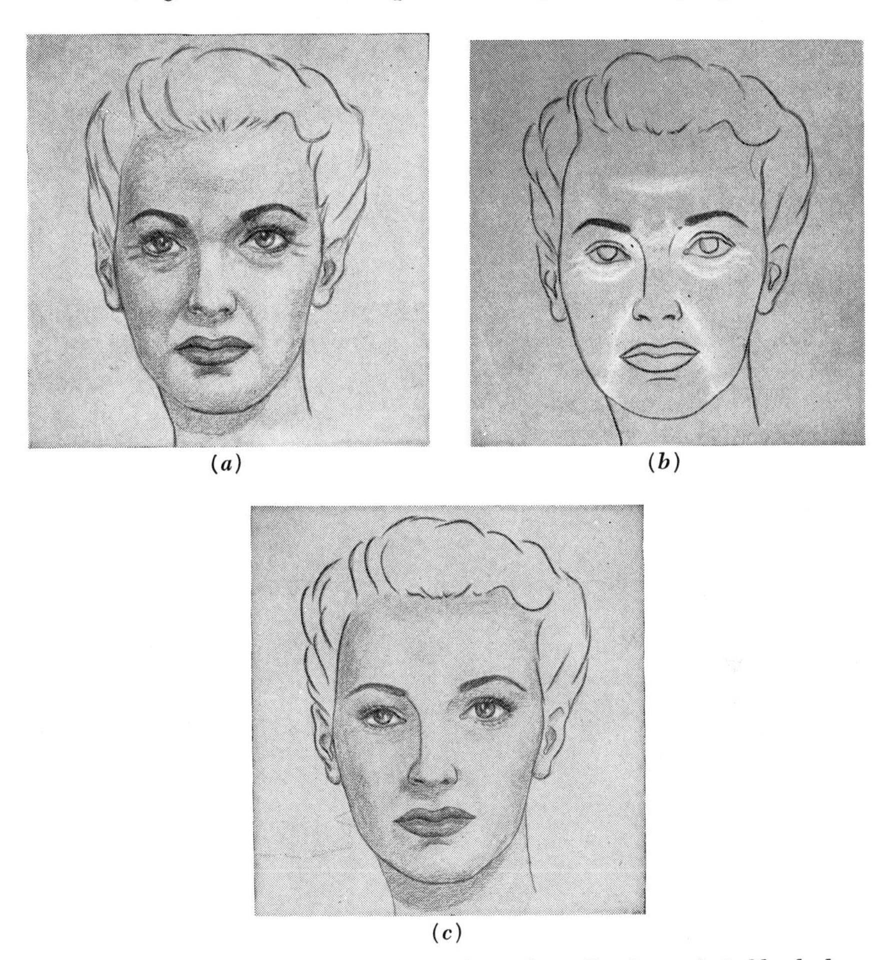

(*a*) (*b*)

(*c*)

Fig. 17–1. Special make-up devised by Dick Smith to disguise undesirable shadows caused by top light. (*a*) Typical top lighting of television. Note bags under eyes, shadow between cheek and upper lip. (*b*) Highlight make-up applied to shadow areas. (*c*) In top light the light make-up helps remove the unwanted shadows seen in *a*. (Drawings by Dick Smith.)

manner, and the make-up requirements under flat lighting are much like those of the stage. In the television studio, however, where modeling light is used, the make-up must be much subtler.

Each studio is different because of different lighting installations and may even vary from day to day. The way in which the cameras are functioning will influence the way the make-up comes across. Another factor is the tone of the backgrounds, which will change from one production to another or between sets on a single show. Light backgrounds, for example, tend to make the face appear darker, while dark backgrounds make it seem lighter in tone. The make-up man should be on hand for rehearsal in any but the most routine productions so that he can adapt to whatever conditions may exist.

In earlier years television camera tubes exhibited strange reactions to colors; and one of the purposes of television make-up was to alter the normal colors, avoiding some and exaggerating others, so that the monochrome effect would look natural. Today's image-orthicon tubes are about as faithful in their translation of colors into tones of gray as panchromatic film, and the consideration of color response is no longer of any great importance.

Television lights are predominantly ceiling-mounted and illuminate the subject from above. Shadows under the eyebrow and beneath the eye are a constant problem which lighting cannot altogether solve. The make-up man can assist in disguising these effects if he applies a lighter tone of base make-up in the shadowed areas (Fig. 17-1). Care must be taken not to overdo this operation, however, since too much lightening is worse than the shadow.

MATERIALS OF TELEVISION MAKE-UP

A make-up foundation called Pan-Stik is now preferred for all careful work, where Pancake was once the standard. It is more natural, less opaque than Pancake. Pan-Stik is used in the "N" series (1N to 11N) for black-and-white television; the series for color TV is CTV-1W to CTV-10W.

Lipsticks are made in a number of medium or dark red shades, almost any one of which may be used on television. The only exception is the light red or orange lipstick, which is simply too light in tone to contrast with the skin when transferred to monochrome.

The rest of the items in the make-up cabinet are standard stage and film equipment. It is not necessary to go to the great lengths in detail which films require, but many of the film devices, such as rubber noses, for example, are necessary, where putty noses are adequate for the stage. Rubber, of course, cannot be used in connection with grease paint, since the grease will deteriorate the rubber. Max Factor's Rubber Mask Grease Paint must be used instead.

PROCEDURE IN THE USE OF TV MAKE-UP

In the network studios practically everyone who needs make-up will have it done for him, although in a small station the performer may be left to his own devices. Not all performers need make-up, however, and even in color TV it is common to skip make-up entirely on extras and actors with minor parts who are not shown in close-ups.

It generally takes 10 to 20 minutes for a make-up artist to give a leading man a complete straight make-up. Straight make-up for a woman may take from 30 minutes to an hour. If complex character make-up is required, the actor may spend as much as two hours in the make-up chair.

One of the hardest problems to solve in television make-up is the quick change which must be made during the show itself. This problem is unknown in film but occurs fairly often in the theater. Television writers are frequently unaware of the make-up problem and often advance an actor's age 20 years during a 30-second commercial. It is almost impossible to accomplish any kind of extensive make-up change (according to Dick Smith) in less than a minute, no matter how many make-up people can work on the actor. The problem is usually complicated by the fact that the actor must be making a costume change at the same time. The wise producer contacts the make-up man before he finally accepts a script, describes the nature of the make-up changes, and determines whether or not the writer has left enough time.

The most common requirement in the quick change is the graying of hair. Yet there is no really quick method of whitening a whole head of hair properly. Face powder, silver powder, white mascara, and a liquid mascara developed for color TV (treated beige to prevent it from looking bluish) are standard materials for this purpose, but they must all be applied skillfully and with considerable care.

One solution to the problem is to apply wigs or gray hair pieces at the temples, fastening them on with spirit gum, rather than to try to gray the actor's natural hair.

When a face must age in a quick make-up change, the actor is sometimes given two faces. First the actor is made up as an old man. This make-up is applied in grease paint and then powdered so that it will set and become waterproof. Then right on top of the old face, a young face is applied, this time in a water-soluble type of make-up. When the quick change is made, all that is necessary is to sponge off the first layer and the older face is quickly revealed. This may be done a little at a time if the aging is to occur between several scenes. There are, of course, certain additions which must be made in the aging process, such as various hair pieces, noses, bags under the eyes, and drooping jowls; but the time-consuming job is already done.

When Claire Bloom played Victoria Regina in 1957, Dick Smith, who did the make-up, had to make three make-up changes. Between the end of Act II and the first scene of Act III, Miss Bloom had to change from a young queen to a stout and middle-aged dowager. In 2 minutes 50 seconds she had to run from one end of the studio to the other, change part of her costume, have her wig redone, and have a partial mask of foam latex and a nose glued on. Involved were two costume handlers, two hairdressers, three make-up artists, and a prompter. The purpose of the prompter was to hold a stop watch and cue the actions of the seven other people.

After that scene Miss Bloom had to age another 20 years in 1 minute 21 seconds. A gray wig and bonnet went over her brown wig, a shawl with a hump went over her shoulders; bags, eyelids, lower lip and chin and more make-up were added.

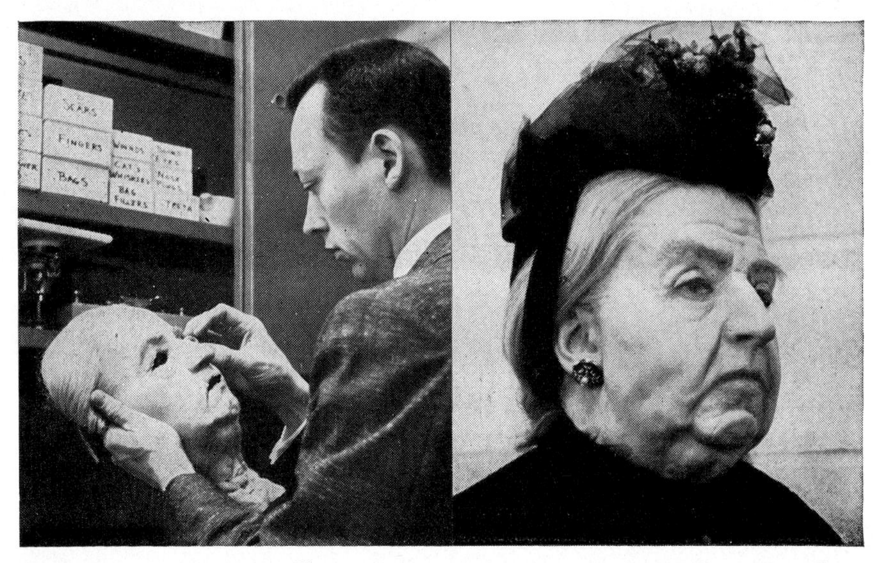

Fig. 17–2. An entire flexible mask created for "Victoria Regina" starring Claire Bloom. (Photo left: courtesy NBC. Photo right: Dick Smith, latex masks, Larchmont, N.Y.)

There was one more short scene when she was 80. But here Dick Smith drew the line. The scene was played by a young actress with a complete foam latex mask to make her look like Miss Bloom as Victoria but still older. The deception worked so well that most viewers did not suspect the double.

With the advent of video tape, quick changes like this have become a thing of the past, a development for which the make-up artists feel profound gratitude.

MINIMUM MAKE-UP FOR NONDRAMATIC PERFORMERS

For the station which is not intending to go into dramatic production and will not require make-up which includes great change of age or character, a few minimum materials will suffice. Pan-Stik is probably the most useful item, and this can be used not only on dark beards which are likely to show through the skin but also on circles under the eyes. A few of the intermediate shades of make-up will be useful, especially when an actor has an extremely pale skin. The rest is standard cosmetic material: face powder, lipstick in standard shades, eyebrow pencil, etc.

Minimum equipment	*Additional items*
Foundation, etc. Factor's Pancake: At least one each of the following: 1N–11N, Light Egyptian, Dark Egyptian Powder: Factor's Translucent Powder puffs Sponges	Factor's Pan-Stik: 1N–11N Factor's Rubber Mask Grease Paint: 1N, 4N, 6N, 10N
Eye make-up, etc. Pencils: Brown and black Mascara: Waterproof Grease eye shadow (any color) Mehron's Lashes (type B) Johnson & Johnson's Liquid Duo adhesive Small scissors	Eyelash curler Tweezer
Lip make-up, etc. Lipstick: Medium (any brand) Dark (any brand) Medium reddish brown (Factor's Moist Rouge Panchro No. 7) for men	Light (any brand) Lipstae
Brushes Lip brushes Make-up shading brushes Spirit-gum brushes Mascara brushes Powder brushes Hairbrushes	Toothbrushes (for graying hair)
Character make-up, etc. Stein's lining color sticks (for beard cover): No. 22, No 23, No. 24 No. 15 white	Nonflexible collodion Stein's black tooth wax (for blocking out teeth) Artificial blood

Minimum equipment	*Additional items*
Character make-up, etc. (*continued*)	
Spirit gum	Lampblack water color (in tube)
Hair whitener	K Y Jelly (mixed with above for quick-change dirt and smudge effects)
Factor's Plasto Wax	Clown white
	Burnt cork (minstrel make-up)
Hair materials, etc.	
Crepe hair, straight and kinked:	Hair nets
Assorted colors	Bandoline
Combs	Wave set
Tuck combs	Scalp Masque (for darkening scalp where hair is thin)
Hairpins:	Rubber bands (for hairdressing)
Brown	
Black	
Extra large	
Bobby pins:	
Brown	
Black	
Solid brilliantine	
Atomizers	
Solvents, etc.	
Alcohol	Sea Breeze or astringent
Acetone	Brilliantine
Witch hazel	Glycerin
Hair lacquer or Liquinet	Mineral oil
Disinfectant	Murine
Equipment	
Barber shears	Hand mirror
Palette knife or spatula (for distributing lipstick)	Plastic make-up cape
Bottles for cleaning lip brushes	Eye dropper
Tape measure	
Razor	
Miscellaneous	
Tissue	Brushless shave cream
Cotton	Styptic pencil
Cold cream	Adhesive tape
Soap	
Razor blades:	
Single edge (for sharpening eyebrow pencils)	
Double edge	
Toupee tape (double-faced adhesive used for attaching mustaches, side burns, etc., in comedy shows where it doesn't matter if they happen to come off)	

HOW TO APPLY STRAIGHT MAKE-UP (FOR A WOMAN)

Following are ten steps in the application of straight make-up for a woman:

1. Cleanse face. The skin should be free of all traces of cold cream or oils of any kind.
2. Apply Pan-Stik foundation with sponge or fingers evenly and sparingly.
3. Apply and blend corrective shadows.
4. Apply moist rouge.
5. Apply highlights, those around eyes last.
6. Powder, starting with highlights below the eyes. Do not powder eyelids.
7. Apply eyelines and eyeshadow. Powder shadow if necessary.
8. Apply mascara and pencil eyebrows.
9. Apply lipstick.
10. Apply body make-up, using matching shade of Pancake.

18

Television Lighting

Television lighting is no more a new and different art than TV make-up, TV camera work, or TV writing. During the first ten years of TV development, when the industry was in the technical stage, the theories propounded by engineers were given great weight. Men who knew little about photographic or stage lighting laid down the rules for TV lighting. Thus it was, for example, that banks of fluorescent tubes were highly favored because of their efficiency. They provided more light per watt of current than incandescents, and they had a high blue content which fitted in very efficiently with the high blue sensitivity of the existing image-orthicon camera tube. The engineer was happiest when the light was flat—everywhere the same, having no perceptible source of emanation.

OBJECTIVE OF TV LIGHTING

The technical objectives behind the engineer's demands are the following: (1) To illuminate the scene before the camera and make possible a satisfactory picture signal safely above the noise level. (2) To provide good "picture quality," which includes good resolution, a realistic balance of tones, and a lack of spurious effects. These objectives concern quantity of light and balance between the intensity of various sources.

The artistic objectives, of which the engineer was largely unaware, are as follows: (1) To assist in achieving a pleasing composition by the distribution of light and shadow. (2) To support the illusion of reality which is attempted in the setting (i.e., sunlight, moonlight, firelight, or other "effect" lighting). (3) To support dramatic values and help in creating or sustaining mood (as in low-key and high-key lighting). (4)

To help bring out the depth dimension in the scene: the roundness of objects and their three-dimensional form are revealed by modeling light; edge lights and back lights separate foreground objects from background. (5) To add sparkle to the picture by the use of highlights, back lights, etc. (6) To add beauty and glamour to the face by smooth soft lighting; often a special "eye light" is used to bring out the highlight in the pupil of the eye. (7) To correct an actor's looks, bring out the good side of his face, and play down undesirable features.

THE LIGHTING DIRECTOR

In any other photographic field, the cameraman has charge of the lighting of the scene: indeed, it is usually his primary concern. In television, however, the cameraman is only an operator and never has anything to do with lighting. In many stations lighting is a responsibility of the engineering department. Where a special lighting man is not available, the practice in many studios has been to set up an even, flat illumination to cover the studio satisfactorily from all possible camera angles, and to leave it there. This provides a very inexpensive but totally dull kind of studio lighting. In some stations a special lighting man is designated; and although he may be basically an engineer, he usually endeavors to learn as much as possible about the creative methods of lighting employed in film and theater and to familiarize himself with the best lighting methods in use in television. A few stations have delegated the responsibility for studio lighting to the program department or have at least installed a lighting man who is primarily responsible to the program manager instead of the chief engineer. In such cases the lighting man is more likely to have had production experience in theater or film, or perhaps in still photography, and approaches his problems with the background of knowledge he has acquired in these fields. The best lighting man, however, must have in addition a pretty thorough understanding of the technical side of television and particularly of the pickup characteristics of the camera tube. He should be able to judge technical quality. Not only should he be able to create and experiment on an artistic level; he should also be expected to veto any lighting effects which result in poor technical quality of the transmitted signal. He should not make it necessary for this action to come from another source.

It is essential that the lighting director have the confidence and cooperation of the technical staff.

LIGHTING PROCEDURES

The function of the lighting director in a small station, where live shows are few and are repeated week after week, is of course quite different from that of the network lighting director who must light two or three new multiple-set shows each week.

The lighting director will usually have some rather definite feelings about working in the TV medium. He will observe that most TV lighting is a compromise. Lights can really be properly adjusted only in relation to the camera, and if the director uses several cameras on the same scene, shooting from widely differing angles, a lighting effect set up for one camera angle may be quite a different effect indeed when seen from the opposite side. The more widely divergent the camera angles on a scene, the greater the compromise necessary in lighting actors effectively from all angles.

Directors of TV dramatic shows have individual styles of working: some preplan every detail of prop position and actor movement before studio rehearsal; others prefer to leave things as flexible as possible and try not to set actions and positions until final camera blocking. Naturally lighting directors greatly prefer the former method of working, since changes in blocking of action or camera angle during camera rehearsal require constant changing of lights.

In general, the lighting director will go through the following steps in lighting a new show.

Plotting. This is the preplanning stage, unnecessary in the case of simple productions but generally followed by network lighting directors on complex productions. Position and movements of actors are indicated by the director of the program on a copy of the designer's floor plan. Then on an overlay sheet, or a tracing or copy of this plan, containing a plan of the overhead light grid, at least nine-tenths of the lights are penciled in and given an approximate position on the grid and approximate area of coverage.

Blocking. Working from the light plot, the electricians can place the necessary lights even without the presence of the lighting director. He will usually supervise the directing of the lights, and whatever trimming can be done before he has actually seen the action on the set.

Trimming. Each light will be adjusted in intensity, beam shape, and direction and in quality during the camera rehearsal. The lighting director watches rehearsal on a monitor, often having a regular position in the control room, and takes what opportunities he can find during breaks to make these finer adjustments.

Recording. If the same lighting setup is to be repeated at a later date, and is of sufficient complexity that it cannot be accurately remembered, a light plot as described above is made at this point—or the original plot is corrected to reflect accurately the final disposition of the lighting equipment.

COMPARISON OF STAGE AND TELEVISION LIGHTING

The greatest difference between stage and television, as far as lighting goes, is that on the stage one is lighting a scene which is to be perceived directly by the human eye, whereas on television lighting must be picked up and transferred electronically by an intermediate system. The human eye is the most marvelous optical mechanism known. It has built-in automatic exposure control. It can function within a brightness range of 1 to 100,000,000. It can register a large range of gray tones at one time, seeing detail in the darkest shadow and also in the brightest light. It is not blind to colors.

A great number of lighting effects are possible in the theater which cannot be accomplished, at least by the same direct methods, in television. Shafts and pools of light so dramatic on a darkened stage will not look the same to the television camera as they do to the eye. Even the simple spotlight effect, standard on the vaudeville stage, imposes quite a strain on television equipment. These effects can be achieved, and often with good effect on television, but only with cooperation from the video engineers.

Stage lighting involves a concept of two kinds of light: general and specific, much like the basic and modeling light of television. General, nondirectional light is provided by the overhead border lights of the stage, plus the footlights and whatever other front illumination is provided from other parts of the auditorium. Specific illumination is provided by spotlights which cover certain areas of the set, with the purpose of highlighting, modeling, accenting, and in general bringing out the form of objects and the depth of space on the stage.

Acting-area light on the stage will range between 2 and 25 lumens per square foot (foot-candles).* Although the image-orthicon camera tube will pick up an image under these lighting conditions, it is usually considered best for optimum performance to have 60 to 100 foot-candles in the television studio.

COMPARISON OF MOTION-PICTURE AND TELEVISION LIGHTING

Motion-picture lighting, just like television lighting, must be designed to fit the particular means of reproduction which is to be employed. Lighting for color film, for example, is entirely different from lighting for black-and-white. In general, film has a wider range of sensitivity than TV, can record darker shades of gray without going pure black, and can record lighter tones without completely washing out.

* Samuel Selden and Hunton D. Sellman, "Stage Scenery and Lighting," Appleton-Century-Crofts, 1959.

In physical placement, the lighting in a motion-picture studio is quite different from that in television. Many of the lights are on movable stands or towers which rest on the floor. Some are attached to the scenery itself, which is built strongly enough to support a platform around the back (the parallels). From this position, electricians can handle the spotlights which are fastened to, and shoot over, the back of the sets. A few motion-picture studios have permanent catwalks above the working area, and certain very intense lights with a long throw are worked from there.

A common method in smaller sound stages is to build temporary scaffolding in the form of catwalks hung from the ceiling rafters, and position these above each set wall. A new set coming into the studio, of course, means at least a day's time of a suitable crew to strike and rebuild the scaffolds, not a practical method for the television studio.

There is usually lots of room in a motion-picture studio, and wide use of the floor for the placement of lights creates no problem. In television, on the other hand, floor space is always limited, and what little there is must be kept free for the movement of cameras. The television lighting man will try to use as few floor lights as possible, preferring to pull lights down from the ceiling on extension mounts when low light sources are desired.

One of the primary problems of television lighting is the microphone boom. This is a factor that must be considered in motion-picture lighting as well. The microphone boom must never pass through the beam of a spotlight, or it may produce a sharp and recognizable shadow on the background. On the motion-picture set there is enough time to work out precise movements of boom, lights, and camera, so that these shadows will not be picked up. In television, on the other hand, such accurate and detailed rehearsal is not possible. The entire studio must be prelighted so that wherever the mike boom must go, it will not cast a shadow. In most applications the boom is placed centrally and spotlights are used only around the back and sides of the set. Floodlighting does not present as much of a problem as spotlighting. Under fluorescent banks, once in common use as a matter of fact, the boom could move around without casting a shadow at all. Where modeling light is concerned, however, the lighting man's only solution is to apply his spotlights from a position where the boom *isn't* and *won't be.*

THEORY OF CREATIVE LIGHTING

The most important quantities of any particular light are, first, the *direction* from which it comes; second, its *intensity;* and, third, its *quality,* in terms of softness or hardness. The type of lighting fixture that produces it is not too important, nor are its color or any of the other qualities which a light may possess, except as they influence direction, intensity, and quality. It is not possible, for example, to look at a television picture and determine whether the studio where it originates is using fluorescent or incandescent lights. (The soft fill light of the fluorescent bank can easily be achieved by a group of incandescent bulbs or floods with diffusers.) It *is* possible, however, to determine which *direction* a light is coming from, whether it is *soft* or *hard* in quality, whether it is relatively high or low in *intensity*. The control of lights in the television studio is built around the control of these three elements.

Light is best known by the way in which it is used. Direction, quality, and intensity will depend on this. The several types of light listed below could be produced by almost any kind of light source. They differ only in the way they are used and, of course, in the three essential qualities mentioned above. They are classified into two groups: (1) lights intended primarily to illuminate the performers; and (2) lights intended to illuminate the set rather than the people in it.

SUBJECT LIGHT

Key light. According to the best practice, the key light is the first light to be set and it remains the main source of illumination on any given area. Key light is highly directional light which builds up highlight areas, casts shadows, and brings out the form of objects. The lighting director usually attempts to set his key light above and forward of the actors and to one side or another of the primary camera angle. Generally only one key light is used on a given area and it is often necessary to devote several instruments to this purpose before all areas in a set are key-lighted. Sometimes action may require that a microphone boom move across a key light. In such a case the lighting director may set two key lights on the same area, using one until the boom must move across its beam, then cross-fading to the second to avoid boom shadow. If more than one key light covers a subject simultaneously, a multiple shadow will result, which can look very unnatural if it becomes obvious.

Back light. Back light, generally the second light to be set on an area, is named for the direction from which it is used. It is placed behind the subject, opposite to the camera and trained primarily on the subject's head and shoulders. The effect is an added sparkle as a gleam appears on the subject's hair and a rim of light around the top of the shoulders. This is usually described as having the effect of separating subject from background. This is partly a function of its modeling effect, bringing out the three-dimensional quality of the subject, and partly a matter of achieving sufficient contrast of tone so the edge of the subject stands apart from the background. Back light (along with key light) is a modeling light.

Back light can only be successfully provided by spotlights which should be placed as low as possible behind the subject without being so low that they reach the camera lens and cause a flare in the top of the picture. Too high a position for the back light will cast light on the subject's forehead, nose, and cheeks and cause dark hollows under the eyebrows. A 45-degree elevation from the horizontal is considered best, although the small size of TV studios dictates a 75-degree angle most of the time.

Fill light. Fill light is used for illuminating or "filling in" shadow areas on the subject left by the modeling lights. It must be a soft and diffuse light, if possible, so it will not cast its own set of shadows on the background.

Fill light was once considered of primary importance in TV lighting, being given the name of "base light." The lighting director began each light setup by establishing a certain minimum over-all level of flat non-directional light which constituted a base on which he could build further with his modeling lights. In ultimate result, of course, the base light served the purpose of filling in the shadow areas. Today, fill light is usually added after the key and back lights have been set, in the same manner as still or motion-picture lighting is done.

A hopeless confusion in terms existed during a period when this "base light" was called "key light" by TV engineers, and it was impossible for film or photographic people to discuss TV lighting with them without violent disagreement.

Fill light may be provided by almost any type of instrument positioned so as to illuminate the side of the subject opposite the key light. A soft light casting no particular shadows, it may come from many sources but should be lower in intensity than the modeling lights or it will destroy their effectiveness.

In photography fill light often originates from the direction of the camera. If the light unit is placed as close to the camera as possible, it will "see" the same portions of the scene that the camera does and illuminate every shadow no matter how inaccessible. In flash photography, a flash bulb is commonly placed on the camera, even when one or more other bulbs are held closer to the subject for modeling light. (When only one bulb is used, as in newspaper photography, it is set off at the camera and illuminates the scene with completely flat light.) Lights are sometimes placed on or near the TV camera lens for fill purposes.

BACKGROUND LIGHT

Unless the action takes place within a few feet of the backgrounds, lights intended for the performers will not also cover the walls and background props. It is general practice to have a number of units devoted only to illumination of the background.

Occasionally special lighting effects which involve the background of the set will be needed. Shafts of light, areas of light and shadow, or patterns of various types are projected by means of special background lights. In those film studios where the incandescent spot is used for every lighting need, backgrounds are often lighted by many small spots so that there is a considerable play of tone between light and dark areas. The barn doors are often partially closed down (feathered) on these spots to cast the light in irregular patterns rather than circular areas.

SPECIAL LIGHTING TERMS

There are several other terms which are also applied to lights according to the way in which they are used. Since these terms will not be used in the text which follows, they need only be defined and related to the more common terms which have been covered above.

Accent light: Usually a back light, although it may be from the side. Its purpose is to add a highlight where one is needed.

Kicker light: Same purpose, usually from the side. For these purposes spots are always used because an intense light must be concentrated on a small area from a relatively distant point.

Crosslight: This term is applied to modeling light when it comes from the front and side of the set, "across the subject."

Rim light: Back light.

Edge light: Back light.

Floor light, cross back light: These also are terms which describe a light by the direction from which it comes.

Clothes light: A motion-picture term for additional light necessary on dark clothing.

Eye light, or eye catch light: A special light placed so that an image of it is reflected from the performer's eye. It is necessary only in close-up but it makes a big difference. A close-up without eye light looks very dead; the addition of the tiny glint in the eye brings it to life.

HIGH-KEY AND LOW-KEY LIGHT

In this connection "key" has another meaning and should not be confused with "key light." High-key is the effect of a brightly lighted room or exterior; low-key the effect of dim or spotty light. Reference to the accompanying table of light levels will reveal that the low-key effect is achieved by applying a low-fill and leaving the key lights unchanged. Conversely, high-key is really high-fill.

INTENSITY OF LIGHT

It is always a good plan to measure the lighting, once a good setup has been achieved, and record the position of lights and the areas they cover so that the same conditions can be reproduced again quickly if desired. The final proof of the lighting must be the picture as it appears on the monitor; and the lighting man must have a jeep monitor at his control point which is kept in perfect adjustment at all times. Although final adjustments will be made by eye, to "light it so it looks right," and a certain variation will be found in technical requirements owing to different camera tubes or other equipment, the following table will provide a close approximation of the usual light intensities used in television studios.

Light intensity is measured in foot-candles, or lumens per square foot. A lumen is a basic quantity of light (the total amount of light which one candle emits). Any light gives out a certain number of lumens, and the number of these which fall on a square foot of surface is a measure of the light intensity at that point. Naturally the farther this square foot of surface is removed from the light source, the fewer lumens will fall on it. This illumination may be called lumens per square foot, or foot-candles, which is a more familiar but a more complex term.

LIGHT LEVELS

The level of intensity of the lighting will depend on the sensitivity of the camera tube and on the lens opening (*f* stop) employed. Some studios prefer a smaller opening (higher *f* stop) because of the greater depth of field, and thus must work at a higher light level. A larger opening (lower *f* stop) will result in less depth of field—a desirable condition in many cases when it is distracting to see all background elements as sharp and clear as the foreground, but certainly more trouble for the cameraman. However, more effective lighting is always possible when the levels are kept lower.

Studios using the vidicon tube must be lighted to about twice the levels given below; NTSC color cameras, about five times. The accompanying figures assume the use of the 5820 image-orthicon tube or its equivalent in sensitivity.

High-key	*f/4 to f/8*	*f/8 to f/16*
Key light	60–80 ft-c	100–150 ft-c
Back light	80 ft-c	150 ft-c
Fill light	30–60 ft-c	60–100 ft-c
Low-key		
Key light	60–80 ft-c	100–150 ft-c
Back light	80 ft-c	150 ft-c
Fill light	15–25 ft-c	25–40 ft-c

The ratios between key and fill light shown in the chart are about 2 to 1 for high-key and 4 to 1 for low-key. Naturally a much greater contrast range will exist between dark and light objects on the set before light is ever applied, and the lighting contrast range will depend on subject contrast. A 5-to-1 ratio is common, and there have been exceptional shows where sets were all in the median range, no one wore white or black clothes, there were no platinum blondes or refrigerators to light, and the key-to-fill ratio could be as high as 8 or 9 to 1.

The lighting man will often block out the lighting on a television set several hours before cameras will be operating in the studio, and he must wait to check his results. In order to ensure even lighting, he will generally use a light meter of the incident type, reading in foot-candles (lumens per square foot). In order to register the light which is seen by the camera, the meter should be pointed at the camera. This means that the light-sensitive area of the meter is held in a vertical plane, since vertical planes (walls of sets, sides of furniture, fronts or backs of people) make up the major portion of the camera's view. It is obvious that a meter faced up or toward the back of the set will register a lot of light which does not affect the camera since it falls on surfaces which the camera does not see. Back light, of course, is an exception and must be measured by facing the meter toward the light.

LIGHTING AND VIDEO

One of the purposes of TV lighting is that it meet the minimum basic requirements of the particular camera tube employed. There are times when the video engineer will be unable to achieve requisite picture quality, even though the levels are not particularly low, and will ask for "more light." In most such cases, according to Carlton Winckler at CBS, what is really at fault is the balance between the various light sources. If the contrast is not excessive (key to back to fill: 1:1:½) and there are no unusually bright hot spots due to highly reflective subject matter or overlap of key-light beams, there should be no video problems.

LIGHT SOURCES

There are only four basic types of light source around which the actual lamps are built. Light instruments of various types have been designed for each of them. The light source is the luminous material *within* the lamp which emanates light. The four light sources are: (1) the incandescent filament, (2) the incandescent gas, (3) the carbon arc, (4) the fluorescent tube. Some new light sources which are combinations of the above are being experimented with. However, at the present time, all light units used in television are built around one or another of these basic light sources.

The incandescent filament. The incandescent filament is the original light source known to electricity, the type of light bulb that Edison first invented. A filament of tungsten wire is heated by the passage of an electrical current which is too great for the size of the wire. It heats up under the strain and radiates heat and light (much more heat than light, as any performer can tell you) and can be built into a light unit with a reflector so that these radiations can be concentrated into a beam.

The incandescent gas. The most familiar example of this type of lamp is the colored neon, argon, or xenon tube spelling out the name of your local bar. The combination of gases determines the color. Lamps containing mercury vapor were used experimentally in the early days of television but proved unsatisfactory because of their extreme blue color, upsetting the color balance of everything on the set, including flesh tones.

The carbon arc. The arc is a spark that jumps across a gap between sticks of carbon. It operates in the air, requiring no vacuum or gas envelope, and gives off a very intense light from a small source. Arcs were experimented with in early television stations but have been pretty well eliminated as impractical.

The fluorescent tube. The fluorescent tube is a development of the incandescent gas lamp and contains mercury vapor, which is the original source of the light. A large part of the radiation from the mercury gas is ultraviolet light. There are many fluorescent chemicals which will glow under ultraviolet light and change these invisible radiations into visible light. The interior of the fluorescent tube is coated with a mixture of some of these phosphors. The ultraviolet light radiated from the interior of the tube is transformed by the phosphor coating into visible light, the color of which will depend on the mixture of phosphors used. This produces the most efficient type of lamp. More light is produced from the same amount of current than by any of the other means.

Although all four types of light were experimented with in the development of television, only the incandescent filament proved capable of the flexibility and artistic control necessary for effective lighting.

LIGHTING INSTRUMENTS

Lighting instruments are characterized mostly by the distribution of the light they put out. An open lamp without any light unit built around it will radiate light equally in all directions. This is highly inefficient, since the subject to be lighted is usually within a very small segment of the space into which all this light is radiated. Only a fraction of the total emitted light would go in the right direction. In order to concentrate more of this light onto the subject area, the reflector was designed. The reflector is usually a curved mirror or other highly reflective surface. It intercepts the light which is leaving the lamp in unwanted directions and turns it back toward the subject. This forms the light into a beam. The light unit can be pointed toward whatever portion of the subject is to be illuminated, and the light will be concentrated on that area.

Different types of reflectors produce different-shaped beams. A light which delivers a wide-angle beam is usually referred to as a *floodlight*, or *broad*. A light in which the beam is narrow is called a *spot*. Spotlights can usually be focused so that the width of the beam is adjustable (Fig. 18-1).

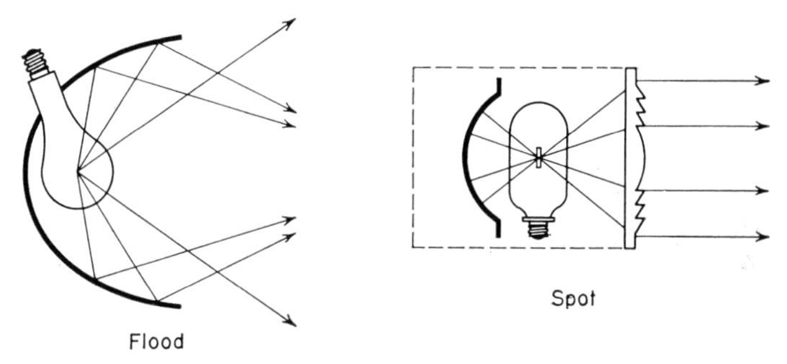

Fig. 18–1. Formation of light beam in wide-beam floodlight (left) and narrow-beam spotlight (right).

Both the flood and the spot type of light can be produced by the internal-reflector lamp, which has the proper type of reflector built and sealed into the bulb. These lamps require no housing of any kind and are used widely in television studios when relatively small amounts of light are necessary. The width of beam is not adjustable in these lamps, however, since the distance between filaments and reflector is fixed (Fig. 18-4).

THE INCANDESCENT SCOOP

The scoop is a floodlight with a very wide beam. A reflector with a parabolic shape is built around a lamp base which will take anything from a 750-watt to a 2,500-watt lamp. Lamps of 1,000 or 2,000 watts are generally used. NBC has standardized on these lights, mounting them overhead to shoot into the sets at an angle, and using them for fill light. Scoops are often used on floor stands when fill light must come

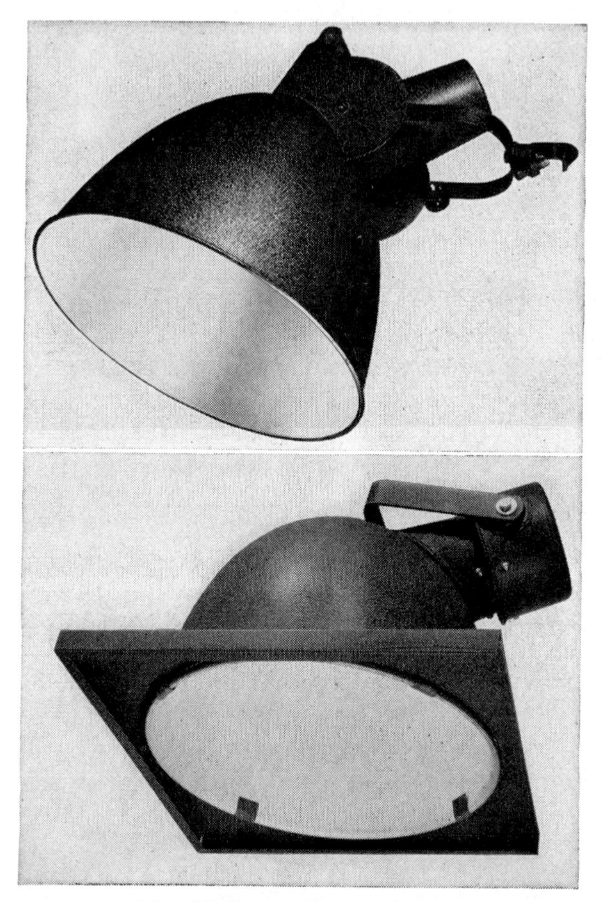

Fig. 18–2. Incandescent scoops.

from a low angle. The scoop puts a lot of floodlight into a single unit not too large in size. For this reason, when lights are taken out of the studio for remote pickups, the scoop is very often preferred.

INTERNAL-REFLECTOR BULBS

These bulbs come in two types, the R40 and the PAR 38 (Fig. 18-3). Each of these is made in a narrow-beam projector (spot) version and in a wide-beam projector (flood). Lamps of 150 and 300 watts are available, and the R40's can be obtained in the very much brighter but shorter lived photoflood type. The standard R40's are rated at 1,000 hours. A bank of several of the projector-spot lamps will create a directional beam and can be used for modeling.

A small studio can make very excellent use of these lamps at a great saving, of course, since the lamp is its own lighting unit. One or two spots fastened with spring clamps to the back of the set and directed properly will provide nice back lighting for limited areas. In the case of a pianist, for example, where an accurate position is known and the lamp does not have to be too far distant, a single R40 projector spot will

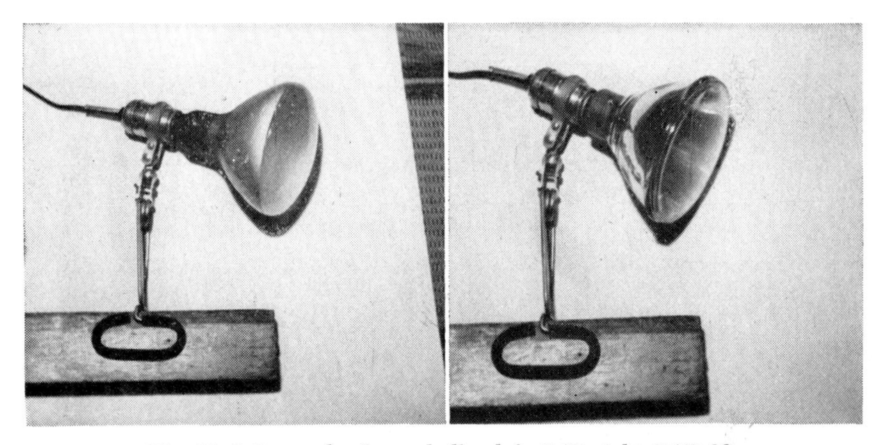

Fig. 18–3. Internal-reflector bulbs: left, R40; right, PAR 38.

suffice. In the use of effects lighting, where lamps must be placed below the cameras, hidden in the foreground scenery or behind ground rows, these lamps are very useful because of their small size. Any other type of light unit with external reflector, housing, etc., would take up a great deal more space.

To increase the usefulness of the projector spot for back light, a clip-on metal baffle is available which prevents spill light from reaching the camera lens. It is a series of concentric bands on edge through which the light can project forward but is prevented from leaving the lamp at an angle. The heat of these unprotected bulbs, especially the photoflood type, makes them dangerous to place where someone might touch them or where they might come in contact with scenery or props. To guard against this, a second type of clip-on is available which puts a protecting shield around the edge of the lamp. In a later section on special-effect lighting, there is an account of how these lamps have been built into homemade projectors for background patterns and long-throw accent lighting.

The internal-reflector *photoflood* bulbs, available at almost any photographic store, give a great deal more light. These are really low-voltage lamps which are run at a higher-than-rated voltage when used on 110-volt current. They burn very brightly but are short-lived (6 to 8 hours) and constitute a certain hazard because they occasionally end their short life in a burst of glory, showering the set with bits of glass. Additional light can be obtained safely from PAR 38's by running them at a higher voltage than the normal 110 for which they are rated. Several studios transform the voltage going to these lamps and run them at 150 volts. Their life is materially shortened, but they give off a great deal more light.

STRIP LIGHTS

There is very often a need for a light unit which will provide general light along a strip. The strip light (Fig. 18-4) is well known in the

Fig. 18–4. Strip lights.

theater as the border and is used in television for many of the same purposes. It can be laid on the floor behind a ground row or mounted on a stand vertically to illuminate a cyclorama from just behind the edge of a set. It is frequently used for background light. The strip light is built with reflectors for standard lamps or without reflectors (at a very great saving) for the use of R40 lamps.

THE FOCUSING SCOOP

The focusing scoop and the beam projector (below) are transitional forms which have some of the qualities of the spotlight and may perform some of the same functions. The width of the beam that a scoop throws out is dependent on the position of the lamp within the reflector. In this particular light the bulb can be moved back and forth to produce the wide beam of the regular scoop or a narrow soft-edged spot very similar to what a fresnel-lens spotlight of equal wattage would produce.

THE BEAM PROJECTOR

The beam projector operates on the principle of directing all possible light from the lamp backward into a highly polished parabolic reflector which then focuses the light into a high-intensity narrow beam. This also produces a rather hard light.

FLOODLIGHTING BY REFLECTOR

The reflector is not a light, but a surface which reflects light coming from some other source. The size and texture of the reflecting surface will change the quality of the light, making it softer and more diffuse. Many kinds of reflecting surfaces can be used, depending on the need. At one end of the scale is the glass mirror or highly polished metal reflector which exhibits "specular" reflection. The light beam is only changed in direction; it is not altered. At the other end of the scale is the diffuse surface, such as white plaster or paint. A light beam reflected by such a surface is diffused in all directions by the myriad tiny facets throughout the surface, and it casts as much light (looks as bright) in one direction as in another. Neither of these is exactly what is necessary in creating floodlighting with a reflector. A surface which retains a semblance of the beam carries the light for a longer distance. Pebbled aluminum foil or silver paper works well for the purpose in television as it has in photography. In motion-picture work a pebbled gold surface is often used to reflect sunlight into the shadow areas of close-up shots. The warm color of the reflected light seems to be especially flattering to skin tones.

In small studios where playing areas are fairly constant from one show to the next, reflectors have been installed that produce a soft and shadowless fill light. They are not readily movable, however, and have no application where lights must be rehung for each show.

Fig. 18–5. Aluminum-foil reflectors used by Karl Weger of WPTZ. These were inspired by a stage-lighting technique used by Mariano Fortuny shortly after 1900, and have been nicknamed "Fortuny reflectors." The white board hanging below the reflectors is only a baffle to keep unwanted light off the studio beyond.

A common practice is to use the floor as a reflector and bounce a spotlight beam off the floor for a soft fill light on the subject from below.

THE FRESNEL SPOT

The term "fresnel spot" covers all types of spotlights which are equipped with a fresnel lens. These lenses, easily recognizable by the concentric grooves, or steps, on their front surface, form the light into a soft-edged beam. Within the spotlight, the lamp and reflector are movable and can be adjusted by a screw-and-crank arrangement in the larger lights or by a simple slide mechanism in the smaller ones. As the lamp bulb is moved closer to the lens, the spotlight beam is widened out; and when the lamp is moved as far back in the housing as possible, the spot is at its narrowest. If the spot were to be made any narrower by further adjustment, the lamp would be coming into the focal point of the lens and an image of the lamp filament would be cast on the scene.

Fresnel spots are made in some six or eight different sizes, depending on the manufacturer, and range from the tiny 100- to 150-watt "dinky-

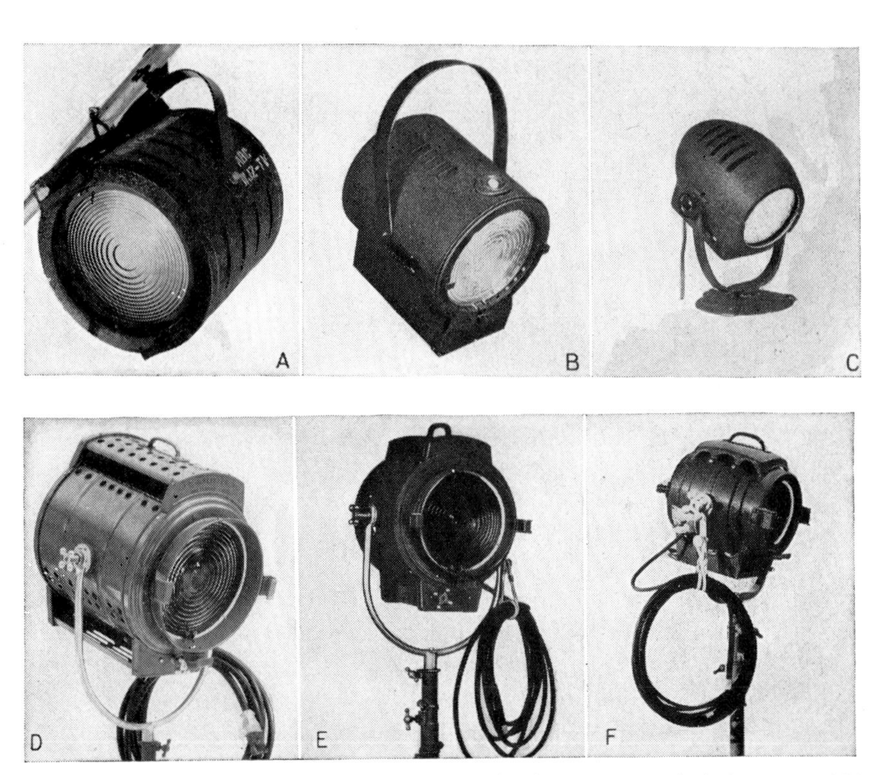

Fig. 18–6. Representative fresnel spots. (*A*) Kliegl 2,000 watt; (*B*) Century 1,000 to 1,500 watt; (*C*) Century 250 to 750 watt; (*D*) McAlister Senior 5,000 watt; (*E*) Junior 1,000 and 2,000 watt; (*F*) Baby 500 to 750 watt.

inky," with a lens only 3 inches in diameter, to the 5,000-watt "senior," with a 14- or 16-inch lens. Neither of these extremes is used often in the television studio, but the 750-, 1,000-, and 2,000-watt sizes are everywhere to be seen. Some of these units may take several sizes of lamps (Fig. 18-6). The 5,000-watt spot is in common use in color TV studios. The incandescent spotlight is the backbone of photographic lighting. Many motion picture studios use it almost exclusively—for fill as well as modeling light. It is not surprising, therefore, that TV studios as well depend heavily on fresnel spots.

Fig. 18–7. Set for CBS physics series "Why Is It So?" showing fresnels and scoops suspended from battens on sky hooks.

THE PROJECTION SPOT (*ELLIPSOIDAL*)

This type of spotlight projects a sharp-edged spot which can be focused and also can be shaped into any rectangle desired. A reflector is used which is ellipsoidal in shape, and this concentrates more of the light into the lens. Whereas the usual spotlight design places the lamp ahead of the focal point of the lens so that an image of the lamp filament is not projected on the scene, this type of unit avoids that effect by placing the lamp *behind* the focal point of the lens. Shutters can then be placed in the focal plane, and a sharp-edged image of these shutters is projected. There is no spill light. Tests have indicated that this design of light is about three times as efficient as the regular spotlight. Century claims 30 to 40 per cent efficiency for their Lekolite, which means that 30 to 40 per cent of the total lumens emitted by the lamp is to be found in the projected beam. This is exceptionally high.

Projection spots can be equipped with iris shutters if desired, or special patterns may be inserted in the focal plane if the unit is adapted for this purpose. They are excellent for long-throw highlighting of small areas. Kliegl makes this type of light in two sizes: the junior, which will take a 250- to 750-watt lamp; and the Master Klieglight, which will take 1,500- or 2,000-watt lamps.

Fig. 18–8. Projection spot (Century Lekolite).

THE LARGE PROJECTION SPOT

These are the largest light units used in the television studio. They are 43 inches long and built on the same principle as the units just described, except that a 3,000-watt lamp is used. An iris shutter in the focal plane can be adjusted to give a sharp-edged spot of any size, and curtain shutters top and bottom can form this circle of light into a wide oblong shape (Fig. 18-9). Kliegl's Dyna-beam has an extra lens which

(*a*)

(*b*)

Fig. 18–9. Large projection spots. (*a*) Century Lekolite; (*b*) Kliegl Dyna-beam.

can be quickly put in place, and this has the effect of spreading the ordinarily narrow beam to twice its width. The maximum spread is about

24 degrees with the spread lens, 12 degrees without. These lights are primarily intended for long-throw purposes. In theaters which have been adapted to television, one will usually see two or three along the balcony rail. While one may be used as a follow spot for theatrical effects, the others are used for front fill light (in the spread-beam adjustment).

Since the Dyna-beam unit is very large and heavy, it is never mounted above the studio but is always used on a floor stand. If it is necessary for its light to come from a high point, it may be placed temporarily on a platform for the purpose.

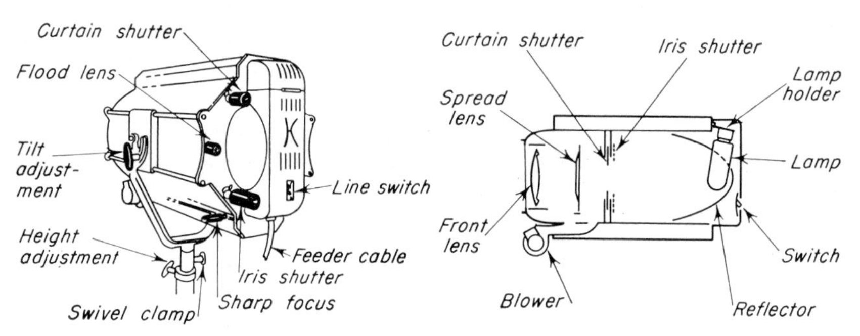

Fig. 18–10. Construction of Dyna-beam spotlight.

MOUNTING OF LIGHTS AND CONTROL OVER DIRECTION

Although many of the smaller stations have equipped their studios with permanently mounted lights which cannot be adjusted in any way (except to be turned off or on selectively), any studio which attempts to do artistic lighting will have given considerable thought to control. A light must be placed where it will give the best effect. It must be directed toward the proper subject. Often it must be changed in quality by the addition or removal of diffusing screens. Barn doors and goboes must be adjusted to prevent spill light from reaching the camera lens or to keep the light off certain areas of the scene.

In lighting for still photography, where all the lights rest on floor stands, the photographer has only to reach out, and he can quickly make any adjustment he wants. In motion-picture work, although the photographer may not handle the lighting equipment, every light is under manual control. If a light is to be adjusted, an electrician can be quickly beside it, with his hands on it, making adjustments according to the cameraman's directions. In television, on the other hand, lights must be kept off the floor and consequently are relatively inaccessible. Several methods of reaching these lights have been devised, none of which is entirely satisfactory.

THE PIPE GRID

The use of a pipe grid is perhaps the most common method of handling lights in television studios. Heavy pipes are run across the ceiling, 4 to 8 feet apart, and anywhere from 14 to 20 feet above the studio floor. A similar set of pipes is run at a right angle to these. Lights are clamped to the pipes. This allows one to place a light in any part of the studio ceiling; and if the pipe squares are 4 feet wide, the greatest compromise between where a light should be and where it can be placed is 2 feet. This is only mounting, however; what about control?

In this kind of installation lights are usually adjusted by the ladder method. Setting up a ladder is slow; it ties up the rehearsal while a light change is made; it requires a couple of men (one to hold the ladder), in addition to the lighting man or director who is watching the effect of the light. The advantage, however, is that the electrician gets his hands on the light. Some good remote-control devices have been developed, but these usually go no further than directional control.

The Bill Eddy three-cord method was once considered very useful: a great maze of nylon cords across the ceiling and down the wall made possible the control of pan and tilt for each light unit. Since the units were thus incapable of repositioning, the system was used primarily for fill light in studios where little more than flat light was attempted.

Some of the large network studios have installed a motorized remote-control pan, tilt, and beam adjustment apparatus which is offered by Century. Kliegl has developed an instrument with special fittings to take a hook at the end of a pole. Adjustments in pan or tilt and in beam width may be made from the floor without a ladder. Diffusing screens can't very well be put in place at the end of a stick, and adjustment of barn doors is awkward. At least for spotlights devoted to key or back light, direct manual control is necessary.

COUNTERWEIGHTED BATTENS

The counterweighted batten is an old stage device. In the theater, pipe battens the width of the stage are suspended by ropes, and on these the spotlights used for specific lighting are mounted. It is only when the space below is completely clear that battens may be lowered to the floor, however, and television studios are rarely known to be clear for any length of time. Besides, adjustments of lights are made only after the sets are up. The result is a recourse to the ladder method.

A studio which is devoted to complex dramatic productions will have constant need for varying the height of the lights from the floor. Often a set must be two stories tall, as when the action takes place at the top and bottom of a staircase. It is just as likely, in such a show, that the neighboring set will be half the height. And any set which requires an extremely long shot—as in the case of classic ballet when an entire company must be seen at once—will require considerable height, or the camera will be forced to show large areas of foreground floor. Unusual height is also necessary for low-angle shooting. When you shoot up at an actor you are also shooting up at the back studio wall and ceiling. The stage solved this problem by hanging tormentors in front of the light

Fig. 18–11. Lights mounted on counterweighted battens (ABC-TV, New York, Studio 1).

battens so the audience in the front rows would not be blinded by the overhead lights. A very high background will often suffice for the TV camera. When this won't work, the solution is to put a ceiling on the set, a design element which permits dramatic low-angle shooting but which is the despair of the lighting director. The movable batten method is probably necessary if the lights must be adjusted quickly to a wide range of heights, even though ladders must be used to trim and adjust them.

CATWALKS

Many TV studios have been built with catwalks around the sides of the studio, and occasionally across the middle. This indeed makes it possible to reach some lights, but unless the studio is very small, a catwalk is of little help in reaching most of the lighting.

A disadvantage of the usual catwalk is that it is difficult to light anything properly which happens to be set just beneath it. Strip lights have been mounted below catwalks, but they give only top light, which is not very desirable. Back light and cross light are the problem. In a small studio it is always desirable to set scenery right up to the studio wall, and the space beneath the catwalk cannot be sacrificed. If in studio construction the catwalk space were taken from some other portions of the building, so that the catwalk were built over a hall running alongside the studio, for example, this problem would be eliminated.

A variation on the catwalk has been in use at some of the CBS studios in New York, where narrow walks of planking have been laid down over the entire studio above the pipe grid. This enables the electricians to reach at least the clamp which mounts a light, even though the unit itself may be hung on an extension which puts it several feet lower. Cables, connectors, outlets, and so forth, are also readily available to the electrician above the set.

INDIVIDUAL LIGHT MOUNTINGS. CONTROL OF ELEVATION

Many studios are using a type of pantograph, or lazy-tongs, mounting which enables a man with a hooked pole to pull the light down to camera level or push it up against the ceiling. Figure 18-12 shows an NBC studio equipped with these adjustable devices. Beam spread, barn doors, etc., can be adjusted by lowering the light within reach, and final directional adjustments can be made after the light is again raised to operating position. Another device is the "sky hook"—a vertical telescoping pipe provided with a counterweight to balance the light unit so that it will rest at any extension. Counterbalancing in the lazy-tongs variety is achieved by means of a spring which can be adjusted to match the weight of the light that is used.

A simpler device than these consists of a long rod with setscrew and safety stop which slides through a fitting clamped to the grid. The light is more difficult to adjust by this method but can be raised and lowered the length of the rod. Two people are required to adjust the larger lamps, one on a ladder below holding the lamp, and one at the setscrew in the fixed fitting where the rod is clamped to the grid.

LIGHTS ATTACHED TO SETS

The fastening of lights to the top of sets is standard motion-picture practice, but it is not done in TV studios where canvas scenery is used,

Fig. 18–12. Lights mounted on individual pantographs. Note use of short adjustable cross members on the grid. (Photo courtesy of NBC.)

except for light clip-on R40 units. The networks now use a sturdier type of scenery, almost as strong as that used in motion pictures. The standard motion-picture set-hook is thus sometimes used in TV studios—a sort of double hook which hangs over the top of the set with a mounting for a fresnel spot which can be adjusted up or down within a range of a foot or two. These are often called "Trombones."

FLOOR LIGHTS

Lights on floor stands are generally to be avoided in the TV studio. There is little enough room in most studios for camera movement, and every square foot of floor space is precious. In addition, floor lights must be manned so they can be moved with the cameras or all flexibility is lost. Key lights are sometimes used on floor stands but more frequently it has been floodlights which were so mounted. Studios with excess top or ceiling light (as in the case of early TV studios which plastered the ceiling with fluorescent tubes) required floor lights to fill in the ugly eye-socket shadows caused by the top light.

LIGHTS ON CAMERAS

It is standard motion-picture practice to mount a small eye-light on the front of the camera. This light is useful only when the camera is shooting close-ups, to provide some fill light and give the eye a sparkle by reflecting in the pupil. In TV studios eye-light is no less necessary. The need for front fill is often felt when the camera moves in so close to the subject that it begins to intercept the key light and throw its

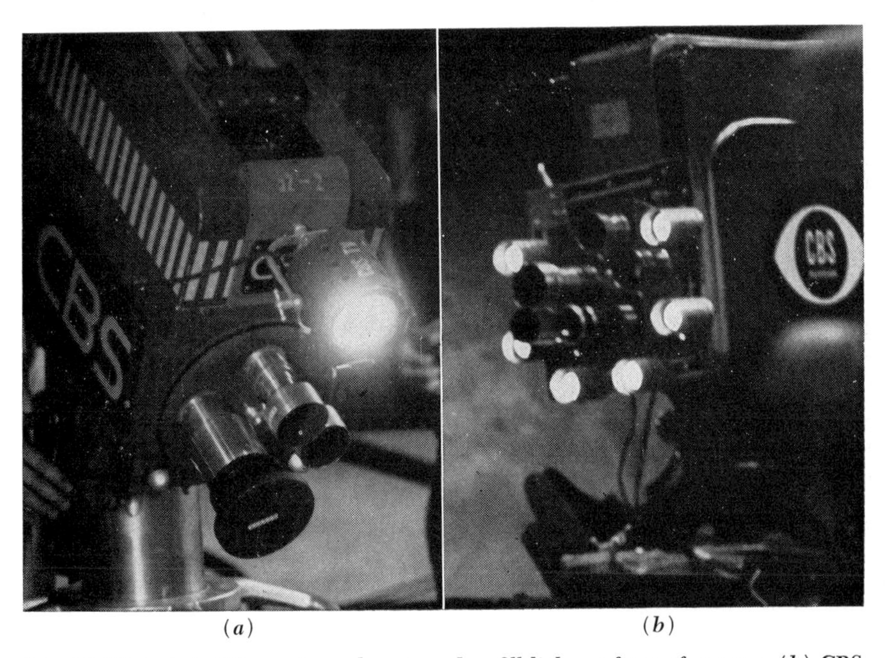

(*a*) (*b*)

Fig. 18–13. (*a*) **A 150-watt fresnel spot used as fill light on front of camera.** (*b*) **CBS camera with a ring of small lights (25 watts, 110 volts) provides a softer fill light.**

shadow across the actor. Then the key must be dimmed out and the camera fill light used to replace it. The camera frequently will shoot into the set through a window or port of some sort, where because of the presence of the set wall there can be no fill light from the direction of the camera unless it is provided by lights on the camera itself. Again, this practice is generally limited to shots where the camera is within 4 feet of the subject. CBS has had success with a circle of eight 25-watt reflector floods surrounding the camera lens. A small fresnel spot (dinky-inky) is frequently used for this purpose (Fig. 18-13) although it is often considered too directional for the best fill light.

LIGHTING THE CEILINGED SET

Mention has been made of the need for ceilings on sets when the director wishes to shoot from low angles. Of course a three-walled set completely covered with ceiling would leave no access for lighting except from the direction of the camera, resulting probably in flat lighting and great danger of boom shadows unless spots were eliminated. In appreciation of this, the designer will generally allow some openings, perhaps between wall and ceiling, or behind low-hanging beams, where light can be directed onto the set without the opening being visible. Failing this, and there are always areas that cannot be reached from these limited openings, the lighting director must have his key lights hand-held, move them into place when the camera angle will allow it and move them back out of the set when the camera withdraws. Clip-on R40's are used in this application since the lights must often be held at arm's length above the head.

CONTROL OF QUALITY

Light from a fresnel spot may be made harder (although less intense) by removing the fresnel lens and lighting with the open lamp. This will be resorted to when sharp-cast shadow effects are desired.

The factor which determines quality is the size of the light source. A sharp-edged shadow can be cast only by a light which originates in a very small source. Frosted lamps enlarge the source to include the entire lamp bulb and produce a softer shadow than clear lamps of the same type, since in a clear lamp the light source is the relatively small filament.

A spot may be softened by adding one or more diffusers in front of it. A diffuser, sometimes called a "scrim," is a metal frame holding a sheet of spun glass, or two or three layers of window screen. Diffusers are also made with such materials as silk or plastic-filled screening, but nonflammable types are necessary. The effect of the diffuser is to enlarge the actual source of light, since now the light originates from the entire area of the diffuser, rather than just from the filament in the lamp plus its reflections in the instrument's reflector.

Scoops are generally lamped with frosted bulbs for softer light, yet must often be diffused further to avoid casting multiple-shadows with the fill light. Some studios always diffuse all scoops, although diffusing a light always cuts down on its intensity. This is partly because the diffuser absorbs a certain amount of light and partly because the light beam is broadened.

"Half-scrims" are often used in key lights not so much as a control over quality as a means of balancing the intensity of the light. Since light intensity varies inversely as the distance from the source, an actor in the foreground will receive much more illumination than an actor in the background, twice as far away. The half-scrim is a diffuser, the top half of which is open. This has the effect of cutting down the intensity of light on the foreground to approximate that in the farther reaches of the beam, and relieves the lighting man from having to dim the light up or down as action moves upstage or down. Half-scrims are sometimes used vertically when overlapping light beams tend to create hot spots in the set. The overlapping portion of each beam is scrimmed down so an actor may walk in even illumination from one key light into the next.

COLORED LIGHT

The use of colored light, even in color TV, is very limited in television. In color TV (see Chap. 21) such lights are used only on the backgrounds when they have not been painted to give the desired effects, but never on the faces of performers except for special effect. Colored light is, of course, provided by inserting gelatin filters in front of standard instruments, and a tremendous range of colored gels is available for use in the theater where subtly or strongly colored light is very important. Extensive experimentation has found very little application to TV, however.

An exception is the practice, in black-and-white TV, of lighting dark Negroes with an amber gel which, it is generally agreed, results in a better rendition of various tones on the skin, avoiding a flat over-all black. This is possibly because the amber light is more completely reflected by the warm skin tones than white with its high blue component, which is absorbed. At the same time the amber will not overilluminate clothes, props, or lighter-skinned people in the same light beam, as white light might do.

CONTROL OF LIGHT INTENSITY

Control of intensity is generally achieved by means of dimmers. Well-equipped studios can put each light on a separate dimmer, so they can be individually adjusted in intensity. Dimmers are thus used constantly for balancing the intensity of the lights and only secondarily for light changes and effects. No studio can do really effective lighting without them.

There are four main types of dimmers, operating on separate electrical principles, which are found in theaters and are adaptable for television studios. These are (1) the resistance dimmer, (2) the autotransformer dimmer, (3) the reactance dimmer, and (4) the electronic tube dimmer.

The resistance dimmer. This is the standard type of dimmer used in most theaters. The dimmer consists of a long wire (compactly arranged into a circular coil) through which the current must pass before it reaches the light. An adjustable arm runs a contact around the coil and either shortens or lengthens the amount of resistance wire the current must pass through. The more resistance in the circuit, the less voltage left to light the lamp and the weaker the light. The rest of the voltage, however, is dissipated in heating up the dimmer. It takes just as much current to run a lamp which is dimmed way down as it does to run a lamp without a dimmer. This is inefficient in comparison with the other methods listed below. Because of the bulkiness of these dimmers and the heat they generate, plus their inefficiency in operation, television stations are following the lead of the newer theaters in installing dimmers of the other, superior types.

The autotransformer dimmer. Several types of autotransformer dimmers are on the market today and are the most common type being built into television dimmer-control systems. The Powerstat, the Autrastat, and the Variac are the chief brands. The operating principle is similar to that of the regular transformer. The main-line current flows through a coil (the primary) which is wound on the same iron core as another coil (the secondary), which is in turn connected with the light. There is no direct connection between the two circuits, but when current flows through the primary coil, another current is induced in the secondary. This can be either a larger current with a lower voltage or a smaller current with a higher voltage, depending on the relative size of the coils. In the case of dimming a lamp, the voltage is gradually reduced. The autotransformer dimmer works on the regular transformer principle, except that the same coil is used for both primary and secondary. A sliding contact is run along the surface of this coil to change the voltage going to the light.

Only as much current is utilized as is necessary to light the lamp, so these dimmers are more efficient than the resistance type and need not be cooled in operation. The operator may stand and work the dimmers directly at the control point or remotely by a motor system which enables him to work from a seated position at a console.

The reactance dimmer. The reactance dimmer has been in operation in theaters such as the Radio City Music Hall for many years. It lends itself to remote control, so that the entire dimmer apparatus does not have to be mounted in the lighting-control board.

The principle is as follows: The alternating current flowing to the lamp passes through a coil which is wound around a second, or "control," coil. Through this control coil is passed a small amount of direct current. The passage of this current sets up a voltage in the main coil, which opposes the main-line current, cuts it down in voltage, and dims the lamp. All that the light board needs to control is the small current which flows through the control coil, and the dimmers themselves can be installed elsewhere in the building. Reactance dimmers can also be built without a control coil, a movable iron core having much the same effect.

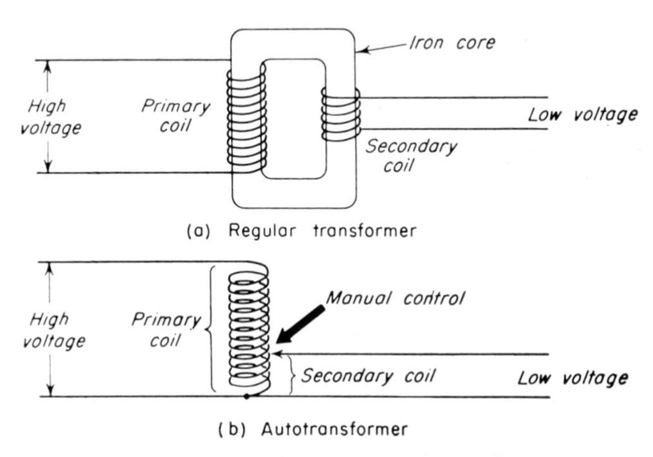

Fig. 18–14. Principle of autotransformer dimmer.

This, however, requires mechanical operation instead of electrical, and remote control is more difficult. Reactance dimmers have been installed in several large television studios.

The electronic-tube dimmer. The most advanced and in many ways the most flexible type of dimmer utilizes electronic tubes to control the flow of current. The main-line current flows through a thyratron tube which acts as a valve to allow greater or smaller amounts of current to flow. The action of this large tube is controlled by a smaller control current which can be remotely operated.

Being a remote-control system, the electronic-dimmer system allows one person to operate a great many lights in any possible combination, working from a seated position. The control location can be placed anywhere. The first lighting board of this design, built by George Izenour at Yale University, was equipped to handle 44 circuits, but there is no serious limitation on the total number that can be controlled. One light board at CBS, Hollywood, handles 60 dimmers and 400 load circuits; two CBS studios are equipped with boards containing 90 dimmers and 600 load circuits each.

The silicon-controlled rectifier dimmer. With solid-state semiconductor devices replacing vacuum tubes throughout the electronics industry, it was to be expected that lighting control would be no exception. The S.C.R. solid-state dimmer acts much as does the thyratron tube, constituting a kind of valve which can be opened or closed by means of a small control current. The S.C.R. dimmer, however, has great advantages over other systems in its very small size, light weight, lack of noise or heat dissipation during operation, and long life expectancy. While reactance dimmers and thyratrons had to be installed in rooms distant from the studio, S.C.R. dimmers could be installed in the studio proper, at the control point, or even on the light pipes alongside the individual lighting units, thus saving on the distribution system.

A great convenience of the S.C.R. dimmer is the fact that it cannot be overloaded. Instead of blowing fuses or tripping circuit breakers, an overload simply causes the unit to operate at reduced voltage; the lamps continue to burn but at less than full intensity.

LIGHTING-CONTROL BOARDS

Most built-in dimmer installations in television studios are specially constructed to meet the specific needs of the particular studio. Whereas some television studios contain lighting switchboards which do not include dimmers, any studio which attempts complex live shows will be provided with facilities for dimming at least a certain proportion of the total light units. Fill light, for example, might never be touched during a dramatic show; the only lights in need of intensity adjustment would be the spots which create modeling and back light. On the other hand, when low-key lighting effects are desired, common practice is to keep the major highlights as they are and lower the intensity of the fill light to something like a quarter of its normal level.

Lights going off in a room, dusk falling in an exterior set, or theatrical effects associated with dance numbers, for example, would call for dimming the fill lights. It should be possible to group any light units together and change that grouping at will.

CROSS-CONNECT SYSTEMS

Whereas in an ideal situation each light should be connected to its own dimmer, this is not economically feasible in practice. Cross-connect systems permit a few dimmers to serve a large number of lighting circuits. In a temporary setup, such as a great many television studios have, this is accomplished by leading the cable from every studio light down to a central point, where they all terminate in a great confusion of wire and terminal plugs on the floor behind the control board. The lighting man has these marked in his own code and changes lights on the dimmer simply by hunting down the right terminal plug and plugging it in.

PATCHBOARDS

A lighting patchboard will work much like an audio patchboard or a telephone switchboard, except that the terminals are much heavier to take the necessary lamp current. Each light is terminated in a connector on the board, of which there may be 100 or more. It is a simple matter then to use short patch cords and connect the desired terminals on the patchboard with dimmer connections on the dimmer board. Lights which are not to be dimmed are patched instead to a non-dim board which is fed by the main-line current. It is possible to connect any set of lights to the dimmers, and these may be changed during the show if necessary.

One of the big advantages of this method of connecting lights to dimmers is that it is impossible to overload the incoming electrical circuits. Electrical codes require that the capacity of the incoming lines should equal the total wattage of lamps which it is possible to connect to them. Allowing for the fact that a studio may install a great many more lamps than it will use at any one time, the codes generally allow a 15 per cent diversity from this total, and the incoming lines must be capable of carrying at least 85 per cent of the total wattage of all the light units installed. The result of this rule is that the capacity of incoming lines must be very great or the number of light units installed in the studio is artificially limited.

The patchboard method removes this limitation, since although there may be any number of lights installed and any number of cables terminating in the patchboard, there are only so many receptacles on the plugboard (beneath the patchboard in Fig. 18-15) and this determines how the incoming lines will be loaded. Thus it is impossible to overload the incoming lines no matter how many lights are installed in the studio, since only a certain number of them can be plugged in at one time.

Kliegl makes a board with individual switches (circuit breakers) at each plug-in point, with a flange on each plug which fits under the switch when it is in "on" position. Thus a plug cannot be removed without pushing the switch into the "off" position, nor can it be inserted unless the switch is thus out of the way. This prevents interplugging while the circuits are hot, and the resultant burning out of the connectors due to arcing.

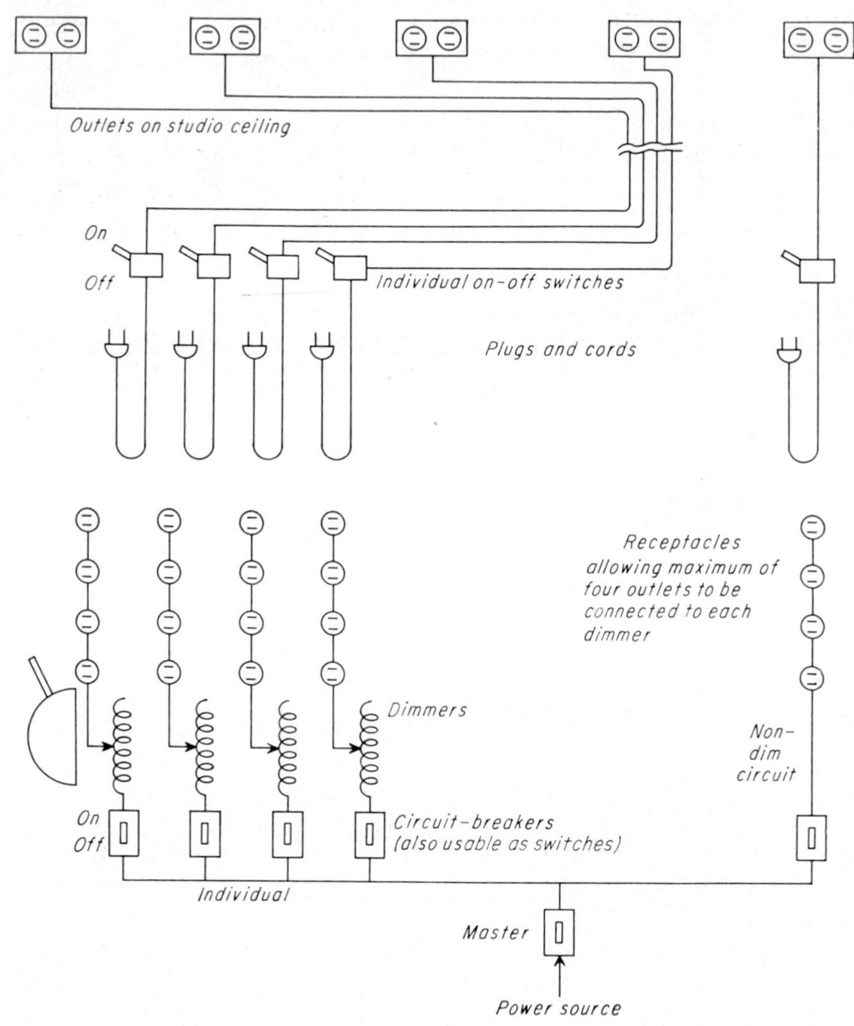

Fig. 18–15. Diagram of a simple patchboard. Only a few circuits are shown.

THE ROTOLECTOR BOARD

A simplified method of connecting lamps to dimmers has been developed in Kliegl's Rotolector board (Fig. 18-17). When this equipment is in use, each lamp circuit in the studio terminates on the board in a rotary selector. Each rotary selector is surrounded by a series of contacts, representing 12 dimmer circuits. (In most boards there are only 10 dimmers, the other two circuits being non-dim circuits controlled only by switches.)

(*a*)

(*b*)

Fig. 18–16. (*a*) An NBC patchboard. This board provides for the patching of 1,200 individual lamp circuits. Plugs above and below are connected to individual lamp outlets. Receptacles at back are connected to source of power through dimmers and switches. (*b*) An NBC dimmer board comprising 36 individual autotransformer dimmers plus master and submaster controls.

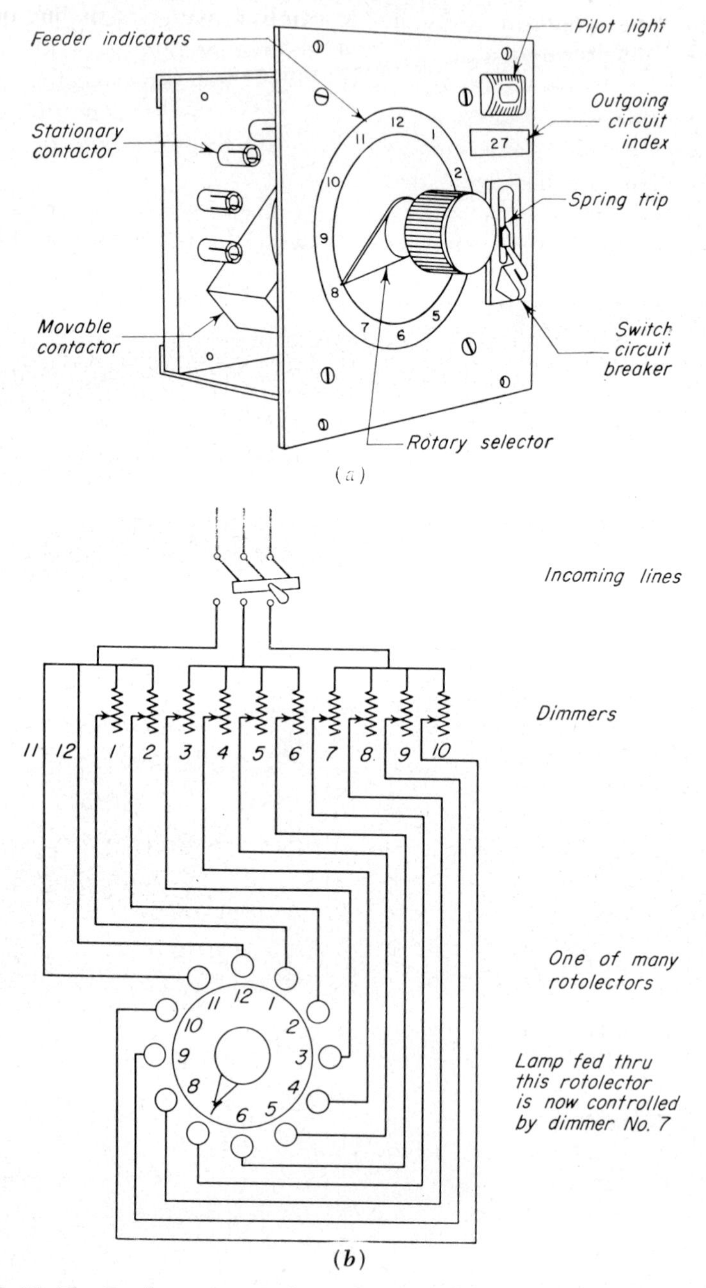

Fig. 18–17. The Rotolector unit and its relation to dimmer circuits. Each Rotolector is wired to the same dimmer circuits in this manner.

Connecting a lamp to a dimmer is simply a matter of pulling out the selector knob, turning it to the desired dimmer number, and pushing it back in. It has been unplugged and plugged in again to another circuit. As many lamps as desired may be connected to the same dimmer by selecting the same dimmer number on the Rotolectors, provided of course that the dimmer is not overloaded.

A circuit breaker incorporated into the Rotolector serves three purposes: it forms a convenient on-off switch for the light unit, it serves

Fig. 18–18. Large Rotolector board at NBC, Hollywood. One hundred and seventy 24-contact Rotolectors are used: 24 dimmers.

as an individual fuse for the lamp circuit, and it prevents arcing at the contacts because it trips automatically as the selector handle is pulled out, so that all plugging and unplugging is done cold. Master circuit breakers on each dimmer circuit will open if the dimmer is overloaded.

On all the patchboards described there is no satisfactory way to keep track of how much wattage is placed on each dimmer, except by examining the entire board and totaling up the wattages of the lamps which are plugged into each. However, this information is not necessarily provided even on the Rotolector board. White china-marking pencil can be used to write the wattage or description of the lamp on the face of the Rotolector plate, but this is hardly satisfactory.

The NBC Rotolector board in Hollywood has overcome some of these difficulties (Fig. 18-18). In place of the standard white pilot light on each Rotolector, lights of different colors have been substituted to indicate the wattage of the lamp in use. (Red indicates 2,000 watts, green 1,000 watts, etc.) Beyond this, NBC has had each dimmer equipped with its own ammeter to register the current it is carrying. Provided that the dimmer is up full, a glance at the ammeter will tell the electrician immediately whether a particular dimmer will carry any more lights or whether it is already fully loaded.

PRESETTING

An important feature of a good lighting-control board is the possibility of presetting. The operator may set in advance the level of the lights which are to be changed on the next light cue, and at the moment of the change he need move only one handle and every light changes to its next setting. The Century Izenour board incorporates an automatic fader and 10 presets so the operator can be set up 10 changes ahead.

In design this electronic preset system is somewhat similar to a two-bus fading system, described in Chap. 7, Television Switching Equipment. A master fading handle "dissolves" from those lights which have been preset on preset channel 1 to those which have been preset on channel 2. Individual lights may be switched onto the preset system or out of it if desired, in which case they are operated by their own individual dimmer controls. This is important, since it would be a great waste of time to preset every light in the studio for a change involving only one or two lights. (If such a change were made by the preset method, all the lights which did not change would also have to be preset for the same level they had just had.)

THE LIGHT PLOT

Light plots can serve two basic purposes. The plan plot, which the lighting director may prepare on a complex production serves as a guide to the rough positioning of the lights. The record plot makes it possible to reproduce accurately a given lighting setup at a later time. It should indicate types of instruments, their placement, direction, and tilt, width of beam, and diffusion, if any. The information contained on the plot cannot be complete or it would be unreadable and take so much time to prepare that it would defeat its own purpose. Some light plots record little data beyond type of instrument, placement, and direction; others

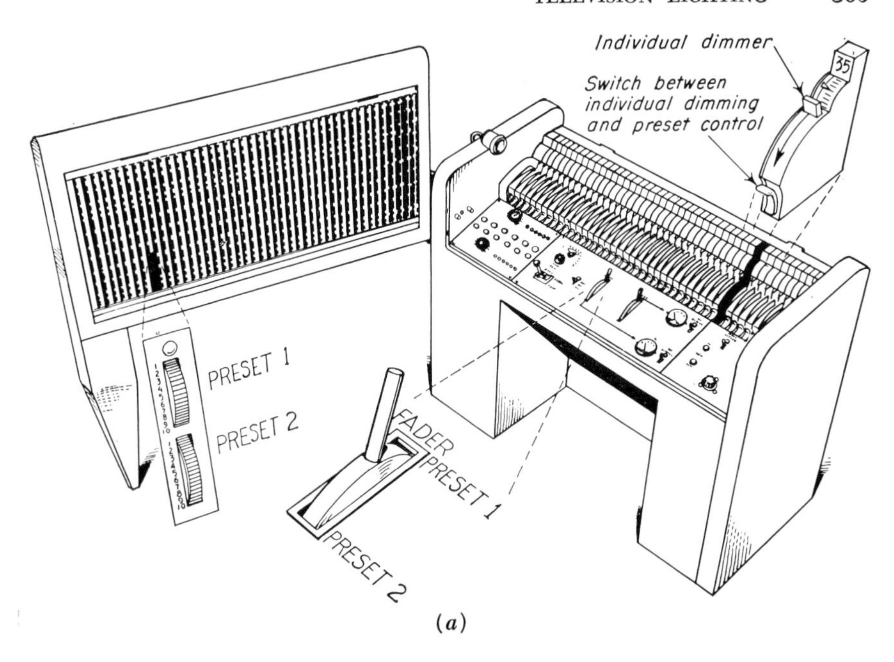

(*a*)

(*b*)

Fig. 18–19. (*a*) **Control board and preset board for electronic tube dimmers.** (*b*) **Large Izenour board at NBC, Hollywood.**

are more complex, recording tilt, beam width, and diffusions as well. No one has found an easy way to record height from the floor.

A studio floor plan, to be useful as a light plot, should include the overhead light grid. This is sometimes shown on a basic studio floor plan in half tone or color or by dotted lines, to distinguish overhead features from floor indications. Sometimes this indication of the light grid is provided as a transparent overlay.

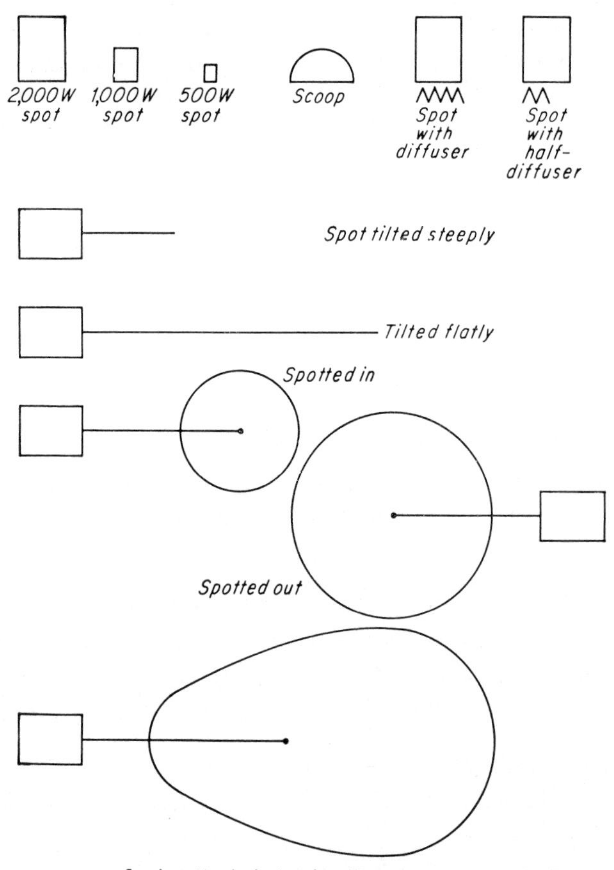

Fig. 18–20. Symbols for use on light plots.

A code of symbols for various lights should be established (Fig. 18-20); a template or stencil can be cut out of heavy plastic to make it possible to draw these quickly and uniformly. Some manufacturers have distributed such templates as production aids.

Drawing the correct type of instrument on the correct place and facing in the correct direction establishes these three items. The use of a diffuser can be indicated by a line drawn across in front of the instrument. Further information is more difficult to diagram. CBS lighting directors draw a straight line from a spotlight to the point where the center of the beam would strike the 6-foot level (the approximate level of the actor's face, which is the subject of illumination in most cases). A short line thus indicates a steep tilt, a long line a shallow tilt, and the end of the line very nicely pinpoints the area of action which is being illuminated.

Now all the information is included except the width of the beam. Two factors will vary with beam width: one, the area covered by a given light and the other, the light intensity at any given point. One method of showing beam width is to use a compass and draw a small or large circle around the end of the beam-center line. This may be done at the 6-foot level, or the line may be continued until the point where it strikes the floor and the circle drawn there. This is more symbolic than graphic, except in the case of down lights, since a beam coming from an angle would cast an ellipse instead of a circle, and the area covered can only be very generally approximated from a circle.

Perhaps the most accurate method, and of course the most complex, is to sketch an ellipse indicating the area covered. When very few lights are involved, lines can be drawn radiating from the instrument to the sides of the ellipse, indicating the sides of the light beam. It is easy to see that when dozens of lights are plotted, such a diagram would become hopelessly complex. (No problem is faced in diagramming a scoop, incidentally; since it has no well-defined beam, no line or circle is needed.)

The best solution for a specific application will lie in the area of compromise. The whole purpose is to save time, anyway, and if the preparation of the light plot takes the lighting director more time than he would otherwise spend in relighting a scene from scratch, it can hardly serve a useful purpose. At NBC, Burbank, most lighting directors operate on this theory and do without light plots entirely. In most studios, however, a few graphic notes will help greatly when a production is to be repeated, especially if relatively inexperienced people are setting the lights.

SPECIAL-EFFECT LIGHTING

Firelight. The light from a flickering fire, cast on the faces of a group around the fireplace, is frequently called for. A spotlight is placed at floor level in the approximate location of the fireplace, to cast light upon the faces. Then a piece of cloth cut into ribbons is fastened to a stick and shaken in front of the light. This creates an uneven flicker (Fig. 18-21) which is more realistic than the Gloccamorra, which is sometimes used for this effect (Fig. 18-22).

Lightning. Very often the effect of lightning does not call for the entire set to be bathed in sudden flashes of light—only the scene out of a window or onto a terrace needs the effect. A special floodlight of very high intensity can be built by mounting half a dozen sockets on a board and lamping them with internal-reflector photoflood bulbs. These bulbs are similar to the R40's except that they burn for a shorter time and with

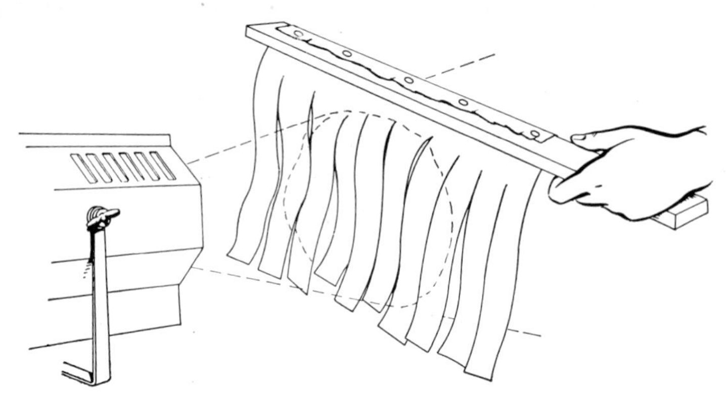

Fig. 18–21. Firelight-effect method.

Fig. 18–22. Gloccamorra for firelight or other uneven or flashing light.

a great deal higher intensity. All six are controlled by a single switch. Lightning is used as a back light or cross light only, never from the front. Front lightning would illuminate everything evenly and give no better effect than turning up the gain electronically for brief flashes of overexposure.

Passing lights and shadows from a train window. The effect of passing lights calls for a smooth movement which, although spaced at random, should not be irregular in speed. It requires a rotating disk or drum in front of a light. The Gloccamorra (Fig. 18-22) is usable when the effect is to be seen on the faces of people sitting near the window. If it is to register instead as moving shadows across the window, it will be accomplished by rear projection on the back side of tissue paper, oiled duck, or other translucent material. The circular-disk movement of the Gloccamorra may be undesirable here; therefore a horizontal drum called the cyclodrum is used (Fig. 18-23). Sometimes the problem may

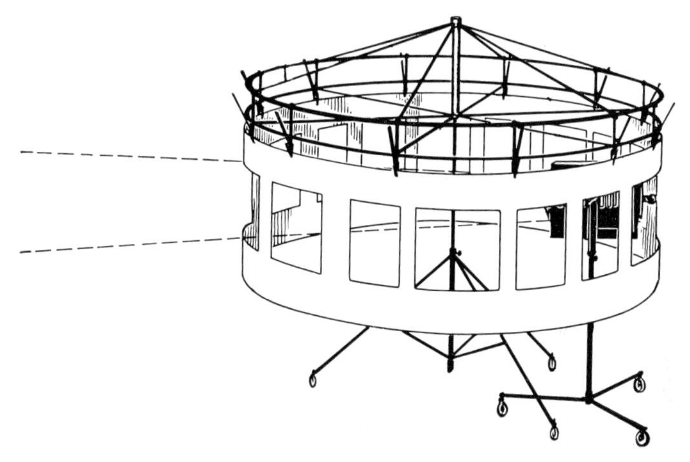

Fig. 18–23. Cyclodrum.

be to show the lights of a moving train flashing across the faces of people standing on the platform. Either of the above devices can be used, but a drum of mirrors is more frequently employed, especially in motion-picture studios. Pieces of mirror are mounted around a vertical cylinder, and the light from a single spot is reflected off this cylinder onto the scene. Each small mirror casts its own area of light, which looks like the patches of light cast by moving windows. The intensity of this light does not have to be very great, since a moving area of light or shadow is always clearly defined.

Bizarre and grotesque lighting. When the main source of light comes from an angle opposite to what is usually accepted, a bizarre effect is achieved. This means low light, from in front, either directly below or cross-lighted from the side. Sinister effects, scenes in hell, grotesque characters are all enhanced by low light. The host who introduced NBC's "Lights Out" program is a typical example (Fig. 18-24) of how a perfectly friendly fellow (Frank Gallup) can be transformed into the embodiment of evil by a little acting on his part and a lot of low light. Low front light is also of very great value in creating theatrical effects involving large shadows thrown against a cyclorama behind a dancer. Chapter 12 includes a discussion of the problems involved in creating shadows and silhouettes, which has application here.

Fig. 18–24. Frank Gallup on the NBC program "Lights Out."

Texture lighting. It is sometimes desirable to light an object in such a way as to bring out the texture of its surface. The reverse is usually true in lighting the human countenance, where the texture often gives an undesirable effect and lighting must be arranged so as to eliminate it as much as possible. Texture is, of course, the tiny hills and valleys in the surface. Light from the camera's angle or flat light of any kind will illuminate hills and valleys equally, and no texture will be visible. A hard light shooting across the surface from a point which is almost in the same plane will bring out every detail. The tiny hills cast long shadows just as mountains cast shadows in the light of the setting sun.

PROJECTED BACKGROUND PATTERNS

Much can be done in television lighting to provide background patterns by the simple method of front projection. In a studio which does not provide a great variety of elaborate scenery, the lighting man should be able to supply a change of background pattern. Karl Weger at WPTZ was able, with a few simple units of his own construction, to create the effects of shafts or patterns of light in great variety. His principal tool was a tin-can spotlight of the projection type built around a PAR 38 spot-type lamp (Fig. 18-25). Two tin cans were used, a larger one about the diameter of the lamp, with a smaller one soldered in front of it like a snoot. The second can was as long as the focal length and as large around as the diameter of a lens mounted at the front end. Thus a projection spot was obtained, with a focal plane at the point where the two cans were joined together. A cutout pattern may be placed in this plane and it will be projected. These cutouts are made of thin aluminum in

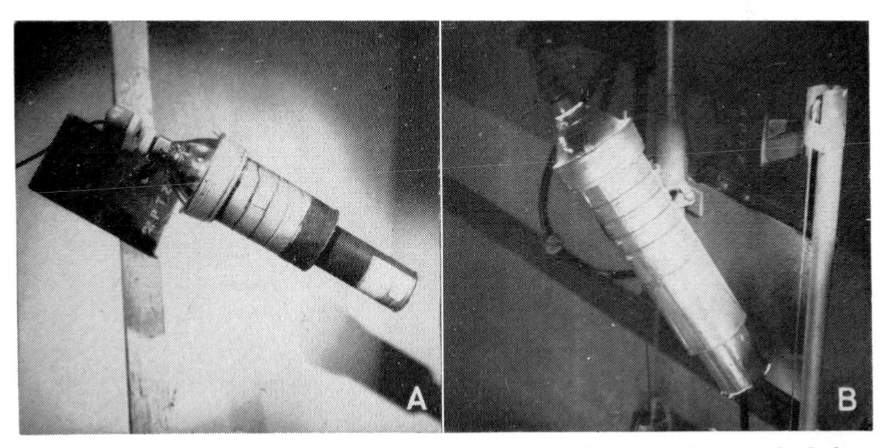

Fig. 18–25. Fuddle projectors, using PAR 38 lamps. (*A*) Fastened to standard clip-on shield and supported at the lamp socket; (*B*) heavier model supported centrally.

order to withstand the heat and can be used for many purposes. The shadow of bars, venetian blinds, shafts of light streaming across a wall may all be projected from above and in front by means of some such simple device. A Lekolite or Klieglite spot can also be adapted for the purpose if an arrangement is made to slide a cutout into the focal plane. The heat inside a projection spot, however, is particularly great, and aluminum will not stand up very long. It has been found that metal caning (grillwork used to disguise radiators, etc.), which is available in a great variety of openwork patterns, is very useful for background patterns and holds up well in the focal plane of a Lekolite. If two of these perforated patterns are rotated against each other, an almost endless variety of changing geometrical patterns can be projected and this sparkling, changing effect is useful for abstract backgrounds behind singers, etc. This calls for a special lamp design, however, as it is impossible to reach the focal plane of the projection spot in order to rotate anything while the lamp is in use.

Fig. 18–26. Projected patterns produced by fuddle projectors.

A cruder method of projecting background patterns involves the use of an ordinary 2,000-watt spot and a cardboard cutout known as a "cucalorus" (Fig. 18-27). Whereas this method is not as efficient as far as the intensity of the projected light is concerned, it can be used to project a larger or a softer shadow and so is equally valuable.

Fig. 18–27. Cucalorus used for background pattern on CBS program.

It has been found that a lower level of light on the background flats can be tolerated provided that a pattern of some kind is projected onto the area. The use of the pattern thus solves two problems, retaining the low-key effect, since the major portion of the background area remains dark, and at the same time raising the level of electrical signal to the point where the total picture quality is improved.

LIGHT CUES

A light cue is any change which must be made in a light during a program. Most light cues are minor adjustments in intensity and balance brought about by camera movement or change in camera angle. Some programs have so many that it is standard practice for the lighting director to work in the control room with a special intercom system to his crew at the switchboard in the studio. A few studios have put the lighting controls either in the production control room or near enough that there can be visual contact with the show director. Some of the complex network programs have necessitated almost as many light cues as camera shots.

TIPS ON HOW TO LIGHT A SIMPLE SET

1. Use the fewest possible instruments on any acting area. Three will do for one or two people in a fixed location.
2. Keep spots away from the mike boom. If the boom is placed center, use key lights from side angles. Try the mike in its various positions while the lights are being set.
3. Key-, fill-, and back-light each area where action is to take place.
4. Squint at the subject for the best guess as to the effect of lighting when seen on camera.
5. Diffuse the fill light so it will not cast shadows. One cast shadow is natural; multiple shadows are distracting and are caused by using more than one key light on the same area.
6. Don't worry about shadows of actors or mike boom cast on the floor or among background props. They will not be noticed.
7. Be careful of hot spots where the key-light level is unusually high, and keep key lights off white refrigerators, etc.
8. Do not add lights to "wash out" cast shadows. Remove such shadows by altering the existing lights. Don't "add light to bad light."
9. When in doubt turn all lights off and start over, key light first.

19

Television Audio

The relative importance of audio to video in dramatic television is a point about which there has been wide disagreement. The proper criterion to use, of course, is the end result, and it has been demonstrated many times that imperfect sound is less noticeable than imperfect camera handling, lighting, set construction, and a great many other visual elements of the program. Of course this generalization cannot apply to everything, and it is certain that those programs which are based on music or singing depend for their primary appeal on the most perfect reproduction of music which the sound department can achieve. A sacrifice of video to audio would in such cases be inevitable; in most other types of shows, however, the audio perfectionist must take a back seat.

SPECIAL PROBLEMS OF TELEVISION AUDIO

First of all, the source of sound, in television, is often in motion. Action must be free, and the microphone must be able to follow it around. Whereas in radio microphones are fixed and form the focal point of the dramatic-show production, in television they must follow along, all but forgotten by the actor, who is too concerned about his gestures, his expression, his movement, and consciousness of the changing red lights on the television cameras to think much about the pickup of sound.

A second problem is that microphones, at least in dramatic shows, must be hidden. This means that either they must be outside the frame of the picture, as with the ubiquitous boom microphone of the television studio, hovering always an inch above the top frame of the picture, or they must be disguised in some way within the scene. When the microphone is suspended overhead and moved about to follow the action, a problem of microphone shadow is created whenever the mike must pass through beams of light. This is less of a problem in the motion-picture studio because sufficient rehearsal is always available immediately before the shooting of a scene and the boom operator can usually find a route over which to move the microphone so that it will not cast a shadow. In television, however, adequate rehearsal is notoriously lacking, and microphone shadows are a frequent occurrence.

Very often a set is so large and the shot which the camera takes of it is so wide and high that the usual boom microphone can hardly get within earshot of the performer without showing in the picture. In such case it is almost mandatory that the designer plan some spot in which to hide the microphone. Sometimes mikes can be placed in the bottom of hanging chandeliers. Sometimes a garden scene can feature a prop bush or vine sufficiently close to the performer. When a boom-microphone shadow is inevitable the set designer can often devise a foliage cutout or a chandelier shape to attach to the mike so that the necessary shadow will seem to be part of the set.

The radio engineer who takes up audio handling in the television studio is usually aghast at the great distance from which a microphone must pick up dialogue. In radio, actors usually stand a foot or less from the microphone, and actors farther away than this are considered "off-mike" and sound as if they are in the background. It is seldom, however, that the microphone on the end of the television boom can reach closer than 2 or 3 feet from the actor, and often the pickup must be made from a distance of some 4 feet or more. Under these conditions room reverberations and background noise become much more noticeable, and television studios must consequently be made acoustically "dead," a problem which will be considered a few pages hence.

A fourth problem in the pickup of television sound is involved with the relation of sound to picture *perspective*. Close-up pictures require close-up sound, and distant shots must be accompanied by a quality of sound which seems to match the distance of the source. This is solved easily in motion pictures by making separate sound pickups for each shot. In television, however, shots are not made separately, but all at once, with a single microphone and several cameras, and if changes of perspective are to be made, they must be achieved during the continuous sound pickup either by moving the microphone or by altering the quality of the sound after it has been picked up.

AUDIO EQUIPMENT

The audio equipment which is installed in the typical television studio is very much like that which a large radio studio would have. There are outlets in the studio wall into which a certain number of microphones may be plugged, and an assortment of different types of microphones and various stands to hold them is provided. Each microphone outlet is numbered; a mike which is plugged into outlet 1, for example, automatically becomes mike 1 on the audio control console (Fig. 19-1).

The audio console consists mainly of a number of fading dials, or "pots" (short for potentiometer), each of which controls the volume of the microphone which is connected to it. There are other sources of sound also, besides the studio microphones (sound-film projectors, sound effects, turntables, remote sources), and these can also be controlled by pots on the audio console. The output of all these faders is mixed together into one outgoing channel, and one final "master-gain" fader at

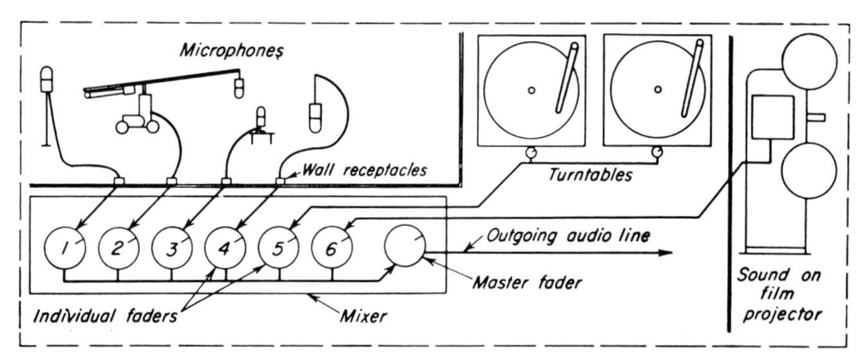

Fig. 19–1. Diagram of audio equipment in the typical small television studio.

the far right of the console controls the level of this outgoing line. The fact that sound from many sources is mixed together in this manner has led to naming this portion of the sound-control apparatus the "mixer."

Two turntables are usually provided in the television control room, within reach of the audio engineer, although in complex production he may have an assistant to help him with the records.

A rack-mounted ¼-inch tape recorder is standard equipment, and when the rack cannot be placed within reach of the audio-operating position, a broadcast-quality portable machine is mounted near the audio console. The audio portions of announcements, commercials, and many programs will originate from ¼-inch tape.

Another piece of audio equipment, is usually provided nearby—the audio patchboard. This is usually a complete mystery to nontechnical personnel, looking more like a telephone switchboard than anything else, with patch cords and innumerable jacks into which they can be plugged. Actually it is a very flexible switching apparatus with which any item of equipment in the audio system can be isolated, taken out of its position in the circuit, or rearranged so as to replace some other piece of equipment which may be defective.

BASIC PROBLEMS IN PICKING UP SOUND WITH A MICROPHONE

People who are unfamiliar with the use of microphones are frequently amazed to notice how differently the normal sounds of a room appear when they are picked up by a microphone and heard on a loudspeaker in another room. Scuffling of feet, coughing, creaking of chairs in the back of the room are very evident and confuse the pickup of the main source of sound; street noises which would never be noticed at all in the room itself seem to be amplified out of all proportion in the microphone pickup. The main reason for this is that the microphone is inferior to the human hearing apparatus in that it consists of only one ear. All sound, to the microphone, is one-dimensional. It has no way of telling the listener in another room from which direction any particular sound is originating or (except by secondary characteristics of sound quality) how far away the source of sound may be. The binaural human apparatus can be selective. Knowing that some sounds originate outside the room, it can then eliminate these from the listener's attention. It is powerless to do this, however, when all sounds are given to it from a single source, the loudspeaker in the other room. When the listener is in the same room with the sound itself, his two ears register different pickups of the same sounds. A sound originating at the left side of the room, for example, will sound very loud in the left ear and may not reach the right ear directly at all but be heard in that ear a split second later by reverberation from the right-hand wall. The audio center in the brain immediately evaluates this information and sends up a report to the center of consciousness that the noise took place at the listener's far left.

Since extraneous noises are so noticeable when picked up by a microphone, studios must be carefully soundproofed to keep out street and building noises. The best radio studios are suspended by springs or rest on feet of rubber so that they are completely isolated from the rest of the building they are in and a rumble which might ordinarily find its way into the studio, transported through the rigid core of the building from elevator motors or traffic in the street, is absorbed before it can be heard. Some television studios have been built in this fashion, especially when they are situated in a newspaper building where heavy presses are running. Special acoustics are necessary in the radio studio, and silence in the background must be maintained. This is something which is very difficult to achieve in television. There is seldom a dramatic show on the air which does not at some time or another puzzle the television viewer with various creaks, slaps, clanks, and groans, not to mention occasional small crashes taking place off screen. It is safe to say that few of these extraneous noises are noticeable to the actors or anyone in the studio. They are painfully evident to the personnel in the control room, however, and the anguished voice of the director screaming "Quiet in the studio" has on occasion escaped from a cameraman's headphones and found its way into the broadcast audio to add to the alien noises.

It is interesting to note that with the development of video tape TV studios in some locations are able to relax the high standards of sound isolation necessary for live radio and television and operate like many film studios. An occasional airplane overhead may necessitate a retake of a scene, but do no greater damage.

WHAT DETERMINES SOUND QUALITY

Sound quality is determined by a number of factors, perhaps the most important of which is the quality of the microphone and associated audio equipment. A school, for example, may install inexpensive public-address (PA) equipment for teaching purposes which would be inadequate for broadcast use. The main difference would be in the "fidelity" of its response to sounds of different pitch. "High-fidelity" equipment is necessary for FM broadcasting and for television too, since the sound portion of television is broadcast by the FM method.

The average ear is sensitive to sounds of a wide band of frequencies all the way from about 50 cycles per second up to 15,000. (A cycle is a single vibration.) All speech is contained within the first 2,000 cycles. The next 12,000 cycles contain overtones. It is not difficult to construct a receiving and reproducing apparatus which is able to transmit intelligible speech without handling any great range of frequencies. The telephone is an example; the dictaphone or the old gramophones can reproduce every note on the piano keyboard, but anyone who has listened to them will immediately notice that they give a far from realistic reproduction of sound. The main reason is that the sounds they carry lack the higher frequency overtones. A general idea of the sound quality possible with a microphone or reproduction apparatus can be conveyed by naming the high-frequency cutoff point (beyond which sounds are not picked up or reproduced). The higher this cutoff point, the higher the fidelity of the apparatus. The telephone cuts off around 2,500 cycles. Most small radio sets cut off at 4,000. The best AM sets on the market cannot handle more than 8,000 cycles, and AM broadcasting stations rarely transmit frequencies higher than this.

FM broadcasting, using a different method of modulating the carrier wave, readily carries the entire range of frequencies up as far as the ear can hear. Good FM sets with high-quality loudspeakers and properly built cabinets can receive and reproduce this entire range. Small low-quality loudspeakers, such as are installed in many table-top television receivers, cannot take advantage of the high-fidelity FM audio which accompanies the television picture. Thus the frequency response of first the microphone, then the amplifier and transmission circuits, and finally the method of transmission and reception will determine to a large extent the quality of the resultant sound.

There are other factors involved, however. One of these is the proportion of direct to reverberant sound which is picked up by the microphone.

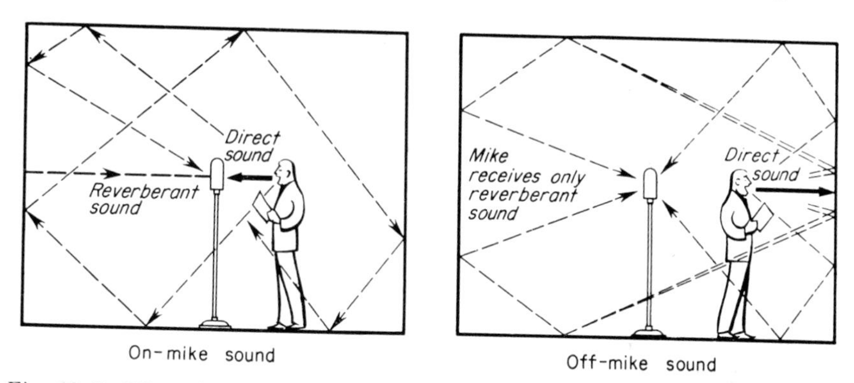

Fig. 19–2. When the ratio of direct sound to reverberant sound is high, the actor sounds "on-mike." When the reverberant sound becomes equal to or greater than the direct, however, the actor sounds "off-mike."

Reverberant sound is actually composed of echoes, which in the usual-sized room follow so closely after the direct sound itself that they cannot be distinguished from it.

If the microphone is close to the source of sound, the direct sound pickup will be large in proportion to the sound which enters the microphone after having bounced back and forth between the walls, floor, and ceiling of the studio. This will give rise to the effect of being "on mike." When the source of sound is farther from the microphone, the direct sound is weaker in comparison with the reverberant sound and the "off-mike" condition is noticed. In a room which has a low reverberation time (a "dead" room) the microphone can be further from the source of sound without the pickup sounding off-mike (Fig. 19-2).

CHARACTERISTICS OF MICROPHONES

A microphone is an instrument for translating sound vibrations in air into variations in electrical current. Although the design of microphones is based on several different principles, each type of mike actually creates a weak electrical voltage by the physical movement of a ribbon, or diaphragm, or some other element under the vibrating force of the air. The most common types of microphone will be described presently according to the basic principles of their design.

The first factor which contributes to the sound quality of a microphone is the range of frequencies it can pick up. Some of the cheaper types of mikes, such as the carbon-button microphone used in telephones and the crystal microphone used in inexpensive home-recording machines, are not capable of much over 4,000 cycles. Most of the standard microphones used in broadcasting respond to frequencies up as high as the ear can hear (15,000 cycles per second). There is considerable variation, however, in how well a microphone will respond to the low frequencies below 300 cycles.

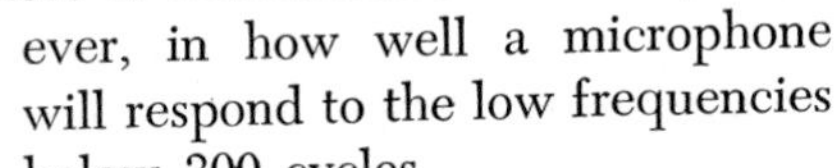

Fig. 19–3. RCA 77DX polydirectional microphone.

Even though two microphones both respond to the entire frequency range, each will have its own variations in response along the scale, and the fact that one microphone is "down a little" in its response to the low frequencies or "falls off" after 10,000 cycles will make it sound quite different from another which may be up to normal response at these frequencies but is low somewhere else.

It is sometimes desirable to alter a microphone's sensitivity to low-frequency sounds. Voice actually picks up better if these low frequencies are not well reproduced. Some microphones, such as the RCA 77DX (Fig. 19-3), are equipped with an adjustment screw marked *M* and *V*, meaning "music" and "voice." When set as *M*, the microphone responds fully to all the bass notes and music sounds full and rich. The *V* setting, however, attenuates (cuts down) these frequencies and allows the voice to pick up somewhat more distinctly than when the bass tones are strong. Making this adjustment is sometimes called "strapping" the mike for voice or for music.

Microphones are designed to have different directional patterns in the attempt to make them to some extent selective. A nondirectional microphone picks up sounds coming from all directions equally well. There is no selectivity. A unidirectional microphone, however, is so designed that only the sounds which come from one direction can be picked up, at least directly, and all other, unwanted sounds are discriminated against. Some microphones are bidirectional, which means they have two live sides but are deaf to sounds originating elsewhere.

Nondirectional microphones are useful for on-the-street interviews, for example, so the interviewer does not need to be constantly pointing the microphone back and forth between himself and his guest. A round-table discussion can be picked up most satisfactorily by a nondirectional microphone in the center of the table, provided, of course, that the table is not too large. On a microphone boom, however, the nondirectional

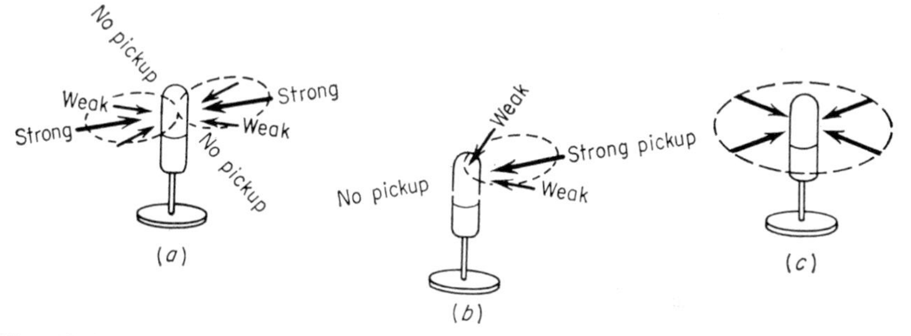

Fig. 19–4. 77DX used (*a*) as a bidirectional, (*b*) as a unidirectional, and (*c*) as a nondirectional microphone.

microphone is so unselective that it picks up reverberant sound from the ceiling of the studio and many other directions, and this reverberant sound is usually rather loud because the boom mike is relatively far from the subject and the gain (amplification) is up high.

The bidirectional microphone, the most common example of which is the RCA 44A (Fig. 19-10), is standard equipment in radio studios, where it finds its greatest usefulness in dramatic shows. Actors may stand on either side of the microphone holding their rustling scripts to the dead side of the mike and can achieve the effect of going off mike very easily simply by moving around to the dead side of the mike. The bidirectional mike has found little use in television, however, except for an off-camera chorus or in a case where it can be shown in the picture and placed a very short distance from the speaker, and then it is generally used only because it happens to be on hand. On a microphone boom it would pick up excessive ceiling reflections.

Some microphones exhibit a directional pattern called "cardioid" (heart-shaped). This is essentially a unidirectional pattern except that the beam is wider and the pickup is stronger on each side. A microphone of this type is better on the overhead boom than a unidirectional microphone since there is less need for accuracy in directing the microphone toward the source of sound.

The directional characteristics of a microphone are usually plotted on a "polar" graph (Fig. 19-8). The microphone can be considered as located at the center of the circle and facing toward the top. The radii of the circle then indicate different directions from the microphone. When the response in any particular direction is high, the line of the graph is far

Fig. 19–5. Microphone placed at focal point of parabolic reflector for highly directional pickup.

from the center; it comes in closer to the center in directions where the response is poor.

It should be noted that the directional pattern of almost any microphone will be quite different when measured at different frequencies. Thus a mike which is nondirectional to sounds of the lower frequencies becomes a unidirectional microphone as far as sounds above 8,000 cycles are concerned.

A microphone may be made highly directional by placing it in the focal point of a large parabolic reflector (Fig. 19-5). When the parabolic reflector is then aimed at a distant source of sound, the mike should pick up only that sound which is within the narrow beam of the reflector and discriminate against all else. It has been used in radio broadcasting, for example, to pick up the sound of a band on a football field when the band is located in the stands on the other side of the field. Parabolic mikes have been tried for music and voice pickup, especially in the television theater, where it is difficult to place a mike boom. Placed in the balcony or on a platform in the orchestra pit, they can pick up sounds adequately which occur over 50 or 100 feet away. They have not been too satisfactory, however.

High-frequency sounds tend to travel in straight lines; they reflect well off hard surfaces and can be focused by a reflector as described above. Low-frequency sounds (below 200 cycles) are not so obliging. Lows go around corners, diffuse from a surface instead of reflecting cleanly, and the directivity of the parabolic microphone is practically nothing in the low-frequency range. Low-frequency sounds, well off the beam, still find their way into the microphone. The result is that when an actor speaks from a position only slightly off the beam of the mike, all high frequencies vanish, the lows continue to be heard, and the voice sounds tubby and boomy. Clearly, when there are several actors, each of whom may speak at any time, it is impossible to keep them all equally centered on the beam, especially when they are in motion, and the resultant constant change of sound quality makes the use of this microphone impractical for such a purpose. A line microphone, or "machine-gun mike," has been tried out with the same results. This microphone achieves its highly directional quality by virtue of a large number of hollow tubes of varying lengths which are aimed at the source of sound and will not admit sounds coming from other directions.

TYPES OF MICROPHONES

The design of microphones has been directed not only toward wider and more accurate frequency response, sensitivity, and directional control but also toward reduced size and weight. In recent years several microphones which are smaller than an inch in diameter have reached the market, representing each of the principal types. This is desirable in television since microphones must be small to be hidden, and they must be small even if they are going to show in the picture (lest they detract from the performers).

Dynamic microphones. The most successful microphones are designed on the principle that movement of a wire in a magnetic field will generate a voltage within that wire. The *dynamic,* or pressure, microphone is equipped with a diaphragm which vibrates as sound strikes it, thus moving a small coil of wire back and forth within the field generated by a small permanent magnet. The very weak voltage so generated is carried over the microphone cable to the control room, where a preamplifier raises it to a useful level. Examples of the dynamic microphone are the BK1A, BK6B, and the Electrovoice 642. The RCA 88A, while now out-

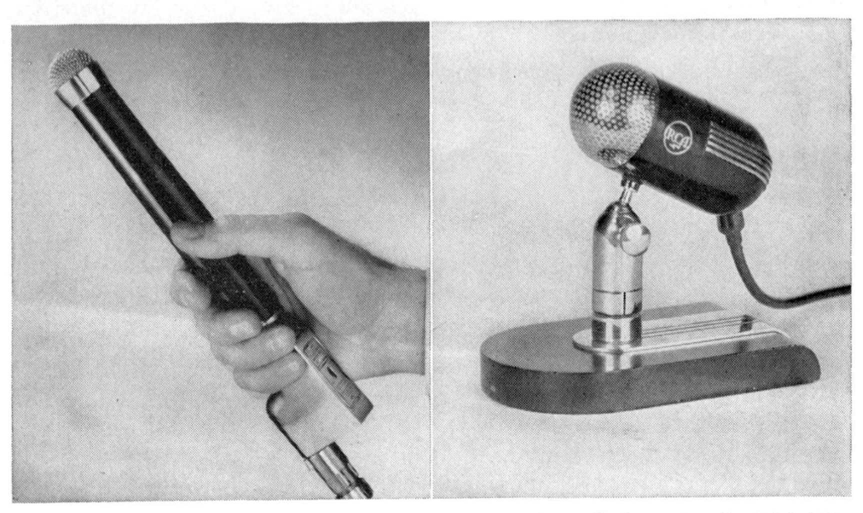

Fig. 19–6. Small dynamic: the Electro-Voice.

Fig. 19–7. Small dynamic: the RCA 88A.

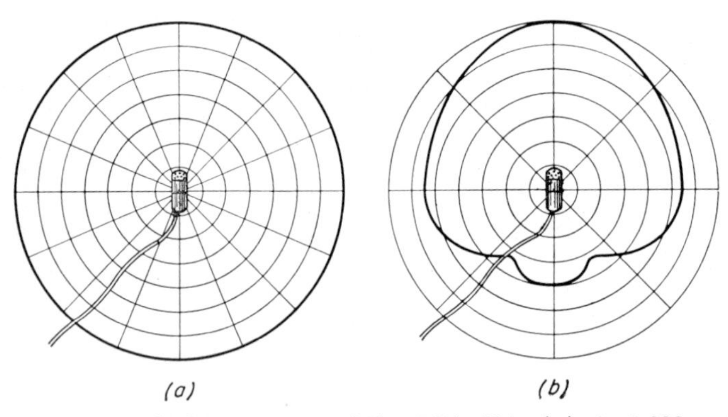

Fig. 19–8. Directional characteristics of the RCA 88A. (*a*) At 1,000 cycles it is nondirectional; (*b*) at 4,500 cycles it is almost unidirectional.

moded, is a classic example of the rugged small dynamic. It was often used where microphones had to be hidden on the set, in desk drawers, etc. Its frequence response, however, as Fig. 19-9 shows, rendered it unsuitable for music or other high-fidelity purposes.

Velocity microphones. The velocity, or ribbon, microphone has been widely used in radio studios. In this design a ribbon instead of a wire is vibrated within a magnetic field, and it is the "velocity" of the ribbon rather than the pressure on a diaphragm which creates the microphone signal. Ribbon mikes are excellent for high-fidelity pickup but are not so rugged as the dynamics just described. Since sound may reach the ribbon from either side, this type of mike can easily be made bidirectional, a pattern which is important in radio but finds little use in tele-

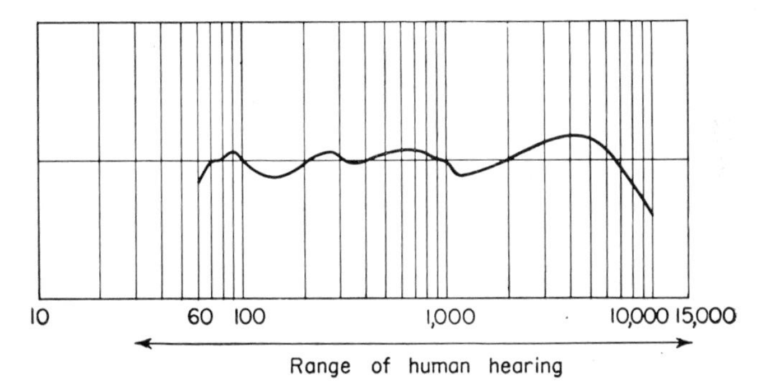

Fig. 19–9. Frequency response of the RCA 88A.

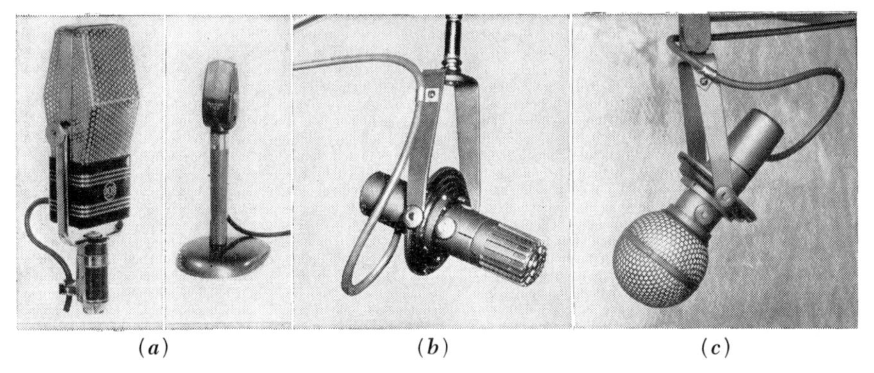

(*a*) (*b*) (*c*)

Fig. 19–10. Typical velocity microphones (bidirectional). (*a*) The RCA 44A and the RCA Bantam KB2C. (*b*) RCA BK5A microphone on boom. (*c*) RCA BK5A with wind screen.

vision. The RCA 44A, standard in radio studios, is shown in Fig. 19-10, and the RCA Bantam KB2C is shown beside it. The Bantam approximates the performance of the 44 without quite the frequency range. It is also bidirectional.

The most useful velocity microphone in the TV studio is the RCA BK5A. This is the first microphone which, to the writer's knowledge, was designed primarily for use on a boom. Called "uniaxial," it has a wide unidirectional beam. It is painted a dull gray to make it as unobtrusive as possible when, like all boom mikes, it makes an occasional unexpected entrance into the shot. It is mounted by means of a rubber collar, thus removing the necessity for a complex rubber band arrangement as shown in Fig. 19-16. It is also provided with a "blast filter" (layers of screening and cloth) to reduce damage to the ribbon from gun blasts and other violent noises.

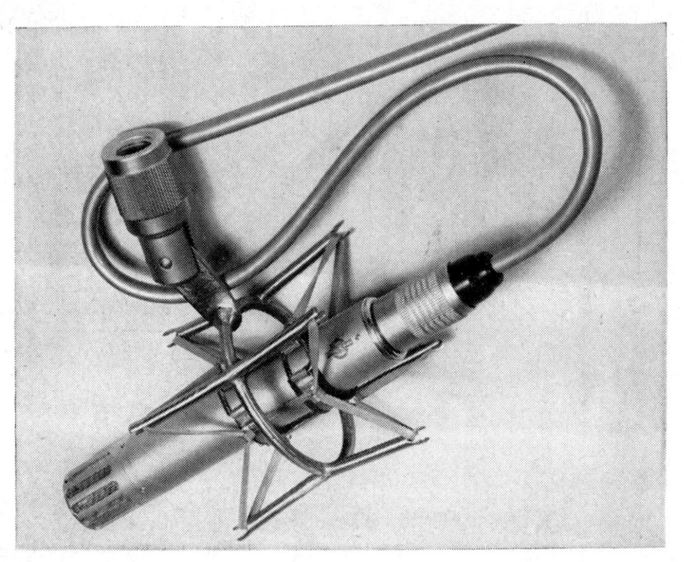

Fig. 19–11. Neuman condenser microphone in rubber band suspension for boom use. Over-all length of microphone: 5 inches.

COMBINATION MICROPHONES

Some microphones can be adjusted between several directional patterns; examples are the RCA 77DX (Fig. 19-3) and the Western Electric Cardioid (Fig. 19-12). The second of these is in reality two microphones contained within the single housing, one of which responds to pressure in the manner of the dynamic mike, while the other is a velocity-actuated ribbon. The unidirectional pattern of the RCA 77DX is nearly cardioid, and both this and the Western Electric microphone, when set for the cardioid pattern, function well on a microphone boom.

Condenser microphones. A third type of microphone, called the condenser mike, which is neither dynamic nor velocity has become popular in recent years. The principle of this microphone is that the sound moves a diaphragm which is actually one of the plates of a condenser. As the condenser plates are moved together or apart, the capacitance changes and a current which is fed through it will vary in strength. The Altec-Lansing button-sized microphone was the first small mike of this type

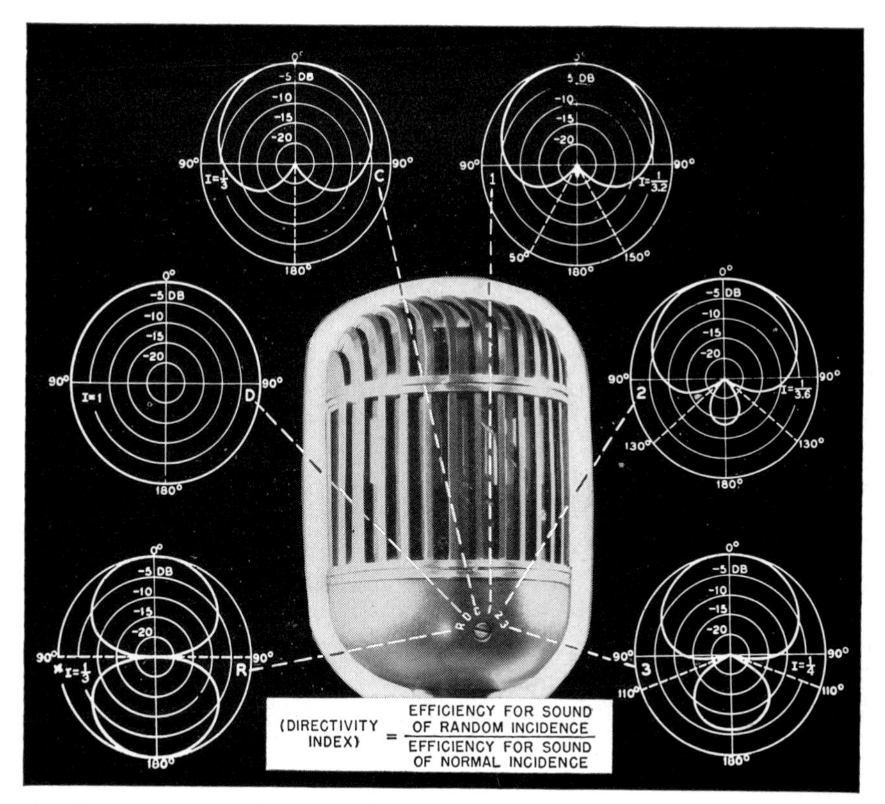

Fig. 19–12. Western Electric Cardioid microphone, showing variety of directional patterns.

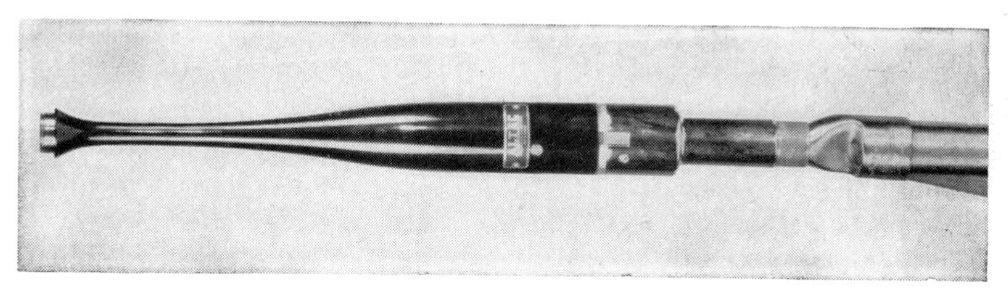

Fig. 19–13. Altec-Lansing condenser microphone.

(Fig. 19-13). Nondirectional, it has a satisfactory frequency range for broadcast purposes. The microphone itself is only 0.6 inch in diameter and ¼ inch high, but it must be used on the end of a shaft which contains a small one-tube amplifier. A special power-supply unit must also be used, but this can be placed as distant as 400 feet from the microphone. The Altec mike has found frequent use as a hand mike for an interviewer or MC to hold.

MICROPHONE PLACEMENT

The most common placement of the microphone in the television studio is to suspend it overhead on the end of a boom. Occasionally a microphone is suspended above one spot, either on its own cable or by means of a cord. This is known as a hanging mike. A third placement for microphones is within the set, hidden from the camera, and a fourth type of placement is in the set, with no attempt made to hide the mike from the camera. Whatever placement is chosen, all microphones which are to be used on a single scene should be of the same model, or noticeable changes of sound quality will result when the pickup changes from one to the next.

The audio man will be careful not to place a microphone close to a hard reflectant surface such as a wall or table top, knowing that the reverberant sound reflected from the close surface will be very loud in the microphone's ear and will impair a good pickup of the direct sound. Tables are usually covered with cloth when microphones must be placed on them. Sometimes a small mike such as an 88A will be hidden by laying it in a partly opened desk drawer, just below the performer. However, the drawer will impart a strange hollowness to the sound unless the mike is laid on a piece of hair felt or other strongly sound-absorbent material. Actors should be kept away from hard walls. When hard-walled sets are used, it is important that no two walls be quite facing each other, as in the case of a box-shaped three-walled set, or standing waves may be set up which will cause strange results with almost any microphone placed between them.

The directional selectivity of unidirectional microphones is so great that unwanted sounds in the background will be picked up clearly simply because they happen to be on the beam. When the microphone is directly overhead, for example, footsteps sound much louder than one might expect, and this is one of the problems connected with hanging mikes. A boom mike, too, will exaggerate rustling paper out of all proportion; the producer who must have someone open a package under a microphone will do well to wrap it in very soft paper or dampen the paper which surrounds it so that the crackling is eliminated. Dishes or hard objects on a table top are another source of trouble; the use of a tablecloth or other cover will help greatly where these are concerned.

Although the best positioning of a microphone can be obtained only when it is controlled by an operator and can be moved about and pointed this way and that, it often happens on many types of shows that dialogue must be picked up in a spot which the boom microphone will not reach. In such cases a hanging mike is used. Since such a microphone cannot be pointed toward a person who is speaking, it should have as wide a beam as possible so that almost any position within a 3-foot radius will be suitable for good pickup of sound. This calls for a nondirectional microphone or a cardioid (unidirectional with a very wide beam). There have been television dramatic shows which used a great many such hanging mikes. Perhaps the record was set in one production of "Suspense" which so filled the studio that there was no place to put a microphone boom. Paul Hale, the audio engineer, solved the problem by stringing up 16 hanging mikes to cover all the areas where dialogue was taking place. Hanging mikes are to be avoided if possible, however, since they can cover a limited area at best and any attempt to try to rehearse actors so that they will deliver their dialogue only in the right spots and facing the right directions produces very uncertain results.

Fig. 19–14. RCA lavaliere microphone (BK6B), a small dynamic. Name comes from classic jewelry pendant.

Perhaps the most commonly used microphone, next to the boom mike, is the lavaliere, named for the necklace-and-pendant type of jewelry made famous by a mistress of Louis XIV. Barely over 2½ inches long this type of microphone, while not invisible, is certainly not intrusive, and its presence has come to be an accepted convention in programs of the actuality type.

THE WIRELESS MICROPHONE

There frequently are situations where an overhead boom is impossible, the hiding of a large number of mikes is impractical, and the trailing cable of a lavaliere or hand microphone would so restrict the movement of a performer as to make it most undesirable. The answer then is a wireless microphone.

When a microphone is used without a wire, several additional items must accompany the mike: an amplifier, a transmitter, batteries to operate these, and a transmitting antenna. These can all now be made so small that they can be effectively hidden even on a girl wearing an

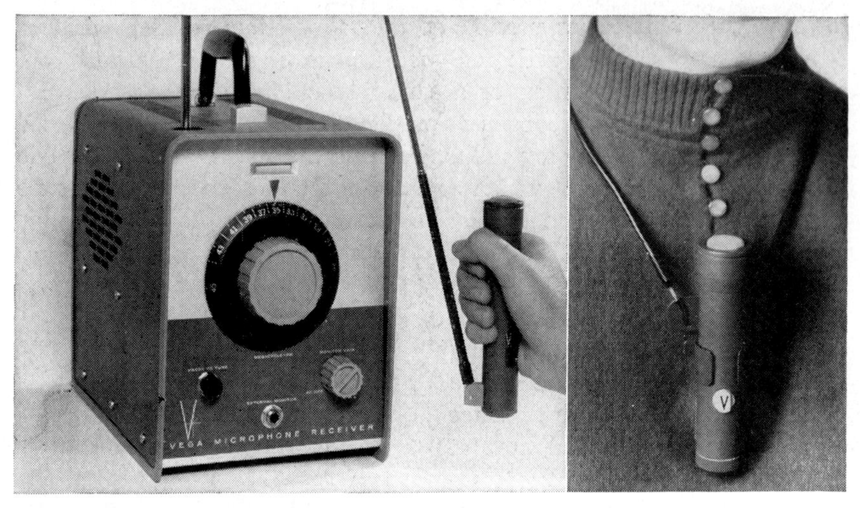

Fig. 19–15. Vega wireless microphone. Receiving unit on left. Mike may be used in the hand with telescoping antenna or may be worn as a lavaliere, in which case the neck strap acts as an antenna element. Several Vega microphones may be used with one receiving unit, either on the same frequency (in which case they all operate together without individual adjustment) or on different frequencies (in which case they can only be used separately, since the receiving unit must be retuned between them).

evening gown. A standard-size receiver is of course necessary at the control point to pick up the signal off the air and feed it into the audio console. Several such microphones have been used simultaneously on programs such as Ed Murrow's "Person to Person."

THE MICROPHONE BOOM

Several types of microphone booms are in use in television studios, the most common and also the most complex of which is the Mole-Richardson boom. This is motion-picture equipment which has been taken over bodily without modification for the television studio. The other types of booms are for the most part nonextensible. They are radio equipment which can best serve in the television studio in place of hanging microphones where a little more control is needed. Several stations use a giraffe boom (Fig. 19-16) which is equipped with a hand grip for rotating and tilting the mike. A microphone can be controlled both in tilt and rotation, and it is possible to use a unidirectional mike and face it around toward whichever person is speaking. This boom can be panned in a circle or tilted so that it will raise and lower, but extension must be done bodily by rolling the base of the boom in or out. This is by no means difficult, since the boom base is very light, and some studios prefer these giraffe booms to the more elaborate, expensive, and cumbersome Mole-Richardson booms.

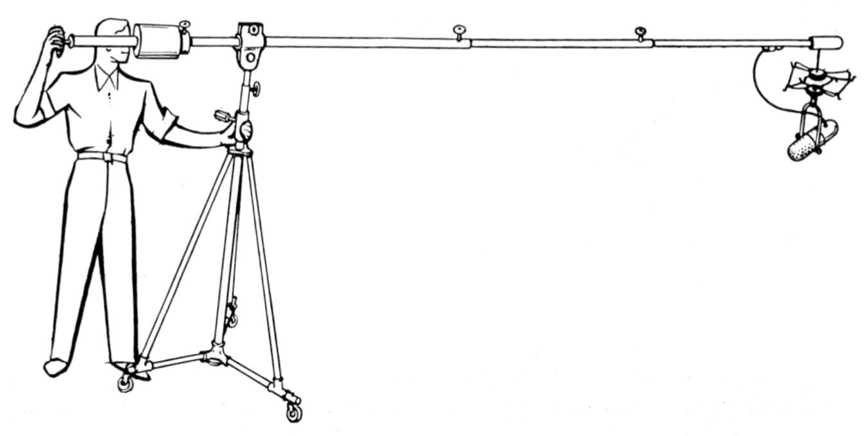

Fig. 19–16. Typical small giraffe boom.

Fig. 19–17. Mole-Richardson microphone boom.

The Mole-Richardson boom (Fig. 19-17) is capable of several simultaneous adjustments, including the extension of the boom arm. The adjustments are: (1) panning of the boom arm (360 degrees); (2) tilting of boom arm (45 degrees above horizontal to 45 degrees below horizontal); (3) extension of mike boom (from a minimum length of 7 feet

4½ inches to an extended length of 17 feet); (4) rotation of microphone at end of boom arm. Whereas these adjustments can all be made simultaneously by one operator, a fifth adjustment, height of central column, can be made before the boom is in use. The boom may rest horizontally at a minimum height of 6 feet 5 inches, or the central column may be raised so that the boom is 9 feet 5 inches from the floor. It is ordinarily used at a height of about 7 feet. The operating platform of this model raises with the boom.

The sides of the operating platform, shown in Fig. 19-17 folded down, will open up flat, and the operator stands on the right-hand side of the boom. His right hand operates the crank which extends or retracts the boom. His left hand holds a handle (shown projecting straight up) which, when he pulls it down, rotates the microphone. Panning and tilting of the boom are also controlled with this hand, by direct effort instead of a twisting movement. All controls can be locked by large-handled setscrews, so that when the boom is being moved and there is no operator at the controls, it will not swing wildly about. The microphone cable running to the boom is usually dropped down from overhead so that it will interfere as little as possible with operations in the studio. The only control which is lacking on this microphone boom is a means of tilting the mike. This has been found desirable in motion pictures, and Paramount added such a control to the boom so that the same hand which handles the crank for boom extension could also control microphone tilt.

The base of the microphone boom is provided with three large wheels with pneumatic tires, only one of which is steerable. There is a tendency, at least in the smaller studios, to think of the boom base as more or less permanent and immobile. This does not have to be the case at all. In many dramatic shows the boom is wheeled about from place to place throughout the show, repositioning almost as freely as the cameras. It is possible to end one scene with the boom at one end of the studio and begin the next scene across the studio with the same microphone. Naturally this calls for a very rapid move. The microphone dollyman will have the base of the dolly aligned so that he does not need to waste time in backing and steering. The audio engineer watches his script closely, and as soon as the last word is spoken, he releases the boom for its move. The director can help this process greatly and reduce the risk of losing dialogue if he will add a few seconds of silent action to the end of the first scene or to the beginning of the second.

Since this boom base was designed for motion pictures, it is not very well adapted to the television studio. It is much too large (the base occupies a floor area of about 4 by 6 feet). It is unmaneuverable, having only one steerable wheel. The operator's platform is built on only one side, so the entire base must be moved if the boom is to pan as much as 180 degrees, or the operator will find himself with no place to stand. To adapt this equipment better to the television studio some stations, such as WTVJ, Miami, purchased only the extensible boom portion and built their own base. Thus they could provide a triangular base with three swivel casters (tops in maneuverability) and a circular platform for the operator.

For quick repositioning and dollying, the mike boom, just as the camera, must be mounted on a dolly all the wheels of which are steerable. Figure 19-18 illustrates the Fisher boom, which is the first such equipment specially designed for the needs of the TV studio.

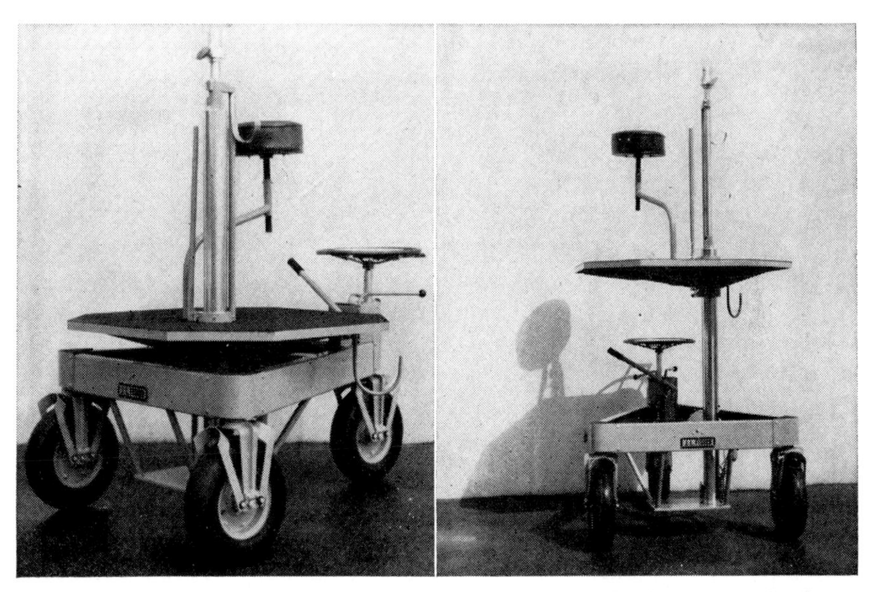

Fig. 19–18. Fisher microphone boom base. Designed specifically for TV, this boom perambulator features a circular platform (operator can't fall off from panning the boom too far); cable guards, shown in raised position (operator can't fall off because of sudden stops against cables); and 3-wheel synchronous steering (maximum maneuverability). It is also provided with a braking mechanism.

The boom man must be a highly skilled operator, or the audio quality will suffer noticeably. A good boom operator must be thoroughly aware at all times of the pictures that the cameras are taking. Since he has no view finder, he must make use of the floor monitor, which is usually placed within his range of vision, although it is frequently across the studio and pretty hard to see. In the interests of good sound pickup he must keep the microphone just as close to the actor as he can without getting it into the picture. When the camera is holding a close-up, he not only finds it possible to get the microphone closer but knows it is highly desirable for it to *be* closer for the proper sound perspective. Consequently he pays close attention to the sequence of shots, watching the floor monitor during rehearsal and constantly dipping the microphone into the picture so that he can see how close he is to the top edge of the frame. (Directors and other control-room personnel who are unfamiliar with this practice worry greatly over the constant appearance of the microphone during rehearsal.)

While the show is on the air, the boom operator listens closely to the director's instructions to the cameramen. When he hears the director say "Ready One," he immediately glances over at camera 1 to see what lens it has in position. If it is a long lens, he knows that immediately after the take he can drop the microphone in a little. If the next ready cue is for a camera which is set up with a wide-angle lens, the boom man will immediately begin to lift the microphone up so that it will not show in the following shot. Often the cameraman will remind him to raise the boom. It is a joint responsibility of cameraman and boom operator to keep the microphone out of the shot, and a moment's negligence on the part of either will produce the seemingly inevitable appearance of the microphone at one point at least in every show. Of course, this is not inevitable and rarely occurs with more highly skilled operators both on boom and on camera. It is important, in this respect, that the director have his shots planned accurately and take the same shots on the air that he took during rehearsal. On the unrehearsed show, of course, the boom operator must play safe at all times, keeping the microphone out of range of even the widest angle shot the director is using since he may receive little warning of a take (the ready cues may be followed immediately by the take cues). A proper match of sound and picture perspective is also of less importance in this type of production. Some boom men keep a cue sheet of moves and microphone positions which they make during rehearsal and refer to during the air show. Others rely on memory and the cues which they receive through their headphones from the audio engineer.

It is necessary for the boom operator to hear several things at once in his headphones. He must monitor the program sound in order to know whether or not his microphone is picking up the sound properly. He must hear the director so that he can keep track of the cameras which are about to be used, and he must be given certain cues by the audio engineer. This is accomplished by a split headset, one earphone of which carries program sound, while the other carries control-room cues. It is generally set up so that the director's line feeds into this earphone at all times except when the audio engineer has something to say, at which time he throws a switch and comes in on the director's line.

It is often desirable to ask an actor to delay his speech a split second while the mike boom swings across the set to reach him, but this is rarely successful. It is even difficult to expect an actor to remember not to speak out of set, away from the boom. Many audio men feel that such technical limitations should not be placed on the actor—that if the actor wants to speak away from the microphone it is up to the audio department to place another microphone or move the boom base so that this dialogue can be picked up. This is a very generous view, but not altogether realistic. There are certain microphone techniques that the performer simply must learn, just as he must learn acting techniques and adapt these to the camera. One of these is not to talk into the floor. No microphone can pick up sound which is directed down, unless it happens to be hidden under the rug, while the overhead boom mike will receive an "echo-y" reflection from the floor as a result of dialogue which is spoken in this direction. Another technique the actor must learn is not to turn his head quickly and speak immediately in another direction. This puts a tremendous strain on the reactions of the boom operator. Since the mike is generally kept a foot or so in front of an actor for best dialogue pickup, when the actor suddenly turns, the mike must quickly move 3 feet or more in order to stay in front of him. A split second must be allowed for this movement, or the first words delivered in the new direction will sound off-mike.

THE OPERATION OF THE AUDIO CONSOLE

By and large the audio-console equipment used in television studios is identical with that used in radio broadcasting. A large studio, however, will make many changes and adaptations to this standard equipment, and, in some cases, specially designed television audio consoles will be installed. The NBC television audio console is described at the end of this chapter as an illustration of what can be done in designing special audio equipment for television. The RCA Consolette (Fig. 19-19) will be described first. Although not the latest model it is probably the most commonly used console, and other equipment will be related to it.

The first thing the student operator learns about the audio console is that each of the fader dials, or "pots," in the middle of the panel controls a separate source of sound. These are called interchangeably "pots," "faders," "attenuators," "fading dials," "mixer positions," or "mixers." There are six, in this particular console, four of which are normally connected (normaled) to four studio mikes. The last two are reserved for sources of sound other than the studio microphones, such as sound-on-film projectors, turntables, or remote lines coming into the studio from outside. Any one of eight such sources of sound may be connected to each of these last two faders by means of rows of push buttons on the upper right-hand corner of the console. These push buttons are labeled "mixer 5 input" and "mixer 6 input." Since these buttons control only two pots, only two of these incoming lines may be used at once. It is important to know, in relation to these selector buttons, that mixer 5 takes precedence over 6, and if the same button should be pressed in each row, mixer 5 would carry the sound while mixer 6 would have

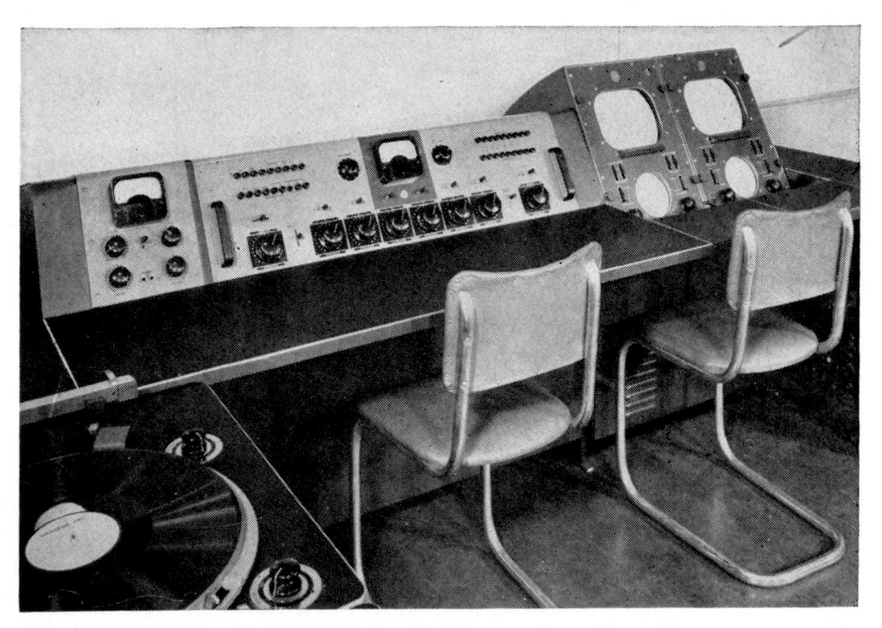

Fig. 19–19. RCA Consolette. Typical small console.

nothing. It is as though the incoming lines entered the console from above, passing through the top row of buttons (mixer 5 input) and terminating in the bottom row (mixer 6 input).

Two other pots are included on the face of the console, separated from the middle six. The one to the left is only a control for the level of the monitor (control-room loudspeaker) and normally has nothing to do with the broadcast program. The pot on the far right is called the "master gain" and controls the total output from the console. All the signals from the other channels are mixed together and go out through the master gain on their way to the audio transmitter. If the master gain is set at a low point, all the microphones will have to be turned up high on their individual pots for the proper outgoing level of sound. If the master gain is set high, each individual pot can be opened only a small way before the outgoing level is too high. This may be a disadvantage, since most pots are built with a series of contact points over which a rotating arm rides, and a low maximum setting of the microphone pot may mean that the sound will reach full volume in only a few steps, each of which will mean quite a noticeable change in volume. A low master-gain setting and a high maximum setting on the microphone pot, however, will make it possible for the same amount of increase in volume to take place in a large number of steps, so many that the difference between each of them is indistinguishable.

An important part of this or any other console is the volume-indicator meter mounted at the top of the panel. This is an exact measure of the volume of the outgoing signal. If this meter were not there, it might easily be possible for the audio engineer to fool himself by establishing a high volume level on his control-room loudspeaker and then holding down the volume from all his microphones so that it sounded correct to him, yet was too low to be distinguishable at home. The meter is calibrated in volume units (VU) as well as in per cent of modulation. As speech or music is picked up by a microphone, the needle jumps back and forth, registering each peak of volume. The audio man watches these peaks and keeps them generally below the 100 per cent mark on the dial. Speech must peak at least at 80 per cent, or the viewer at home will be leaning forward to adjust the sound on his set. Peaks of more than +1 or +2 volume units are likely to set into operation at the transmitter certain automatic equipment, known as limiters and compressors, which protects the transmitter from overloading but results in distorting the sound. A peak that is too high will sound raspy or buzzy instead of being a good clear sound.

It is a small television studio which can limit itself to only 4 microphones, as this console normally provides. Some complex shows have used as many as 16. If more mikes are necessary, at least 2 more are provided for in this console by feeding them through a switch and into the fourth position mixer. The switch is located just at the right of the pots, between the sixth mixer and the master gain. When this switch is in the middle position, as shown in the illustration, microphone 4 is feeding through the fourth position pot in normal manner. If the switch is thrown up, however, another mike (labeled on the panel as a remotely located announce mike) is switched into the fourth mixer and mike 4 is disconnected. If the switch is thrown into the lower position, still another microphone, labeled as a local announce mike (placed perhaps in the control room itself), is switched into the same circuit and the first two are inoperative. It is only radio-station operation that gives rise to the remote- and local-announce-mike labels; actually any microphone used for any purpose can be attached to this switch provided that it is plugged into the right wall receptacle in the studio.

TURNTABLE OPERATION

Most television studios are equipped with two turntables, each of which must be provided with the necessary pickup heads, filters, and other controls so that it can play the great variety of types of disk recordings which are on the market today. Besides this it must have a heavy-duty motor and a large flywheel so that its speed of rotation is even and the highest quality reproduction is possible at all times.

Records may play at one of three speeds, 78 rpm (revolutions per minute) for standard home phonograph recordings, 33⅓ rpm for broadcast transcriptions, standard record library material, and microgroove long-playing records, and 45 rpm.

Fig. 19–20. Typical control-room turntable. Two pickup arms are included. The one at the back is a special lightweight arm for long-playing microgroove records. Left knob, speed selector; right knob, lateral or vertical cut selector.

The audio engineer will handle records only in the smallest studio. Usually he is so busy with watching the action and controlling his console that handling of the records is delegated to an assistant engineer or record spinner. This operator must check many things as he puts a record on the turntable. First he must determine the speed at which it should be run and set the speed control on the turntable to accord with it. Then he must look to see whether it is a lateral or vertical recording and set the lateral-vertical switch. Finally he must "cue the record up" so that it will start immediately at the beginning of the music when the director calls the cue. Cuing up the record is done with the aid of a small cue speaker or, if this is a disturbance in the control room, with a set of headphones. The proper turntable is switched into the headphones, and the record man listens as he spins the record around on the turntable by hand. When he hears the music start, he backs up the record until he finds the exact point at which the needle first encounters modulation and then backs the record up another quarter turn (in the case of 33⅓ recordings). With 78-rpm records this is half a turn. In many studios it is the audio man who then starts the record, opens the appropriate pot, and feeds it onto the line.

When he hears the director say "Stand by with the music," the audio man reaches over and starts the turntable running but immediately puts his hand on the record so that it will not turn, letting the felt-top turntable spin under it. At the same time his other hand is ready on the

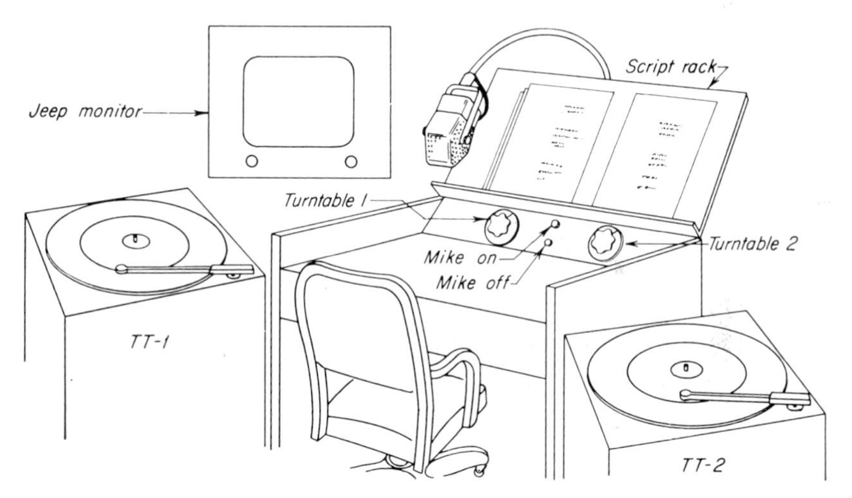

Fig. 19–21. Turntable equipment set up in announce booth.

mixer knob which controls that particular turntable, holding it in the "off" position. At the cue "Hit the music," he releases the record and watches as it makes the requisite amount of turn. Just before it completes its half or quarter turn as the case may be, he turns up the pot and the first notes of music go out loud and clear without any record noise or needle scratch before them. If the record is not backed up the proper amount, the pot may be opened before the record is up to speed and the very undesirable effect known as the "wow" will be heard. A wow makes any music sound like the opening note of a siren.

In some setups the record spinner has complete control of the turntables, having two individual pots on a little mixer of his own and feeding the output of this into one of the last two mixer positions on the audio console. This console position is then left open during the show, and all turntable control is done by the record man. This is a preferred procedure since it relieves the audio man of this responsibility and also releases one of his all too few mixer positions for other uses.

AUDIO SPECIAL EFFECTS

There are two special audio effects which are used frequently wherever dramatic shows are produced: the sound-effects filter and the echo chamber. Controls for both of these are built into the console in elaborate equipment but must be added in the case of the RCA Consolette and most other small consoles.

The sound-effects filter is a device which can be adjusted to cut either high- or low-frequency sounds (or both) out of a microphone signal, so that the sound will seem to come from a telephone or will take on an unreal, dream, or otherworldly quality. Two controls are provided on a filter (Fig. 19-22), one for low-frequency and the other for high-frequency

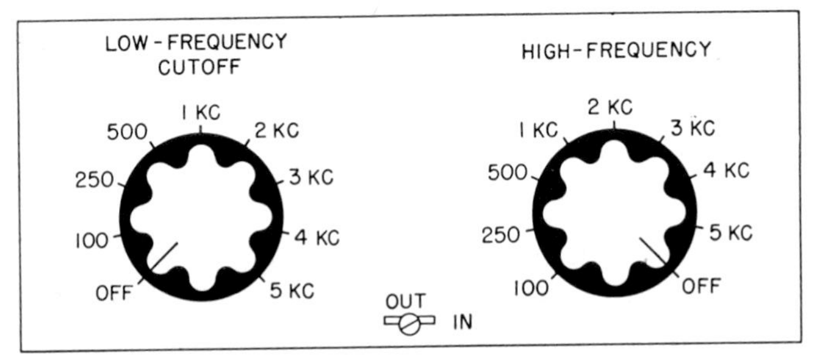

Fig. 19–22. Control panel of typical sound-effects filter.

cutoff. Each of these is calibrated in frequencies, and it is possible to obtain a great variety of filtered sounds by cutting off varying amounts of low or high frequencies. For example, if the low-frequency cutoff is set at 250 cycles, frequencies lower than this are not heard. If the high-frequency cutoff is set at, say, 2 kilocycles, frequencies above this point are eliminated. Thus only that portion of the sound which falls within the 250- to 2,000-cycle range will be transmitted, and it will sound like a telephone voice or a short-wave radio.

The echo chamber is a method of obtaining the echo and reverberation of a large hall or underground cavern when the original sound may be picked up by a regular studio microphone. The echo is added later by feeding the sound into a loudspeaker which is mounted in a concrete room, preferably long and narrow, usually in the basement of the studio building. At the other end of this chamber a second microphone picks up the sound again, this time richly enhanced with echoes, and feeds it back again into the audio console. By running the direct sound through one fader and the echo through another, the two may be intermingled in any proportion and any desired degree of echo can be obtained. Sometimes just a touch of echo will improve the sound of a musical pickup or add importance to an actor's speech (Fig. 19-23).

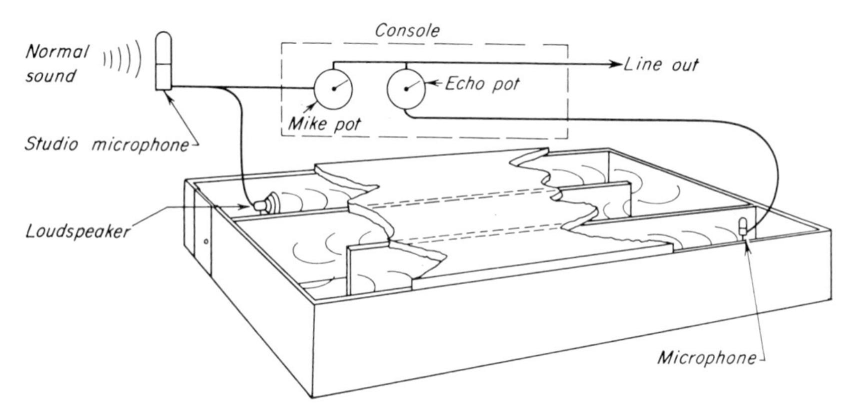

Fig. 19–23. Typical echo chamber.

Echo may also be imparted to the sound by using one of several synthetic devices, which are all termed electronic echo equipment. Several stations have imported a German product from Electromesstechnik which occupies a box 3 by 6 feet in size and 6 or 8 inches deep.

TELEVISION AUDIO CONSOLES

Both the CBS and the NBC networks have built special television audio consoles. A television audio console designed by the general engineering department at NBC will be described in detail.

A glance at the console shown in Fig. 19-25 will at first reveal that there are 12 individual microphone faders. There are no switches. At the end of this description an example will be given in which it will be shown how even this large number of mixer positions can be exceeded in a fairly complex network show. Whereas 12 microphones are normaled into individual faders, there are included another 11 microphone circuits which, by means of two keys on the lower right of the console, can be interchanged with other mikes on one or another of the 12 faders.

In the center of the control panel on a lower row are five master faders. Only one of these is the master gain, the one on the right. The middle three are *submasters,* the use of which will be described presently. The one at the left is called the "nemo master." The word "nemo" was adopted by NBC many years back to apply to any incoming line originating at a remote source. Two remote lines can be connected

Fig. 19–24. Artificial reverberation apparatus, made by E.M.T., West Germany, shown with cover removed. A flexible metal plate (black) is suspended behind white porous damping plate. Handwheel at top sets amount of damping and thus controls echo time.

Fig. 19–25. Special NBC audio console.

to this gain control. These may be used for sound from a film projector or the output of another studio or remote pickup point which is being integrated with the studio show.

The value of the submaster is that a number of microphones which are to be used together can be opened at once or closed at once. A musical program may employ a large orchestra, necessitating a pickup with several mikes, yet the musicians may not be playing throughout the program. If these several mikes, which always work together, are put

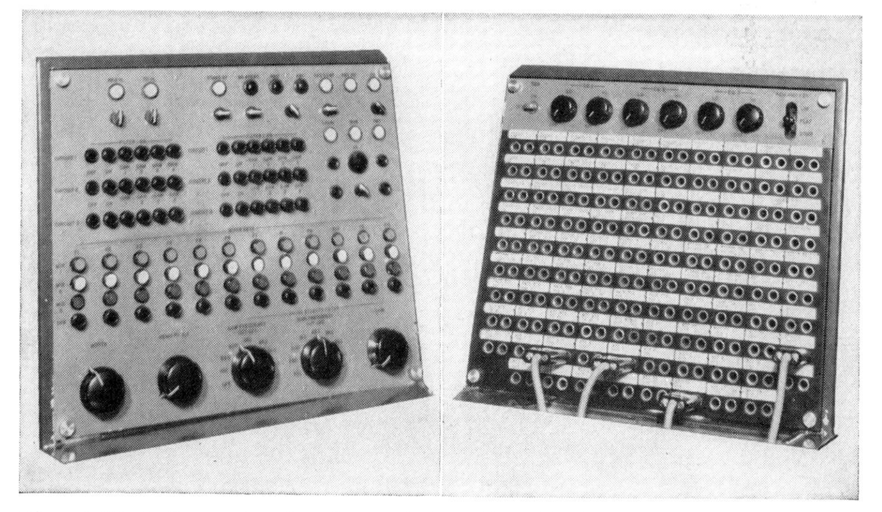

Fig. 19–26. Left panel and right panel (patchboard) of NBC television audio console.

on one submaster, they can be taken out all at once. In a dramatic program the pickup of dialogue on a set may take several microphones also, and when the scene is over and a new scene begins, the audio man may have only a few seconds in which to turn them all off and turn another group in the next set all on. The use of submasters makes this considerably easier to do. The output of all the submasters feeds through the master gain.

To make it possible for the audio man to keep track of which faders are in operation and which are controlled by each submaster, a color system is used. The knobs of the three submasters are colored red, white, and green. Behind a little window over each individual fader are three lights of the three colors. The left-hand panel of the console (Fig. 19-26) carries 12 vertical rows of push buttons, a group of 4 for each mixer position. One of each set is red, one white, one green. The fourth in each row is an "off" button. These are the selectors, which determine the submaster to which a microphone will be connected. If the "off" button is pushed in the F7 row for example, fader 7 is not connected to any of the submasters and feeds directly through the master gain just as in the operation of any console. No light appears in the window above fader 7. If, however, the red button is pressed in the fader 7 row, a red light appears in the window above the fader and the microphone on this position will be controlled by the red submaster, as well as the master gain. When all the microphones have been assigned submasters, there will be a number of red lights, a number of white, and a number of green lights above the fader controls. All the reds can be faded out by turning down the red submaster without affecting the remaining microphones. Turning down the submasters or turning down the individual faders will not turn off the lights behind the windows, however. These will disappear only when the off button corresponding to their number has been punched on the left-hand panel of the console. The lighted panels above each microphone pot are faced with ground glass on which the audio engineer can mark a name or number which will identify the microphone to him. Such indications as boom 1, boom 2, chorus, commercial, etc., will provide quick and positive identification, which is very important in a complex show when so many microphones are in use. As a further aid in this direction a light has been placed behind a plastic panel on which each fader knob turns. This light will go off only when the pot is completely turned off. Thus the audio man is always conscious of each microphone that is open without having to scan the entire console and check each pot. The CBS-designed TV audio consoles, while not at all as complicated as those of NBC, go a step further in this one respect and make each fader knob of transparent plastic with a light inside it, so that the whole knob lights up when it is in operation.

MICROPHONE EQUALIZING

Another feature of the NBC console is a method of changing the frequency response of the microphones at the console itself. The procedure of "strapping" a microphone for voice or for music has been described earlier in this chapter. Many microphones have switches on them which enable the user to select either a full low-frequency response for music pickup or an attenuation of the low frequencies, which is more desirable for voice. Very often in television it is necessary to make such a change during the program, when the microphone is inaccessible. Accordingly, the mike is left on music (full lows), and the change is made by means of a small knob above the patchboard at the right of the console. Three equalizers are provided so that three microphones may be controlled at one time in this manner. Each of the equalizers has two knobs, one of which will attenuate (cut down) the low frequencies coming from the microphone, and the other of which will control the highs.

MATCHING SOUND AND PICTURE PERSPECTIVE

It has been stated before that sound perspective and picture perspective should match and that the main factor in sound perspective was the distance from microphone to source of sound. The best way to match the two, then, would be to move the microphone closer in for close-ups and farther back for long shots. This is not always possible, however, and the NBC console has included a method of producing almost this same effect by different means. Not only does a closer microphone pick up less reverberation, but it also picks up more highs and more lows. The method used here is to increase the "presence" of the sound pickup at the moment of the cut from medium shot to close-up by suddenly cutting in a little more low and high response and boosting the sound level a certain amount. Since there is no change in the component of reverberant sound, this is not an entirely accurate effect but it does help to keep the sound pickup as realistic as possible.

A microphone which is to be controlled in this manner must be switched in quality exactly at the same moment at which the cameras are switched from medium shot to close-up. If the change in sound quality should come a few moments after the visual cut, the effect would be noticeably bad. For this reason it was necessary to tie in this audio switching with the switching of cameras. When a microphone is properly patched in, and preset on the top bank of buttons (Fig. 19-26, left), it will automatically switch to a filtered condition every time a particular camera is switched onto the air.

The change in quality is made by switching the microphone through a special-effects filter. The lows and the highs are reduced for the distant perspective, and the gain is slightly reduced at the same time. Switching the filter out of the circuit again restores the full frequency response and raises the level slightly, to provide an effect of greater presence for close-ups. Provision is made for the use of two special-effects filters, although only one is actually built into the console, and each of these has three circuits through which microphones can be fed and switched on and off the filter by means of the video switching. Thus a maximum of six microphones can be set up at once for this kind of control.

A typical audio problem in television dramatic shows concerns the telephone conversation in which the cameras switch back and forth, sometimes holding on one end of the line for a few speeches, sometimes switching on every speech. The sound must follow the picture accurately. While camera 1 is on, picking up Joe at one end of the line, microphone 1, which picks up Joe's voice, must sound normal, while mike 2, picking up Al at the other end of the line, must be heard on filter. However, when we switch to camera 2 on Al, we must hear microphone 2 in normal sound and mike 1 on filter. Ordinarily this is a feat of prestidigitation and mind reading by the audio operator, unless the director adheres strictly to his script, with which the audio man has had thorough rehearsal. With the video switching feature in the NBC console, however, this situation is no problem to the audio engineer, and the director can feel free to change his cutting from what he followed in rehearsal without throwing the sound out of synchrony. Microphone 1, which must sound filtered only when camera 2 is on the air, is punched up to work with camera 2, while mike 2, which must be on filter when camera 1 is on, is punched up to go on filter every time camera 1 is switched on the air. Thus a cut from one end of the phone conversation to the other will always result in a simultaneous reversal of the filter effect. One filter is all that is necessary, since both mikes should be filtered identically, and they work alternately. Mike 1 could be patched into the first line of punch buttons (marked filter 1, circuit 1), while mike 2 could be patched into the second row (marked filter 1, circuit 2).

The use of the NBC console on a typical complex production is described below. Audio may originate in at least a dozen locations, some of which must be covered by more than one microphone. In the example given, the audio engineer used 17 different microphones, plus two remote sources and one studio turntable. Since the console has only 12 positions, some of these microphones were alternated with others, so that 2 of the mixer positions could be used for more than 1 microphone.

On position 1 were placed the applause mikes. Four microphones, situated in different parts of the house, are used for applause, and all are fed together through one preamp and into the one mixer position. Four extra pots were added, through which each microphone could feed. This is "low-level mixing"—"mixing," since each microphone may be adjusted individually in volume without the others being affected, and "low level," because the mixing is done before the signal has been amplified. If audience mikes are fed through this mixer, it is possible to choose applause from selected portions of the house and turn down the upper-balcony mikes if the teen-agers in that part of the audience let their enthusiasm run away with them and begin to whistle and yell. The audience mike position (position 1 on the console) was placed on the white submaster. No other microphones were used on the white submaster.

The next four positions were devoted to microphones covering the house orchestra in the pit, one mike position each for the sax section, the rhythm section, the strings, and the brass. All these orchestra mikes were placed on the green submaster.

The remaining seven console positions were all placed on the red submaster. These comprised several stage locations, as listed below, and two boom microphones.

An on-stage orchestra was still to be provided for. This involved two additional microphones. However, this orchestra never played at the same time that the house band played; so two of the positions (positions 4 and 5) ordinarily connected to house-orchestra mikes were used for these extra microphones. This was accomplished by utilizing the special keys at the right of the mixer panel. Each of these keys has two positions, and these appear on the patchboard. Both keys were used in the "up" position (position 1) until the part of the show where the on-stage orchestra played, at which point both keys were thrown into the "down" position to connect mikes 13 and 14. This orchestra, just like the house band, was then controlled on the green submaster.

Two remote, or "nemo," sources were also included in this program, nemo 1 being a feed from NBC master control, nemo 2 from a sound motion-picture projector operating into a studio image-orthicon camera back stage. There is one mixer position for nemo feeds, located next to the submaster faders on the lower row at the far left. Called the "nemo master," it will carry one or another of two possible nemo feeds, depending on the position of the "nemo switch" just beside it. When the nemo switch is in the center position, nemo 1 or nemo 2 will be chosen automatically according to the video switching. As soon as the TD punches up his nemo 1 picture, the sound will automatically cut in at the same time.

20

Remote Pickups

The remote pickup of sports and other events outside the studio sometimes accounts for a large part of a station's schedule. Remote programs are usually quite long in comparison with studio shows and of course require very much less in the way of preparation and rehearsal. This is because the program material of most remotes is not created by the station staff. Shows are transmitted which already exist, which would be put on in any case, television or no television, for the benefit of an assembled audience.

Almost any kind of show, event, or sport which is interesting enough to attract an audience of spectators will make a good television show as well. A slow game like cricket, however, with a very limited appeal in this country, is a possible exception. The advantage of all such events is that they take place in a limited area, where the cameras can be stationed and, like the spectators, see everything. An event which covers distance (like a boat race or a golf tournament) is more difficult to pick up, and often two or more remote crews with duplicate equipment must be stationed at strategic points along the route.

The importance of the *place* in which a program originates cannot be overemphasized in the analysis of television programming; one of the special characteristics of this medium is its ability to convey actuality. The audience is able to be in two places at the same time. But the audience will have this feeling only if the distant place is real. The more you make of the location, the more fascinating the pickup will become. It is relatively uninteresting, for example, to tune in a ball game and never see anything but the diamond or to watch the pickup of a speech and see nothing but a close shot of the speaker.

Fig. 20–1. Scene from "Subway Express," a dramatic show that originated entirely from the IRT carbarns in New York City.

FIELD EQUIPMENT

The accompanying diagram illustrates in a simplified fashion the relationship of the essential units of equipment when they are set up for a remote pickup. Two cameras and two microphones are picking up the program; in this particular case, one of the mikes is placed near the cameras, presumably for interview purposes, while the second is back by the control equipment for the commentator (announcer), who sits in front of a jeep monitor, so that he can watch the shots as he describes them. The point at which the camera-control units, switching units, and audio units are placed is called the "control point." This is most often in the mobile unit truck, although it can as well be set up in a darkened corner or a small room under the stands. Many different intercommunication hookups are used. In most cases the director is in constant communication with the cameramen at all times. The video relay link and audio phone line back to the studio are indicated, plus two "cue lines" for phone communication, one for engineering and one for production. More often only one such line is used for all purposes.

Minimum operating personnel engaged in a two-camera remote pickup such as the one diagramed here are as follows: two cameramen, video engineer, switcher, audio engineer, supervisor (has no operating duties and so is not shown), program director, and back at the studio in master control at least two more people (usually an engineer and a production man) devoting part of their time to the same broadcast. The posts at the relay transmitter and receiver are not continuously manned; the intercom is necessary at this position only when lining up the relay link.

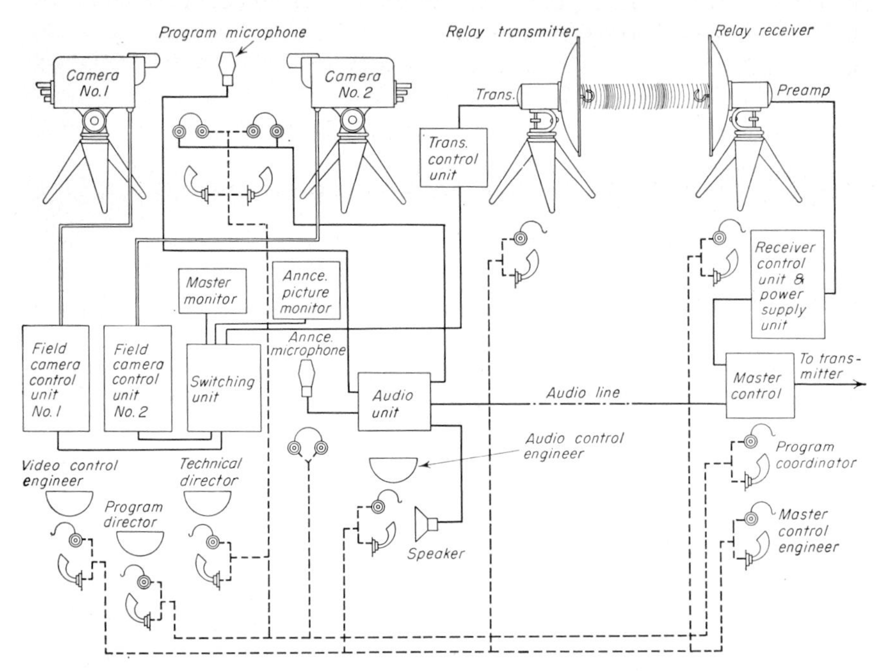

Fig. 20–2. Diagram of essential units for two-camera remote pickup.

CAMERAS AND CONTROL EQUIPMENT

All television manufacturers make field camera equipment. These units are portable and have been equipped with carrying handles for one- or two-man transport. They can be set up or broken down in relatively short order and transported in any type of conveyance that affords at least a little protection against the shocks of the road. In most operations, however, permanent positions are found for the control equipment in the mobile unit truck so that interconnecting cables need not be detached from one program to the next.

A simple diagram (Fig. 20-3) will serve to make the relationship of the various field units clear. Each camera sends its signal to a camera-control unit, which in turn feeds the switching system, from which the selected signal is then fed to the relay transmitter. A master monitor also receives this selected signal. Power-supply units which produce the necessary currents of various voltages feed each camera-control unit, the switching unit, and the master monitor.

The sync (synchronizing-pulse) generator is the heart of the television system. It performs three vital functions: (1) It provides the *driving pulses* that keep the electron beam in the camera tube scanning back and forth at the correct rate across the picture. Driving pulses to synchronize the horizontal movement of the beam are produced at the rate of 15,750 per second, and vertical driving pulses are produced at the rate of 60 per second. (2) It provides the *blanking pulses,* which turn off the beam between each line so that it will not scan during the return trace. (3) It provides a *synchronizing signal* (usually referred to simply as sync) which is added to the camera signal in the switching system, producing what is

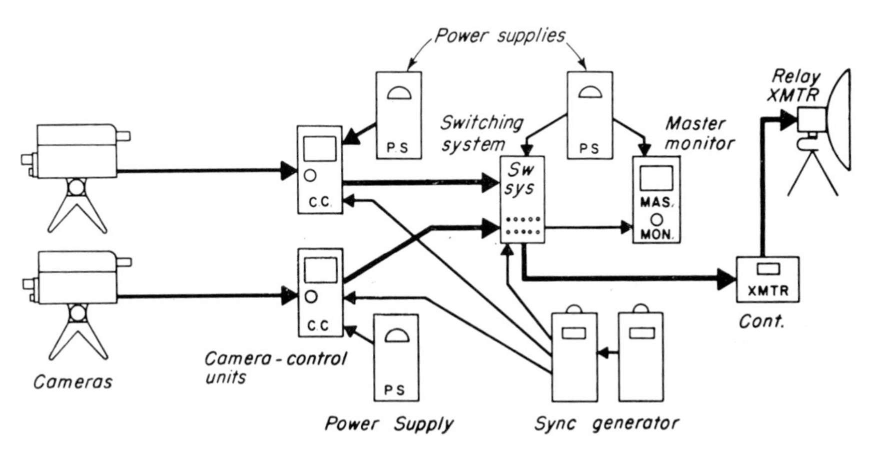

Fig. 20–3. Diagram of video equipment for two-camera remote pickup. (RCA equipment shown.)

known as a composite signal. The camera signal before this point is considered pure video. These sync pulses control the operation of the receiving sets, ensuring that they stay in exact synchrony with the scanning of the camera.

WIRELESS CAMERAS

Small vidicon cameras which can be carried freely away from a control point, without need of power or transmission cables of any kind, are very useful in a variety of remote applications. They are sometimes known as R.F. cameras because of the radio-frequency transmission employed, sometimes as "Back-pack" because of the small power and transmission unit carried on the cameraman's back, but perhaps most commonly simply as "walkie-lookie" or "creepie-peepie" equipment.

During the 1960 political conventions as many as fifteen of these cameras were in use simultaneously. Some were made by Dage, some by

RCA. Figure 20-4*a* shows such a camera manufactured by a French firm in use by the BBC in London. The cameraman has an optical view finder similar to that of a 16-mm-film camera, a pistol-grip handle, and a unipod base which can be rested in a cup at the base of a neck strap.

(*a*) (*b*)

Fig. 20-4. Wireless TV cameras. (*a*) French radio-camera used by the BBC; (*b*) small experimental vidicon by RCA. Small electronic view finder is hung on chest.

VIDEO LINK TRANSMISSION

The program signal originated by remote equipment must be sent back to the station and rebroadcast over the regular transmitter. This can be done over ordinary telephone wire if necessary, although if the distance is more than a few hundred feet, so much signal will be lost that the picture will not be usable. The telephone company will run a special parallel-conductor wire, similar to receiver antenna lead-in wire, which is capable of carrying an adequate signal over much greater distances.

For permanent installations, regular coaxial cable is necessary. This is also a two-conductor wire, one of which is a cylinder which completely surrounds the other. Since both conductors thus have the same axis, it is called coaxial. Light coaxial cables are now available at a few cents per foot.

When a great variety of pickups are anticipated, many of them at quite a distance from the studio, it is necessary to invest in a microwave relay link (Fig. 20-2). The relay link consists of two parts, a transmitter and a receiver. To all appearances they look exactly alike. The transmitter must be placed on a high point no farther than 400 feet from its control point and must have line of sight to the receiver.

The transmitter itself is contained in the small cylinder, or "ash can," which is fastened to the back of the large "dish." The transmitted signal is not broadcast directly, however, but goes into a rectangular tube, called a wave guide, which is hooked around so that it finally releases the signal facing back toward the dish. The mouth of the wave guide is in the point of focus of the reflector; so it beams the signal out just as the reflector of a searchlight forms a beam of light. When a 4-foot reflector is used, all the energy is concentrated into a narrow beam of 3 degrees or so, increasing the effective strength of signal at any point in the beam by a factor of 5,000 times over what it would be if the signal were broadcast equally in all directions. The nominal power output of the transmitter is then only ½ watt, while the effective strength is that of a 500-watt transmitter.

A 6-foot parabolic reflector will bring this factor up to 11,500 times (or an equivalent power output of 1,150 watts). Of course the receiver on the other end of the link is built in the same way and works in reverse, concentrating 5,000 times as much signal into the mouth of the wave guide as if no reflector were in use. The total "gain" of the system, then, is 25 million times in the case of the 4-foot reflector, and 132 million in the case of the 6-foot reflector.

When the 4-foot reflector is used, the maximum range of the link is about 25 miles. A longer jump can be made possible by using the 6-foot dish. Both these reflectors make beautiful sails in the wind and must be securely lashed down, or a sudden gust may send them crashing into the street. A solution for this problem was found in Cleveland, where winter storms off Lake Erie not only threaten to blow any projecting objects off the tops of the buildings but coat with ice anything that stands immovable. Plastic domes (Radomes) devised to protect radar antennas during World War II were found to be very useful for this purpose and were later adopted by others as standard equipment where permanent exposed positions must be used (Fig. 20-5).

Some stations have found that smaller reflectors are useful for short distances and don't catch the wind so badly. WTMJ-TV had several 3-foot reflectors built for them by Milwaukee Metal Spinning Corp. Once in Cincinnati, an engineer forgot to put the wave guide on as he was setting up the transmitter; of course the parabolic reflector was then inoperative because the signal was radiating directly from the front of the transmitter. Since the distance was only a few blocks, the signal was entirely usable. Many stations now do not bother with the reflector and wave guide at all for extremely short distances.

Since the beam which the link transmitter produces is only 3 degrees wide, it must be carefully aimed at the receiver (which is usually placed part way up the regular transmitting tower). The receiver, too, must be aimed directly into the beam in order to receive the strongest signal. This means that an accurate method of aiming each dish must be provided. Sometimes they are mounted on regular camera tripod heads, so that they

Fig. 20-5. Plastic Radome protects microwave receiver atop Radio City from wind and weather.

can be panned or tilted with complete freedom. When the equipment is being lined up, the engineer in master control must watch the picture and direct the aiming of both receiver and transmitter. (The single cable running to these units carries intercom circuits.) Some stations pay their engineers for steeplejack work ($10 a trip to go up the tower and adjust the receiver dish). Others have acquired equipment for remote control which permits this operation to be done from below. A remote-control mount for this purpose is pictured in Fig. 20-6.

When the remote location is first surveyed, a position for the relay-link transmitter must be chosen which will provide a direct line of sight to the link receiver back at the station. If this is impossible because of high buildings, hills, or other obstructions, sometimes a double jump is used

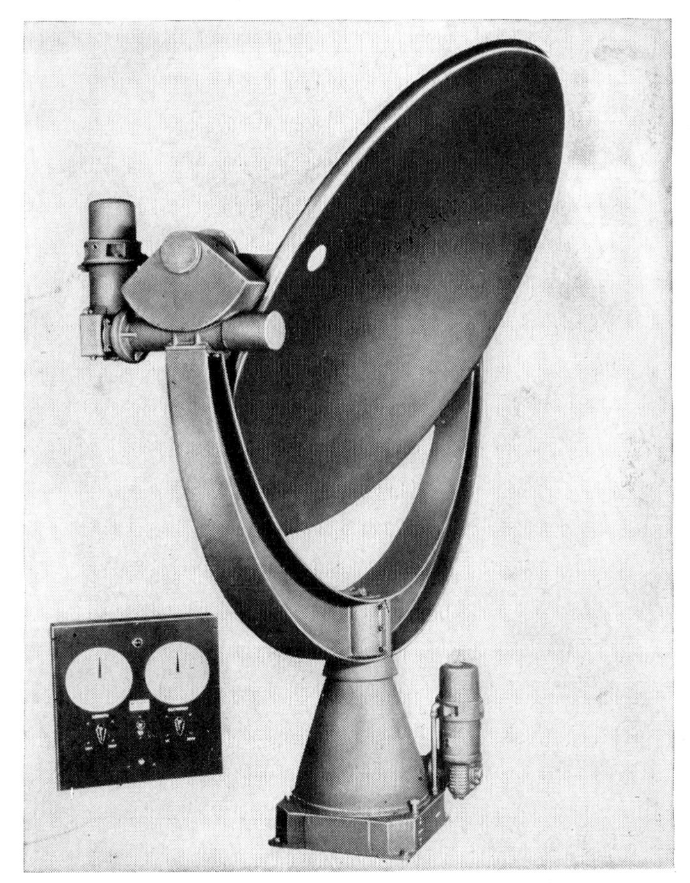

Fig. 20–6. Houston-Fearless remote control for microwave receiver. Controls at left include direction and tilt indicators.

(Fig. 20-7). Most of the larger stations have more than one set of microwave relay equipment. A second receiver and transmitter are positioned at some intermediate point which can see both the remote point and the station, and the signal is relayed a second time from there. This is often necessary when the relay link is used from a point in the downtown section of a city. Tall buildings interfere with line of sight, and it often takes more than the maximum 400 feet of cable to put the relay transmitter on top of one.

Sometimes a double jump is not necessary even though there is no line of sight between the link transmitter and its receiver. A very high-frequency carrier is used for the microwave link, and these ultrashort waves reflect very readily off a variety of surfaces, especially when the surfaces happen to be wet. CBS-TV sent in the picture from Ebbets Field for a couple of seasons without having to build a tower above the stands for line of sight to their main transmitter on the Chrysler tower. Experimentation revealed that if the beam were pointed in almost the opposite direction and bounced off the side of a Brooklyn warehouse, it

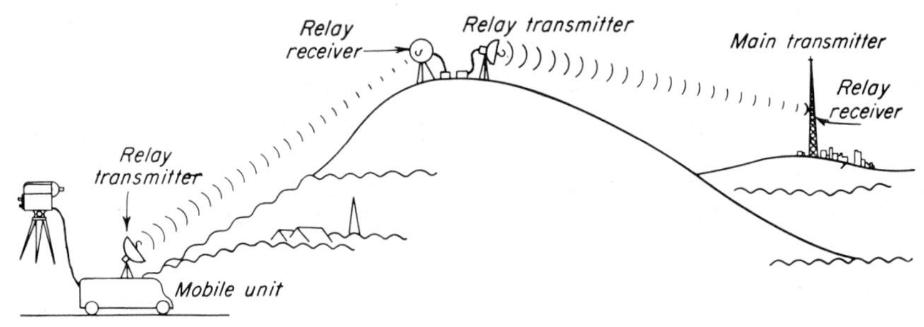

Fig. 20–7. Double jump is used when line of sight is obstructed.

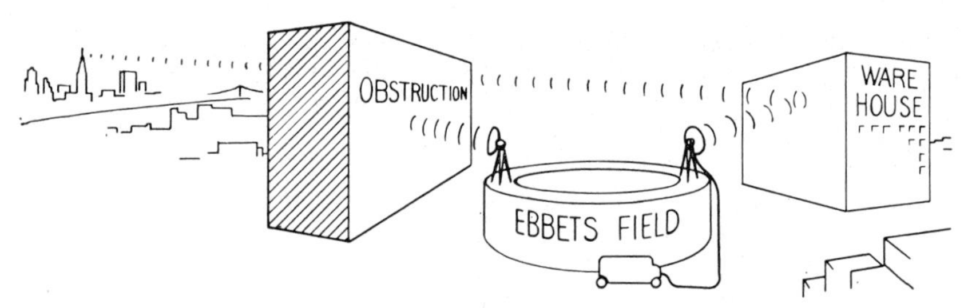

Fig. 20–8. Reflecting the beam is another method of getting the signal in when line of sight is lacking.

brought in a consistently good signal (Fig. 20-8). The signal was good until the third season, when the warehouse changed hands and its new use required that all the windows be left open. This sufficiently reduced its reflecting properties so that a tower finally had to be constructed to provide the direct line of sight.

Station WABD in New York once had difficulty with their wrestling pickup from Ridgewood Grove arena. Week by week the picture seemed to deteriorate. Finally something had to be done about it. They tested the transmitter in another spot, and the picture came in fine. Back on the roof of the arena it was weak again. Then they got out the original maps which are usually worked out in detail for a long jump such as this. The maps revealed that the beam narrowly missed the top of a hill somewhere in Queens, on its way to New York. Arriving at the hill, investigators found that a large, new apartment building had been going up there, right in the path of their beam. While the building had been only a frame, there was no particular obstruction; as the brick walls rose, the picture began to weaken.

AUDIO EQUIPMENT FOR REMOTES

The discussion of equipment will be brief here, since a more detailed description of audio consoles, microphones, etc., is given in Chap. 19, Television Audio. A representative portable audio console is the RCA BN6B (Fig. 20-9) which has four microphone channels, one of which can be switched between two inputs.

Fig. 20–9. RCA transistorized portable console BN6B. Four microphone positions and master gain are provided.

It is rare that a remote pickup calls for the use of a microphone boom, unless it be a special dramatic program where the creation of illusion requires that the microphone be kept out of the picture. A telescoping mike boom is a very heavy and clumsy piece of equipment to move around, and is best left in the studio. Smaller booms are available, such as the giraffe boom pictured in Fig. 19-16, which are collapsible and thus highly portable. When a small nondirectional mike can be used, the operator will frequently handle it on the end of a "fish pole," holding it sometimes below or to the side of the frame rather than above.

When a dramatic illusion is not involved, it generally does not matter whether microphones show in the picture. Stand mikes are occasionally used; for interviews the hand mike is often best, especially when these take place in crowded and noisy places. Holding the microphone close to each speaker has the advantage of raising the volume of direct sound in relation to the background noise.

Occasionally a microphone will be used in a parabolic reflector for picking up sound from a considerable distance away. The mike is placed in the focal center of the parabolic dish and receives a greatly amplified sound from a very narrow field. Such microphones are very useful at football games for picking up the sound of a band across the field or the voice of a cheerleader down below the stands.

An important piece of audio apparatus which is used more and more with special-events remotes is the radio microphone, once known as the

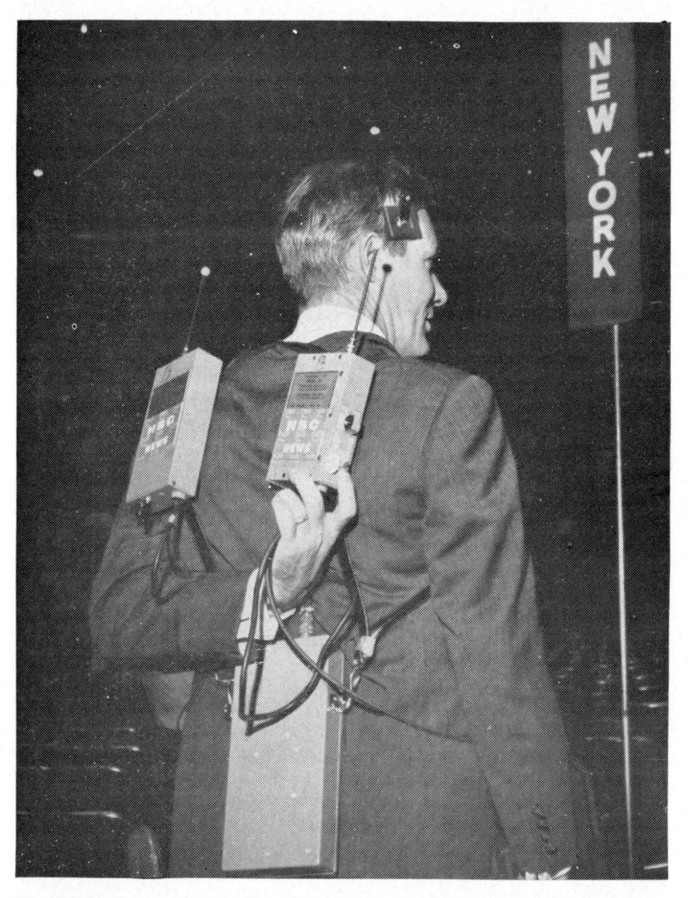

Fig. 20–10. NBC commentator Frank McGee carries portable audio receiving and transmitting equipment to allow him freedom of the convention floor.

"walkie-talkie." The use of transistors rather than vacuum tubes in its construction made possible the design of smaller units. Several makes of wireless microphones are available, the components of which are small enough to be hidden in a performer's clothing, even when, in the case of some attractive performers, this amounts to very little indeed. A small lavaliere microphone is generally provided with these units, which can also be made largely unnoticeable. The Vega microphone (Fig. 19-15) is entirely self-contained; a case the size of a standard lavaliere mike holds microphone, power supply, and transmitter. The neck strap doubles as the antenna.

A useful piece of audio apparatus which has been found valuable in radio remote work is a special type of cable reel which enables the

Fig. 20–11. Port-o-reels for power and microphone cable. The microphone may be used while the reel is in operation.

microphone to be used even while the cable is reeling up or unrolling from the reel. Ordinarily while the inside end of a reeled-up cable may be plugged into the audio equipment so that the entire cable need not be taken off the reel, it must be disconnected again if more cable is to be payed out, because the center of the reel must turn just like the outside.

The Port-o-reel eliminates this problem by providing a continuous sliding contact at the center of the reel.

THE MOBILE UNIT TRUCK

Every station that can boast a set of image-orthicon field equipment will also have some kind of special conveyance for carrying it around. This will vary from luxury busses, in which the investment is justified in large part as station promotion, down to simple station wagons and light pickup trucks, which can be used for hauling props and many other purposes as well. Some of the stations have adapted large house trailers for the purpose. Each of the major TV manufacturers offers a specially adapted truck with various built-in features that make it almost a traveling studio.

A well-designed mobile-unit truck must serve several purposes:

1. It must provide a means of transporting at least the major part of the operating personnel.

2. It must provide a quick and convenient means of transporting the television equipment from station or headquarters garage to and from remote location.

3. It must provide a control room with adequate desk space for operating personnel and some standing room for additional assistants or important visitors.

4. It must provide a well-organized storage system for all necessary equipment so that any item can be quickly located and will not be damaged during transit.

5. It must provide space for equipment maintenance of a simple sort; a small workbench with a few tools will suffice.

6. It must provide a suitable platform and working space for cameras on top of the truck, to be used as a vantage point at parades and special events when other convenient camera positions are lacking.

7. With all this space provided inside the vehicle, the over-all length must not be so great that the truck is not maneuverable in traffic or in towns with narrow streets and sharp corners.

8. It must be cooled in summer and warmed in winter. Insulation of the floor, walls, and roof is necessary for both purposes; a heating system must be installed; and if a cooling system cannot be afforded, at least forced-draft ventilation should be provided.

9. If the truck is large enough, it may also provide a position for an announcer or commentator with a small desk and jeep monitor.

10. The truck is generally considered a traveling advertisement for the station; and the appearance of the outside, plus the shipshape condition of equipment and personnel during operation, is a constant medium of station promotion in the local market.

There have been several types of trucks and busses adapted for television mobile units, and a great variety of interior layout designs. None of these meets every requirement satisfactorily, but each has something to recommend it.

RCA MOBILE UNIT

A representative small mobile-unit truck is supplied by RCA. This mobile unit is built into a Chevrolet 1½-ton truck of the school-bus

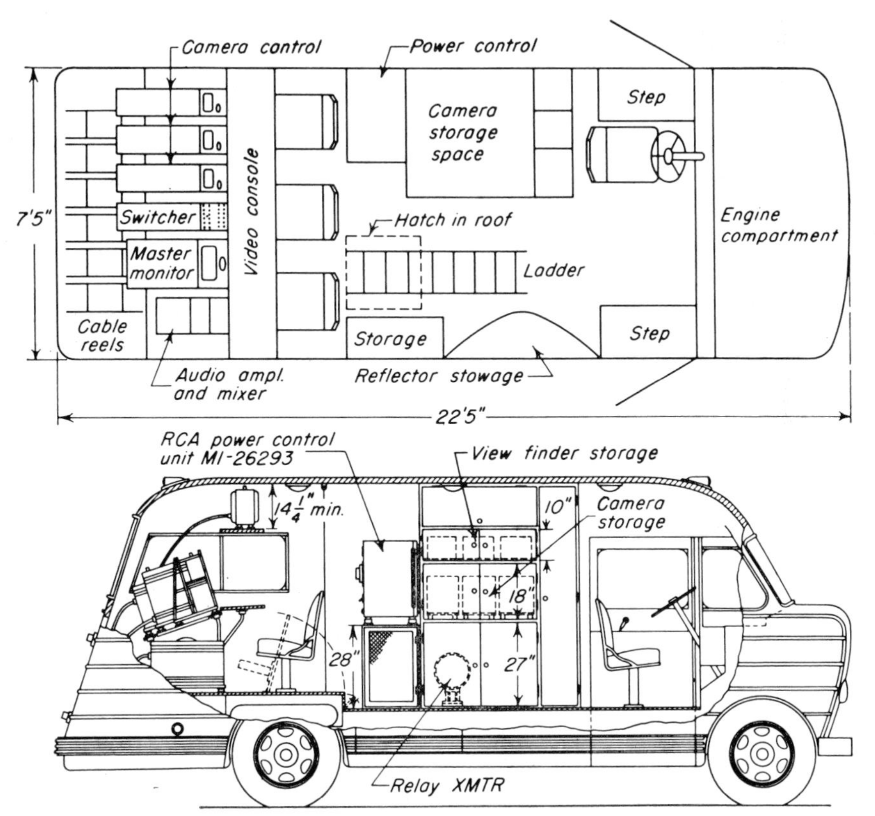

Fig. 20–12. Plan and elevation of RCA mobile-unit truck.

type. It is also the smallest of the various trucks which will be described. There are smaller trucks in use, but they are inadequate unless used in connection with other vehicles; so they are not called upon to fulfill all the functions that have been listed here.

The control-room section of the truck is at the rear, where the various camera-control units, switching system, master monitor, and audio equipment are set up in console form. The truck elevation (Fig. 20-12) shows

Fig. 20–13. Back of RCA truck.

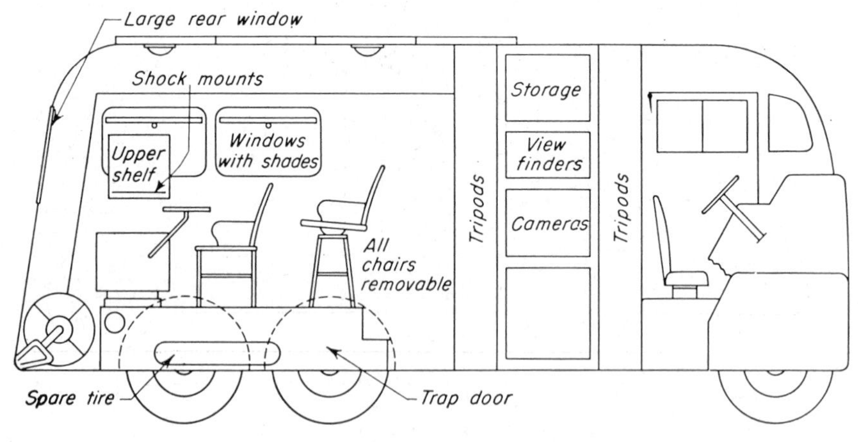

Fig. 20–14. Plan and elevation of General Electric mobile unit.

how the power supplies, sync generator, and other units requiring little attention during operation are placed just beneath. Only three chairs are provided, and this is of course not adequate unless the producer does his own switching. If a switching engineer is used, the other two chairs must be occupied by video and audio engineers and the director is re-

Fig. 20–15. Six representative mobile units. Top left, WEWS, Cleveland, adapted Sparton House trailer. Top right, KPIX, San Francisco, adapted Ford truck. Center left, WKY-TV, Oklahoma City, adapted Flexible bus. Center right, NBC "crash" unit includes audio and video transmitters and gas-driven generator. Bottom, NBC, Hollywood, color TV mobile vans.

quired to stand behind. A production assistant must then stand behind him, and the truck soon becomes hopelessly congested.

The video console faces a large back window, on the theory that the truck could be backed up to an event; this would serve as a kind of control-room window. Actually, the author knows of no case where this window has been found necessary or has even been put to good use; the truck can only rarely get right up next to an event but is usually parked behind the stands or in a side street. The rest of the truck is used for storage of cameras, view finders, relay-link transmitter, and other equipment that cannot be left permanently set up in the truck.

Wide doors open at the back of the truck (Fig. 20-13), where a series of cable reels are mounted for the long camera, power, and transmission cables that are required. Each reel will hold 200 feet of cable, and there is space for six reels. Any further cable (and more is often necessary) must be carried on the floor of the truck or in someone's car.

(*a*)

(*b*)

Fig. 20–16. (*a*) BBC Roving Eye mobile unit, containing two cameras and a transmitter. (*b*) BBC Roving Eye with 45-foot pneumatic mast erected.

Figure 20-16 shows a mobile unit constructed by the BBC which is completely mobile in every sense. The unit is very small and maneuverable, but provides for the following functions: (1) a mobile placement for two cameras, (2) a traveling control room, (3) a built-in generator to provide current for the equipment, and (4) a mobile sound and picture transmitter with a pneumatically operated mast which can raise the antenna to 45 feet and keep it automatically on the proper bearing no matter which direction the van may turn. One camera operates through a wide window in the left side of the vehicle; the other protrudes from the top, and is mounted on a circular track 3 to 4 feet in diameter within which the operator stands, so he can have the same operating space behind the camera whichever direction he may choose to shoot.

Fig. 20–17. Interior of BBC Roving Eye. Camera well and part of camera, which protrudes through roof, can be seen. Camera is roller-mounted on a circular track, so it may be swung around to face any direction, while the operator remains always behind it. Vertical adjustment screw shows at left of track.

MOBILE FILM UNITS

European television production centers have often incorporated film and slide pickup equipment into their remote units, a practice which is quite the exception in this country. The West German manufacturer, Fernseh, offers mobile units, marvels of functional design and space utilization, and includes in the larger models either 16-mm- or 35-mm-film pickup apparatus. A small 2- by 2-inch slide projector (dia-geber) is available as an attachment for the vidicon camera, which can also be used for live pickup simply by hinging the projector out of the way.

The Italian television service, RAI, possesses a special mobile film unit containing not only a 16-mm film chain, but complete film processing and editing equipment. Thus events, such as bicycle races, which cannot be covered in their entirety by live transmission, can be reported within a very short time by film transmitted directly from the event. The RAI unit includes a trailer containing the film-processing machine and two editing tables, plus a tractor unit containing the film pickup camera and apparatus for picking up sound from ¼-inch tape.

MOBILE VIDEO TAPE

Video-tape equipment can be nearly as well operated when truck-mounted as in the studio, and the use of this equipment on location can greatly extend the quality of television reporting. Highlights of a game can be played back during intermission or after the end; commercials and other inserts can be integrated and transmitted with the same quality as live pictures. In the future much film for television, and eventually, probably, film for theater purposes, will be made electronically with the TV camera and video recording instead of photographic equipment and films. The mobile video-tape unit is extending the range of "electronic motion pictures" to include location shooting with practically the flexibility of film production.

SEA AND AIR MOBILE UNITS

Many television pickups have been made from boats or ships and in several cases from submerged submarines. TV cameras have covered events from airplanes and helicopters. One Swedish station, however, has equipped a permanent mobile-unit ship, and an American station has kept a "telecopter" unit in constant readiness for news events which can be covered from the air.

The Swedish mobile-unit ship is at Göteborg, a harbor city where most events take place along the waterfront. An old ferry was acquired, on which the remote truck is kept. For events on land the truck may be easily driven off the ferry.

KTLA, an independent Hollywood station, is the first to have a regular helicopter mobile unit. A General Electric vidicon camera equipped with a Pan Cinor zoom lens is directed at the scene from the side window. The cameraman uses a wire-frame view finder for convenience, but can check framing and picture quality on a monitor carried inside the aircraft.

(*a*)

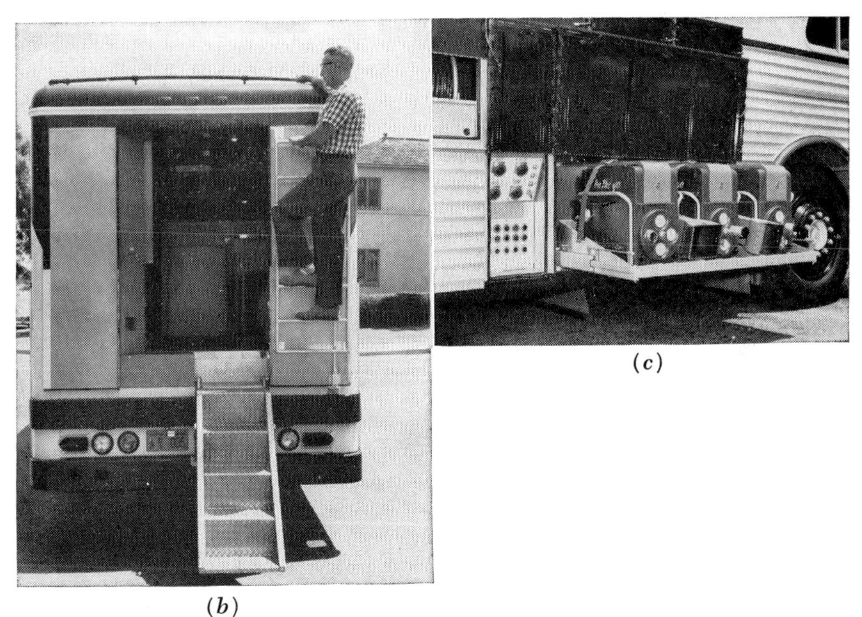

(*b*)

(*c*)

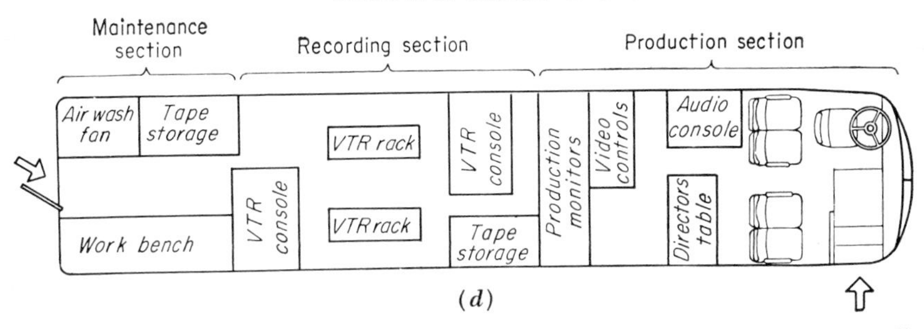

(*d*)

Fig. 20–18. Mobile video-tape van made by Crown Coach. (*a*) Technician pulls camera cable from reel on side of vehicle. (*b*) Rear view shows roof access. A video-tape console can be seen inside the vehicle. (*c*) Shelf for camera storage slides out for easy access. Camera and microphone inputs and video outlets are on panel at left. (*d*) Diagram of interior layout.

(a)

(b)

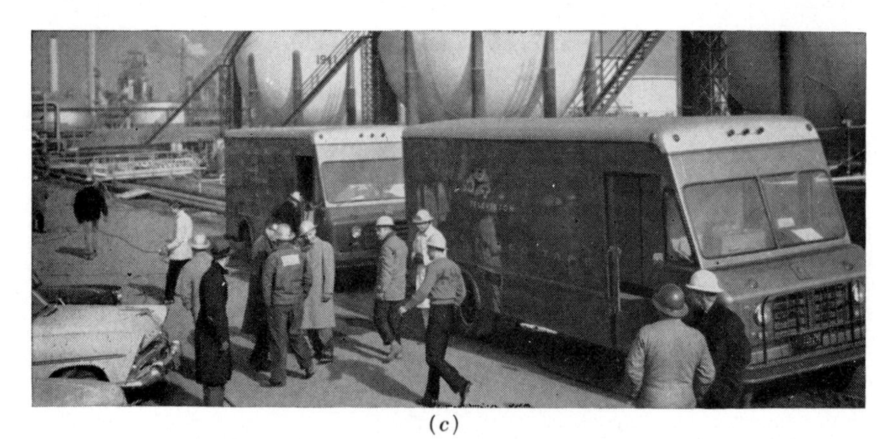

(c)

Fig. 20–19. Various mobile video-tape vehicles. (*a*) Plane used by Mobile Video Tape, Inc. (*b*) Intercontinental Television unit in Europe. (*c*) Two MVT units on location at oil refinery.

Fig. 20–20. KTLA Telecopter over Los Angeles. GE vidicon camera with Pan Cinor zoom lens and open frame view finder protrudes from cockpit window. Transmitter antenna, below, must be raised before landing.

The helix antenna below the fuselage (Fig. 20-20) puts out a saucer-shaped nondirectional beam, and a receiver with a parabolic disk at the station's transmitter on Mt. Wilson tracks the helicopter as it moves. In covering emergencies this helicopter has been used as a relay point between remote truck and transmitter to make a double jump quickly possible.

EXTRA-HEIGHT DEVICES

Extra height is very often a necessary thing in remote work, sometimes for satisfactory camera placement, sometimes to obtain line of sight to the main transmitter for the microwave link. Stackers and fork trucks have been used sometimes for camera vantage points, the advantage of these devices being that the camera can be mounted at ground level and hoisted 10 or 15 feet in the air. Where these devices are used, it is usually because they happen to be handy at the scene and can be utilized without added expense. The fork truck makes an excellent camera dolly with the added possibilities of vertical movement but is of value only on remotes when the microphones are used close to the announcer.

To lift the microwave dish as high as possible, some ingenious methods have been attempted. One station solved the problem by calling up the local fire department and borrowing the hook-and-ladder truck. The city fire department generously sent out the truck with a man to run it, and the microwave dish could be raised to a height of 80 feet. It is not always possible to borrow equipment like this, and the station is often obliged to build some kind of tower as quickly and as cheaply as possible. Wooden platforms are sometimes constructed for camera positions, but these are usually considered permanent installations and are neither particularly quick nor cheap to put up.

Several manufacturers make a kind of tubular scaffolding of which very solid towers can be built in a few minutes' time. "Upright scaffolds"

Fig. 20–21. Upright scaffold used for camera placements at Hollywood event (KNBH).

made of aluminum alloy are particularly well adapted to this purpose. Figure 20-21 shows an upright scaffold put up by KNBH in Los Angeles for camera placement at a tennis match. Two men can put up this lightweight scaffolding in five to ten minutes' time. Each section folds together into a flat package weighing only about 60 pounds. Several stations have invested in this type of scaffolding. WTMJ-TV in Milwaukee has a tubular aluminum Safeway tower which can be assembled to the height of 60 feet in an hour or so. There is almost no limit to the structure which can be built with tubular scaffolding. Figure 20-22 shows a 70-foot tower of scaffolding. Contractors will erect scaffolding like this for special jobs, but enough sections to build small towers for camera placement can easily be carried to and from the scene and stored in relatively little

Fig. 20–22. Seventy-foot tower of scaffolding erected by WXYZ-TV, Detroit.

space. The scaffold shown in Fig. 20-21 when folded up and stacked away should occupy a space not over 2 by 4 feet and 6 feet high.

GAS-DRIVEN GENERATORS

Very often the mobile unit will be asked to make a pickup from a location where there is no available supply of alternating current. To broaden the scope of remote pickups, many stations have invested in a 5-kilowatt generator permanently mounted on a small trailer. The trailer can be hauled behind the remote truck or any other vehicle and placed a few hundred yards from microphones so that the noise of its gasoline motor will not interfere with the sound pickup. A fairly even frequency of current is necessary to run television equipment since all the synchronizing and driving pulses are based on the 60-cycle alternating current (a-c current reverses its direction of flow 60 times every second: hence 60-cycle). If the frequency is not accurately controlled and goes down to 58 or up to 62 cycles, receivers may lose sync and the picture occasionally will roll up the screen.

WCAU-TV in Philadelphia has had one of these generators in operation for several years and finds that frequency control is maintained as

(*a*) (*b*)

Fig. 20–23. Extra height. (*a*) NBC camera rises 75 feet on high-reach apparatus from Sign Maintenance Company. (*b*) Similar equipment used by Illinois Bell Telephone Co. to raise microwave transmitters to the same height.

long as the generator is not overloaded. It is not satisfactory, for example, to operate more than two cameras; three will overload the generator just enough to lose the steady frequency.

PROBLEMS OF REMOTE PICKUPS

In planning the pickup of remote events, many things must be taken into consideration. So much preplanning and setting up have to be done at the usual remote that stations often estimate that a "one-shot" pickup from beginning to end costs $300 to $500. Of course when the problems can be solved once for a long series of pickups from the same place, the unit cost becomes far less. Most of this cost is man-hours, surveying the location, arranging for the necessary rights, stringing cable overhead where it will not interfere with the movement of crowds, etc.

On the other hand, some stations have found that simple one-camera remotes can be handled by only two men, reducing the cost to very little indeed.

THE POWER-SUPPLY PROBLEM

Approximately 5 kilowatts of power is usually necessary to operate remote equipment. Five kilowatts means a 50-ampere current, which can usually be obtained from the entrance equipment of a nearby dwelling or field house, since a 60-ampere line is provided for most installations. This much current cannot be taken out of a lamppost or a wall socket, since these lines are generally fused for 15 to 30 amperes and the wires involved would heat up dangerously or even melt if 50 amperes were put through them.

The person who is surveying the remote location will hunt up the main fuse box and entrance switch, usually in a cobwebby basement, and check to see whether or not it is rated at 60 amperes capacity. When the remote pickup is made, the power cable is then connected either by heavy spring alligator clips (which are illegal in some localities) or by lugs which can be screwed or bolted to the incoming lines.

LOCATION OF CONTROL POINT

The location of the control point is dependent on several factors, one of which is cable length. Normally camera cables may not exceed 1,000 feet in length. If the transmitter control unit is kept in the truck or at the control point, then only 400 feet of cable is allowed from control point to transmitter. Finally, the available power-supply cable (which is the heaviest and most expensive of the cables involved) will determine how far distant the control point can be from the source of power.

Usually the control equipment will be kept in the truck, and selection of a control point will involve only finding a suitable place to park the truck where it will be in the shade, removed from crowds, and close enough to things so that tremendous amounts of cable are not necessary. If the truck cannot be parked near enough to the scene or if cables cannot be run to a suitable parking spot, then the equipment must be taken out of the truck and a special control point established elsewhere. This cannot be outside, because the monitors must be shaded, so that a picture can be seen. If there is no nearby room, a canvas can be stretched overhead to make a kind of tent for the purpose. It is not necessary for the operators at the control point to see the event itself or have any further communication with the cameramen than the regular talk-back earphone setup. At ball parks a small room or office can usually be found under the stands for this purpose.

THE RELAYING OF AUDIO AND VIDEO SIGNALS BACK TO THE STATION

The problem of relaying the signal back to the station is of vital importance and should be considered very early in the survey of the location. This is usually done on topographic maps of the locality before going out to the location, to make sure there are no obstacles in the way between the transmitter and receiver of the proposed microwave link.

Audio was originally relayed back from the remote point by means of telephone wire, whether the video transmission was by wire also or by microwave relay. Some stations acquired separate audio link transmitters which were set up side by side with the video gear. Eventually, however, audio channels were incorporated into the standard microwave transmission equipment so that both audio and video are now carried on the same beam.

PERMISSIONS, RIGHTS, AND CLEARANCES

A great share of the time involved in preparing for a remote pickup is spent on securing the right permissions and legal clearances for the job. Some municipal governments are less involved in red tape than others. Police permission must be obtained for parking the truck on the street, or private permission for parking it elsewhere. If any construction of platforms or special poles or rigging is to be done in connection with the running of the cables, city or private permission must be obtained. Fire laws are involved in most of this planning.

COORDINATION WITH THE STUDIO

It is necessary that the producer of the remote program have sufficient communication with the studio so that proper coordination of beginning and end of transmission will be possible and filmed commercials which must originate at the studio will be smoothly integrated. For this purpose a second audio line is provided as a cue line. The technical director at the remote is always handy at the end of this private line, and the other end usually terminates in the station's master control room. It will be used for engineering purposes as the equipment is set up, particularly in aiming the microwave transmitter. Immediately before and during the broadcast the private line will be used for production purposes. There is usually a production man in master control (called the coordinator or the broadcast supervisor). It is his responsibility to coordinate the beginning and ending of the remote program with whatever other program material or spot announcements are to be run from the studio, and especially to direct the running of the film commercials which occur during the broadcast of the remote.

To enable the remote crew to coordinate better at their end of things, an air monitor is provided so that the actual program which the station is putting on the air can be watched in the remote truck. This is of course nothing more than an ordinary receiver and antenna set up in the same way as any other home receiver.

Without a sync-lock system it is impossible to make a dissolve between a remote picture and a studio picture. It is impossible to superimpose news bulletins, for example, originating in the studio, on pictures coming from the remote point. Two sync generators are involved, and it is not possible to keep them working in synchrony with each other. The field equipment has its own sync generator, providing the sync pulses that keep the receivers working in time with the remote cameras, and the studio has another sync generator, sending out similar pulses to keep the home receivers working in time with the film-pickup camera which is picking up the news bulletin. If a dissolve is made between these two picture sources or if the dissolve is held (a superimposure), two sets of sync pulses will be going to the receivers at once. If these are not together, the receivers will have to choose one or the other and one picture will be seen to roll constantly up or down the screen. Even a direct cut from studio to remote may catch the new sync pulses at an in-between point, and the receiver picture will roll once up the screen until the receiver gets locked in synchrony again. Consequently all transitions from studio to remote, or vice versa, must be made by a fade to black and a fade back in.

The manufacturers have met this problem with a device called the sync lock, or the "Gen lock" in the case of RCA, which locks together the pulses of the two sync generators. The method is to lock the studio sync generator as a slave to the field sync generator as a master. Some stations have built their own equipment to do this. Only where such equipment is in use, however, is it possible to superimpose studio and remote pictures, lap-dissolve, or make a direct cut from one to the other.

THE SURVEY

To summarize the various points made above, a typical survey form is included here. This form is a composite of many, developed at many places over the years. It is intended to be filled out by the engineer and production man who make the original survey of the remote location. Every possible question is included. If any real problems arise, the chances are they will be pretty well solved during the process of the survey, and any unsolved problems will be indicated as such under general remarks at the end of the form.

REMOTE SURVEY FORM

1. Date of this survey
2. Name of program
   Name of series
3. Date of first broadcast ______________ Time ______________
4. Type of program
5. Studio integration required?
6. Place of broadcast ______________ Exact address ______________
   Nearest phone
7. Director
8. Technical director
9. Contact man at location ______________ Telephone ______________
10. Video transmission. Number of links required
    a. Location of link transmitter
    b. Location of power source
    c. Video cable required
    d. Power cable required
       (Note: if additional links needed, enter above information under Remarks, No. 26)
11. Sound transmission
    RL and PL termination location
    Audio link transmitter location ______________ Cables ______________
12. Power source location ______________ Power cable needed ______________
13. Cameras

Camera	Location	Lenses	Cable length
1			
2			
3			
etc.			

14. Lighting
    Location ______________ Existing light level ______________
    Extra light needed/approx.wattage ______________
15. Microphones
    Location ______________ Use ______________ Type of mike required
    Cable length
16. Commentator location
17. Announce monitor
    Location
    Power source
    Power cable
    Video cable

18. Off-the-air monitor
    Location
    Antenna location
    Lead-in
19. Additional video monitors required
    Location ______________ video cable ______________ power cable
    ____
20. Additional off-the-air receivers required
    Location ______________ Antenna location ______________ Lead-in
21. Special electrical installation required
22. Electrical contractor employed by location
23. Special carpenter construction required
24. Contractor employed by location
25. Miscellaneous equipment needs
26. Remarks
27. Show all locations on sketch map (north at top)

Signed ______________________________
Director (or production representative)

____
Technical Director (or engineering representative)

METHODS OF COVERING THE MAJOR SPORTS

The problems of camera placement, choice of lens, etc., have been purposely omitted from the preceding section because they belong more properly under the more creative production problems of picking up the event. It is, of course, impossible to cover all the types of remote events which have been picked up by television crews. Some of the most interesting problems have been faced when one-shot pickups of unusual subjects have been made. A more detailed discussion of the standard games will serve, however, to establish the basic principles, which can then be applied in individual cases as the need may arise.

WRESTLING AND BOXING

The pickup of wrestling and boxing is perhaps the simplest of the various sports, although this does not mean that the director can relax and take it easy on this type of show, any more than on any other. He still must be Johnny-on-the-spot with the right shot at the right time. His job is simplified, however, by the fact that he rarely has to direct the cameramen, since there is but one pair of fighters to watch, and he can devote his attention to proper switching between the shots.

Only two cameras are used for wrestling and boxing, and these are usually placed on special platforms, either above and behind the spectators if it is a small arena or in the aisle if the arena is large. The placement of the camera far back in a large arena is to be avoided since long lenses must be used. A long lens exaggerates any lack of smoothness in camera handling, and vibrations of the camera platform are easily seen in the picture. If the camera position is high as well as distant, the long lens will have a further undesirable effect. Long lenses shrink depth. The fighter in the ring will be shrunk in height if seen from a high angle and will look like an unimpressive dwarf.

The cameras cannot be placed too close to the ring, or they will be in the way of spectators. If the cameras are placed low, in the aisles, the ropes and corner post are in the way. Sometimes a camera has been placed at ringside and has produced an extremely dramatic low-angle shot, but this cannot be done everywhere since at some rings the camera will be shooting up into the lights.

One station was able to put up a platform in the aisle about 10 feet from the corner of the ring, without blocking anyone's view, and high enough so that the corner post would not interfere. The advantage of such a close position is that big close-ups are possible without the use of such a long lens that the following of action would be very rough and uneven.

The announcer is usually placed at ringside in the pickup of these two sports, but it is very important on which side of the ring he is placed. If he is on the opposite side from the cameras, for example, he will have a difficult time keeping left and right straight in his own mind (the fighter on the left of the screen will be seen on his right, etc.). For this reason and also to make it possible to show the announcer and an occasional interviewee, he is almost always placed on the same side of the ring as the cameras.

RACING

In the pickup of racing (flat racing, harness racing, stock car racing, etc.) the action takes place on a very large stage, sometimes a half mile long. All races run counterclockwise in this country, which means that the action is left to right on the screen in the foreground and right to left in the back stretch. Admittedly, it is impossible to be close to the entire action. The finish line is the place to be, of course; and the press box at the race track, as well as at any other grandstand, is placed in the best position to see the important moments of the action. Whereas it is usually possible to obtain space in the press box or on the roof of the press box if it is strong enough, this is not always the best vantage point for the television camera. In racing, just as in any other sport, the high-angle assures coverage of everything, but at the sacrifice of dramatic pictures. Tiny horses moving across the screen, seen from above like toys on a table top, are not at all impressive, as they would be from a low angle near the track, sweeping toward the camera, looming larger in the shot as they come. The shot of the horses as they go down the back stretch is almost universally bad, making them look like the moving ducks in a shooting gallery.

Fig. 20–24. WKRC-TV camera on grandstand roof at Cincinnati race track.

The placement of cameras at all remotes is dependent upon a great many other factors than simply the best position for the best possible pictures. The design and construction of the grandstand may be a determining factor, as well as the policy of the owners in regard to the use of cameras and the quality of pickup they are prepared to allow the television station to make.

Methods of programming the races will dictate to a great extent the placement of cameras. A camera may be placed in the paddock, for example, and devoted to the before-the-race examination of the horses. Of course it is better if this camera can also be used for another purpose so that fewer cameras will be required.

Action on the race track takes up only a small portion of the time of a race-track remote, and the producer must be prepared to pick up something of interest to the viewing audience while there is nothing on the track. In harness racing there are usually some horses on the track warming up, and the announcer can ramble on about past performances and interesting angles of the sport; but in flat racing the track is dead between one race and the parade to the post for the next one. A camera in the paddock will give the viewers what they would be looking at if they were actually at the track; and when this fails, the producer will usually try to ring in some interviews with the race-track officials, celebrities in the audience, etc. A New York station has programmed a full-fledged quiz game, with panel of contestants and master of ceremonies, for the interval between harness races.

If a camera can be used for more than one purpose, maximum efficiency is attained. Thus at the race track in New Orleans, WDSU-TV has placed one camera on the clubhouse porch, where it can be used on the race itself and can be turned around for interviews against the lush background of the exclusive clubhouse. CBS at Jamaica Race Track on Long Island used a camera in the paddock and later dollied it out on the lawn to watch the crowds surging to the rail. One camera is always placed high on the top of the grandstand for horse racing and is used as the basic camera for the major portion of the race. CBS placed a camera at Jamaica down at the rail near the finish line and used it for the finish of the race as the horses came down the final stretch into the camera. This camera was also useful for good shots of the crowd during the race, long shots of the grandstand before the race, and a close-up of the bugler calling the horses to the post.

WBKB in Chicago used a different technique, something that producers had talked about for a long time. A camera was placed in the infield so that an adequate shot would be obtained of the action in the far stretch. Stringing wires across the track was of course impossible; so about 600 feet of camera cable was snaked through a conduit under the track. Running cable to a camera on the far outside of the track could be done, but the direction of motion of the horses would be reversed and the audience might become confused as to the position of the horses on the track, proximity to the finish line, etc. By keeping all cameras on one side of the action, this confusion is eliminated.

Of course the technique of cutting from one camera to another had to be very carefully considered in this setup. Figure 20-25 illustrates the positions of the three cameras that WBKB used. The routine of cutting was as follows: After the start, camera 1 followed the horses as they moved from left to right down to the "clubhouse turn." Before they were definitely going from right to left on the screen, a cut was made to camera

2, placed closer to this turn and able to see the action in his portion of the track. In camera 2's shot the action turned and was soon moving from right to left on the screen. At this point the infield camera could take over and follow the action all around the back stretch. Just as the horses began to round the far turn, the director had to cut back to camera 1, however, so that the action would be right to left in both shots at the moment of the cut. If the horses had been allowed to round the turn too far, however, a good cut would have been impossible. Whereas the horses would still have been going right to left for the infield camera, camera 1 would have shown them moving from left to right.

At the finish of the race it is usually considered best to hold the camera on the finish line after the winner crosses to show the other horses come in. Of course, this cannot be done with too close a shot, or the following horses will flash through with such a blur that they will be unrecognizable. Sometimes a single shot of the winner is used up to the finish line, and a cut is made to a wider shot as the other horses come through. Too

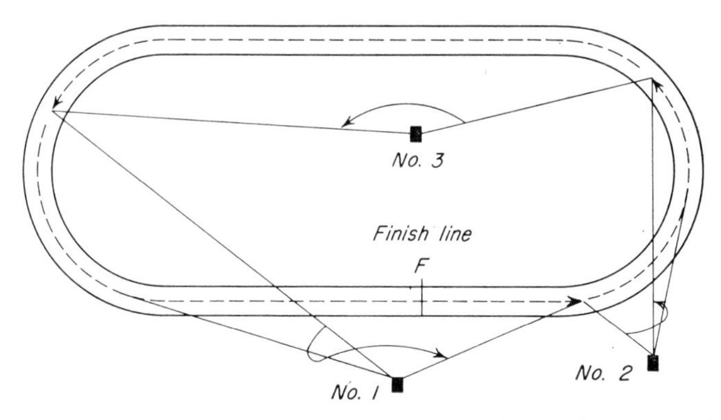

Fig. 20–25. WBKB race-track pickup with camera in the infield. Range of usefulness of each camera is shown.

close a shot on the contest at the finish of the race defeats its own purpose, however, since the important thing is to watch how the horses approach the finish line, and both the horses and the approaching line have to be in the shot for a certain length of time for this to be entirely satisfactory. If there is no contest for first place, often the camera will forget the winner and concentrate on the contest for second place.

A typical cutting routine in race-track pickup can be exemplified by WDSU-TV at the race track in New Orleans (Fig. 20-26). Only two cameras are used; camera 1 is on the clubhouse porch, about 100 feet to the left of the finish line and only half as high as camera 2, which is placed in the press box on the top of the grandstand. Camera 2, with a

25-inch lens, takes the start of a typical race (far side of the track) and carries the horses on around the far turn except for a section of the back stretch, when a group of live oak trees in the infield of this particular track obscures the horses from camera 2; and camera 1, which is lower and can see under the trees, is briefly cut in with a 13-inch lens. Number 1 then changes lenses to a 135-mm and is cut into the sequence as the horses come down the straightaway until they are nearly opposite the

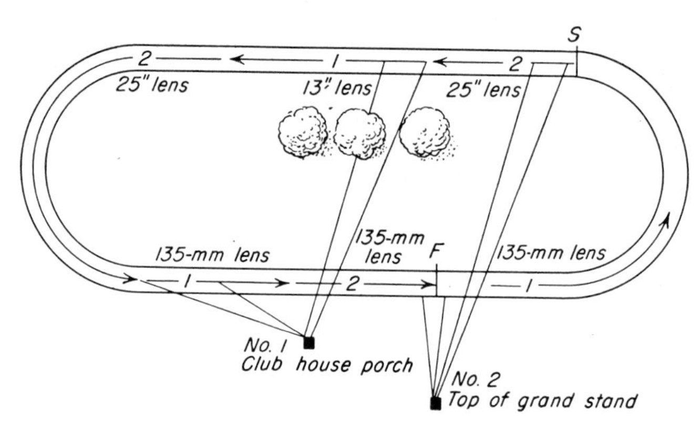

Fig. 20–26. Camera placements for WDSU-TV two-camera pickup at New Orleans track.

camera. Then camera 2, which is closer to the finish line, takes over with the same lens, carries them to the finish line, and holds as they all go through.

FOOTBALL

Football is one of two major sports where an intimate knowledge of the game is a very valuable attribute for both director and cameraman. Some of the new developments in the game of football leave the position of the ball a mystery to all concerned for several moments after the beginning of a play, and the cameraman is often no exception. If he knows more about the game, he can better anticipate the plays and be ready with the right lens or follow the right player more often.

The television director's primary responsibility is to show the audience what they want to see, when they want to see it, and to leave no confusion in their minds about it. The greatest sin a director can commit is to fail to show the audience what they know is happening, what they would be looking at if they were there. Yet this is surprisingly easy to do.

Sometimes it is mere sluggishness; sometimes, lack of a cover shot; sometimes it is a confusion caused by too much cutting.

Most stations use two cameras on football and place them together on the 50-yard line, usually in the press box or up on the roof at the top of the grandstand. A position halfway up the stands is often used, just above an entrance, where there will be no one to jump up suddenly and wave his arms in front of the lens. KTTV once used four cameras on football, two on the press-box roof, and two halfway up the stands, one on each 40-yard line. That was before they had acquired a zoom lens. One camera with a zoom lens can do the work of two at a football game.

The extreme height of most football-stadium press boxes makes the shot down on the field more nearly vertical than horizontal. Often the closest part of the field is more than 300 feet away. The disadvantages of high-angle shooting and long lenses (both mentioned under Wrestling and Boxing) combine to make a pickup from this camera position alone rather uninteresting and undramatic. Don Hallman used three cameras at Briggs Stadium in Detroit, one in the high press box on the 50-yard line, one halfway up the stands on the 25-yard line south, and one only 10 feet above the field placed on the 40-yard line north. Many remote men are convinced that placing cameras higher than 20 or 30 feet (unless no better positions are available) is undesirable. Thirty feet is high enough to see the action separated on the field, so that near players do not block off the view of farther action; higher camera positions serve only to dwarf the players and increase the necessary focal length of the lenses. The camera on the field is a particularly valuable thing from the dramatic point of view. It is only from the low angle that the player really looks impressive; and plays occurring on the near side of the field, especially when they happen to come close to this camera, make the most exciting and dynamic shots in the game.

The use of the camera on the field was improved by WPTZ in Philadelphia when they mounted a camera on a microphone-boom base borrowed for the occasion from the studio (Fig. 20-27). High enough to give the camera an excellent vantage point over the heads of players, linesmen, etc., it interfered with spectator vision and could be used only when the game was not in progress. It could be quickly rolled into place, however, and picked up some excellent shots of the stands and of celebrities in the audience.

The ultimate in field-level coverage is the camera mounted on a jeep. This too had been talked about for many years, but in the 1950 season KTTV in Hollywood actually put the idea into practice. The jeep was converted to a "camera car" by bolting on a channel steel support which extended a foot or so out from the back, on which could be mounted the

Fig. 20–27. WPTZ camera on field mounted on studio mike-boom base.

Fig. 20–28. KTTV camera mounted on jeep.

rotating turret of a studio Sanner camera crane (Fig. 20-28). Although this camera was not used for trucking shots, it could easily keep abreast of the line of scrimmage and a very dramatic low shot down the line was obtained which could be used just before the start of each play.

The jeep camera is practical only where the stadium has a wide track between stands and field and where the stands are high enough so that the camera will not interfere with spectators' view of the game. The jeep ran close to the field, dragging the camera cable behind it. When it turned around, it swung wide and turned toward the field, while the cable was laid back toward the stands out of its way.

The Zoomar lens first began to be used in football and baseball in 1947, and now a zoom lens is considered practically indispensable in covering these sports. The great advantage is freedom from cutting. The moment of the cut is always a moment of confusion, especially if the director isn't too sure where the ball is and has to punch buttons trying to find it. The cameraman with a zoom lens may zoom the lens in or out at any time, without running any risk of confusing the viewer. Even if the cameraman should lose the ball and zoom in on the wrong player, he can always zoom back out to a wider shot and go into a close-up again only when the position of the ball is clear. On a forward pass, the camera can go in for a close-up of the passer as he fades back, stay with him if he decides to run instead, or zoom back out into a wider shot as he passes the ball. Without a zoom lens, either the pass would have to be carried on the same lens, which would mean a very rapid panning with the ball and considerable confusion about where the ball had gone, or a wider shot would be used, with the risks of confusion involved in the cutting. Cameramen must learn, incidentally, to control their initial enthusiasm at handling such a lens and refrain from zooming it at top speed. A smooth and controlled zoom, although a little slow, is much better than a lightning swoop that carries the audience in breathless flight across the field. The one serves only to show the audience what they want to see; the other calls attention to the camera and the viewer's kinesthetic sense.

BASEBALL

By far the most complicated of all the sports, and one of the most difficult to direct in the field of television, is baseball. When things start happening in this sport, they happen so fast that there is no time for instructions to be given. Director and cameramen must have all their moves worked out and rehearsed in advance and must operate together with flawless teamwork. An infield play, for example, batter to shortstop to first, will be over in about 3⅘ seconds. There is no time for anyone to hesitate or wait for instructions. Here more than anywhere else, the director and the cameraman must know the game. It has been said that they are as much a part of the television ball game as the players on the field. They must know what plays are likely to be made, where particular batters will hit the ball, whether or not the pitcher on the mound is good at picking off base runners, whether he makes batters hit pop flies or whether they usually hit into the dirt.

A few top-notch television directors became expert at directing baseball through very intense study of the game. Some of the best baseball directors, however, have been players themselves.

Nowhere else does the slow-witted or excitable director show up to poorer advantage than in baseball. Action happens rapidly, often in many parts of the field, and the director must be quick with his cuts. But more than this, he must be calm. An excitable director is almost worse than none at all. Cameramen have been known to pull their earphones off rather than listen to a lot of inarticulate screaming. Others have reported (and they were baseball cameramen) that they dread working with certain directors but look forward to working with others because they themselves do such a better job.

A brand-new station in Boston with a brand-new crew once found itself obliged to make the pickup of the World Series game for the benefit of what was then the East coast network. There are directors and cameramen in the industry who have been doing baseball for years and are still improving. Few would have wanted their first attempts on the cable. It was inevitable that the Boston station took a roasting in the press. The management wisely refused to reveal the identities of director or cameramen, mentioning rules against "personal publicity." Critics of the same station's baseball coverage today tell a somewhat different story.

Confusion or dullness or both result from poor handling of baseball. If the director plays it safe, sticks to the wide-angle lenses, he won't miss the action so easily; but the players will be so tiny on the screen that the audience will yawn. If, on the other hand, he gets too reckless with the long lenses, he can get caught trying to follow action that is too fast and can confuse the audience by switching without proper orientation. *Variety* complained of claustrophobia on the Boston games: too many close-ups, too slow to pan with the ball, "a monotonous and cramped depiction of a ball game." The baseball director is between two evils. If he is too conservative, the show will be dull; if he is reckless, confusion will be the result. Precise switching, accurate teamwork, quick reaction can do much to make a ball game interesting. But the director must have his cameras in the right places, or his problems are multiplied.

The placement of cameras. About half the stations which televise baseball use two cameras. The other half use three. Some stations have used four or five cameras, but in such cases one was devoted entirely to the commercials. There is no doubt that three cameras are better than two, and those stations using two would probably prefer three if it were economically possible.

The placement of cameras will depend primarily on the design of the particular ball park where the pickups are to be made. Some of the smaller parks have single-tier stands. Some are oriented differently, and the direction of the afternoon light will be a factor in camera placement. In most ball parks, a press box is already available where space can usually be found for one or two television cameras, and the position of this press box will determine the kind of shots the camera can get. In some cases special platforms have been built for the cameras; WPTZ and WEWS have both built crow's nests underneath the upper stands, to place the camera at the best height (Fig. 20-29).

Fig. 20–29. WPTZ's camera 1 at Shibe Park, Philadelphia, in cage under upper stands.

The cover shot. As a general rule the first camera is placed where it will give the best "cover shot." This is the basic shot of the ball game, and the greater part of the load rests on this camera. A director will usually have this shot on the screen during more than half the total time of the game. The cover shot will generally include the pitcher and the batter-catcher-and-umpire trio at the plate. It is used for almost every pitch and can quickly become a pan shot into the outfield in case of a hit. In the case of an infield hit, many directors use no other shot and simply pan the camera with the ball as it is picked up and thrown to first. If a zoom lens is used, the cameraman may zoom in to a closer shot either on the player who nails the ball or on the play at first. Sometimes he will do both, zooming back slightly to a wider angle as the throw is made to the first baseman. The best cover shot is obtained within a rather narrow range of camera positions. It must be somewhere behind home plate and not too high above the ground.

The cover shot must be taken by a camera behind home plate, or it will be impossible to include both pitcher and batter in the same shot. To be sure, a wide-angle shot from the side of the ball park would show them both, but they would look like ants. In case of a hit, a camera behind home plate does not have to pan as far to follow the ball to the outfield as a camera on either side line would have to do. Figure 20-30

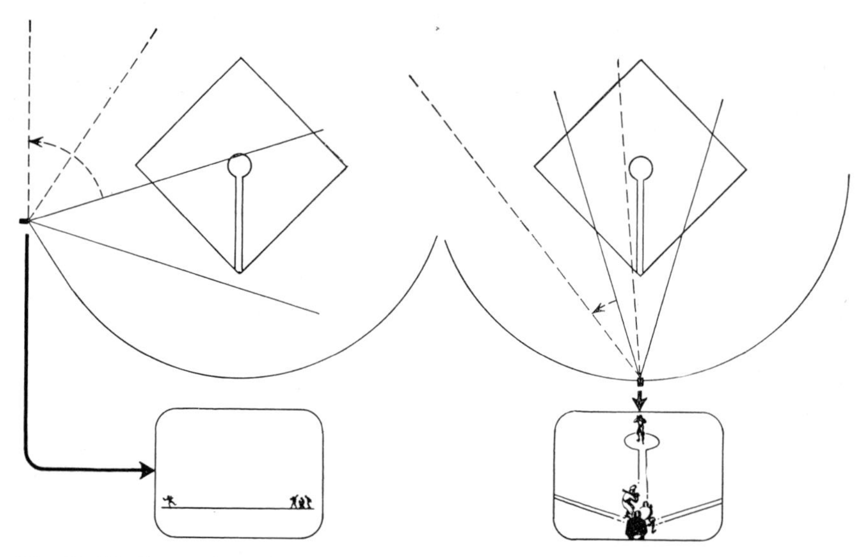

Fig. 20–30. Cover shot taken from third base compared with cover shot taken from behind home plate.

compares the arc in which a camera behind home plate would have to pan to follow the ball to left field with the amount of panning a camera at third base would have to do.

The height of the cover camera is important also. If the camera is too low, there is too little separation between near and far parts of the field, foreground players may obscure the action behind them, and the audience does not get a good view of the game. If the camera is placed too high, there is so much separation that a very wide-angle shot must be used to bring both batter and pitcher into the field of the lens. Again the players are too small in the shot. The angle of elevation is the important thing, as Fig. 20-31 indicates. If the stands are far back from the plate, a higher camera position will give the same shot except that a longer lens is used. Of course, too long a lens from a low position behind the palte will tend to contract the distance between pitcher and catcher, and the effect will be ludicrous. If the camera is 50 feet back from the plate, it should be about 20 feet high. If it is as far as 75 feet from the plate, it can be as high as 30 feet without making the use of too wide a lens necessary. There is great variation in the positioning of this camera, however, owing to conditions peculiar to each park. Few stations say they are entirely satisfied that their cover camera is in the ideal position.

In some cases a camera behind the plate is impossible. The foul net may interfere. If the camera can be placed within a few inches of the net, the mesh will be so far out of focus that it will not show in the shot. In some ball parks, stations have installed sheets of unbreakable "herculite" glass in front of the cameras when they are so placed. In a single-tier stand the only two choices of camera position may be at the front of the stands, almost at ground level, or on the top of the grandstand roof,

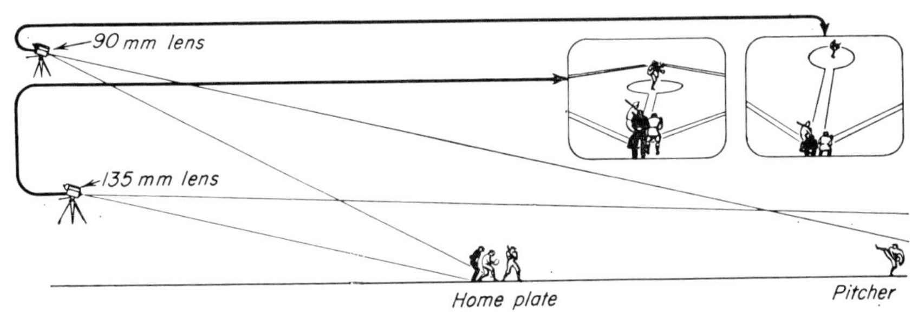

Fig. 20–31. Effect of camera height on cover shot.

usually more than 75 feet high, neither of which is usable. In cases where the cover shot must be taken by a camera on the third- or first-base line, the director may often give up trying to show both batter and pitcher in one shot and must use two shots for every pitch, a close-up of the pitcher for the windup and delivery, and a shot of batter, catcher, and umpire as the ball reaches the plate.

Recently the use of a camera located in the center-field stands with a very long lens (90- to 100-inch) has been occasionally seen. This provides a shot of pitcher, batter, and catcher over the pitcher's shoulder. While the distant perspective makes the depth between mound and plate look unnaturally short, it provides a very striking shot.

An interesting variation on the standard behind-the-plate cover shot was in use for several seasons by KSTP in Minneapolis. The ball park was small, a factor which made for better coverage because the cameras could be closer to the action and shorter focal-length lenses could be used. The cover camera in this setup was operated without a cameraman. It was placed behind home plate, about shoulder height, peering through a small hole in the fence. It was said to give a sensational shot, showing the pitch almost from the batter's point of view (subjective camera). It was even reported that one could see the ball break in a curve. Keeping the camera on one shot all afternoon had a tendency to burn the picture permanently into the tube, but the crew were always able to erase the image afterward. With no cameraman to pan the camera, this shot could not be used to follow a hit unless it should go directly into center field.

The second camera. The placement of the second camera is disputed. Some believe it should be widely separated from the first so that it can get a different angle on the action. If it is placed near first base, for example, where most of the action in a ball game occurs, it can get good shots of the plays without having to employ too long a lens. Some directors believe that this camera should be placed on a line with third and home so that it can cover action along this base line.

The majority opinion, however, favors keeping the two cameras together, either side by side or one above the other so that they both get the same angle on the field. This makes cutting easier on the audience. Switching cameras is a necessary evil, because during the moment following the switch the viewer must reorient himself to his new point of view. If the shot is from a different angle, it takes him longer to grasp its meaning. He may mistake one player for another or third base for second, for example. This period of confusion may last only a fraction of a second, but it is enough to lose a fast play.

If the second camera is placed next to the first, it can also be used for a cover camera in case of failure of the first (a rare occurrence, but something that the sponsor will consider). If camera 2 is placed directly *above* the cover camera, it will probably be most useful. The setup that WPTZ has used at Shibe Park in Philadelphia with such good results is of this type, one camera low and one camera high directly above it (Fig. 20-32*b*).

The third camera. The same considerations apply when a third camera is placed in the park. Most stations will place it with one of the other cameras or with both of them if these two are together. Many will use three cameras behind home plate at the front of the upper-tier stands, no farther separated than the extension of the first-base line on one side and the extension of the third-base line on the other. The third camera, placed in line with home and first, will be able to get certain shots, such as a front close-up of a left-handed hitter, while the other two cameras can show only his back. It can look down into the first-base dugout and show the scramble for foul balls on that side of the field.

If all three cameras are not behind the plate, they will be placed either between home and first or between home and third. Only rarely is a camera placed beyond first or third base. In general, it can be said that if three cameras are placed along the third- or first-base line, they will not be spread beyond a position directly behind home plate. This will keep them all on the same side of the pitcher-batter line. A poor choice was an early method used by WLW-C in Columbus, which placed one of two cameras opposite first base and the other about halfway down the third-base line. Although the author received no comment on the pickup which this station turned in, it is his guess that the game was pretty hard to follow. From neither of these camera positions is a good

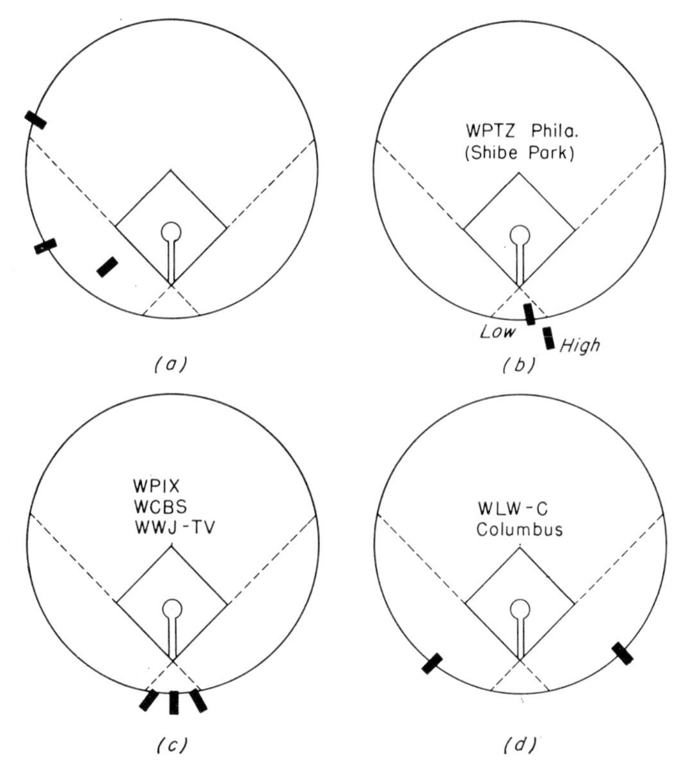

Fig. 20–32. Several methods of placing cameras, used experimentally in the first few years of televised baseball.

cover shot possible; so the director probably tried to cut from pitcher to batter on every pitch. Because of the reverse angle, however, both pitcher and batter would be facing to the same side of the screen, and runners on either the first- or third-base lines would change screen direction with each cut (Fig. 20-32*d*).

Some of the stations have placed their third camera down on ground level, either next to the third-base dugout, as in the case of WBKB, or next to the first-base dugout like WOR-TV in New York. When a fourth camera is available, one has been placed at each dugout. This low angle is very valuable from the dramatic standpoint and puts a punch into the game which no other shot can do. The ground-level camera gives the best possible angle on the batter as he steps up to the plate. From the low angle he is silhouetted against the stands, his expression is clearly visible, and the shot may even be used occasionally to show him swinging at the ball. For this purpose the position near the first-base dugout is best, since most batters are right-handed.

The 40-inch reflector lens is often used on a camera in this position to provide a big close-up of the batter's face. This camera may also be

Fig. 20–33. Two CBS cameras cover the play at Ebbets Field from behind home plate. An early photo, this picture shows the cameras in use without electronic view finders.

used on a close-up of the pitcher and on action on the bases when necessary and is particularly valuable for close-ups of nearby players, team managers, coaches, and action on the near side of the field. WBKB once used a mirror in front of their camera to reflect an image of the players in the nearby dugout, although off-guard shots of the players in relaxed moments were not always flattering to the team involved. This camera was also mounted on a Ritter dentist-chair lift for quick adjustment of height. After it was found that the most dramatic shot was taken from ground level, a hole was dug in the ground for the cameraman to stand in, a practical measure except in rainy weather, when the cameraman stood ankle-deep in water and cursed the whole idea.

Other cover shots. An important consideration in the placement of cameras is the possibility of obtaining cover shots showing both ends of an action, or two or more actions which happen in quick succession, without the need of switching cameras. The standard cover shot is valuable, for example, because both the pitch and the swing, and often the flight of the ball as well, can be covered without cutting.

A camera behind third base can get a good shot across the diamond with the pitcher in the foreground and the runner leading off base in the background. When there is a man on first who likes to steal, the pitcher's windup may develop into a pitch to the batter or he may fire the ball to the first baseman. At the very last moment in the delivery, after which the pitcher cannot change his mind and throw to first, the runner is off. It enhances the drama of the situation greatly if both pitcher and runner can be shown simultaneously on the screen. Thus if the director has a camera behind third, he can cover both ends of this situation, and the action which may result, without cutting. A camera placed beyond first base and shooting toward third can obtain this same kind of shot, with the runner in the foreground and the pitcher in the distance. The only other way to show both the pitcher winding up and the runner trying to rattle him is to use two cameras in a split-screen shot. To include both the pitcher and first base, a shot from any other position in the park would have to be so wide that the players would be too small to recognize.

Switching sequences. Two schools of thought govern baseball directing. One favors the cut; the other opposes it. A simple infield play (pitcher to batter to shortstop to first) could be covered in one shot or in two or even three separate shots. Many directors will do it with one shot, usually with a Zoomar lens, at least during daytime games. Most directors pan with the ball on their basic cover shot and cut to a closer lens only for the play at first. Other directors do it with three takes, the cover shot to show the hit, a close-up on the shortstop throwing to first, and a close-up on first, for the play. Remember, the time necessary for a runner to cover the distance from home to first is only $3\frac{4}{5}$ seconds. These cuts have to be very quick.

In the case of an outfield play, the same thing holds true. The cover shot which is taken with a Zoomar lens can pan out to the outfield with the ball and zoom into a fairly big close-up of the fielder going for it. Without the Zoomar, the usual routine is to cover the fielder with the second camera and a very long lens (17 to 20 inches) and cut to a close-up of the catch as soon as it is evident which player will have the ball.

In panning with the ball, it has been found impossible to keep it visible throughout the pan, except with the best luck; and any attempt to follow it up in the air and back down will result only in a blurred pan in which nothing can be seen at all. The cameraman usually pans out to the section of the field where the ball is going, and the next time the ball is seen is just before it enters the fielder's glove.

As soon as the ball is fielded and thrown back in, the field of view must again widen. The Zoomar will do this smoothly, concentrating again on a close-up of whatever play should result. Lacking the Zoomar, the director may cut back for the throw-in to his cover camera with the original lens and expect the second camera to make a quick switch of lenses and whip down to the base for a close-up of the play.

When there are men on base, this situation is more complicated and the advantage of having a third camera is quickly felt. If there is a man on first, for example, a possible play at second is indicated and perhaps a relay to first for a double play. In such a case the third camera will be instructed to follow the runner, while the other two cameras cover the play at first in the regular manner. If there is more than one man on base, the play is usually made on the more advanced runner and the third camera will concentrate on him. Under most conditions the director will keep his cameras on the ball at all times; but when there are advanced runners likely to score, he may cut away from the fielder and the throw-in to show a runner rounding third or crossing the plate. That is certainly what the observer at the game would do. It may be that there is room for more cutting back and forth at moments such as this, provided that the viewer is kept properly oriented.

A common problem is the situation where a runner is taking a lead off first base. One solution to this problem involved matting out a small area in the upper corner of the shot of the pitcher, and inserting a round image from the second camera showing the runner on first. (For details on the technique of matting see Chap. 12.) This problem was also solved by off-setting the turrets on both cameras, so that the picture was evenly divided down the middle with pitcher on one side and runner on the other. When electronic split screen was available this solution was generally preferred.

SPECIAL EVENTS

The wedding of Princess Margaret of England to Antony Armstrong-Jones was an event which so captured the interest of the world that it merited elaborate remote coverage. Both the BBC and the ITA covered it; the program of the former was fed to the Eurovision network and seen live in sixteen European countries. It was taped by the three American networks and the Canadian Broadcasting Corporation at the London Airport, whence it was flown quickly back across the Atlantic in time to be aired on the evening of the very day on which the events took place. The program was sent by kinescope recording to such distant points as Australia, Nigeria, and Hong Kong. While not the most significant event of our times, it is representative of the kind of international television which will be increasingly common.

Twelve foreign commentators seated at Broadcasting House before twelve picture monitors translated the proceedings for separate audio feeds to each country. The picture originated, of course, in the English 405-line standard and had to be converted to 525 lines for North America, 819 lines for France, and 625 lines for the rest of the continent, a problem faced in doing any broadcast over the Eurovision network.

To cover this complex special event, it was necessary for the BBC to bring into London its mobile units from its Scottish, West, Welsh, and North Regions. A total of 25 cameras were involved.

The first three cameras centered about Buckingham Palace, one on the roof of the palace, looking down the Mall, the other two on the Victoria Memorial opposite the palace, to cover the bridegroom's departure for the Abbey and the couple's return after the wedding.

The next three were stationed in the vicinity of Clarence House, where the bride would leave for the ceremony. A key point on both the outward and return journeys was Horse Guard's Parade and Horse Guard's Arch, and four cameras were deployed in this area. Five cameras were placed outside in the vicinity of the Abbey, and six within.

A total of fourteen video tape recorders were in use on this broadcast, most of them in mobile vans parked at the London Airport and engaged in recording tapes to be flown immediately to America. The BBC also recorded the picture on 16- and 35-mm film and on video tape.

In studying Fig. 20-34, it is important to note the "emergency" and "reserve" equipment. It is good practice in television production to provide duplicate and sometimes triplicate equipment at every step of the way. For example (not shown on the chart), the central control room was connected by "Omnibus" intercom with all the mobile control rooms at once; in addition, there was a separate intercom to each, as well as an open phone line at each point. Examples shown on the chart include a double feed from each mobile unit, one to the switching center at Broadcasting House and a second to an emergency switching center set up by General Post Office. Both a cable and a radio link were maintained from Broadcasting House to the London Airport (Skyport Exchange). A reserve standards convertor and video-tape machine are shown at the top. If the Television Centre convertor should fail, Kingswood Warren, picking the picture off the air from the London transmitter, would be converting it to American standards and feeding it via Broadcasting House to Television Centre, where it would be ready if needed and could be switched immediately onto the line. Or if, through power failure, Television Centre should fail completely, this Kingswood Warren feed

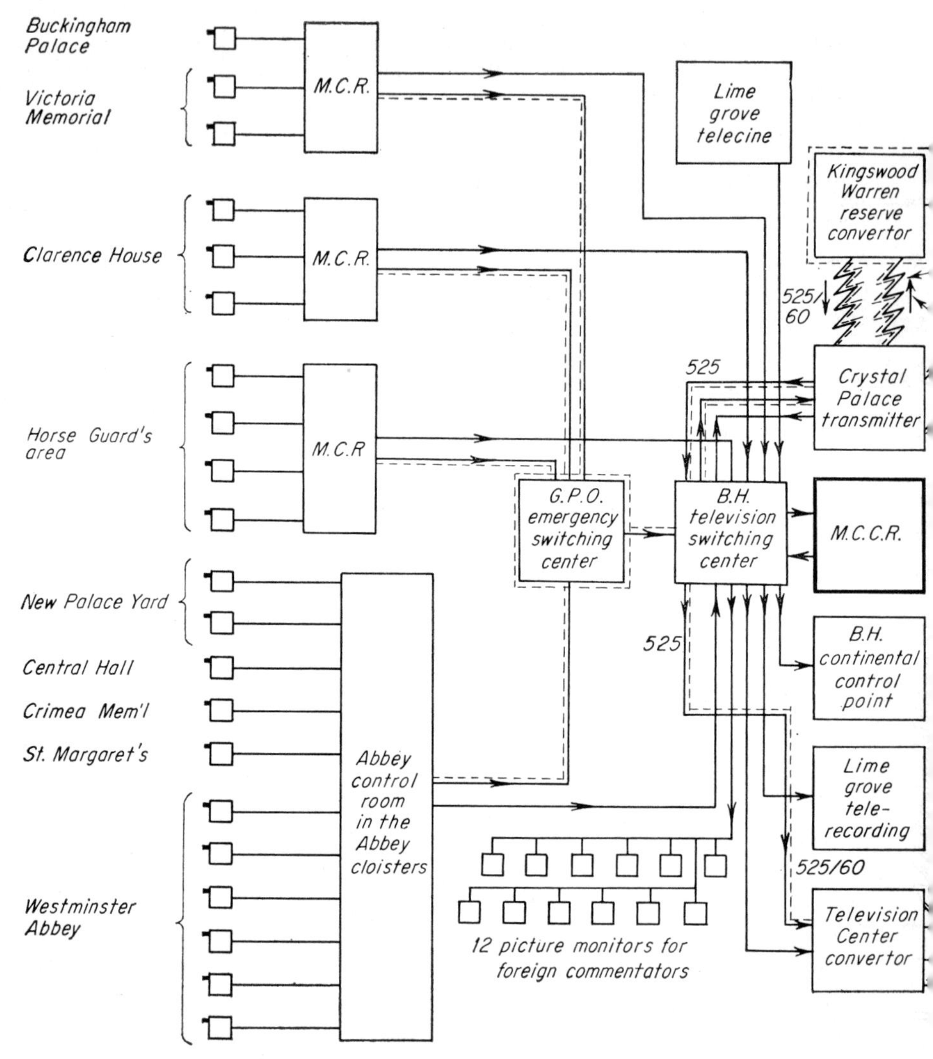

Fig. 20–34. Simplified schematic of BBC arrangements fo

could be switched at the Crystal Palace transmitter to go directly to the airport via the radio link.

THE POLITICAL CONVENTIONS

Among the most complex remote pickups regularly attempted is the coverage of the American political conventions. All-out competition between the networks and several local independent outlets as well

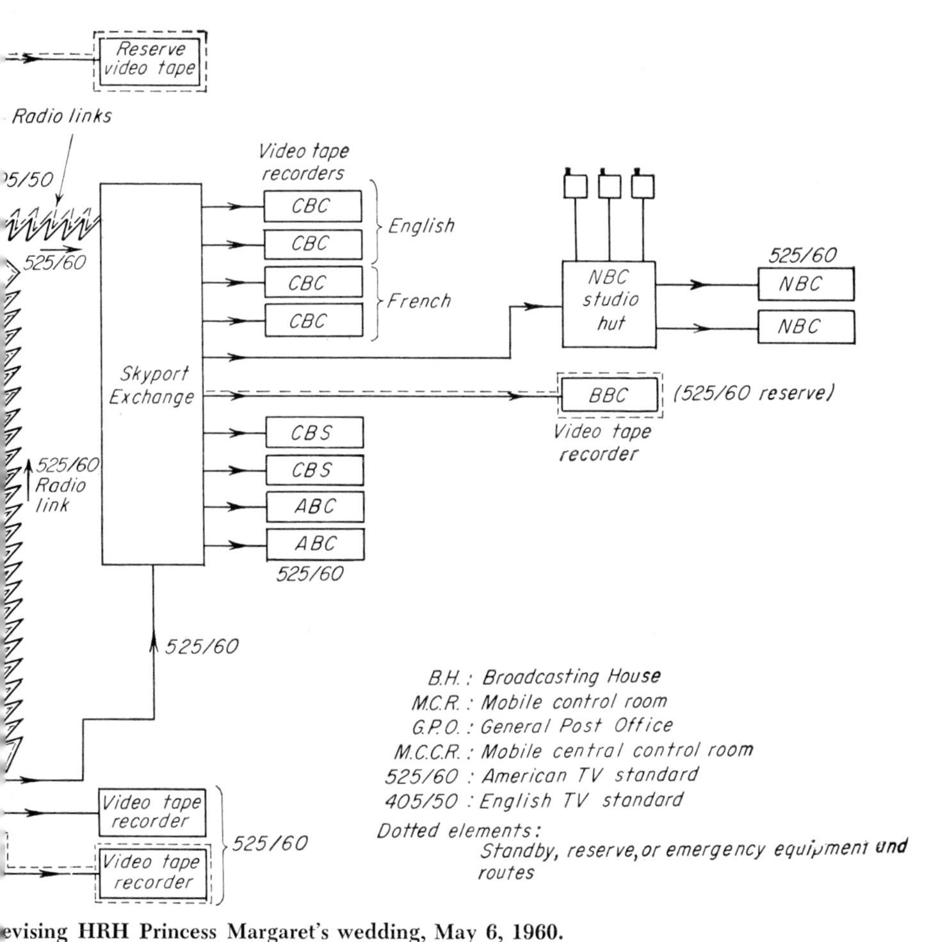

evising HRH Princess Margaret's wedding, May 6, 1960.

results in a total of close to one hundred cameras in almost simultaneous operation.

The coverage of the speeches and other activities on the convention floor is done on a pool basis. This is a standard procedure at many events, not only desirable from an efficiency standpoint, but often required by the management of the event because of limited camera placement space. When three or four organizations want coverage from as many as five or ten camera positions, it can become impossible to accommodate them.

At a convention there will be a pool control room, where directors from each of the networks will alternate in handling the seven or more cameras comprising the pool coverage. At the same time each of the networks will have its own master control room in which its own director will integrate

Fig. 20–35. Main BBC control center for the royal wedding. (*a*) Outside Broadcasts van outside Broadcasting House. (*b*) Peter Dimmock, head of Outside Broadcasts, at control desk with two assistants. (*c*) Mr. Dimmock faces an array of 10 monitors displaying the various inputs and outputs to the switching center. Pickup from the Tower Bridge (top center monitor) does not show on the chart. The purpose of this was to show the royal yacht leaving for the honeymoon.

its own program sources, using the pool coverage at his discretion as it comes from the pool director. The network director would have such program sources as his own commentators at the "anchor desk" or booth overlooking the convention floor, interviews with personalities originating in a small studio off the convention floor, interviews with people on the floor either covered by extremely long lenses from high in the auditorium (in some cases lenses as long as 100 inches have been used) or picked up by small roving wireless cameras. Arrivals and departures of key figures are often covered by camera after camera almost every foot of the way from distant arriving motorcade, through entry halls, pressing crowds, up stairways, to final arrival at the speaker's rostrum. Competition is so keen that the value of all such coverage is measured in terms of the ability

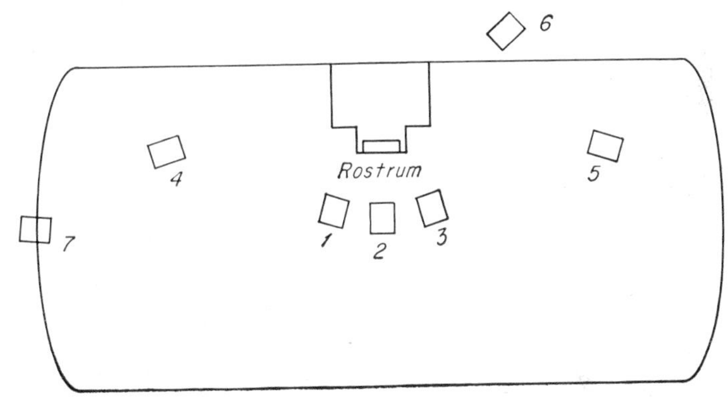

Fig. 20–36. Diagram of camera positions used in pool coverage at the 1960 Democratic convention. 1, 2, and 3: basic front shots. 4 and 5: side angles. 6: high-angle over-the-shoulder position. 7: high-angle end view for wide-angle establishing shot.

Fig. 20–37. Cadillac self-contained mobile unit used by NBC to cover a presidential arrival. Both camera and microwave transmitter are mounted on circular track and may be rolled around the periphery of each operating well to point in any direction.

to keep one's share of the audience. If the candidate is en route somewhere, and further action is suspended until he arrives there, the station which is showing him and his progress on the screen will keep its audience, and any station which may be so unlucky as not to show

Fig. 20–38. (*a*) **Interior of sports arena at start of session. Circled are the three major camera positions surrounding podium (arrow). At top of picture large screen TV projection can be seen.** (*b*) **Mobile camera outside sports arena mounted on Fisher mike-boom base.** (*c*) **CBS cameraman in blimp picks up aerial view of Los Angeles sports arena during 1960 Democratic convention.**

him will find its viewers sampling other channels to see what the competition is doing.

To cover the various arrivals at and departures from the major scenes of action, each network will employ two or more mobile units which are completely mobile; that is, they are self-contained and can generate power and transmit signal while traveling. In addition, each network establishes a control point, with half a dozen cameras, in the headquarters hotel.

The hotel, generally a remnant of pre-electronic era construction, becomes a great tangle of wires hanging in stairwells, running along corridors, looping from window to window, and otherwise festooning the outside of the building. Crews try to be so well organized that they can cover any point in the hotel within five minutes of notification.

Wireless audio communication had become such a commonplace by the 1960 convention that even the political managers themselves were

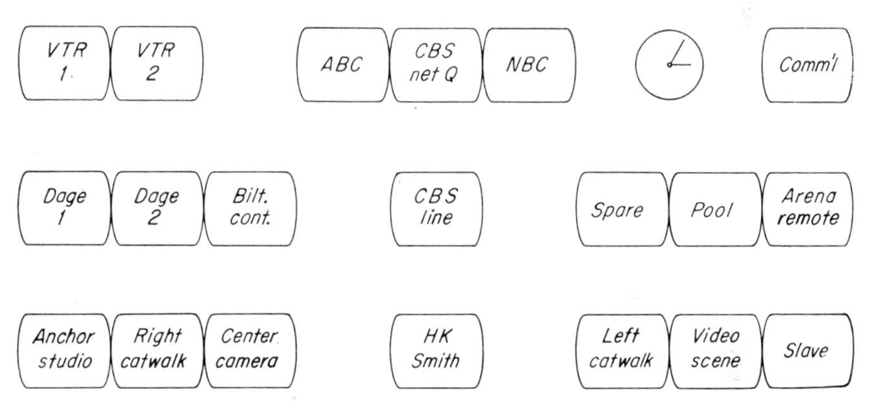

Fig. 20–39. Diagram of CBS control-room monitor display. From the upper left: two channels for tape playback; the three networks together so CBS could be instantly compared with the competition; a monitor representing the output of a special commercial studio and control room. Second row: two Dage wireless camera channels; the output of the control room at the Biltmore; the main program line; a spare; the pool coverage; a remote unit near the arena. Bottom row: one of the cameras in the anchor studio (Walter Cronkheit and Ed Murrow); four separate cameras in odd places in the arena, with the one in the center on commentator H. K. Smith; far right, two cameras involving the VideoScene effect (see page 283). (This effect was used constantly, putting the view of the arena and the rostrum in a window behind the commentator's desk in the anchor studio. In the studio, the window was backed by a blue-lighted cyclorama.)

keeping in constant touch with all staff members by transistorized walkie-talkie equipment. It was estimated that more than fifty simultaneous audio transmissions were crisscrossing the convention hall, causing much confusion at first because of overlapping frequencies. More than once an NBC commentator was heard over the CBS transmission, and vice versa. Fifteen wireless cameras were in use in 1960, nine in the convention hall and six at the headquarters hotel.

NBC instituted a new control-room method during the 1960 conventions which proved very valuable. A TV director normally has two basic things to concern himself with: the program on the air with the immediate

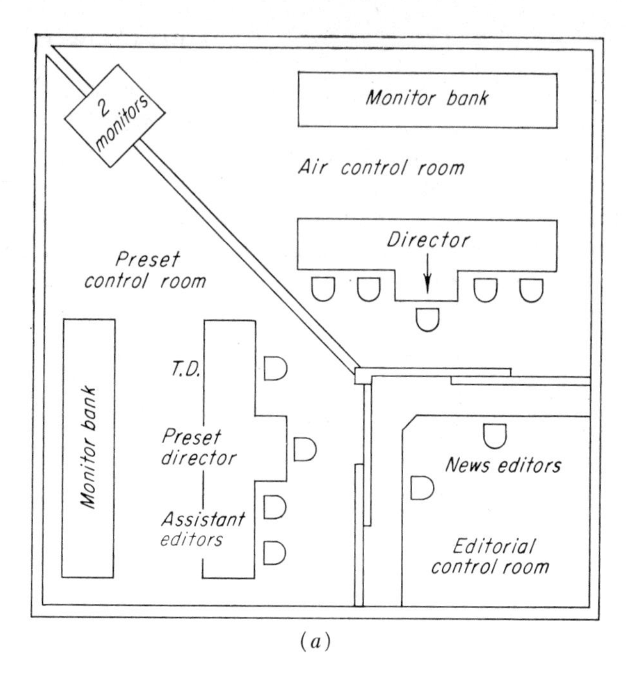

(a)

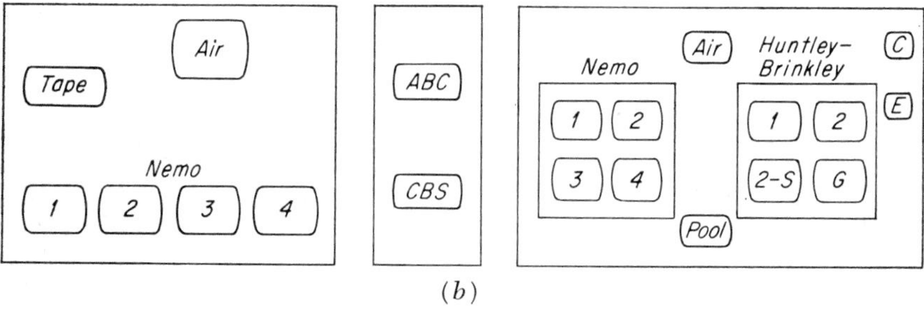

(b)

Monitor	Nemo 1	Nemo 2	Nemo 3	Nemo 4
Sources: Priority 1	Long lens 1 High reach	Long lens 2 Exterior	Wireless cam 1 Caucus roof	Wireless cam 2 Fork lift
Priority 2	Open Pram	Open H.Q. hotel	Burbank Cadillac	Mobile 1 Mobile 2

(c)

Fig. 20–40. (*a*) **Plan of the NBC three-part control room used at the 1960 political conventions.** (*b*) **Layout of the monitors in NBC three-part control room used at the 1960 political conventions. Left: monitor bank in preset control room. Center: two monitors visible to both control rooms showing output of competing networks. Right: monitor bank in air control room. Huntley-Brinkley monitors included cameras 1 and 2 from reverse angles, each favoring one of the commentators; a third camera, able to show both in a two-shot (2-S); and a fourth camera source for studio graphics (G). Top right: a monitor to preview the commercial studio (C), and below this an effects preview monitor (E).** (*c*) **Chart showing sources available to the preset director for each of the four nemo monitors. Each had four inputs, two in each of two priority groups.**

cameras which are in use and the setting up of the next camera or scene which will be needed. Usually an assistant director can be used to relieve the director of this second aspect of his work. In this case an entire control room and crew were so employed.

The two control rooms were placed in an L-shape, and in the corner of the L, with visual and verbal communication into each control room, were placed the executive news directors, the men whose decision it was whether to interrupt a speech for an interview with another politician or to stick to the speech, and so forth. Sixteen different sources of picture and sound could be previewed and readied on four preset monitors in the first control room. These four monitors were duplicated in the main control room where the air director could refer to them as preview monitors when he got the word to put a certain thing on the air. Thus neither the air director nor anyone else in the air control room had to be concerned with talking with cameramen, production assistants, or commentators in lining up special interviews, remote pickups, or playback of previously taped segments.

21

Color Television

Color television has been slow to get under way throughout the world. During the early 1940s it was felt by many that television broadcast standards should include color from the start, but indecision concerning the merits of several competing technical systems led to a standardization on black and white initially and a long period of official indecision ending in 1950 with the FCC decision to standardize on the field-sequential method of color TV. This was the so-called CBS whirling-disk method, requiring a series of filters to be moved in front of the camera and a similar series of three filters, constituting the three primary colors, to move over the face of the receiving tube in exact synchrony. Thus a picture was taken through a red filter, and at the receiver viewed through a red filter; a fraction of a second later the same procedure followed with green, and then with blue. This method was not accepted by the United States television industry, and in 1953 the FCC changed the color TV standards to the NTSC (National Television Systems Committee) method. Very much more complicated than the field-sequential, the new method had the prime advantage of compatibility (NTSC color broadcasts could be received in black and white on standard black-and-white receivers). NTSC receivers were placed on the market and began to sell at a slowly increasing rate.

Regular programs in color were broadcast by the networks, and soon 20 per cent of the independent stations in the country had installed minimal equipment to at least broadcast the network color programs, slides or film, while 7 per cent installed live cameras so they could originate local color programs. At the date of writing the future of color TV is uncertain. There has been some backtracking. Improved methods of color pickup or reception may make their appearance: it is certain that full public acceptance waits for a rise in the quality and a reduction in the price of the color receivers.

What will be said about the problems of color TV in this chapter applies particularly to the NTSC system, and yet in general will hold good for whatever color system may be encountered. The introduction of color motion pictures required much the same adjustments on the part of motion-picture technicians and production people as TV people are making today.

Most color TV production problems are the same as those of black and white. It is primarily in lighting, in the painting of sets and visuals, and in the make-up and costuming of performers that new problems are encountered. Everything which can be done in black and white can be done in color—even elaborate electronic matte effects—as long as the more stringent limitations of the color medium are understood. Crew and personnel in the color studio are the same as in black-and-white production, except that video adjustments are very complex and it is always necessary to have one video man on each camera-control unit, whereas in black and white one video man is often used to ride video on two or more cameras.

The fact that a color broadcast must also be received in black and white (by the great majority of the set owners) must not be forgotten. This raises no new production problems, however. The major point is that adjacent colors which contrast pleasingly to the eye or the color camera must also have sufficient *tonal* contrast to register as separate tones on the gray scale. Since program and preview monitors in a color control room are generally duplicated with black-and-white monitors showing the same picture, it is easy for the production staff to check the effectiveness of a program in both media.

WHAT IS COLOR HARMONY?

Production people beginning to work in color for the first time may justifiably exhibit marked eagerness to learn the rules of color harmony. Much thought and experimentation have gone into this subject. Elaborate systems of classification of colors have been devised, such as the famous Munsell and Ostwald systems, and scientific methods of choosing pairs and triads and larger groups of colors have been devised. However, most creative artists have always preferred to flout rules and scientific methods and choose their color harmonies by feel or instinct. Having the right people with the right feel and instincts is undoubtedly the best technique for achieving color harmony. Certainly poor taste in the use of color can lead to gaudiness, even color clashes where one color vibrates against another. Color poorly used can be a dividing rather than a unifying influence, and too compelling a use of color in the wrong places can distract from elements in the scene which should have emphasis. Most TV production people have had some occasion to work with color in other fields, and for those who have not, there is an extensive literature on the subject.

THE TECHNICAL LIMITATIONS OF COLOR TV

The color camera is more limited even than the monochrome in the range of tones it will accept and correctly reproduce between black and white. This is true also of color film compared with black-and-white film.

Whereas in black-and-white television a light gray reflecting over 70 per cent of the light that falls on it registers as white, in color every tone down to a 60 per cent reflectance gray registers as white. Thus the tints of all colors (pastel shades—the hue mixed with white) generally look lighter than expected.

Hues usually reproduce pretty much as they look to the eye. One of the most difficult things to reproduce, however, is a plain gray surface. Minor defects and misadjustments turn the gray into a color of one sort or another.

Whereas it is not possible for the home viewer to know what colors were painted on sets and props and thus judge the faithfulness of color reproduction, when human flesh appears on the scene an immediate judgment can be made by anyone. Thus it is concluded that the flesh tone (reflectance 35 to 40 per cent) is the most important tone in color television. It is for this reason that for many years each CBS color program started, if possible, with a close-up of a face. This enabled viewers to adjust their color sets until the skin tone reproduced to their satisfaction. Then, theoretically, the rest of the tones and colors would reproduce well.

The reaction of color television to extreme contrasts appears to remove a well-known limitation in black-and-white operation. Shiny objects are avoided in black and white because they create black halos, streaking, or other spurious effects within the image-orthicon tube. With the color camera, however, proper color balance requires a different method of operation of the image-orthicon tube (highlights are run below the knee of the curve, technically speaking), reduction of halo is a happy by-product, and shiny objects are reproduced quite naturally.

Many lighting directors in black-and-white studios balance key versus fill and back light by eye, and this practice is also followed in color. The use of a photometer or other light meter, while common, is rarely considered mandatory.

SCENERY FOR THE COLOR STUDIO

It has been found generally that the color camera is more critical of scene-painting techniques than the black-and-white. Painted moldings, shadows, etc., are often revealed to be two-dimensional by the color camera, and actual three-dimensional construction has had to be relied on to a large extent.

The use of colored light will be discussed presently, but in connection with scenery it should be observed that the colors of a scene are much better achieved by painting them onto the settings than by relying on the use of colored light. The reason is, of course, that the colored light will distort the skin tones of any performers working under it, and so must be avoided where it may touch the actors (except, of course, for special effects).

Designers have found that large backings or other areas of solid color generally reproduce badly, the color being uneven, and they have learned to break up such areas wherever possible.

Experimentation with glossy- versus matte-surface paints has shown that in color as in black and white, the matte surface is best. Matte paints and velour rather than shiny fabrics give better color reproduction.

Some stations have wanted to standardize on their color paints, just as they have calibrated paints for black and white according to the gray scale. This involves, then, a simplification of the color palette, which in itself is an aid in choosing color and tonal combinations. One station has done this as follows: Ten hues were chosen and provided in their most saturated form. Then each hue was mixed with white in varying quantities to make three "tints," mixed with black to form two "tones," and mixed with black and white together to form one grayed "shade." Each hue with its six variations then brought the total palette to 70 individual colors which were ready-mixed and kept handy for use.

The question of when a system is an aid and when it becomes an end in itself naturally arises here. It can be pointed out that in terms of a six-tone gray scale, certain hues such as yellow fall in the high values to begin with, and the addition of three "tints" of yellow would very likely create several light yellows which would be indistinguishable from each other; whereas the second "tones" of blue or red, for example, might easily be too close to the tone of black to register separately. This objection could be easily overcome by varying the number of "tints" or "tones" according to the gray-scale value of the pure hue. The point is that a standard series of paints can be prepared and pretested, and its effectiveness in both the color-TV picture and the black-and-white picture can be predicted without the need for constant uncertainty and experiment.

COSTUMES AND MAKE-UP FOR COLOR

In the area of costuming, it has been found that stage costumes, although usable on black-and-white television, often turn out to be too light or too contrasty for the narrower contrast range of color. Accordingly, costume people find that much more designing of special costumes is necessary for color.

Advice from the make-up department is usually fairly simple: just use less make-up than you would in black and white. Women with good, light complexions need almost no make-up at all. Natural red lips, for example, are often lightened rather than emphasized with lipstick, and men's lips must be paled out entirely for fear too red a color will come through. When people with considerably different complexion casts are to play in tight shots together, as, for example, a swarthy man and a very light-skinned girl, the color system may exaggerate the difference between them, and make-up must be used to lighten the darker-skinned person, darken the lighter one, or both.

LIGHTING FOR COLOR

In the area of TV lighting, color causes considerable change in technique from standard practice in black and white. To begin with, more light is necessary. This is again because of the three-tube camera. The light entering a color TV camera is divided up according to the three primary colors and approximately one-third of the entering light goes to each tube. Thus there must be three times as much light to begin with in order for each tube to end up with the same amount it would receive if it were in the camera alone. Actually absorption and reflection losses within the complex optical system and a difference in method of video operation bring this requirement up to something more like four or five times the light a black-and-white camera would require. Thus it is generally considered that 400 foot-candles of illumination are required, at least on the actors, if the cameras are to record an acceptable skin color. Some studios have used 500 foot-candles.

COLOR TEMPERATURE

One quality of light becomes important in color television which is of little matter in black and white, and this is its color temperature. To define this complex concept in a very simple and inaccurate way, one might say that color temperature is a measure of the color of white light. There are many colors of light which look white to the eye, but color film and color television are very sensitive to subtle differences between one white light and the next. We are all pretty familiar with the changing colors of daylight and have probably had the experience of taking color pictures less than an hour before sunset, and then been surprised to see how red all the faces appeared. The color temperature of the light had changed (lowered) as the sun lowered in the sky until it had exceeded the range for which the film was balanced.

Light from incandescent lamps, for example, is 3200° Kelvin color temperature, whereas the light from a blue sky at midday is around

Fig. 21–1. At least four times as much light is needed for NTSC color TV, necessitating the use of many 5,000-watt floods and spots and much flat lighting. The large floods are not lighted above because of the small playing area. Two senior (5-kilowatt) spots, one from each side, give essentially flat front light. Modeling is achieved by other seniors used as kicker and back light (this is revealed by the shadows of the desk). (Photo courtesy of NBC.)

5000° Kelvin. Color films are made in indoor and outdoor types, each balanced for the light it will receive. The color TV camera too may be balanced for either indoor or outdoor use, but cannot be used interchangeably without readjustment.

The reason that this quality of light is defined in terms of degrees of temperature is as follows: the standard against which light is compared and measured is a theoretical filament or radiating body. To measure the color of a white light one would heat this theoretical "black body" until it glowed with the same color of light as the unknown light being measured. The temperature to which it must be heated will be lower if it must glow red hot and give off a reddish light, higher if it must glow white hot, and highest of all if it must glow blue like the light from the open sky.

The Kelvin temperature scale starts at absolute zero, and is thus 273° higher in reading than the centigrade scale. It does not mean, in the case of a 3200°K incandescent light, that the filament of the bulb is operating at that actual temperature. It means that a perfect radiator (a "black body" which absorbs all light that falls on it and therefore radiates all energy with which it is supplied) would have to operate at 3200° to produce the same kind of light. Actually the incandescent filament does operate at very close to that high a temperature. It can be noted, also, that if standard incandescent lamps are supplied a higher voltage, they will give off a higher color temperature, but will run hotter and last a shorter time.

Matching the color temperaure of various light sources is important in color television because, although there may be little or no apparent difference to the eye, the camera will show a difference if the color temperature varies as much as 100°K between the light which illuminates one side of a face and that which illuminates the other. This is, of course, not always undesirable.

One other aspect of color temperature is the limitation on dimming of lights. Dimming is accomplished in most cases by lowering the voltage of the current which operates a lamp. The average lamp loses ten degrees of color temperature for each volt the current is lowered. Thus a lamp could vary 1100°K between zero voltage and 110 volts, a range which exceeds by ten times the maximum tolerance of 100°K beyond which differences are visible.

Theoretically, light intensities between key, fill, and back light should be balanced by other means than dimmer adjustments, but in actual practice dimmers are used much as they are in black-and-white television. Some manufacturers have developed shutters and irises to control light intensity, but these are rarely used in practice.

In any area of production, practice is generally a compromise between the ideal and the expedient, with the practical solution falling most often closer to the latter. Theoretical considerations, also, often turn out to be less important in practice than they were expected to be.

UNWANTED SHADOWS

Shadows, wanted or unwanted, are uncommon in the color TV studio because of the large number of instruments which are required, and hence the many sources of light, each erasing the other's shadow. The mike-boom shadow problem is thus not as great as it is in black-and-white television.

The RCA three-tube color camera is considerably bulkier than black-and-white cameras and is thus more likely to throw its own shadow on the subject when it moves in close. Where the RCA black-and-white camera extends about 8 inches above its taking lens, the color camera rises 22 inches above. Thus key lights must often be used from a higher angle than desirable to avoid camera shadow when the camera is working close.

COLORED LIGHT

It has already been mentioned that colored light cannot be used on skin tones except for special effects, but can generally be used only on sets and backgrounds. Occasionally it is desirable to create colors on gray backgrounds, or to accentuate colors which are there, or even to help harmonize the colors in a set which may not have all been part of the designer's plan. A difference in color between modeling light and fill light can assist in modeling a subject, provided it is not on a person whose skin tones might be affected. Colored light or changing colored light can provide certain dramatic effects not possible with white light. Finally, certain natural effects, such as firelight, moonlight, etc., can be enhanced by the use of color in the lighting.

Colored light is obtained by filtering the light as it emerges from an instrument, the filter having the effect of absorbing and thus subtracting all the wavelengths of light except those of the desired color. Thirty to 90 per cent of the light intensity is lost as a result. Because unusually high light intensity is required in the color TV studio, it is not very practical to use many color filters. The most commonly used filter in the theater, the pink gel, will fade out after fifteen hours or less at high light level. Cellulose acetate filters last possibly three times as long. Glass, of course, is best, but glass rondels are readily available only in the size for theater border lights and come in a very limited range of colors.

COLOR FILMS IN TV

The producer of color film for the TV system works under more rigid limitations than if he were producing black-and-white film for television, or color film for theater projection. Plenty of fill light is necessary in the shadow areas. A ratio of not more than 2 to 1 (key to fill light) should be used in lighting the original scene if the resultant film is to register proper tones and colors on the TV system.

Large dark areas are to be avoided, with an emphasis on close-ups rather than long shots. Optical effects (supers, dissolves, etc.) usually result in some tonal and color distortion which show up very much worse on the TV system, and thus are generally avoided.

Color contrast between foreground and background is desirable, as it ensures a clear separation between subject and set without the need for a difference in light intensity which could cause poor response. Often complementary colors can be used for this purpose.

The final print of a color film prepared for TV use should be thin or light in density as compared with the best quality of print for theatrical projection.

22

Communication in TV Production

Television is unique among the theater and communication arts in that production in this medium requires the maximum of coordination within the minimum of allotted time. It is obvious that quick and ready communication of all sorts is essential to the success of TV production. Each person taking part in a production must receive a constant flow of information relevant to it. He must know what is happening, what is about to happen, and what he himself must do at each moment in order to play his particular role. These are the functions of monitoring the program, following the script, and taking cues.

Ideally, each one involved in a program should monitor both audio and video and, if the program is scripted, follow a complete script. This is not always possible, because the act of performing his function usually takes a person's eyes away from script and monitor. If everyone could follow a script, cuing would be unnecessary, except as a director would wish to exert a control over tempo, such as a symphony conductor can achieve by cuing his musicians, even though they can all hear each other fairly well and are all following the musical score.

When a person's function is such that he cannot follow the script or the program, he must be cued to act by someone who is able to do so. Most cuing is thus a kind of prompting. There is insufficient time for each person to commit all his actions to memory, plus the words or actions which precede each of his acts. Thus he, or someone else, must follow a script. In programs where there is no script, monitoring is even more important, and coordination by the director is more important as well. In programs which are unscripted decisions must constantly be made, by the director at least, on the spur of the moment, and under such conditions monitoring is even more important. Voice intercommunication, too, is indispensable in the case of ad-lib and unscripted production, since crew activities cannot be set in rehearsal and must be coordinated through cues from the director.

MONITORING

The best production generally results when each participant can see his part in relation to the whole. Most directors feel they can rehearse more in a shorter period of time when people can see what they are doing and grasp the whole effect for which the director is working. Audio and video monitoring facilities are thus provided wherever it is possible for a participant to use them. Program video is generally provided at the following points:

1. The production control room, for the use of the director and his assistants, including the TD.

2. The audio control room, if separate from production, or the audio position in the main control room if the director's program monitor is not visible to the audio man. Video monitoring is needed by the audio man so he can know when to open each microphone and can match sound level and perspective to the picture.

3. The video control point, so the video engineers may observe the matching of picture quality as successive cameras are used.

4. The studio floor, in one or more strategic locations, usually on a movable stand, since these positions change from one program to the next. These are for the use of floor crew and performers. Figure 22-1 illustrates the placement of a monitor on the camera, so the performer may keep his eyes on the camera lens (in contact with the audience) and still see the monitor. This is particularly valuable in unscripted actuality programs and especially those of the lecture or demonstration type. This practice allows the performer to know exactly what the camera is doing at all times, and he can manipulate and describe what he is showing in accordance with the transmitted picture.

5. The announce booth (where the monitor is frequently set into the desk), so the unseen announcer, whose principal function is to read copy for commercial announcements and station identifications, can coordinate with the slides and films being used.

6. The lighting control point, so the lighting director, or electrician, if the lighting director is in the control room, can watch the results of his lighting, coordinate with action, and compensate for lighting problems and deficiencies as they develop.

7. The sound-effects position, to assist the sound-effects man in coördinations with action.

8. Another special position of a floor monitor is often seen. It is built

into a newscaster's desk, so that he may, while on camera, coordinate with still pictures and films which are being shown as part of news programs.

Program audio is usually provided at the following points:

1. The control room or rooms.

2. Headsets on the floor, for special purposes. Program audio will generally be fed to a headset connection somewhere in the studio, so if necessary one or more headsets can be plugged into it. Music conductors,

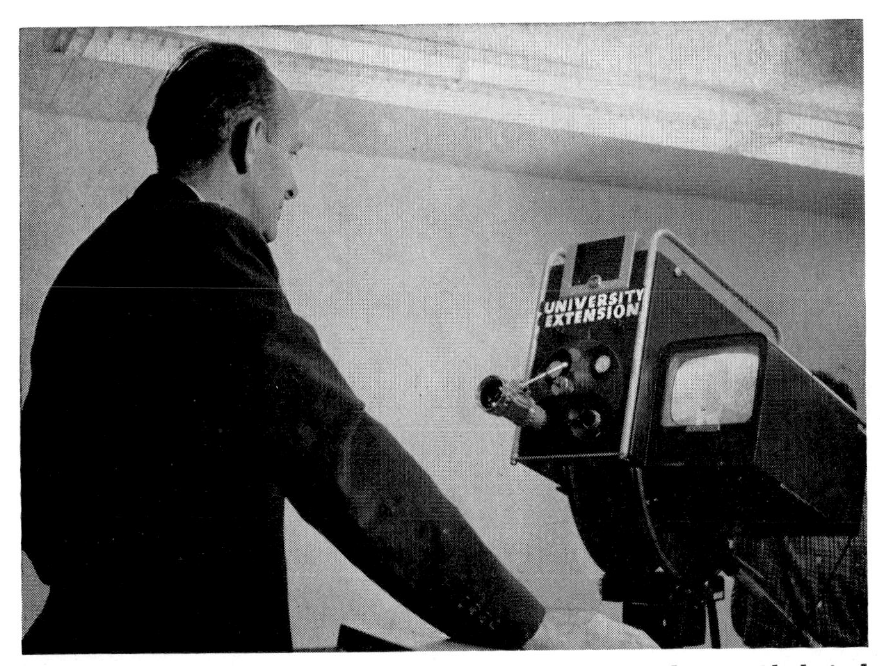

Fig. 22–1. The camera with the picture on the front. This production aid, devised by the author, provides the TV performer with constant knowledge of the program without taking his eyes from the viewing audience.

sound-effects men, and others, may need to follow program audio on the studio floor.

3. One earphone of a split headset for the boom operator. One ear brings him program sound; the other gives him the director's intercom line. When the audio engineer wants to reach the boom operator with cues or directions, he throws a switch which allows his voice to be heard over that of the director in the second earphone.

4. A loudspeaker, to the studio, on occasion; provision should be made for this possibility. It may be that a dance group is to follow music which is being played in the control room, or a "lip-sync" performer is working with a recording which he, or someone else, has previously recorded.

Studio microphones are of course cut when program audio is fed into the studio, to prevent feedback. However, if the music fed to the studio in the example above is not program audio, but feeds directly from a turntable or other source, studio microphones may be open without danger of feedback.

5. The projection room, usually entirely isolated from studio and control room, is generally provided with program audio, so the projectionist may monitor the program.

PREVIEWING

Previewing is similar to monitoring except that it is concerned with what is about to become the program rather than the program itself. This is actually a video term. When applied to audio alone, as in radio, it is sometimes called the "audition" function and sometimes merely "checking out," in the sense of testing the technical functioning of an upcoming channel.

It is a very primitive facility, indeed, which will not permit a director to look at a camera or other source of picture before he gives the cue or punches the button which puts it on the program line. Similarly, sound sources must also be previewed, although in most cases the audio portion of the program only begins after the picture is on the line and there is little to previewing audio beyond checking out the line. This indispensable function is up to the audio operator and is not a production operation.

A special preview monitor is generally provided in the production control room, controlled by a single-bus switching system, so that picture sources which are not displayed on individual monitors can be previewed when needed. The control-room operating method developed by NBC (Fig. 22-2) makes constant use of a different kind of preview monitor

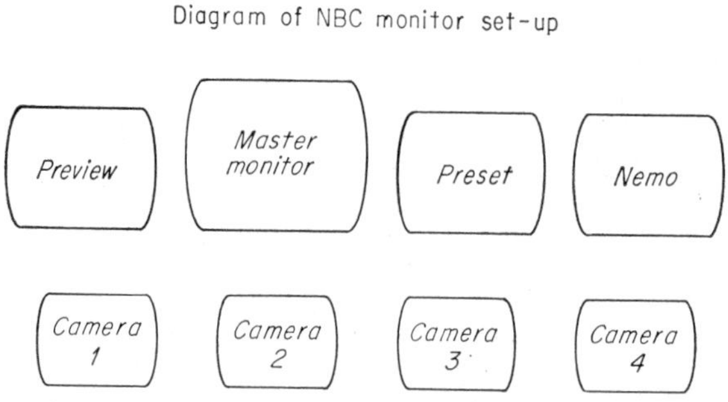

Diagram of NBC monitor set-up

Preview
Master monitor
Preset
Nemo
Camera 1
Camera 2
Camera 3
Camera 4

Fig. 22-2. Typical NBC control-room monitor display. Nemo monitor and individual camera monitors are found in only the larger NBC studios.

(called the "preset" monitor) on which each picture source is previewed immediately before it is switched onto the program line. This progression of picture from the preset to the program monitor is always seen in an NBC studio, even when individual camera monitors are also used. This is a method of operation felt by some to be a simplification over the usual methods since only two basic monitors immediately concern the director: the program monitor and the preset monitor which carries the picture next to go onto the program line. Indeed, some NBC studios have operated without individual camera monitors at all. This practice is a decided disadvantage, however, in the type of ad-lib production where the director cannot know which camera he will use very far ahead of his need to use it and must watch the output of all his cameras at once to make his decisions.

In addition to the program and the preset monitors in the usual NBC studio, there will be found at least one preview monitor which can be used to display additional picture sources at will. The preview monitor, then, might show the second-next picture source in line for the program, if this is known, or it may be used for an auxiliary picture source, such as a film or slide chain which might soon be needed. A large NBC studio control room will have yet another preview monitor, called the "nemo" monitor, "nemo" being NBC's term for remote source. This would be used for a picture coming from outside the studio, from a remote location, or possibly from another studio.

The previewing function became so important in the case of complex special events, such as the political conventions, that in 1960, NBC installed a method of previewing where a separate control room with its own staff took over the task of previewing and selecting pickups from many varied sources, releasing the director from this responsibility so he could be concerned only with the program itself. A further discussion of this technique is to be found in Chap. 20.

CUING

Most cues during a television program originate with the director. Ideally he should give few cues. Whenever it is possible for a crew member or a performer to take a cue from preceding sounds or actions in the program itself, this is generally preferable to having him take a cue from the director. The exception is, of course, when only the director is able to see or hear the program and to judge the proper timing for the action involved. Some methods of operation have placed an altogether unreasonable weight of responsibility on the director: he has even been required to cue the audio man to open microphones and cameramen to execute the most obvious adjustments of the camera. At the other end of the scale, some methods of directing, notably the German, have placed nearly all responsibility for action on the crew members themselves. Once a scene is rehearsed and set by the director, as in the theater, the cast and crew proceed on their own, and the director is free to detach himself from the performance and judge its effectiveness. This, of course, is possible only when sufficient rehearsal time is available. Indeed, this method is possible in theater production only because of the hours of rehearsal for all participants to learn their parts thoroughly.

Cuing, however, is not practical without alerting. Usually this takes the form of the "Ready" signal. The term "Stand by" is also used to alert, but is generally used further ahead of an action than the "Ready." The "Ready" may sometimes be given immediately before a cue, when a decision is suddenly made. The command "Ready" *sets* the shot. When the cameraman hears this word he knows the director is satisfied with the shot he has, and he holds until his camera is used. Of course a person should be alerted for any expected action as far ahead of time as possible. If there is to be no change in the next camera's shot, a director will ready his next camera as soon as he has the preceding camera on the line. "Take two, ready one," and "Take one, ready two" are familiar instructions from a director to his switcher or TD. "Ready to cue talent" is a standard alert from director to floor manager, promising action within seconds, while "Stand by to strike the table" is an earlier warning to the same crew member.

In addition to cues and readys, the studio intercommunication system will carry a steady flow of ongoing instructions. "Camera two, as soon as you are free I want you to flip wide and reposition over to your right for a cover shot." ("Flip wide" is used in some stations to mean "change to the next wider angle lens.")

"Now watch her as she rises. This is where she comes toward you. Pull back with her. Just keep a waist shot as she comes. Now pan down to the table and in on the letter. MUSIC." The cameraman has rehearsed his move, but having the director talk him through it gives him added surety. However, when more rehearsal time is available, the action less complex, or the cameraman more skilled, this amount of director assistance is not necessary and often a director will say very little. This is particularly true where long stretches of action are covered on one camera.

The studio intercom is generally a single "omnibus" system to which all crew members are connected. Complex systems of intercom with individual buttons or switches to cut in or out various members of the crew have been found not only inconvenient to use (directors were much too busy to read the labels on the switches) but largely impractical. Everyone who needs to hear the director's intercom line needs also to hear him give cues to other members of the crew. When a crew member finds it necessary to speak back to the director, this communication can easily involve some problem of which the rest of the crew should be aware. Only relatively isolated functionaries, such as the film projectionist in a distant projection room, find it is better to hear only their own cues than to listen to all the director's conversation. In such cases the director, assistant director, the TD (or whoever is doing cuing for the projectionist) will press a switch to deliver the cue.

Word feeding back from the projectionist to the control room is often necessary. The projectionist may have to inform the technical director which of several projectors has been threaded with a film, or to warn a director or T.D. that a film is running out. Since this information can concern any of several people in the control room, it is conveyed via a small speaker, generally of the squawk-box variety. The projectionist will have a similar squawk-box at his end of the intercom, rather than a headset, so he can move around and work freely. He operates a push-to-talk switch in most cases to contact the control room.

Cues from the director to performers cannot be given directly, as they are in radio production, since the director is not in visual communication with the cast. However, the floor manager generally is, and one of his primary purposes is to relay cues for action. He may level a finger at a performer, for example, to mean "start," or point to the next area or element of the program if it is time to proceed into the next segment. Often he may point to a camera if the performer is supposed to look into the lens and is not doing so, or change and point to the other camera as a switch is made to save the performer having to look for the tally lights.

Time cues given to a performer always indicate how much time he has left, not the time to the end of the program itself, since almost invariably some program elements, if only titles and music, will follow after the point generally referred to as "end of talent."

These cues are generally given by hand, although cards or colored lights have also been used for the purpose. Standard cues are 5, 3, 2, 1 minutes to go, 30 seconds, 15 seconds, and cut. Not all these are always necessary. The proper number of fingers held up, or down, suffices for the minute cues; an index finger crossed by the other index finger is a common 30-second cue. When a floor manager has only one hand free, or a cameraman must give the cue, a crooked index finger is often used. Many stations use the clenched fist to indicate 15 seconds; some will have the floor manager display his open palm at 15 seconds and then slowly close it during the remaining time. Time cues are to a large extent a matter of local usage and may even differ between one station and another in the same town.

Occasionally the performer is provided with a headset, so he may take cues directly from the control room, and is seen wearing these earphones on camera. This is an honest admission of the need for intercommunication, and has become an accepted part of TV production in news, special events, and other actuality productions. Similarly, the visible presence of a microphone in the picture acknowledges the need for close sound pickup and has also become completely accepted by television viewers.

In many cases it is found desirable to provide the performer directly with the information he might require instead of feeding it to him through cues. Thus a clock may be mounted on the newscaster's desk, on the stand supporting the studio monitor, or just below the lenses of the studio camera. Each situation is different, however. Some performers will want 2-minute-, 1-minute-, ½-minute-to-go signals, even though they are also watching the clock. Some prefer the time cues spelled out on a large card for them to read. On some programs the director merely starts sneaking in the music when it is time to break into the performer's conversation. The performer hears this, smoothly terminates his remarks, and introduces the station break. Whichever method works best for the performer is obviously the right one to use.

Lights are often used in cuing, especially if headset intercom is inconvenient. Lights play a very important feed-back function, too. Once something has been done, a button pushed or a pot opened, it is very reassuring to see a light go on to prove it. Again, lights are frequently used just as a means of quick reference as to the state of things, such as numbered lights in the switching system or over preview or master monitors to keep everyone aware which camera's picture is being shown.

The meaning of various colored lights is pretty nearly standardized. Any light at all indicates "on" or "active." Only the absence of a light is used for "off." Red universally means "danger" or "important" in our society, and it is natural that red should be used when it is important for people to notice and act on the knowledge, or where failure to do so would result in some kind of dire consequence. Thus, on-the-air lights outside studios are invariably red, to keep people out of studios. Camera tally lights are red, since awareness of which camera is on the line is important to all studio personnel, if only to keep them from crossing in front of it. Often a performer will be expected to take his cue to start speech or action from the appearance of the red tally light.

One station eliminated the need for the floor manager's closing time signals to performers, and thus nearly eliminated floor managers, by using a system of colored lights. Green, the most relaxing color, the softest spoken, was used to denote "One minute to go." Yellow, a traditional stand-by signal, as in traffic lights, was used for the "30 seconds to go" cue, and red was reserved for "15 seconds to go." If the performer looked as if he were about to exceed the 15-second period before winding up his remarks, he was paralyzed by all three lights at once and quickly obeyed the command to "cut."

PROMPTING

The term "prompting" is used in the theater generally in the sense of "reminding." A performer forgets a line and the prompter reads the beginning of it for him, preferably in such a way that the audience is not aware that prompting has been necessary. In TV the term has been used in a broader sense, to include the furnishing of an entire script, but still with the concept of secrecy involved, the audience presumably being unaware that the performer is reading. If a news commentator's script, for example, is frankly seen on camera, or obviously present although just out of camera range, he is reading script. If, however, it is placed so that he appears, or nearly appears, to be looking at the camera lens and talking spontaneously, he is using a prompter. Actors in daily dramatic programs who do not have time for memorization are regularly provided with prompting devices, on which the entire script rolls up across the front of a large box, several working in synchrony on various sides of the set, so that an actor may readily look over another's shoulder and find his lines. Formal speakers and commercial announcers are other types of performers for whom total script prompting is valuable. Singers and instrumentalists often pretend to perform ad lib but are in reality following the lyrics, and sometimes a full score is being held beside the camera or directly under the lens turret (Fig. 22-3).

Performers who have insufficient time to learn the dance routines they are required to do will sometimes follow the movements of a dance prompter who leads them through the dance, working in some easily visible place beside or between the cameras.

When cards are used, held as close as possible to the side of the camera, it is often desirable to limit the information contained on the cards to outline items. The run-down of the show, key phrases to be used in introducing people, etc., may be all that is required. Informal speakers and announcers, masters of ceremonies, ad-lib news commentators (rarely), and improvising actors (also rarely) may use an outline only. Sometimes performers have these cue cards placed on the studio floor, it being easy to drop one's eyes for a moment, as though in thought, and come up immediately with the proper phrase. Some may use the top of a table which is normally hidden from the camera. Some make no bones about it, and carry a clip-board in a most businesslike manner, referring to it openly.

Fig. 22–3. Fred Waring using cue card. Floor manager, equipped with wireless headset (no talk-back), holds cue card as close to lens as possible.

Fig. 22–4

When cue cards first came into use for full script purposes, they were known derisively as "idiot sheets." The later development of the prompter device into a complex piece of electronic machinery, and the TelePrompTer company into a million-dollar concern, discouraged the use of the term, at least in relation to the prompter machine. The only idiots

Fig. 22–5. TelePrompTer in action on a live commercial.

left were a few producers who imagined that anyone and everyone could read from a prompter and make it look like a spontaneous speech. It could be done, but it took special skill.

The director will usually refrain from cutting between cameras while a performer is reading from a prompter and pretending to be looking directly at the audience. Cutting would necessitate the performer turning from one camera and its prompter, to another camera and prompter, an effect which can be quite obvious, especially if the sudden shift causes him a moment's difficulty in finding the right place in his lines.

Several types of prompter machine have been in use, the most widely used being the TelePrompTer (Fig. 22-4). The device is about 18 inches across the face, and some eight lines of copy can be displayed at once. Half-inch type is used (the system includes a typewriter of this size for the preparation of the sheets), and the lines are 22 characters long.

(*a*) (*b*)

Fig. 22–6. TelePrompTer Tellens device makes it possible to read the prompter while looking into the lens. (*a*) TelePrompTer is shown in a standard position on the front of the camera. The Tellens is a periscope device with two mirrors which is fastened to the front of the TelePrompTer. Performer, not directly in front of the camera and probably seated, is seen through the transparent lower mirror. (*b*) View from front of camera. With TelePrompTer lights off, camera lens and words are superimposed; with lights on, only the script is visible.

At this rate a full frame of script could make some twenty-five words visible at once. The paper is perforated with sprocket holes along each edge, these are engaged into sprockets on the machine, and the sheet rolls upward at a speed controlled by an operator in accordance with the pace of the performer. Control may also be in the hands of the performer himself, through either a hand switch or a foot control. The prompters may be mounted on floor stands, or on the cameras themselves, either above or below the lens. One device utilizes a transparent mirror so the performer may look directly at the lens and see reflected in front of it the TelePrompTer copy (Fig. 22-6). The lens shoots through the mirror to pick up the performer.

Some performers can use the TelePrompTer at a greater distance than others, and in these cases there is less likelihood of its use being obvious. The closer the camera and prompter to the performer, of course, the greater the angle at which he must look away from the lens to see the prompter, and thus the more obvious its use.

Some stations fasten their own roller-towel prompting devices to the camera, utilizing rolls of teletype paper and advancing it by hand. Large-size typewriter type (five characters to the inch or less) has been used in preparing sheets for this purpose. If cues or script must be hand-printed, however, it is best to allow the performer himself to do it, since he will generally have less difficulty interpreting his own hasty scrawls than those of another. Sometimes a newscaster will use both script and prompter so he can look up or down at will and continue to read script

23

Television Recording

Television recording is the middle ground between live television and film. While live television is an instantaneous transmission of reality, it becomes something different when it is changed to a series of recorded images. Regardless, then, of the manner in which the images were first produced, or the manner in which they are recorded, the fact that they *are* recorded, can be stored, and viewed again at will, years later if desired, puts them into the same category as film images.

The first successful method of recording the television picture was known as kinescope recording. Basically, this is the photographing of televised images with a motion-picture camera. Since the TV receiver tube is known technically as a kinescope tube, a movie of its pictures is called a kinescope recording. "Kine" recording has long been a very delicate and inconsistent thing. It has been said with considerable validity that kine recorders are like women—you never find two alike at one time, and you never find one alike twice. They seem to be unpredictable. No matter how good a kine recording is, it must inevitably be substantially less good than the live pickup it records. This is because of the many stages the picture must go through as it is transferred from one medium to another: electricity to optics to chemicals to optics and back to electricity again. In each of these transfers there is a loss of quality. There must always be some loss, although great care and technical excellence can keep it to a minimum. These losses are due to *nonlinearity*.

When applied to one of these transfers in the kine process, linearity refers to the line on a graph—the kind of graph that might represent the ups and downs of a sales campaign. For a simple example, let's take the first transfer in the kine process, the same transfer which occurs in any television pickup: picture in the camera to television signal in the camera cable. The camera forms a visual image of lights and darks, and this optical image is transferred by the magic of the image-orthicon tube into a series of electrical signals—one long continuous electrical current, to be exact, which reproduces all the variations of light and dark as strong and weak modulations of that current.

A certain amount of brightness in the scene generates a certain amount of current in the camera tube. A larger amount of light will generate a larger current. Now, it would be ideal if this relationship

Fig. 23–1. Kinescope recorder made by GPL. A high-definition high-intensity monitor tube is enclosed in the housing at left. At right, focused on the monitor, is a specially built 16-mm motion-picture camera. Cabinet below houses sound equipment and chassis for the monitor tube.

continued in proper proportion. Made into a graph with a scale of dark to light along the bottom and a scale of weak to strong current along the side, this information would result in a nice straight line (linearity) and all the tones of light and dark would be translated faithfully into similar increases of electrical signal. In reality, however, this transfer characteristic is usually more or less nonlinear.

If the camera is focused on a scale of, say, fifteen tones of gray, all equally spaced between black and white, the television picture will generally show very little if any difference between the darkest tones, will reproduce the intermediate tones fairly faithfully (the linear portion of the graph), and again at the top of the scale will show very little increase in signal for the last few lightest tones. This explains why dark tones tend to go black on TV, light tones run together as white, and only the intermediate tones are generally reproduced accurately. This is one kind of nonlinearity which may occur during a transfer. There are other qualities besides tones of gray which must be transferred, such as resolution of detail, and these encounter conditions of more or less nonlinearity at every stage of transfer.

The accompanying chart shows the many stages of transfer through which the picture must pass in the standard kine-recording process, in each one of which nonlinearity may occur. Contrasted with this, in the far right-hand column are the transfer stages involved in the video-tape process.

Stages in standard kine-recording process		*Stages in video-tape process*
0. Video signal	(Electrical impulses)	Video signal
1. Transfer to		Transfer to
2. Kinescope picture	(Optical image)	
3. Transfer through camera optics to		
4. Negative film	(Latent negative image)	
5. Development of negative film	(Photographic image)	
6. Transfer through printing to		
7. Positive film	(Latent positive image)	
8. Development of film	(Storage as photographic image)	Storage as magnetic pattern
9. Transfer through projection to	(Optical image)	
10. Film pickup tube		
11. Transfer to		Transfer to video signal
12. Video signal	(Electrical impulses)	

Another factor which has always caused difficulty in kine recording is the basic incompatibility between the 24-frames-per-second standard of motion-picture photography and the 30-frames-per-second standard of television. The 30-frame (60-field) standard is of course limited to the Western Hemisphere and the Far East, where a-c current is 60-cycle. In most other parts of the world, a-c current is 50-cycle, and the TV standard is thus 50 fields (25 frames) per second. Twenty-four frames-per-second sound film is run at 25 frames without noticeable difference, although some musicians with absolute pitch have complained that TV notes sound slightly sharped. Kine recorders, too, operate at 25 frames per second and record all of each TV frame in perfect compatibility. This is one reason why televised film and kine recording in Europe has always been superior to that in America.

For years, the idea of recording television signals seemed fantastic. Improvements in sound recording had been marked by an increase in the range of frequencies that could be reproduced. The final achievement of high fidelity made it possible to record sounds as low as and higher than the ear could hear. The highest sound the average ear can hear agitates the air at the rate of 15,000 vibrations (cycles) per second.

Although a 15,000-cycle range was fine for high-fidelity sound, it was a long, long way from enough for television. According to our TV standards, there are 525 horizontal scanning lines per picture and 30 pictures per second, which means approximately 15,000 scanning lines a second. A 15,000-cycle recording range could show a difference between each entire line and the next, but the TV screen would look like a kind of grosgrain ribbon and would not create a picture. In order to do so, each line must vary in intensity across its length—it must be capable, if necessary, of 300 to 600 variations in tone.

If 300 variations within each scanning line are sufficient for an acceptable TV picture, we must then multiply the 15,000-odd scanning lines per second by 300 to get the total frequency of variations that must be transmitted or recorded each second. This comes to around four million.* Four megacycles, then, is what we must be able to record if we want to store the TV electrical signal. The more cycles we can record, the better the TV picture we can reproduce.

Knowing what it takes to record 15,000 cycles on disk or tape, we use simple arithmetic to calculate what would be necessary to record TV. A 33⅓ record, for example, turning at that speed, would have to be 100 feet in diameter to record four million cycles. Of course it could be run at 78 rpm, in which case the size could be cut to 42 feet (only half as impossible).

After magnetic audio tape entered the industry, further arithmetic revealed that if we could record 15,000 cycles on a 15-ips (inches per second) tape, we could get four million cycles (4 megacycles) on the tape if it ran at 4,000 ips. Later, with the development of the finer head with the ¼-mil gap, 15,000 cycles could be recorded on tape running at 7½ ips. This made TV tape a little less fantastic, but not much. It figured out to be only 2,000 ips for television. A 14-inch reel would run

* 1 cycle = 1 vibration. 1 megacycle = 1 million cycles.

for almost 30 seconds. It would about get up to speed when we would have to start slowing it down again.

HISTORY OF THE DEVELOPMENT OF VIDEO TAPE

Early in the 1950s Bing Crosby Enterprises startled the TV world by announcing that they had perfected a method of recording TV signals on magnetic tape. The tape ran at a speed of 100 ips and the quality was only about 2½ megacycles. They did this on such a slow-moving tape by using tape an inch wide and chopping up the video signal into eleven different components, which they recorded on eleven parallel tracks. A 14-inch reel ran fifteen minutes. Demonstrations were given in the laboratory, but nothing was said about when a model would be on the market or how much it would cost. Two and one-half megacycle quality, moreover, was no great improvement over conventional kine processes.

Not to be outdone, RCA put full steam on a tape device they had been perfecting, and they were able to announce, and demonstrate, a videotape recorder of 3-megacycle quality. It recorded only one track running at 30 feet per second—that's 360 ips—using a ¼-inch tape and requiring a reel some 17 inches in diameter for four minutes of program. RCA promised a figure on equipment and operation costs but never came through with it. Estimates on when RCA and Crosby would be ready became more and more conservative. In 1954, it was only two years away. In 1955, the figure generally given was five. Some people said it seemed to be getting further and further away all the time.

Meanwhile, the Ampex Corporation, leading manufacturers of sound magnetic-tape equipment, had been perfecting a method based on quite a different principle. Instead of moving a tape across a stationary recording head and contending with the very high tape speeds which must be used, the Ampex engineers *moved the head* as well as the tape. They constructed a wheel with four heads that rotated crosswise to the motion of the tape. Their video tape is similar to standard sound-recording tape except that it is 2 inches wide. A delicate commutator feeds the signal to the first head just as it contacts the top edge of the tape. When it reaches the bottom, a slip-ring contact in the commutator switches the signal to the next head, which is just making contact with the top of the tape. Thus, the forward motion of the tape needs to be only fast enough so the recording track made by the first head is not overlapped by that made by the second, and so on. This works out to the standard recording speed of 15 inches per second. So narrow are these tracks that each linear inch of video tape carries a total of 100 inches of recorded track. Effective head-to-tape speed: 1,500 inches per second.

So that the sound may be recorded along with the picture, a standard sound-record head contacts the tape a half-second after the video recording has been done, and a sound track is recorded along the upper edge of the tape. A similar head contacts the bottom of the tape at the same point and records a series of synchronizing pulses acting like "electronic sprocket holes" which make sure that the tape, when played back, will stay in perfect synchrony with the movement of the rotating heads. In between these sync pulses, there is room for even more recording, so a special cue track is provided where the recording engineer may record special instructions for the playback engineer as the tape moves along.

Fig. 23–2. The Ampex VTR 1000 video-tape machine.

The video recorders look very much like standard audio recorders. They have push-button operation for play, record, stop, rewind, and fast forward. They will rewind an hour's tape in three minutes and stop from playing speed within 2 inches of tape.

Ampex could not only announce and demonstrate their machine—they could take orders, and they had a certain number of handmade prototype models which were ready for delivery. It was the most important development in television since the image-orthicon camera tube.

The dramatic moment was the NARTB convention in April, 1956, when the executives of the American television industry were gathered in Chicago. CBS and NBC each bought three prototype models on the spot and placed orders for more. By November of that year CBS had begun the first regularly scheduled video-tape program: "Douglas Edwards and the News," a rebroadcast for viewers in the Western time zones.

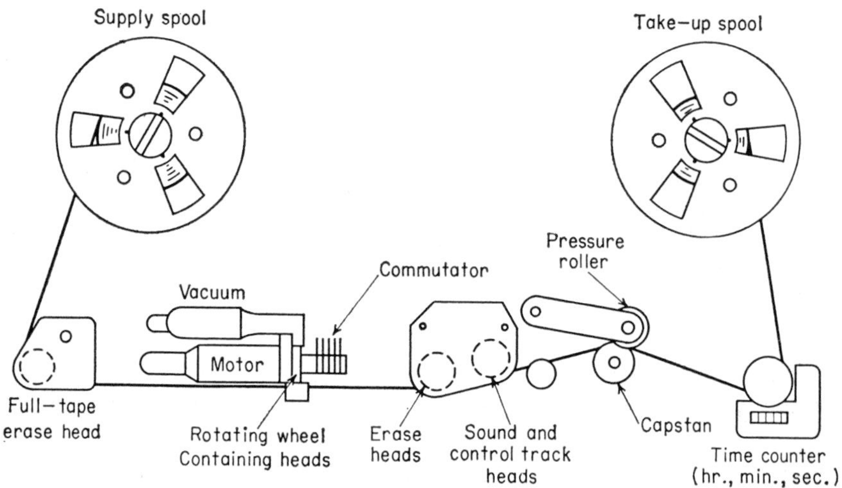

Fig. 23–3. The Ampex VTR 1001, a more compact and portable model than the VTR 1000, with a diagram of its tape transport mechanism. This is essentially the same as that of the first model.

PRODUCTION APPLICATIONS OF VIDEO TAPE

The introduction of a fully satisfactory method of recording television images caused great changes to take place in the television industry. Live production was reduced in favor of recording; video tape gradually replaced film in the production of commercials, then studio programs and

TV dramatic series. Even the filming of on-location action stories has been done by the use of TV recording from mobile unit trucks.

Delayed broadcast. The first utilization of the new technology was the recording of programs for rebroadcast. America is divided into four or five time zones, causing a four-hour difference between New York, for example, and the Pacific Northwest. Since the content and the expected rating of a given show is related directly to the time when it is aired, it has always been the wish of each advertiser to place his program in the same time slot in each part of the country. Before tape, a compromise was often made. A show was done live for the East coast (whether from New York or from Hollywood) and kine-recorded. This was immediately developed and dried (the so-called "hot-kine" process), and was ready to play back two hours later for the Western part of the country. Virtually all evening programs and many daytimers on all three networks were recorded in this manner. Standard procedure was to make two kines simultaneously, one in 35 mm, the other in 16 mm, and to play them back simultaneously. If any fault was detected during the playback of the primary 35-mm film, the secondary 16-mm recording could be instantly cut in, with merely a drop in picture quality instead of an interruption.

Another important use of kine recording was the distribution of network programs by mail. This was necessary in order to serve the many TV stations which were not reached by the growing web of transcontinental cable and microwave routes.

The costs of film stock and developing ran to several hundred dollars an hour. The new video tape, however, could be erased and reused over a hundred times, so the cost of recording stock for an hour's program was only a few dollars. The first video-tape machines paid for themselves very quickly in this one application alone.

More efficient scheduling. The second important application to which video tape was put was the more efficient scheduling of production facilities. A show could be produced at the most convenient time for the utilization of production facilities, and aired at the most convenient time for the viewing audience. Since a taped show looked live on the home receiver, it was to all intents and purposes a live show. This point will be further discussed at the end of this chapter.

Audience-participation programs recorded in the afternoon could be aired on a subsequent early morning, a time when it would be impossible to gather a studio audience for a live show. Studio production hours could be more efficiently filled, since there was no longer any fixed relationship between rehearsal and air time. Even in the small TV station where subsistence comes largely from the production of local live commercials, more efficient scheduling could result. The station could produce commercials during the morning hours, for example, keeping a crew busy on one shift; it could then operate the rest of the day with only a skeleton projection crew on duty, airing the taped commercials during feature films and between network programs.

Further application of this principle made it possible for a TV station to operate on a five-day work week but broadcast a full seven days. Weekend programming was greatly improved because of the possibility

Fig. 23–4. The RCA video tape recorder is similar to the Ampex except that it is rack-mounted.

of obtaining performers available during the week and recording programs which could not be produced on weekends.

Efficient scheduling advantages were also felt in the area of remote broadcasting, where many special events cannot be controlled by a television producer. Here also it was possible to divorce production time from air time, record the fire or the parade at its height, then play it back at the first convenient time.

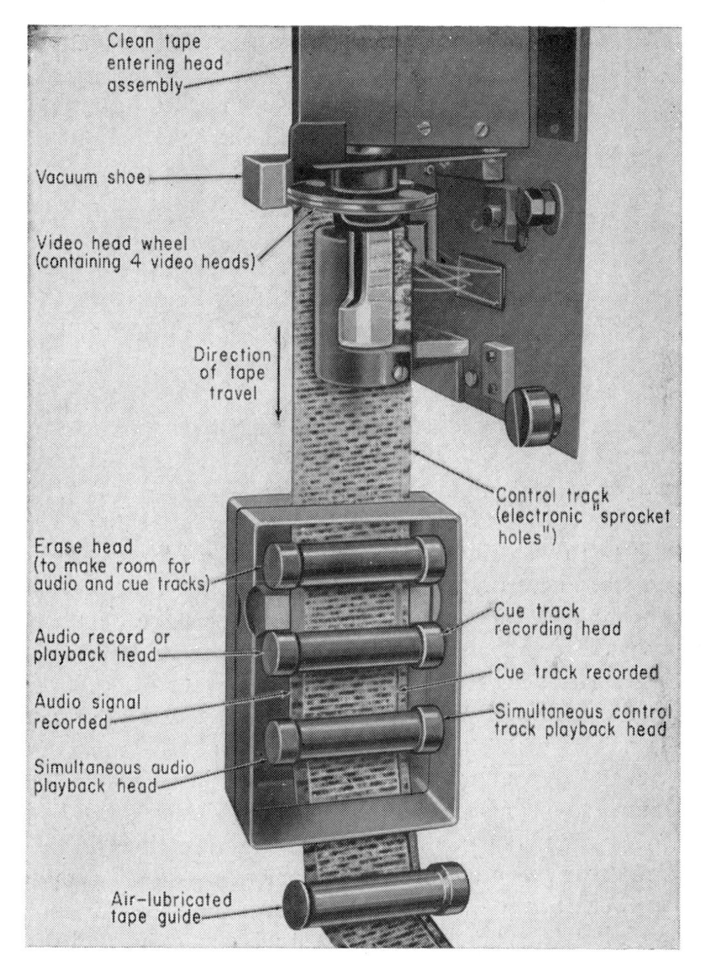

Fig. 23–5. Photodiagram of video tape moving down through audio and video head assemblies of RCA video tape recorder (RCA machine is rack-mounted in vertical position). Photo is retouched to make recorded tracks visible. For clarity the size of the transverse video tracks is exaggerated: they are shown about six to eight times correct width. Simultaneous audio playback head is for use in monitoring the audio recording off-the-tape during recording operations, the main audio playback head being busy recording at the time. Simultaneous control track playback head assures operator that the control track is actually being recorded. A video tape without a control track could not be played back again, any more than a film without sprocket holes could be projected.

THE REPLACEMENT OF FILM

Not only could video tape replace live TV, but it was also soon replacing much of filmed TV. In the first place, tape looked better on TV than film—it had that crisp, live quality which even the best 35-mm film rarely can achieve. Moreover, tape production was faster than film production, and for this reason cost less (some 30 to 40 per cent less according to the first estimates). It could also be recorded and re-recorded several times without noticeable degradation, whereas film loses quality with every generation. Given TV production facilities including the best of special-effects equipment, video tape could record nearly as many special "opticals," wipes, dissolves, and traveling mattes as film, and without extra time and trouble. Primarily, however, tape was superior to film in many applications because of the principle of immediate playback. Much time was saved when producers could see their rushes immediately and did not need any extra takes for protection. The fact that all cast and crew members could see the take as it was played back was a tremendous help in shooting. When a retake was necessary, everyone could see why, whereas in film shooting all must rely on verbal descriptions by the one person, the camera operator, who has been watching the take through the camera view finder. Furthermore, sets could be struck as soon as final takes were approved; there was no need to leave them standing for the screening of rushes just in case retakes should be necessary. Taping on location was less expensive than location filming because once a good take was achieved, the unit could pack up and move on; there was no longer any need for cover shots at different exposures and angles, and if these failed, return trips to the same location for retakes.

The first use of tape in place of film was applied to the production of commercials. The next step was the production of dramatic series for TV tape, using TV cameras and a TV studio instead of film. This led to speculation as to how soon the electronic motion picture would completely replace the photographic. The tape engineers themselves answered this one: whereas the present tape equipment was good enough to pass for live on the home receiver, it would never look like 35-mm film on a screen, much less like some of the current wide-negative and wide-screen techniques.

Electronic motion pictures for theatrical release were in the future, perhaps, but would have to wait for very great improvements in the quality and the detail of television recording.

VIDEO TAPE ON LOCATION

The use of the video-tape machine in a mobile truck or van opened up great possibilities for outside production. The problems and uncertainties of arranging a good microwave-link transmission would be obviated if the tape machine were at the location; another advantage would be immediate playback without the need for microwave links in both directions.

SCENE-BY-SCENE PRODUCTION

In many ways the use of tape in TV production combined the advantages of live TV and the advantages of film. The streamlined all-at-once production methods of live TV could be used when production on TV budgets was needed. But there were advantages in the piecemeal scene-by-scene production of the film studio as well. One of these was the perfection of editing at leisure, a point which will be discussed in the next section. Another was the advantage of being able to use the same studio area on successive days for different scenes or sequences. After finishing with one set and approving the takes, the crew was able to strike the set and erect the sets for the next sequence in the same studio area. Certain limitations of the live theater which accompanied live television as well, such as the need for intermission time to effect costume and make-up changes, were no more a problem in TV tape production than they had ever been in film.

Since the use of tape, many producers have achieved savings in production time due to the reduction in dress rehearsals. Once a scene is played and recorded, that is the end of it, until it is spliced or otherwise edited into the final show. On a live dramatic production one or two complete run-throughs and a dress rehearsal are always considered necessary, so that each part of the production will be as recently rehearsed as possible when the program goes on the air.

EDITING OF VIDEO TAPE

Techniques of tape editing can be divided into two classifications: techniques which simulate the editing techniques of film and try to give the tape editor the conditions he would be used to in working with film; and techniques which more closely resemble the editing of live television programs, where the TV director does the editing.

Film-technique methods of editing are based on the eventual cutting and splicing together of the tape, just as a film is pieced together from individual shots. Live-technique editing, on the other hand, is based on the method of re-recording. Two sections of tape are joined together by re-recording them in succession on a third tape. The editing process is thus very similar to the process of editing a live TV program: it is done by a director, working at a high pitch, watching monitors and calling shots. It is fast and thus economical, but is not capable of the accuracy and perfection desired by film editors.

One of the most valuable contributions that TV production can make to electronic film production is the concept of "pre-editing." Shots in sequence are planned with the greatest care before shooting, and then all of the production—shooting and editing—is accomplished simultaneously. Not only is it less expensive, but this live TV technique requires continuity of performance and thus, in the opinion of many top producers who have worked in both the film and TV media, results in better performances than are possible in the shot-by-shot piecemeal production techniques of film.

Splicing of video tape was at first a haphazard procedure. Having the same mylar base as audio tape, video tape could be cut and spliced with

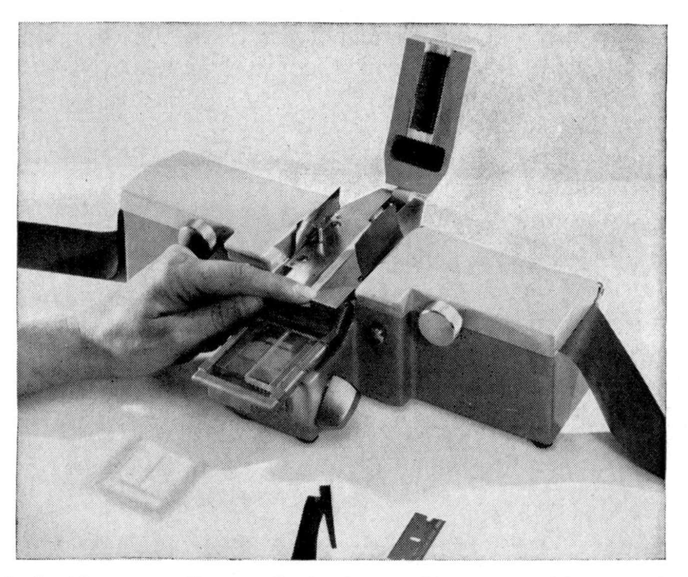

Fig. 23–6. A video-tape splicer made by Ampex. Pressure-sensitive tape is used to hold the two tape ends together, just as in audio-tape splicing.

the same materials, but the editor had no assurance at all that the cut he had made would fall on a frame line. The odds were, indeed, overwhelmingly against it, and every splice resulted in a loss of frame, causing a "roll-over" on monitors and home receivers as the frame line moved up the screen until it locked into sync again.

The 525 lines of video information which comprise one frame of the television signal are recorded on the tape in the linear space of about ½ inch. In other words, if you wanted to cut a single frame out of a piece of video tape, you would end up with a piece of tape 2 inches wide (the width of the video tape) and ½ inch long. The problem was somehow to locate the lines of demarcation between the frames so the splicing could be done at that point.

The solution was to record a special pulse on the cue track at the start of each field (there are two fields for each frame). Then this pulse was made visible so the editor could make his cue in the right spot. The magnetic pattern on tape may be made visible by applying a highly volatile liquid containing iron dust which evaporates immediately, leaving a powder which outlines each recorded track and the pulses on the cue track. Using a microscope, the editor moves each piece of tape back and forth in the splicer until he has lined up the pulses exactly. Then he cuts the two ends of the tape just as in editing audio tape and makes his splice with a piece of pressure-sensitive tape.

While splicing is possible, it is undesirable to handle video tape very much. In comparison with the ruggedness of film, video tape is a delicate material indeed. When one considers the frightful condition that a film editor's work print develops after he has finished editing a difficult sequence, one can see immediately that this kind of editing of video tape —splicing, playing back, resplicing, etc.—would very quickly destroy it. Even a slight crease in video tape can cause trouble as it speeds through the machine.

One solution, developed in Hollywood, was the use of a film work print. The tape editor, working by this method, receives a kinescope recording which has been made simultaneously with the tape, or made later from the tape itself. He proceeds to edit this film in the normal way, and when he has finished, the film work print is matched to the video tape just as in normal film production the work print is matched to the negative. Of course edge numbers are required for this operation, so the correct piece of tape can be matched with the correct piece of film. This has been done visually by printing the numbers on both tape and film, 15 inches apart on the tape, 24 frames apart on the film. It has also been done verbally. A roll of "talking edge numbers" is first produced and then, during the original recording, is played back onto the cue track of the tape and the single-system sound track of the film. Matching then becomes a matter of listening to numbers rather than reading them.

A method of editing holding some promise is the method of re-recording. When close-ups from one camera are to be intercut with long shots from a second camera, for example, each camera's output is recorded separately and played back simultaneously during the editing on two video-tape machines. The editor then watches two monitors, like a live TV director, and using a TV switching system, selects the shots and creates the transitional effects (wipes, dissolves, fades) that he wants to use. The final result is recorded on a third video-tape machine. When one entire scene is to be joined to another by a dissolve, the two may be re-recorded together in this fashion. Scene 1 is played on the first machine until a few seconds before the point at which the dissolve is to begin. Then the second machine is started, comes up to speed, and with the fading handles of the switching system, the editor effects the dissolve between them. Then he can stop the first machine and continue to re-record scene 2. In comparison with photographic film there is very little quality loss in re-recording of video tape, even over several generations.

A problem was initially encountered with this method because each tape machine had its own sync generator. Re-recording could not be accomplished because the differences in sync would cause constant roll-over and break-up on every take or transition. Eventually a device called "Intersync" was developed, which performed the same essential function as sync-lock or gen-lock equipment (see page 439), phasing together all the sync generators of all the video-tape recorders involved, so that the pictures could be intercut, dissolved, or superimposed.

FREEZE-FRAME

Film editors have often felt rather frustrated in attempting to edit video tape because of the impossibility of looking at individual static frames, as a film editor must do to make an accurate cut. Assurances that TV editing has always been somewhat on the approximate side and the public has not complained did not completely satisfy the professional film editor. To make it possible to actually look at a series of static frames so that the exact frame for a cut could be selected, devices were developed which could freeze several still frames as the tape moved through the playback machine.

One such device was developed by John Silva at KTLA and called the TV-Ola. In this device four pictures were displayed on four small monitors (Tonotron tubes) which could hold static pictures for as long as a minute before the images faded away. (Another method developed by Conrac for the Ampex Company displayed four small pictures on four quadrants of a standard-size TV monitor.)

In the TV-Ola a cue pulse was first recorded at a point about 3 seconds ahead of the point in the action where a cut was to be made. As this cue pulse passed through the video-tape machine, it triggered off the display of four static frames on the four Tonotron tubes, each frame being thirty frames (one second) from the one before. Deciding that the point of his cut should lie between the third and fourth of these, the editor could then erase the screens, quickly rewind the tape, and lay out another series of frames, only ten frames apart this time, giving him a closer sampling of the particular part of the tape he was looking for. Deciding again that the point to cut must lie between, say, the first and second of these, he could again reverse the tape, set the machine to show frames only three frames apart, and examine the area of interest in even greater detail. If he was still not satisfied that he had found the exact frame on

Fig. 23–7. The TV-Ola, left, operating in conjunction with a video-tape recorder, right. The four Tonotron tubes which freeze and hold the frames are seen at left; controls for selecting frame frequency are on the console at lower left.

which to make his cut, he could rewind again and lay out four successive frames. The tape could then be marked for the cut and later spliced, a procedure which is standard motion-picture practice.

COLOR TELEVISION RECORDING

Color television had already made a strong beginning when video tape was introduced. Color kine recording had always been a serious problem. While color film could be exposed from a very intense color kinescope tube, the cost of color film stock was prohibitive. Eastman Kodak finally developed a film stock which partially solved this problem during the last two or three years before color video tape was available.

Lenticular film. The Eastman solution to the problem of recording color television was the lenticular film. While far from perfect, it made color kines at least possible. The lenticular film had a standard black-and-white emulsion, its cost was that of black-and-white film, and it called for the same developing techniques. Colors were separated and recorded selectively on the correct areas of the image by means of microscopic cylindrical "lenses" embossed into the film base.

Light rays reaching the film passed through the film base, and were bent in one direction or another according to their wavelength, just as a prism separates white light into colors. This meant that all the red rays which passed through a particular "lens" reached the film emulsion above the lens, all the blue rays were bent to record below it, with the green rays in between. The photographic image, however, was composed as usual of black and white silver granules. The picture did not become color again until it was projected through colored filters.

Color video tape. So poor was the quality of the lenticular film, especially when seen on black-and-white sets, that the industry eagerly welcomed the arrival of color video tape. When it came in early 1958 (from Ampex), the machine was in all external appearance exactly the same machine which was being used for black and white. One rack of electronic equipment was added. The machine was compatible—black-and-white tapes could be recorded and played back on it, and color tapes could be played in color or in black and white. (Black-and-white tapes have not as yet been played back in color, although some enthusiasts are predicting even this.)

RCA followed shortly with a similar machine for both monochrome and color, also externally similar to the RCA black-and-white model. In the case of the products of each manufacturer, existing monochrome recorders could be converted to record color as well as black and white.

SIMPLIFIED VIDEO RECORDERS

The trend in the design of video recording equipment is toward simplification of the design and thus a reduction in what was, to begin with, a fairly high price. One video-tape machine was worth nearly three monochrome cameras or one color camera. Many users of closed-circuit TV, particularly in the educational field, would have purchased the equipment during its first few years had the cost been within their reach.

The Japanese firm, Toshiba, was the first to announce a single-head video-tape recorder at about half the price of standard machines. Most of the technical problems connected with earlier machines had centered around "quadrature," or the proper alignment and synchronizing of the four heads involved. In order to lay down a continuous track with only one head, it was necessary, in the case of the Toshiba recorder, to devise a method whereby the head would be in continuous contact with the tape. This was accomplished in spite of the fact that the track was laid down across the tape as in the original Ampex machine. Each head in the Ampex machine, the reader will recall, travels for three-quarters of the time out of contact with the tape while one of the other three heads is laying down the track. The Toshiba solution was to mount the head in a cylinder around which the tape was wound in a spiral fashion. Thus as the head turned, it laid down a long slanting track starting at the bottom and approaching closer to the top of the tape as the head turned inside the spiral. Reaching the top of the tape, the head immediately contacted the bottom again, but because of the forward motion of the tape, this time a fraction of an inch farther along.

To put the same amount of track on the tape as the Ampex and RCA machines, each slanting transverse track had to be a little over 2 feet long, long enough so that a full field of video information could be included. A drum or cylinder slightly over 8 inches in diameter was needed, and the head revolved within this cylinder at the speed of 3,600 rpm, or 60

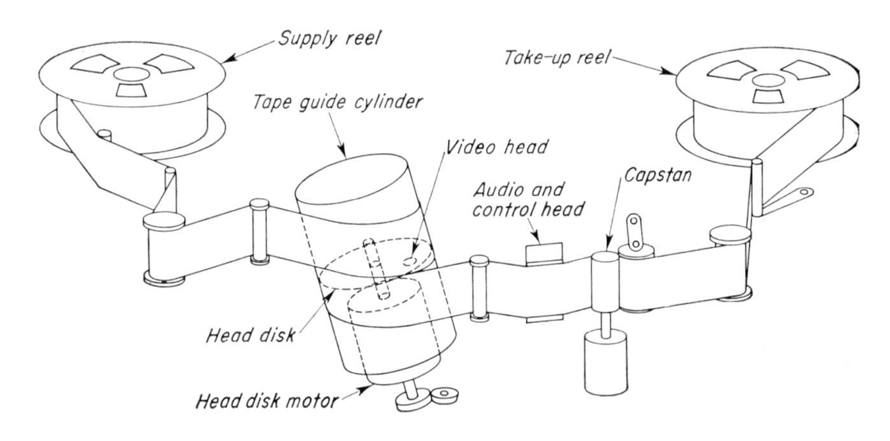

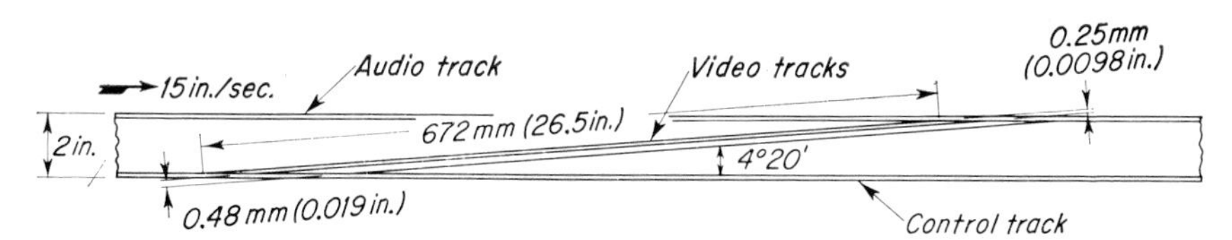

Fig. 23–8. Diagram of the tape transport on a video-tape recorder using a single head (Toshiba). (Courtesy of *Journal of the Society of Motion Picture and Television Engineers.*)

revolutions per second, which is the standard field rate. Splicing was said to be possible and to have some advantages. The splice was 2 feet long and had to follow the track perfectly, but since each track was a complete field, there was no danger of splicing in the midst of a field and causing a roll-over. A conventional splice, directly across the tape, was said to have the effect of introducing the new picture by means of a diagonal wipe.

In the spring of 1961 Ampex demonstrated a single-head machine operating on essentially the same principle as that just described (the VR 8000, Fig. 23-9). The tape ran at the economical speed of 7½ inches per second instead of the broadcast standard of 15. Necessarily incompatible with broadcast models, the VR 8000 was half the price while equal in quality, and engendered great interest in the field of closed-circuit television in industry and education. RCA soon followed with a half-price model of their own. RCA, however, held to the same

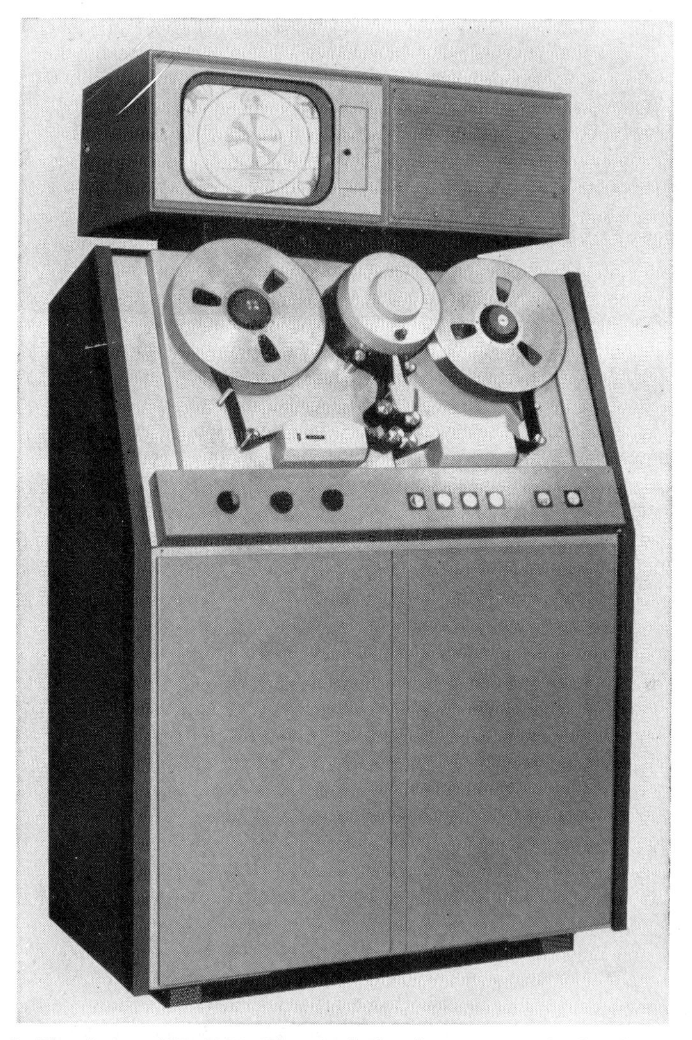

Fig. 23–9. The Ampex VR 8000. The single head rotates inside the drum at center as the tape moves around it in a helical wind.

four-head assembly as the broadcast model, and the same tape speed. It was thus compatible with existing broadcast models by both RCA and Ampex. Tapes made on any of these models could be played back on any other model. While operating costs would be cut nearly in half in the case of the Ampex machine, with tape running at half the speed and only one head to replace instead of four, the factor of compatibility was considered so important, at least by educators, that many looked favorably on the RCA machine. Meanwhile RCA added an inexpensive slant-track machine using two heads and running at half speed.

LIVE VERSUS TAPE TELEVISION

The subject of video tape and its influence over television production cannot be closed without a word about the relative values of tape versus live production. The practical, the technical, and the economic advantages of tape have been mentioned. Now let us consider the artistic.

Television has been hailed by many as a totally new medium, having its own unique characteristics. It has as often, perhaps, been analyzed as merely a new branch of the cinematic art—a new technology, the ultimate purpose and effect of which was identical with that of film. Hard put to defend the first stand, its proponents pointed to the unique sense of "immediacy"—the feeling that what one is seeing on television is happening at that very moment in another, often distant, place. Live productions make the best use of the TV medium, went this argument, when they make the most of immediacy and actuality. Sports and special events are naturals for the medium. In the area of studio programs, situations which use actual people, not actors making believe, in real situations where spontaneous and unrehearsed action is called for, are also natural to the television medium. Some went further and said that live dramatic production could convey some of the feeling of the live theater, in that each performance was an event in itself, a real and actual performance, and therefore conveyed more of the excitement and immediacy of a theater performance to the viewing audience than when the same drama was produced on film.

The arguments for the other side ignored the feeling of immediacy. They pointed out that drama certainly is all illusion and make-believe, that there can be no spontaneity, no actuality without destroying this illusion, and film is fully as effective as live TV in conveying everything that a drama is intended to convey.

The TV medium can easily become entirely a recorded medium like film. Tape-recorded TV looks like live TV; the television audience doesn't know the difference and reacts to the programs as though they were live. Taped TV looks like live TV because the entire technique from the camera work through the titles to the switching is in the style of TV, not that of film. And it looks like TV because the definition and other aspects of the picture quality are better than those of TV film. So the audience reacts to it as live because they believe it to be live. If we rely on this condition, are we not perhaps putting our trust in a foundation of shifting sand?

The television audience in nearly every country today understands the nature of live television. Each viewer has experienced the thrill of seeing at a distance, of watching something happen in another place. Each viewer knows the difference between live television and film. How long will it take before he will feel a difference between live television and tape? The fast transitions where the same actor is left at the end of a scene and encountered immediately, perhaps in another costume, at the beginning of the next, the jumps in action where small cuts are made—how soon will these become a kind of subconscious giveaway to the viewer?

The TV industry has made much of its responsibility not to perpetrate fraud on its viewers. Thus stations generally feel they must announce when a program has been seen on tape. Radio managed to announce without informing, by throwing in the word "electrical transcription" in announcing that a program had been recorded. The term was probably meaningless to most people, especially when announced very casually, and live radio was confused with recorded for years. Was anything lost? Will anything be lost by the same confusion in TV? Is taped television as successful as live television merely because people are taking it for live? Would they accept the same programs if they were done on film? Is tape, then, an intermediate stage between live and film? Is tape a little less live, perhaps, than live TV, but still more live than film, because it was made only a few hours ago while film goes back a few months at least? Is a delayed broadcast which is taped and immediately played, so that the delay is only a matter of minutes, reacted to in a different manner than a program which has been delayed an hour—two hours—three? When does a live show die and become a "dead" recording?

Does the line fall, perhaps, between unedited tape and edited tape, that is to say, between a program which is pre-edited in the manner of a live TV program, or post-edited in the manner of film?

These are questions of aesthetic theory which must be faced by those television broadcasters who take a long forward look into the future of their medium, and ask: What effects can the wide use of recorded television have on the unique qualities of the TV medium? They must answer the question: Is television really unique? Or is it perhaps only a new technological development of the cinematic art—a new method of electronic film, using the electronic motion-picture camera and creating nothing essentially different from the motion picture—moving images on a screen accompanied by synchronized sound?

If this were true, live television could disappear and never be missed. Luckily it is not. But film and television, and the many specific production techniques of each, are due to become, through mutual borrowing and adaptation, even more interwoven and interdependent.

Index